When Christians gather to worship, we recall and celebrate the timeless stories of our faith through word and song. With this in mind, artist Yolanda Durán adorned the letters of the word "Gather" with the stories of our faith. From left to right, the first panels depict Adam and Eve's fall from grace; the miraculous encounters of Noah and Moses with water, the sign of our baptism; and John the Baptist in the desert, dressed in clothing made of camel's hair, foretelling the coming of the promised Messiah. The next panel portrays the peaceful night and new dawn of the joyous Nativity. The panels go on to illustrate the Last Supper, the crucifixion, the empty tomb, and finally, the second coming of Christ, all echoing the words we sing each time we proclaim the mystery of faith: "Christ has died, Christ is risen, Christ will come again."

The spine of the hymnal is crowned with a dove, the symbol of the Holy Spirit. The back cover is framed with the symbols of the four evangelists: Matthew, the divine man, symbol of Christ's incarnation; Mark, the winged lion, symbol of the royalty of Christ; Luke, the winged ox, symbol of Christ's priestly office; and John, the rising eagle, symbol of the grace of the Holy Spirit.

GATHER
COMPREHENSIVE

SECOND
EDITION

GIA PUBLICATIONS, INC.
CHICAGO

PREFACE

The publication of *Gather Comprehensive—Second Edition* marks the release of GIA's tenth hymnal and service book for Roman Catholic parishes in the United States since the Second Vatican Council. Each of these volumes has had a unique character, and while several have been widely adopted by American parishes, the precursor to this edition, published in 1994, has risen above all the others.

The decision to revise a hymnal is essentially dictated by the church community itself. Increasing inquiries about the possibility of a revision along with a significant drop in adoptions readily signal the time to address the matter. To begin this particular project we incorporated a tool that we hadn't used in a number of years.

A large representative number of parishes who had used *Gather Comprehensive* for an extended period were randomly chosen to receive a detailed and extensive survey. For each item in the original edition, we asked if they had used the item; if not, did they feel that they would use it in the future, and if they felt it should be included in a new edition. The results of this survey became a major factor in choosing the contents for this second edition.

In *Gather Comprehensive—Second Edition* the ritual and service music offerings have been considerably expanded making it even more comprehensive than the original. The established mass settings have been retained, several exciting new settings have been added, and the rites of Christian Initiation, Baptism, Funeral, etc. have been added with appropriate service music. The section of psalms near the beginning of the hymnal retains the most widely sung settings, and in keeping with the spirit of the revised *General Instruction of the Roman Missal* and the document *Liturgiam Authenticam,* all of the lectionary psalm refrains for Sundays and solemnities set by Michel Guimont are now included near the back of the volume.

Like its precursor, this edition includes both contemporary and traditional, or folk-style and classical, or piano/guitar-based and organ-based music—depending on how one chooses to identify musical styles—with the mix leaning toward the former in each case. The accompaniments for many items in the first category are clearly pianistic and cannot effectively be played on the organ without adaptation. To maintain the integrity of performance practice, it is our strong recommendation that these pieces be played on the piano as intended. Other accompaniments, of course, can effectively be played on either organ or piano.

It must be remembered that a hymnal is inherently a book for the gathered assembly. While expanded octavo versions for choir and various instruments exist for many of the titles in this hymnal, hymnal items have been edited to be accessible for the most commonly found resources of assembly with cantor and accompanist.

The introductions to the rites and seasons are by Gabe Huck, taken from *Worship—Third Edition.* Further acknowledgment is hereby given to Jeffry Mickus for project direction, editing, engraving, and book layout; and to Philip Roberts, engraver; Victoria Krstansky and Clarence Reiels, proofreaders; Ronald F. Krisman, Spanish editor; Sarah Parker, survey coordinator; Timothy Redmon, permissions editor; and to all who responded to our survey or supplied detailed recommendations.

Soli Deo gloria.

Alexander Harris
  Publisher
Robert J. Batastini
  Senior Editor
Kathryn R. Cuddy
Michael A. Cymbala
Kelly Dobbs Mickus
Stephen Petrunak
  Editors

Contents

Hymns and Songs

Indexes

Morning Praise

The Church's sense for how to pray in the morning comes from our Jewish heritage. Whatever the day, whatever the difficulties, the tradition has been to begin the day with praise for the creator. The sign of the cross, first traced on the Christian at baptism, is again made to begin the new day and its prayer. In the hymn and the psalms, in the scripture and intercessions, each one who prays and the community together finds what it is to stand at the beginning of a new day as a Christian. The morning's prayer gives the day its meaning when, through the years, these prayers become one's own.

OPENING DIALOG

1

Stand

Ho-ly God! Fill us this day with new breath! And we shall be liv-ing words of praise!

Text: J. Tasch Jordan, adapt.
Music: David Haas
© 1986, GIA Publications, Inc.

2   MORNING HYMN

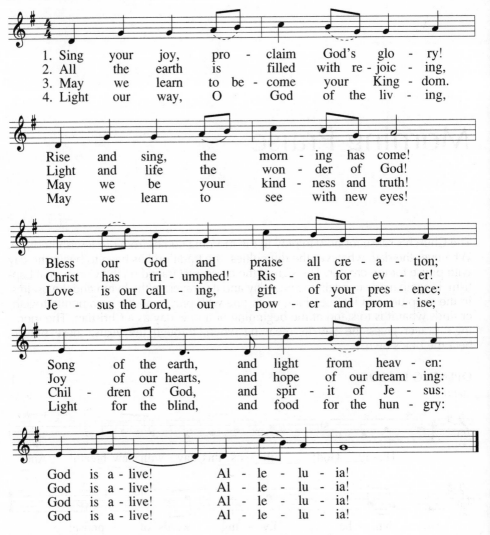

1. Sing your joy, pro - claim God's glo - ry!
2. All the earth is filled with re - joic - ing,
3. May we learn to be - come your King - dom.
4. Light our way, O God of the liv - ing,

Rise and sing, the morn - ing has come!
Light and life the won - der of God!
May we be your kind - ness and truth!
May we learn to see with new eyes!

Bless our God and praise all cre - a - tion;
Christ has tri - umphed! Ris - en for ev - er!
Love is our call - ing, gift of your pres - ence;
Je - sus the Lord, our pow - er and prom - ise;

Song of the earth, and light from heav - en:
Joy of our hearts, and hope of our dream - ing:
Chil - dren of God, and spir - it of Je - sus:
Light for the blind, and food for the hun - gry:

God is a - live! Al - le - lu - ia!
God is a - live! Al - le - lu - ia!
God is a - live! Al - le - lu - ia!
God is a - live! Al - le - lu - ia!

Text: David Haas
Music: SUMMIT HILL, Irregular; David Haas
© 1987, GIA Publications, Inc.

PSALMODY

The singing of one or more psalms is a central part of Morning Praise. Psalm 63, given below, is one of the premier morning psalms. Psalm 51 is commonly substituted for Psalm 63 on Wednesday and Friday, as well as during Lent. Other appropriate psalms for morning are Psalms 5, 8, 33, 42, 47, 66, 72, 80, 85, 93, 95, 98, 100, 118, 148, 149, and 150.

PSALM 63

Sit
Refrain

As morn-ing breaks I look to you; I look to you, O Lord, to be my strength this day, as morn-ing breaks, as morn - ing breaks.

Verses

1. O God, you are my God, for you I long; for you my soul is thirsting.
   My body pines for you like a dry, weary land without water.
   So I gaze on you in your holy place to see your strength and your glory.

2. For your love is better than life, my lips will speak your praise.
   So I will bless you all my life, in your name I will lift up my hands.
   My soul shall be filled as with a banquet, my mouth shall praise you with joy.

3. On my bed I remember you. On you I muse through the night
   for you have been my help; in the shadow of your wings I rejoice.
   My soul clings to you; your right hand holds me fast.

Text: Psalm 63:2-3, 4-6, 7-9; © 1963, 1986, The Grail, GIA Publications, Inc., agent; refrain trans. © 1974, ICEL
Music: Michael Joncas, © 1985, OCP Publications

PSALM PRAYER

Stand
All respond: **Amen.**

WORD OF GOD

Sit
Reader concludes: The word of the Lord.
      Assembly: **Thanks be to God.**

5   GOSPEL CANTICLE

Stand. All make the sign of the cross as the canticle begins.

1. Now ✠ bless the God of Is - ra - el, Who comes in love and pow'r, Who rais - es from the roy - al house De - liv - 'rance in this hour. Through ho - ly proph - ets God has sworn To free us from a - larm, To save us from the heav - y hand Of all who wish us harm.

2. Re - mem - ber - ing the cov - e - nant, God res - cues us from fear, That we might serve in ho - li - ness And peace from year to year; And you, my child, shall go be - fore To preach, to proph - e - sy, That all may know the ten - der love, The grace of God most high.

3. In ten - der mer - cy, God will send The day - spring from on high, Our ris - ing sun, the light of life For those who sit and sigh. God comes to guide our way to peace, That death shall reign no more. Sing prais - es to the Ho - ly One! O wor - ship and a - dore!

Text: *Benedictus*, Luke 1:68-79; Ruth Duck, © 1992, GIA Publications, Inc.
Music: FOREST GREEN, CMD; English; harm. by Michael Joncas, © 1987, GIA Publications, Inc.

MORNING PRAYERS

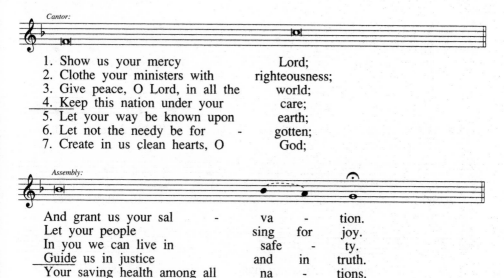

	Cantor:	
1.	Show us your mercy	Lord;
2.	Clothe your ministers with	righteousness;
3.	Give peace, O Lord, in all the	world;
4.	Keep this nation under your	care;
5.	Let your way be known upon	earth;
6.	Let not the needy be for -	gotten;
7.	Create in us clean hearts, O	God;

Assembly:

And grant us your sal -	va -	tion.
Let your people	sing for	joy.
In you we can live in	safe -	ty.
Guide us in justice	and in	truth.
Your saving health among all	na -	tions.
Nor the hope of all to	be de -	nied.
And sustain us in your holy	Spir -	it.

Text: *The Book of Common Prayer*
Music: David Haas, © 1986, GIA Publications, Inc.

CONCLUDING PRAYER
All respond: **Amen.**

7 LORD'S PRAYER

Our Fa - ther in heav - en, hal - low - ed be your
name, your king - dom come, your will be done on
earth as in heav - en. Give us to - day our
dai - ly bread. For - give us our sins as
we for - give those who sin a - gainst us.
Save us from the time of trial and de -
liv-er us from e - vil, for the king - dom, the pow'r and the
glo - ry are yours, now and for ev - er.

Music: David Haas, © 1986, GIA Publications, Inc.

FINAL BLESSING

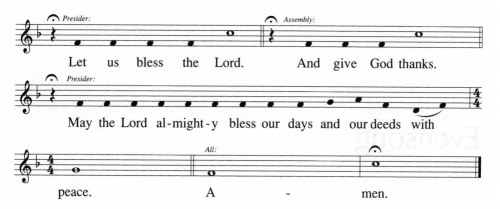

Let us bless the Lord. And give God thanks.

May the Lord al-might-y bless our days and our deeds with

peace. A - men.

Text: David Haas
Music: David Haas
© 1986, GIA Publications, Inc.

Evensong

The Church gathers in the evening to give thanks for the day that is ending. In the earliest tradition, this began with the lighting of the lamps as darkness fell and the hymn of praise of Christ who is "radiant Light . . . of God the Father's deathless face." The evening psalms and the Magnificat bring the day just past to focus for the Christian: "God has cast down the mighty from their thrones, and has lifted up the lowly"; "God has remembered the promise of mercy, the promise made to our ancestors." Prayers of intercession are almost always part of the church's liturgy, but those which conclude evening prayer are especially important. As day ends, the church again and again lifts up to God the needs and sorrows and failures of all the world. Such intercession is the daily task and joy of the baptized.

9 LIGHT PROCLAMATION
Stand

Light and peace in Jesus Christ our Lord. Thanks be to God.

10 EVENING HYMN

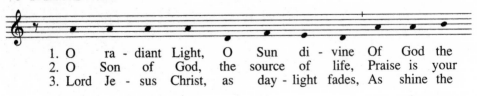

1. O ra - diant Light, O Sun di - vine Of God the
2. O Son of God, the source of life, Praise is your
3. Lord Je - sus Christ, as day - light fades, As shine the

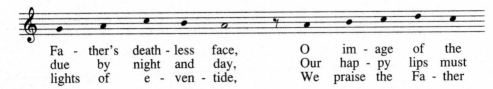

Fa - ther's death - less face, O im - age of the
due by night and day, Our hap - py lips must
lights of e - ven - tide, We praise the Fa - ther

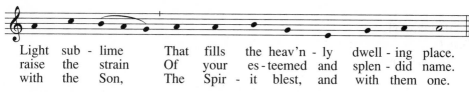

Light	sub - lime	That	fills	the heav'n - ly	dwell - ing	place.
raise	the strain	Of	your	es - teemed and	splen - did	name.
with	the Son,	The	Spir -	it blest, and	with them	one.

Text: *Phos Hilaron*, Greek, c.200; tr. by William G. Storey, ©
Music: JESU DULCIS MEMORIA, LM; Mode I; acc. by Richard Proulx, © 1975, GIA Publications, Inc.

PSALMODY

The singing of one or more psalms is a central part of Evensong. Psalm 141, given below, is one of the premier evening psalms. It is customary to use incense as it is sung. Other appropriate psalms for evening are Psalms 4, 19, 23, 27, 84, 91, 104, 110, 111, 112, 114, 115, 117, 118, 121, 122, 130, 136, 139, and 145.

PSALM 141 / INCENSE PSALM   11

Antiphon

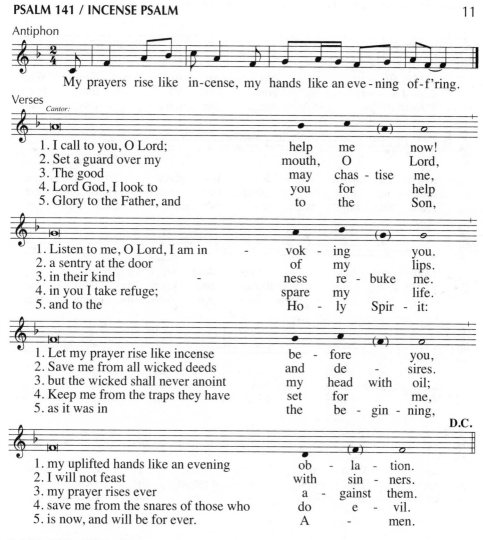

My prayers rise like in-cense, my hands like an eve - ning of-f'ring.

Verses

Cantor:

1. I call to you, O Lord;	help	me	now!
2. Set a guard over my	mouth,	O	Lord,
3. The good	may	chas - tise	me,
4. Lord God, I look to	you	for	help
5. Glory to the Father, and	to	the	Son,

1. Listen to me, O Lord, I am in -	vok - ing	you.
2. a sentry at the door	of my	lips.
3. in their kind -	ness re - buke	me.
4. in you I take refuge;	spare my	life.
5. and to the	Ho - ly Spir -	it:

1. Let my prayer rise like incense	be - fore	you,
2. Save me from all wicked deeds	and de - sires.
3. but the wicked shall never anoint	my head with	oil;
4. Keep me from the traps they have	set for	me,
5. as it was in	the be - gin - ning,

D.C.

1. my uplifted hands like an evening	ob - la - tion.
2. I will not feast	with sin - ners.
3. my prayer rises ever	a - gainst them.
4. save me from the snares of those who	do e - vil.
5. is now, and will be for ever.	A - men.

Text: Psalm 141; Howard Hughes, SM
Music: Howard Hughes, SM
© 1979, GIA Publications, Inc.

PSALM PRAYER

Stand

All respond: **Amen.**

12 WORD OF GOD

Sit

Reader concludes: The word of the Lord.
       Assembly: Thanks be to God.

13 GOSPEL CANTICLE

Stand. All make the sign of the cross as the canticle begins.

1. My ✠ soul gives glo - ry to my God Who
2. God's mer - cy com - forts all who fear, Em -
3. God's jus - tice sends the rich a - way, But

reach - es down with lov - ing grace To lift me
brac - ing with a stead - fast arm That casts the
feeds the poor with lav - ish things. Each hun - gry

from my low es - tate And set me in the
might - y from their thrones, But keeps the hum - ble
soul now fills with joy And joins the song that

high - est place. Mag - ni - fi - cat, mag - ni - fi -
safe from harm. Mag - ni - fi - cat, mag - ni - fi -
Mar - y sings: Mag - ni - fi - cat, mag - ni - fi -

cat! With all my heart, I an - swer
cat! The weak find strength; the wear - y,
cat! To God, Cre - a - tor, Christ, the

Yes   When God an - noun - ces won - drous news.   And
rest.   God's prom - ise sounds from age to age: The
Son;   And Ho - ly Spir - it— tri - une God: All

ev - 'ry age shall call me blest.
need - y of the world are blest.
prais - es to the Three - in - One.

Text: Mary Louise Bringle, © 2003, GIA Publications, Inc.
Music: MAGNIFICAT, LMD; Michael Joncas, © 1979, 1988, GIA Publications, Inc.

GENERAL INTERCESSIONS   14

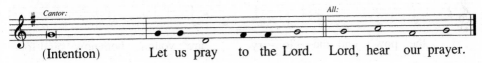

(Intention)   Let us pray to the Lord.   Lord, hear our prayer.

Music: Byzantine chant

LORD'S PRAYER   15

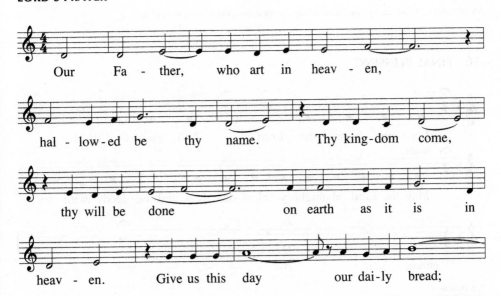

Our Fa - ther, who art in heav - en,

hal - low-ed be thy name.   Thy king-dom come,

thy will be done on earth as it is in

heav - en.   Give us this day our dai-ly bread;

and for-give us our tres - pass-es as we for-give those who tres-pass a - gainst us; and lead us not in-to temp-ta - tion, but de-liv-er us from e - vil. For the king-dom, the pow'r, and the glo - ry are yours, both now and for-ev - er. From now un-til the end of time.

Music: Steven C. Warner; acc. by Karen Schneider Kirner, © 1980, 1993, World Library Publications

16 FINAL BLESSING

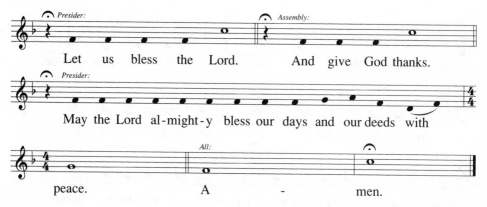

Presider: Let us bless the Lord. *Assembly:* And give God thanks.

Presider: May the Lord al-might-y bless our days and our deeds with

All: peace. A - men.

Psalm 15: They Who Do Justice   17

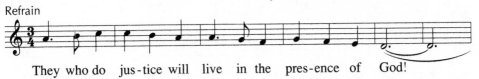

They who do jus-tice will live in the pres-ence of God!

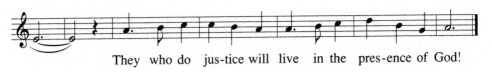

They who do jus-tice will live in the pres-ence of God!

Verses

1. Those who walk blamelessly and live their lives doing justice,
   who keep the truth in their heart, and slander not with their tongue!

2. Who harm not another, nor take up reproach to their neighbor,
   who hate the sight of the wicked, but honor the people of God!

3. Who show no condition in sharing the gifts of their treasure,
   who live not off the poor: They will stand firm forever!

Text: Psalm 15:2-5; David Haas, © 1989, GIA Publications, Inc.; refrain trans. © 1969, ICEL
Music: David Haas, © 1989, GIA Publications, Inc.

18 Psalm 16: Keep Me Safe, O God

Refrain

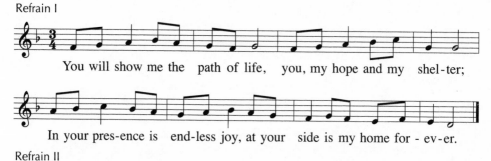

Keep me safe, O God: you are my hope;

you are my hope, O God.

Verses

1. I say to God, "you are my only God, I have no good except in you."

2. I find in God always my cup of joy; and God will keep my life secure.

3. I bless my God: God who has counseled me. At night my heart gives counsel too.

4. I keep my God always before my eyes; with God beside me I'm secure.

5. And so my heart always is glad in God; my body too shall dwell secure.

6. For you will not ever abandon me, or let your servant lose the path.

7. The path of life you have revealed to me, and in your presence is my joy.

Text: Psalm 16; John Foley, SJ, © 1993, GIA Publications, Inc.; refrain trans. © 1969, ICEL
Music: John Foley, SJ, © 1993, GIA Publications, Inc.

19 Psalm 16: You Will Show Me the Path of Life

Refrain I

You will show me the path of life, you, my hope and my shel-ter;

In your pres-ence is end-less joy, at your side is my home for - ev-er.

Refrain II

Keep me safe, O God, I take ref - uge in you.

Refrain III

You are my in - her - i - tance, O Lord.

Verses

1. Faithful God, I look to you, you alone my life and fortune,
   never shall I look to other gods, you shall be my one hope.

2. From of old you are my heritage, you my wisdom and my safety,
   through the night you speak within my heart, silently you teach me.

3. So my heart shall sing for joy, in your arms I rest securely,
   you will not abandon me to death, you shall not desert me.

Text: Psalm 16:1-2, 6-8, 9-10; Marty Haugen, © 1988, GIA Publications, Inc.; refrain III trans., © 1969, ICEL
Music: Marty Haugen; refrain II and III adapt. by Diana Kodner, © 1988, 1994, GIA Publications, Inc.

Psalm 19: Lord, You Have the Words   20

Refrain

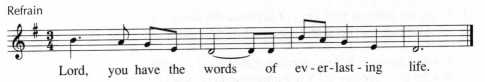

Lord, you have the words of ev - er - last - ing life.

Verses

1. The law of the Lord is perfect, refreshing the soul;
   the Lord's rule is to be trusted, the simple find wisdom.

2. The fear of the Lord is holy, abiding for ever;
   the decrees of the Lord are true, all of them just.

3. The precepts of the Lord are right, they gladden the heart,
   the command of the Lord is clear, giving light to the eye.

4. They are worth more than gold, than the finest gold,
   sweeter than honey, than honey from the comb.

Text: Psalm 19:8, 9, 10, 11; David Haas, © 1983, GIA Publications, Inc.; refrain trans. © 1969, ICEL
Music: David Haas, © 1983, GIA Publications, Inc.

21 Psalm 19: Words of Everlasting Life / Palabras de Vida Eterna

Bilingual Refrain

Lord, you have the words of ev-er-last-ing life.

Tú tie-nes, Se - ñor, pa - la - bras de vi - da e - ter-na.

Verses

1. The law of the Lord is perfect, refreshing the soul;
   The rule of the Lord is to be trusted, giving wisdom to the simple.

2. The precepts of the Lord are right, delighting the heart;
   the command of the Lord is clear, enlightening the eye.

3. The fear of the Lord is holy, enduring forever.
   The decrees of the Lord are true, all of them just.

4. They are more precious than gold, than the purest of gold;
   and sweeter are they than syrup, or honey from the comb.

1. *La ley del Señor es perfecta y_es descanso del alma;*
   fieles las palabras del Señor, instruyen al ignorante.

2. *Los mandatos del Señor son rectos y_alegran el corazón;*
   Son luz los preceptos del Señor alumbrando_el camino.

3. *La voluntad de Dios es santa y para siempre estable;*
   los mandatos del Señor son verdaderos y_enteramente justos.

4. *Más preciosos que_el oro y las piedras más finas;*
   y más dulces que la miel de_un panal que gotea.

Text: Psalm 19:8, 9, 10, 11; Tony E. Alonso, © 2003, GIA Publications, Inc.; English refrain trans. © 1969, ICEL; Spanish refrain trans. © admin. by
Obra Nacional de la Buena Prensa
Music: Tony E. Alonso, © 2003, GIA Publications, Inc.

Psalm 22: My God, My God   22

Refrain

My God, my God, O why have you a - ban-doned me?

Verses

1. All who see me laugh at me, they mock me and they shake their heads:
   "He relied on the Lord, let the Lord be his refuge."

2. As dogs around me, they circle me about.
   Wounded me and pierced me, I can number all my bones.

3. My clothing they divided, for my garments casting lots,
   O Lord, do not desert me, but hasten to my aid.

4. I will praise you to my people, and proclaim you in their midst,
   O fear the Lord, my people, give glory to God's name.

Text: Psalm 22:8-9, 17-18; 19-20; 23-24; Marty Haugen, © 1983, GIA Publications, Inc.; refrain trans. © 1969, ICEL
Music: Marty Haugen, © 1983, GIA Publications, Inc.

23 Psalm 23: Shepherd Me, O God

Refrain

Shep - herd me, O God, be - yond my wants, be - yond my fears, from death in - to life.

Verses

1. God is my shepherd, so nothing shall I want,
   I rest in the meadows of faithfulness and love,
   I walk by the quiet waters of peace.

2. Gently you raise me and heal my weary soul,
   you lead me by pathways of righteousness and truth,
   my spirit shall sing the music of your name.

3. Though I should wander the valley of death,
   I fear no evil, for you are at my side, your rod and your staff,
   my comfort and my hope.

4. You have set me a banquet of love in the face of hatred,
   crowning me with love beyond my pow'r to hold.

5. Surely your kindness and mercy follow me all the days of my life;
   I will dwell in the house of my God for evermore.

Text: Psalm 23; Marty Haugen
Music: Marty Haugen
© 1986, GIA Publications, Inc.

Psalm 23: My Shepherd Is the Lord   24

Antiphon I

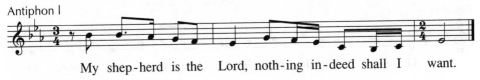

My shep-herd is the Lord, noth-ing in-deed shall I want.

Text: Psalm 23; The Grail
Music: Joseph Gelineau, SJ
© 1963, The Grail, GIA Publications, Inc., agent

Antiphon II

The Lord is my shep-herd, noth-ing shall I want: he

leads me by safe paths, noth-ing shall I fear.

Text: Psalm 23; The Grail
Music: A. Gregory Murray, OSB
© 1963, The Grail, GIA Publications, Inc., agent

Psalm Tone

Music: Richard Proulx, © 1975, GIA Publications, Inc.

Gelineau Tone

¹ **Lord, you** are mỳ **shep**herd;
there is **noth**ing Í shall **want**.

² **Fresh** and **green** are thè **pastures**
where you **give** me ré**pose**.
Near **restful waters** yòu **lead** me,

³ to re**vive** my droopíng **spirit**.

You **guide** me alòng the rìght **path**;
You are **true** tó your **name**.

⁴ If I should **walk** in the **valley** òf **darkness**
no **evil** would Í **fear**.
You are **there** with your **crook** and yòur **staff**;
with **these** you give mé **comfort**.

⁵ You have pre**pared** a **ban**quet fòr **me**
in the **sight** óf my **foes**.
My **head** you have a**noint**ed wìth **oil**;
my **cup** is ové**rflowing**.

⁶ Surely **good**ness and **kind**ness shàll **follow** me
all the **days** óf my **life**.
In the **Lord's** own **house** shall Ì **dwell**
for **ever** ánd **ever**.

To the **Father** and **Son** gìve **glory**,
give **glory** tó the **Spirit**.
To God who **is**, who **was**, and whò **will** be
for **ever** ánd **ever**.

Text: Psalm 23; The Grail
Music: Joseph Gelineau, SJ
© 1963, 1993, The Grail, GIA Publications, Inc., agent

25 Psalm 24: We Long to See Your Face

Refrain I

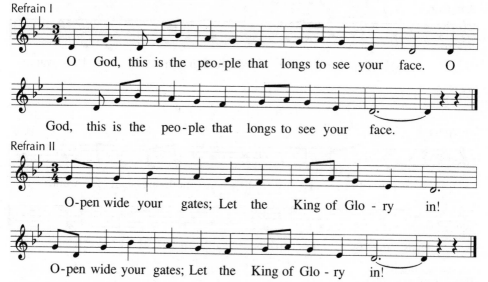

O God, this is the peo-ple that longs to see your face. O

God, this is the peo-ple that longs to see your face.

Refrain II

O-pen wide your gates; Let the King of Glo - ry in!

O-pen wide your gates; Let the King of Glo - ry in!

Verses

1. All the earth is yours, O God, the world and those who dwell on it.
   You have founded it upon the seas and established it upon the rivers.

2. Who can ascend your mountain, God? Or who may stand in this holy place?
   Those whose hands are sinless, hearts are clean, and desire not the vanity of earth.

3. They shall receive your blessing, God, their Savior shall reward them.
   Such is the face that seeks for you, that seeks your face, O God of Jacob.

Text: Psalm 24; Kevin Keil, © 1993, GIA Publications, Inc.; refrain 1 trans. © 1969, ICEL
Music: Kevin Keil, © 1993, GIA Publications, Inc.

Psalm 25: To You, O Lord 26

Refrain

To you, O Lord, I lift my soul, to you, I lift my soul.

Verses

1. Lord, make me know your ways, teach me your paths
   and keep me in the way of your truth, for you are God, my Savior.

2. For the Lord is good and righteous, revealing the way to those who wander,
   gently leading the poor and the humble.

3. To the ones who seek the Lord, who look to God's word, who live God's love,
   God will always be near, and will show them mercy.

Text: Psalm 25:4-5, 8-9, 12-14; Marty Haugen, © 1982, GIA Publications, Inc.; refrain trans. © 1969, ICEL
Music: Marty Haugen, © 1982, GIA Publications, Inc.

Psalm 25: Remember Your Mercies 27

Refrain I

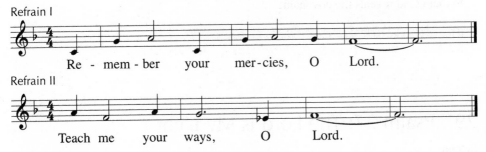

Re - mem - ber your mer-cies, O Lord.

Refrain II

Teach me your ways, O Lord.

Verses

1. Your ways, O Lord, make known to me, teach me your paths.
   Guide me, teach me, for you are my Savior.

2. Remember your compassion, Lord, and your kindness of old.
   Remember this, and not my sins, in your goodness, O Lord.

3. Good and just is the Lord, the sinners know the way.
   God guides the meek to justice, and teaches the humble.

Text: Psalm 25:4-5, 6-7, 8-9; David Haas, © 1985, GIA Publications, Inc.; refrain trans. © 1969, ICEL
Music: David Haas, © 1985, GIA Publications, Inc.

28 Psalm 25: To You, O Lord

Refrain

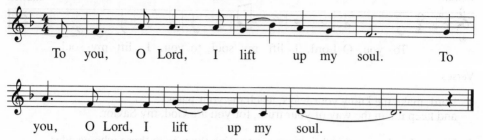

To you, O Lord, I lift up my soul. To
you, O Lord, I lift up my soul.

Verses

1. Lord, make me know your ways.
   Lord, teach me your paths.
   Make me walk in your truth,
   for you are God my Savior.

2. The Lord is good and upright.
   He shows the path to those who stray.
   God guides the humble in the right path.
   He teaches his way to the poor.

3. God's ways are faithfulness and love,
   for those who keep his covenant and will.
   The Lord's friendship is for those who revere him:
   to them God reveals the covenant.

Text: Psalm 25:4-5, 8-9, 10, 14; Stephen Pishner, © 2000, GIA Publications, Inc.; refrain trans. © 1969, ICEL
Music: Based on VENI EMMANUEL; Stephen Pishner, © 2000, GIA Publications, Inc.

29 Psalm 27: The Lord Is My Light

Refrain

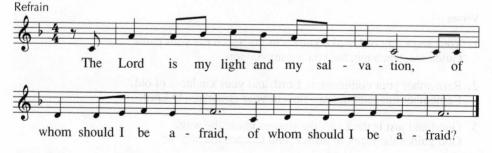

The Lord is my light and my sal - va - tion, of
whom should I be a - fraid, of whom should I be a - fraid?

Verses

1. The Lord is my light and my help; whom should I fear?
   The Lord is the stronghold of my life; before whom should I shrink?

2. There is one thing I ask of the Lord; for this I long:
   to live in the house of the Lord all the days of my life.

3. I believe I shall see the goodness of the Lord in the land of the living;
   hope in God, and take heart. Hope in the Lord!

Text: Psalm 27:1-2, 4, 13-14; David Haas
Music: David Haas
© 1983, GIA Publications, Inc.

Psalm 30: I Will Praise You, Lord   30

Refrain

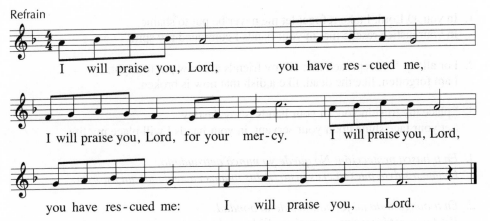

I will praise you, Lord, you have res-cued me,

I will praise you, Lord, for your mer-cy. I will praise you, Lord,

you have res-cued me: I will praise you, Lord.

Verses

1. I will praise you, Lord, you have rescued me
   and have not let my enemies rejoice over me.
   O Lord, you have raised my soul from the dead,
   restored me to life from those who sink into the grave.

2. Sing psalms to the Lord, you who love him,
   give thanks to his holy name.
   His anger lasts but a moment; his favor through life.
   At night there are tears, but joy comes with dawn.

3. The Lord listened and had pity.
   The Lord came to my help.
   For me you have changed my mourning into dancing;
   O Lord my God, I will thank you for ever.

Text: Psalm 30:2, 4, 5-6, 11-13; © 1963, 1993, The Grail, GIA Publications, Inc., agent; refrain, Paul Inwood, © 1985, Paul Inwood
Music: Paul Inwood, © 1985, Paul Inwood
Published by OCP Publications.

31 Psalm 31: I Put My Life in Your Hands / Pongo Mi Vida

Refrain

Ab-ba, Ab-ba, I put my life in your hands.
Ab-ba, Ab-ba, pon-go mi vi-da en tus ma-nos.

Ab-ba, Ab-ba, I put my life in your hands.
Ab-ba, Ab-ba, pon-go mi vi-da en tus ma-nos.

Verses

1. In you, O Lord, I take refuge; let me never be put to shame.
   In your justice rescue me, in your hands I commend my spirit.

2. For all my foes reproach me; all my friends are now put to flight.
   I am forgotten, like the dead, like a dish that now is broken.

3. I place my trust in you; in your hands is my destiny.
   Let your face shine upon your servant, in your hands I will place my life.

1. *En ti busco protección. No quede yo nunca defraudado.*
   Ponme a salvo, pues tú eres justo. A tus manos encomiendo mi espíritu.

2. *En ti pongo toda mi fe; hablaré de tu bondad.*
   Por favor estás siempre conmigo. Tú haces la luz del caos.

3. *Tú eres mi esperanza; sólo tú mi salvación.*
   Con tu misericordia, ven. Escucha mi oración.

Text: Psalm 31:2, 6, 12-13, 15-17 (English); 2, 6, 7-8, 15, 17, 23 (Spanish); David Haas; Spanish trans. by Jeffrey Judge
Music: David Haas
© 1993, GIA Publications, Inc.

Psalm 33: Let Your Mercy Be on Us   32

Refrain

Let your mer-cy be on us, O God,
as we place our trust in you.

Verses

1. Your words, O God, are truth indeed, and all your works are ever faithful;
   you love justice and right, your compassion fills all creation.

2. See how the eye of God is watching, ever guarding all who wait in hope,
   to deliver them from death and sustain them in time of famine.

3. Exult, you just, in the Lord, for praise is the song of the righteous!
   How happy the people of God, the ones whom God has chosen!

4. Our soul is waiting for God, for God is our help and our shield.
   May your kindness, O God, be upon us who place our hope in you.

Text: Psalm 33:1, 4-5, 12, 18-19, 20, 22; Marty Haugen, © 1987, GIA Publications, Inc.; refrain trans. © 1969, ICEL
Music: Marty Haugen, © 1987, GIA Publications, Inc.

Psalm 34: The Cry of the Poor   33

Refrain

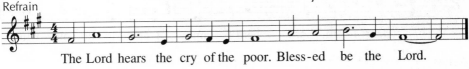

The Lord hears the cry of the poor. Bless-ed be the Lord.

Verses

1. I will bless the Lord at all times, with praise ever in my mouth.
   Let my soul glory in the Lord, who will hear the cry of the poor.

2. Let the lowly hear and be glad: the Lord listens to their pleas;
   and to hearts broken, God is near, who will hear the cry of the poor.

3. Every spirit crushed, God will save; will be ransom for their lives;
   will be safe shelter for their fears, and will hear the cry of the poor.

4. We proclaim your greatness, O God, your praise ever in our mouth;
   every face brightened in your light, for you hear the cry of the poor.

Text: Psalm 34:2-3, 6-7, 18-19, 23; John Foley, SJ
Music: John Foley, SJ
© 1978, 1991, John B. Foley, SJ, and OCP Publications

34   Psalm 34: Taste and See

Refrain

Taste and see the good-ness of the Lord, the good - ness   of the Lord.

Verses

1. I will bless the Lord at all times, God's praise ever in my mouth.
   Glory in the Lord for ever, and the lowly will hear and be glad.

2. Glory in the Lord with me, let us together extol God's name.
   I sought the Lord, who answered me and delivered me from all my fears.

3. Look to God that you might be radiant with joy,
   and your faces free from all shame.
   The Lord hears the suffering souls, and saves them from all distress.

Text: Psalm 34:2-3, 4-5, 6-7; Marty Haugen, © 1980, GIA Publications, Inc.; refrain trans. © 1969, ICEL
Music: Marty Haugen, © 1980, GIA Publications, Inc.

35   Psalm 40: Here I Am

Refrain

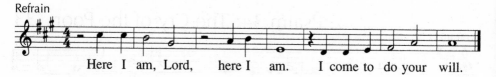

Here I am, Lord,   here I   am.   I come to do your   will.

Verses

1. Long was I waiting for God, and then he heard my cry.
   It was he who taught this song to me, a song of praise to God.

2. You asked me not for sacrifice, for slaughtered goats or lambs.
   No, my heart, you gave me ears to hear you, then I said, "Here I am."

3. You wrote it in the scrolls of law what you would have me do.
   Doing that is what has made me happy, your law is in my heart.

4. I spoke before your holy people, the good news that you save.
   Now you know that I will not be silent, I'll always sing your praise.

Text: Psalm 40; Rory Cooney, © 1971, 1991, North American Liturgy Resources.; refrain trans. © 1969, ICEL
Music: Rory Cooney, © 1971, 1991, North American Liturgy Resources.
Published by OCP Publications.

Psalm 47: God Mounts His Throne 36

Ostinato Refrain*

God mounts his throne to shouts of joy, O

sing your prais - es to the Lord!

Verses

1. All you peoples, clap your hands, shout to God in gladness,
   the Lord we must fear, king of all the earth.

2. God goes up to shouts of joy, sound the trumpet blast.
   Sing praise to our God, praise unto our king!

3. God is king of all the earth, sing with all your skill
   to the king of all nations, God enthroned on high!

May be sung in canon.

Text: Psalm 47:2-3, 6-7, 8-9; Marty Haugen, © 1983, GIA Publications, Inc.
Music: Marty Haugen, © 1983, GIA Publications, Inc.

Psalm 51: Create in Me 37

Refrains

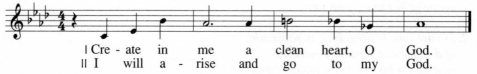

I Cre - ate in me a clean heart, O God.
II I will a - rise and go to my God.

Verses

1. Have mercy on me, O God. In the greatness of your love,
   cleanse me from my sin. Wash me.

2. Stay close to me, O God. In your presence keep me safe.
   Fill me with your spirit. Renew me.

3. Your salvation is joy to me. In your wisdom show the way.
   Lead me back to you. Teach me.

Text: Psalm 51:3-4, 12-13, 14-15; David Haas, © 1987, GIA Publications, Inc.; refrain I trans. © 1969, ICEL
Music: David Haas, © 1987, GIA Publications, Inc.

38 Psalm 51: Create in Me / Crea en Mí

Ostinato Refrains*

Cre - ate in me   a clean   heart, Oh   God.   Cre -

Oh Dios,   cre-a_en mí   un co - ra -zón   pu - ro.

Verses

1. A pure heart create for me, God.
   Steady my weary spirit.
   Do not cast me away from your presence,
   nor take your spirit from me.

2. Save me and bring back my joy.
   Support me and strengthen my will.
   Then I will teach transgressors your ways
   and sinners will return to you.

3. In sacrifice you take no delight.
   Burnt offerings you would refuse.
   My sacrifice, a contrite spirit,
   a changed heart you would not refuse.

1. *Crea_en mí un corazón puro,*
   renuévame con espíritu firme;
   no me_arrojes lejos de tu rostro,
   no me quites tu_espíritu santo.

2. *Devuélveme la_alegría de tu salvación,*
   afiánzame con espíritu generoso:
   enseñaré a los malvados tus caminos,
   los pecadores volverán a ti.

3. *Los sacrificios no te satisfacen:*
   un holocausto, no lo querrías.
   Mi sacrificio un espíritu quebrantado;
   no lo desprecias un corazón cambiado.

The English and Spanish refrains may be sung separately or together.

Text: Psalm 51:12-13, 14-15, 18-19; Tony E. Alonso, © 2003, GIA Publications, Inc.; English refrain trans. © 1969, ICEL; Spanish refrain trans. © 1970,
Conferencia Episcopal Española
Music: Tony E. Alonso, © 2003, GIA Publications, Inc.

Psalm 51: Be Merciful, O Lord   39

Refrains

```
 I  Be    mer - ci - ful,  O  Lord,  we have sinned,  we have sinned.
II  Cre - ate  a   clean heart    in    me,    O      God.
```

```
Be    mer - ci - ful,  O  Lord for  we have  sinned.
Cre - ate  a   clean  heart   in     me.
```

Verses

1. Have mercy on me, God, in your kindness.
   In your compassion blot out my offense.
   O wash me more and more from my guilt, from my guilt
   and cleanse me, O Lord, from my sin.

2. My offenses truly I know them;
   my sin is always before me.
   Against you, you alone, have I sinned, have I sinned;
   what is evil in your sight I have done.

3. A pure heart create for me, O God,
   put a steadfast spirit within me.
   Do not cast me away from your presence, O Lord,
   nor deprive me of your holy spirit.

4. Give me again the joy of your help, Lord;
   with a spirit of fervor sustain me.
   O Lord, open my lips, O Lord, open my lips
   and my mouth shall declare your praise.

The refrains may be sung in canon without the accompaniment.

Text: Psalm 51:3-4, 5-6, 12-13, 14, 17; © 1963, 1993, The Grail, GIA Publications, Inc., agent; refrain trans. © 1969, ICEL
Music: Based on WONDROUS LOVE, Stephen Pishner, © 1998, GIA Publications, Inc.

40 Psalm 51: Have Mercy, Lord

Antiphon

Have mer - cy, Lord, cleanse me from all my sins.

Text: Psalm 51; The Grail
Music: Joseph Gelineau, SJ
© 1963, The Grail, GIA Publications, Inc., agent

Psalm Tone

Repeat for 5 lines

Music: Chrysogonus Waddell, OCSO, © Gethsemani Abbey

Gelineau Tone

Repeat for 5 lines

³ Have **mer**cy on me, **God**, ìn your **kind**ness.
 In your com**pas**sion blot **out** my óffense.
⁴ O **wash** me more and **more** from mý **guilt**
 and **cleanse** me **from** mý **sin**.

⁵ My offenses **trulỳ** I **know** them;
 my **sin** is **al**ways bé**fore** me.
⁶ Against **you**, you a**lone**, have Ì **sinned**;
 what is **e**vil in your **sight** I háve **done**.

 That you may be **jus**tified **when** yòu
 give **sen**tence
 and be with**out** re**proach** when yóu **judge**,
⁷ O **see**, in **guilt** I wàs **born**,
 a **sin**ner was **I** cón**ceived**.

⁸ Indeed you love **truth** ìn the **heart**;
 then in the **se**cret of my **heart** teach mé
 wisdom.
⁹ O **pu**rify me, **then** I shall bè **clean**;
 O **wash** me, I shall be **whit**er thán **snow**.

¹⁰ Make me **hear** re**joic**ìng and **glad**ness
 that the **bones** you have **crushed** may
 ré**vive**.
¹¹ From my **sins** turn a**way** yòur **face**
 and **blot** out **all** mý **guilt**.

¹² A **pure** heart cre**ate** for mè, O **God**,
 put a **stead**fast **spir**it wíthin me.
¹³ Do not **cast** me a**way** from yòur
 presence,
 nor de**prive** me of your **ho**lý **spir**it.

¹⁴ Give me a**gain** the **joy** òf your **help**;
 with a **spir**it of **fer**vor sús**tain** me,
¹⁵ that I may **teach** trans**gres**sors yòur
 ways
 and **sin**ners may re**turn** tó **you**.

¹⁶ O **res**cue me, **Gòd**, my **help**er,
 and my **tongue** shall **ring** out yóur
 goodness.
¹⁷ O **Lord**, **o**pen mỳ **lips**
 and my **mouth** shall de**clare** yóur **praise**.

¹⁸ For in **sac**rifice you **take** nò de**light**,
 burnt **of**fering from **me** you would ré**fuse**;
¹⁹ my **sac**rifice, a **con**trìte **spir**it,
 a **hum**bled, contrite **heart** you will nót
 spurn.

²⁰ In your **good**ness, show **fa**vòr to **Zion**;
 re**build** the **walls** of Jéru**sa**lem.
²¹ **Then** you will be **pleased** with lawfùl
 sacrifice,

(burnt **offerings wholly cònsumed**),
then you will be **offered** young **bulls**
> on yóur **al**tar.

Give **glory** to the **Fathèr Al**might**y**,
to his **Son**, Jesus **Christ**, thé **Lord**,
to the **Spir**it who **dwells** in oùr **hearts**,
both **now** and for **ever**. **Ámen.**

Text: Psalm 51; The Grail
Music: Joseph Gelineau, SJ
© 1963, 1993, The Grail, GIA Publications, Inc., agent

Psalm 51: Be Merciful, O Lord   41

Be mer-ci-ful, O Lord, for we have sinned; be
mer-ci-ful, O Lord, for we have sinned.

Verses

1. Have mercy on me, God, in your kindness,
   in your compassion, blot out my offense.
   O wash me more and more from my guilt and my sorrow,
   and cleanse me from all of my sin.

2. My offenses, truly I know them, and my sins are always before me;
   against you alone have I sinned, O Lord, what is evil in your sight I have done.

3. Create in me a clean heart, O God, put your steadfast spirit in my soul.
   Cast me not away from your presence, O Lord, and take not your spirit from me.

4. Give back to me the joy of your salvation, let your willing spirit bear me up
   and I shall teach your way to the ones who have wandered,
   and bring them all home to your side.

Text: Psalm 51:3-4, 5-6, 12-13, 14-15; Marty Haugen, © 1983, GIA Publications, Inc.; refrain trans. © 1969, ICEL
Music: Marty Haugen, © 1983, GIA Publications, Inc.

42 Psalm 63: Your Love Is Finer than Life

Refrain

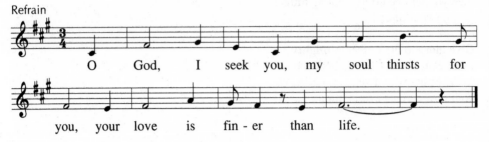

O God, I seek you, my soul thirsts for you, your love is fin - er than life.

Verses

1. As a dry and weary desert land, so my soul is thirsting for my God,
   and my flesh is faint for the God I seek, for your love is more to me than life.

2. I think of you when at night I rest, I reflect upon your steadfast love,
   I will cling to you, O Lord my God, in the shadow of your wings I sing.

3. I will bless your name all the days I live, I will raise my hands and call on you,
   my joyful lips shall sing your praise, you alone have filled my hungry soul.

Text: Psalm 63; Marty Haugen
Music: Marty Haugen
© 1982, GIA Publications, Inc.

Psalm 63: My Soul Is Thirsting   43

Refrain

My soul is thirst-ing, my soul is thirst-ing,

my soul is thirst-ing for you, O Lord my God.

Verses

1. O God, you are my God whom I seek;
   O God, you are my God whom I seek;
   for you my flesh pines, my soul thirsts like the earth,
   parched, lifeless, without water.

2. Thus have I gazed toward you in your holy place
   to see your power and your glory.
   Your kindness is a greater good than life itself;
   my lips will glorify you.

3. Thus will I bless you while I live;
   Lifting up my hands I will call upon your name.
   As with a banquet shall my soul be satisfied;
   with exultant lips my mouth shall praise you.

4. For you have been my help, you have been my help;
   in the shadow of your wings I shout for joy.
   My soul clings fast to you; your right hand holds me firm;
   in the shadow of your wings I sing for joy.

Text: Psalm 63:2, 3-4, 5-6, 8-9; verses adapt. © 1970, Confraternity of Christian Doctrine, Washington, D.C.; refrain by Michael Joncas, © 1987, GIA Publications, Inc.
Music: Michael Joncas, © 1987, GIA Publications, Inc.

44 Psalm 63: My Soul Is Thirsting

Antiphon I

My soul is thirst-ing for you, O Lord, thirst-ing for you my God.

Text: *Lectionary for Mass*, © 1969, 1981, ICEL
Music: Richard Proulx, © 1975, GIA Publications, Inc.

Antiphon II

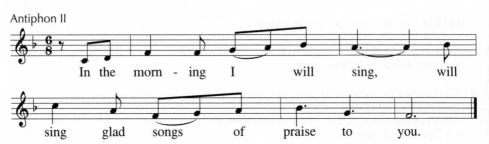

In the morn-ing I will sing, will sing glad songs of praise to you.

Text: *Praise God in Song*
Music: David Clark Isele
© 1979, GIA Publications, Inc.

Psalm Tone

Music: Richard Proulx, © 1986, GIA Publications, Inc.

Gelineau Tone

Omit for 4-line stanza

² O **God**, you are my **God**, for yòu I **long**;
  for **yóu** my **soul** is **thirst**ing.
  My **body pìnes** for **you**
  like a **dry**, weary **lánd** with<u>out</u> wa<u>ter</u>.
³ So I **gaze** on **you** in the **sànc**tuary
  to **see** your **stréngth** and <u>your</u> **glory**.

⁴ For your **love** is **bèt**ter than **life**,
  my **líps** will **speak** your **praise**.
⁵ So I will **bless** you **àll** my **life**,
  in your **name** I will **líft** up <u>my</u> **hands**.
⁶ My **soul** shall be **filled** as wìth a **ban**quet,
  my **mouth** shall **práise** you <u>with</u> **joy**.

⁷ On my **bed** I remèm**ber you**.
  On **you** I **múse** through <u>the</u> **night**
⁸ for **you** have **bèen** my **help**;
  in the **shad**ow of your **wíngs** I re<u>joice</u>.
⁹ My **soul clìngs** to **you**;
  your **ríght** hand **holds** me **fast**.

  Give **praise** to the **Fà**ther Al**might**y,
  to his **Son**, Jésus **Christ** the **Lord**,
  to the **Spir**it who **dwèlls** in our **hearts**,
  both **now** and for **éver**. <u>A</u>men.

Text: Psalm 63:2-9; The Grail
Music: Joseph Gelineau, SJ
© 1963, The Grail, GIA Publications, Inc., agent

Psalm 66: Let All the Earth   45

Refrain

Let all the earth cry out in joy to the Lord;

Let all the earth cry out in joy to the

1.-3. *To verses* | *Last time*

Lord!   Lord!   to the Lord!

Verses

1. Cry out in joy to the Lord, all peoples on earth,
   sing to the praise of God's name, proclaiming for ever,
   "tremendous your deeds for us."

2. Leading your people safe through fire and water,
   bringing their souls to life, we sing of your glory, your love is eternal.

3. Hearken to me as I sing my love of the Lord,
   who answers the prayer of my heart. God leads me in safety, from death unto life.

Text: Psalm 66:1-3, 12, 16; Marty Haugen
Music: Marty Haugen

46 Psalm 72: Every Nation on Earth

Refrain I

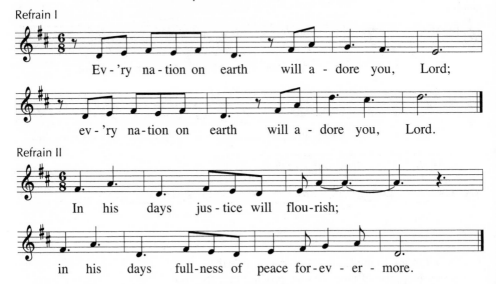

Ev - 'ry na - tion on earth will a - dore you, Lord;

ev - 'ry na - tion on earth will a - dore you, Lord.

Refrain II

In his days jus - tice will flou - rish;

in his days full-ness of peace for - ev - er - more.

Verses

1. O God, with your judgment endow the king;
   with your justice endow the king's son.
   With justice he will govern your people,
   your afflicted ones with right judgment.

2. Justice shall flow'r in his days,
   lasting peace 'til the moon be no more.
   May he rule from sea to sea,
   from the river to the ends of the earth.

3. The kings of Tarshish and the Isles offer gifts,
   those from Seba and Arabia bring tribute.
   All kings shall pay him their homage,
   all nations shall serve him.

4. He rescues the poor when they cry out,
   the afflicted with no one to help.
   The lowly and poor he shall pity,
   the lives of the poor he will save.

Text: Psalm 72:1-2, 7-8, 10-11, 12-13; Michael Joncas
Music: Michael Joncas
© 1987, 1994, GIA Publications, Inc.

Psalm 80/85/Luke 1: Lord, Make Us Turn to You   47

Refrain

Lord,   make us   turn to you,   show   us your face,   and

we   shall   be   saved.

Verses

1. Shepherd of Israel, hearken from your throne and shine forth,
   O rouse your power, and come to save us.

2. We are your chosen vine, only by your care do we live,
   reach out your hand, O Lord, unto your people.

3. If you will dwell with us, we shall live anew in your love,
   O shine upon us, great Lord of life.

4. Lord, we are present here, show us your kindness and love,
   O speak your word of peace unto your people.

5. Lord, let salvation rain, shower down your justice and peace,
   the earth shall bring forth truth, the skies your love.

6. See, Lord, we look to you, you alone can bring us to life,
   O walk before us to light our pathways.

7. You have done wondrous things, holy is your name for all time,
   your mercy and your love are with your people.

8. You are my joy and song, I would have my life speak your praise,
   on me your love has shown, your blessings given.

9. You fill all hungry hearts, sending the rich empty forth,
   and holding up in love the meek and lowly.

Text: Psalm 80:2-3, 15-16, 18-20; Psalm 85:9-14; Luke 1:46-55; Marty Haugen
Music: Marty Haugen
© 1982, GIA Publications, Inc.

48 Psalm 85: Lord, Let Us See Your Kindness

Refrain

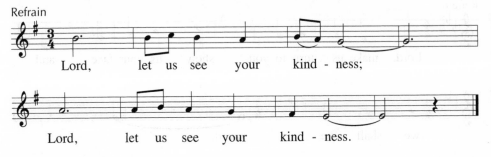

Lord, let us see your kind - ness;

Lord, let us see your kind - ness.

Verses

1. Let us hear what our God proclaims: Peace to the people of God,
   salvation is near to the ones who fear God.

2. Kindness and truth, justice and peace;
   truth shall spring up as the water from the earth,
   justice shall rain from the heavens.

3. The Lord will come and you shall know his love,
   justice shall walk in his pathways, salvation the gift that he brings.

Text: Psalm 85:9-10, 11-12, 13-14; Marty Haugen, © 1983, GIA Publications, Inc.; refrain trans. © 1969, ICEL
Music: Marty Haugen, © 1983, GIA Publications, Inc.

49 Psalm 89: For Ever I Will Sing

Refrain

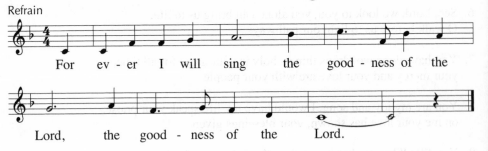

For ev - er I will sing the good - ness of the

Lord, the good - ness of the Lord.

Verses

1. "With my chosen one I have made a covenant; I have sworn to David my servant:
   I will establish your dynasty forever and set up your throne through all ages."

2. Happy the people who acclaim such a God,
   who walk, O Lord, in the light of your face,
   who find their joy ev'ry day in your name,
   who make your justice the source of their bliss.

3. He will say to me: "You are my father, my God, the rock who saves me!"
   I will keep my love for him always; with him my covenant shall last.

Alternate Verses

1. I have found David my servant,
   with my holy oil I have anointed him,
   that my hand may ever be with him
   and my arm make him strong.

2. My faithfulness and love shall be with you,
   in my Name your name will be exalted.

3. He shall cry to me, "My God, my rock of salvation, my salvation."

Text: Psalm 89: 4-5, 16-17, 27-29, © 1963, 1993, The Grail, GIA Publications, Inc., agent; alt. verses 21-22, 25, 27, Marty Haugen, © 1988, 1994,
GIA Publications, Inc.; refrain trans. © 1969, ICEL
Music: Marty Haugen, © 1988, 1994, GIA Publications, Inc.

Psalm 91: Be with Me   50

Refrain

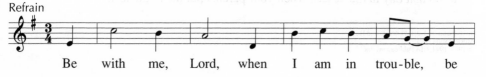

Be with me, Lord, when I am in trou-ble, be

with me, Lord, I pray.

Verses

1. You who dwell in the shelter of the Lord, Most High,
   who abide in the shadow of our God,
   say to the Lord: "My refuge and fortress, the God in whom I trust."

2. No evil shall befall you, no pain come near,
   for the angels stand close by your side,
   guarding you always and bearing you gently, watching over your life.

3. Those who cling to the Lord live secure in God's love,
   lifted high, those who trust in God's name,
   call on the Lord, who will never forsake you.
   God will bring you salvation and joy.

Text: Psalm 91:1-2, 10-11, 14-15; Marty Haugen
Music: Marty Haugen
© 1980, GIA Publications, Inc.

51 Psalm 95: If Today You Hear God's Voice

Refrain

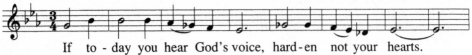

If to-day you hear God's voice, hard-en not your hearts.

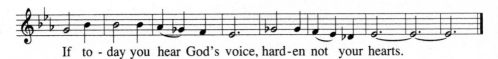

If to-day you hear God's voice, hard-en not your hearts.

Verses

1. Come, ring out our joy to the Lord, hail the rock who saves us,
   let us come now before our God, with songs let us hail the Lord.

2. Come, let us bow and bend low, let us kneel before God who made us,
   for here is our God; we the people, the flock that is led by God's hand.

3. O that today you would hear God's voice, "Harden not your hearts,
   as on that day in the desert, when your parents put me to the test."

Text: Psalm 95:1-2, 6-7, 8-9; David Haas
Music: David Haas
© 1983, 1994, GIA Publications, Inc.

52 Psalm 96: Today Is Born Our Savior

Refrain

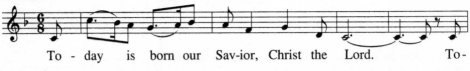

To - day is born our Sav-ior, Christ the Lord. To-

day is born our Sav-ior, Christ the Lord.

Verses

1. Sing to the Lord a new song;
   sing to the Lord, all you lands.
   Sing to the Lord; bless his name.

2. Announce his salvation, day after day.
   Tell his glory among the nations;
   Among all peoples, his wondrous deeds.

3. Let the heavens be glad and the earth rejoice;
   let the sea and what fills it resound;
   let the plains be joyful and all that is in them!
   Then shall all the trees of the forest exult.

4. They shall exult before the Lord, for he comes;
   for he comes to rule the earth.
   He shall rule the world with justice
   and the peoples with his constancy.

Text: Psalm 96; verses trans. © 1970, Confraternity of Christian Doctrine, Washington, D.C.; refrain trans. © 1969, ICEL
Music: Howard Hughes, SM, © 1976, GIA Publications, Inc.

Psalm 96: Sing a Song to the Lord's Holy Name   53

Refrain

Sing a song to the Lord's ho - ly name. May the won - ders of God be pro - claimed. Sing a song to the Lord, now ac - claim. Al - le - lu - ia, al - le - lu - ia! Ho - ly is God's name!

Verses

1. Give the Lord, you families of people, Give the Lord glory and power.
   Give the Lord a heart that is grateful. Let us tell of the glory of God.

2. Tell the world our God rules with justice. Tell the world its praises to sing.
   Tell the world God's people know fairness. Let our voices proclaim God is King.

3. Day by day we count on God's blessings. Day by day we seek for God's strength.
   Day by day may love be our lesson. May our wonder of God have no end.

Text: Psalm 96; Liam Lawton
Music: Liam Lawton; arr. by John McCann
© 1998, GIA Publications, Inc.

54   Psalm 96: Proclaim to All the Nations

Refrain I

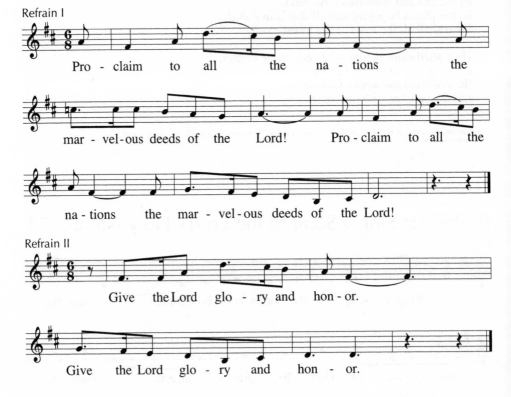

Pro - claim   to   all   the   na - tions   the
mar - vel-ous deeds of   the   Lord!   Pro - claim   to all   the
na - tions   the   mar - vel-ous deeds of   the Lord!

Refrain II

Give   the Lord   glo - ry and   hon - or.
Give   the Lord   glo - ry   and   hon - or.

Verses

1. Sing to the Lord a new song. Sing to the Lord all you lands!
   Sing to the Lord with all your heart, and bless God's name!

2. Announce salvation day by day, God's glory throughout the earth!
   Among all the people in every land, God's wondrous deeds!

3. Give to the Lord, you nations, praise to the Lord of all!
   Sing glory and praise and sing to the name, above all names!

4. Worship the Lord, and tremble, proclaim the one who reigns!
   Say to the nations: "The Lord is King;" who rules with justice!

Text: Psalm 96:1-2, 3, 7-8, 9-10; David Haas, © 1989, GIA Publications, Inc.; refrains trans. © 1969, ICEL
Music: Marty Haugen; refrain I, David Haas; refrain II adapt. by Diana Kodner; © 1989, 1994, GIA Publications, Inc.

Psalm 98: All the Ends of the Earth 55

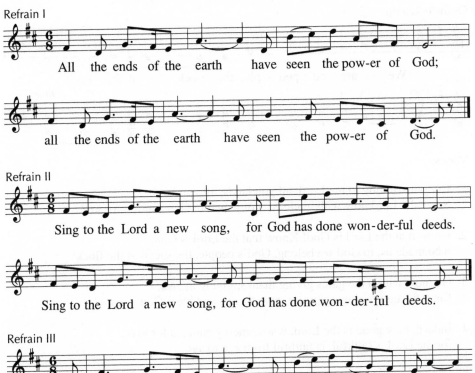

Refrain I

All the ends of the earth have seen the pow-er of God;
all the ends of the earth have seen the pow-er of God.

Refrain II

Sing to the Lord a new song, for God has done won-der-ful deeds.

Sing to the Lord a new song, for God has done won-der-ful deeds.

Refrain III

The Lord comes to the earth to rule the earth with jus-tice.

The Lord comes to the earth to rule the earth with jus-tice.

Verses

1. Sing to the Lord a new song, for God has done wondrous deeds;
   whose right hand has won the victory for us, God's holy arm.

2. The Lord has made salvation known, and justice revealed to all,
   remembering kindness and faithfulness to Israel.

3. All of the ends of earth have seen salvation by our God.
   Joyfully sing out all you lands, break forth in song.

4. Sing to the Lord with harp and song, with trumpet and with horn.
   Sing in your joy before the king, the king, our Lord.

Text: Psalm 98:1, 2-3, 3-4, 5-6; David Haas, Marty Haugen
Music: David Haas, Marty Haugen; refrain II, III adapt. by Diana Kodner
© 1983, 1994, GIA Publications, Inc.

56 Psalm 100: We Are God's People

Ostinato Refrain

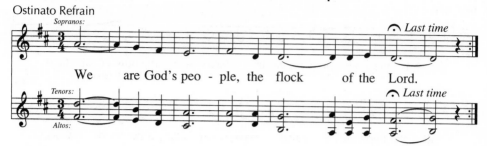

We are God's peo - ple, the flock of the Lord.

Verses

1. Cry out with joy to the Lord, all you lands, all you lands.
   Serve the Lord now with gladness, come before God singing for joy!

2. Know that the Lord is God! Know that the Lord is God,
   who made us, to God we belong, God's people, the sheep of the flock!

3. Go, now within the gates giving thanks, giving thanks.
   Enter the courts singing praise, give thanks and bless God's name!

4. Indeed, how good is the Lord, whose mercy endures for ever,
   for the Lord is faithful, is faithful from age to age!

Text: Psalm 100:1-2, 3, 4, 5; David Haas
Music: David Haas
© 1983, GIA Publications, Inc.

57 Psalm 103: My Soul, Give Thanks to the Lord

Antiphon

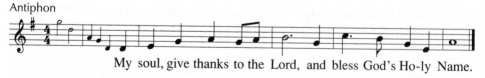

My soul, give thanks to the Lord, and bless God's Ho-ly Name.

Text: Psalm 103:1; © 1963, 1993, The Grail, GIA Publications, Inc., agent
Music: Richard Proulx, © 1986, GIA Publications, Inc.

Psalm Tone

Music: Richard Proulx, © 1986, GIA Publications, Inc.

Gelineau Tone

Omit for 5 lines
Omit for 4-line stanzas

¹ My **soul**, give **thanks** tò the **Lord**,
  all my being, **bléss** God's holy **name**.
² My **soul**, give **thanks** tò the **Lord**
  and **never** for**get** **á**ll God's **bless**ings.

³ It is **God** who for**gives** **à**ll your **guilt**,
  who **heals** every **ó**ne of your **ills**,
⁴ who re**deems** your **life** fròm the **grave**,
  who **crowns** you with **love** **á**nd
  com**pas**sion,
⁵ who **fills** your **life** wìth good **things**,
  re**new**ing your **youth** l**í**ke an **ea**gle's.

⁶ The **Lord** does **deeds** of **jù**stice,
  gives **judge**ment for **á**ll who are
  op**pressed**.
⁷ The **Lord's** **ways** were made **known** to
  Mòses;
  the **Lord's** **deeds** to **Í**srael's **sons**.

⁸ The **Lord** is com**pas**sion **à**nd **love**,
  slow to **anger** and **rí**ch in **mer**cy.
⁹ The **Lord** will not al**wà**ys **chide**,
  will **not** be **á**ngry for **ev**er.
¹⁰ God does not **treat** us ac**cord**ing tò our
  sins
  nor re**pay** us ac**cór**ding to our **faults**.

¹¹ For as the **heav**ens are **high** abòve the
  earth
  so **strong** is God's **love** fór the **God**-
  fearing;
¹² As **far** as the **east** is fròm the **west**
  so **far** does hé re**move** our **sins**.

¹³ As **par**ents have com**pas**sion on their
  chìldren,
  the Lord has **pity** on **those** who **á**re
  God-fearing;
¹⁴ for he **knows** of **what** wè are **made**,
  he re**mem**bers th**á**t we are **dust**.

¹⁵ As for **us**, our **days** are like **gràss**;
  we **flow**er like the **flów**er of the **field**;
¹⁶ the wind **blows** and **wè** are **gone**
  and our **place** never **sées** us a**gain**.

¹⁷ But the **love** of the **Lord** is ever**làst**ing
  upon **thóse** who **fear** the **Lord**.
  God's **jus**tice reaches **out** to children's
  children
¹⁸ when they **keep** his **cov**enant **ì**n **truth**,
  when they **keep** his **wìll** in their **mind**.

¹⁹ The **Lord** has set his **throne** in **hèav**en
  and his **king**dom **rúles** over **all**.
²⁰ Give **thanks** to the **Lord**, all you angels,
  mighty in **pow**er, fulfilling **Gòd's** **word**,
  who **heed** the **vóice** of that **word**.

²¹ Give **thanks** to the **Lord**, **à**ll you **hosts**,
  you **ser**vants wh**ó** **do** God's **will**.
²² Give **thanks** to the **Lord**, all his **works**,
  in **every** **place** whère God **rules**.
  My **soul**, give th**á**nks to the **Lord**!

Give **praise** to the **Fa**ther Al**mìgh**ty,
to his **Son**, Jésus **Christ**, the **Lord**,
to the **Spir**it who **dwells** in **ò**ur **hearts**,
both **now** and for **év**er. **Amen**.

Text: Psalm 103; The Grail
Music: Joseph Gelineau, SJ
© 1963, 1993, The Grail, GIA Publications, Inc., agent

58 Psalm 103: The Lord Is Kind and Merciful

Refrain

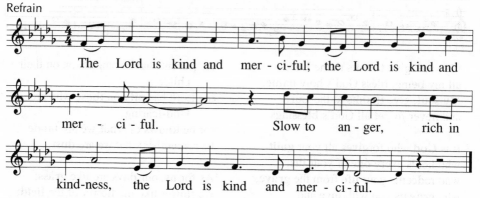

The Lord is kind and mer-ci-ful; the Lord is kind and mer-ci-ful. Slow to an-ger, rich in kind-ness, the Lord is kind and mer-ci-ful.

Verses

1. Bless the Lord, O my soul; all my being bless God's name.
   Bless the Lord, O my soul; forget not all God's blessings.

2. The Lord is gracious and merciful, slow to anger, full of kindness.
   God is good to all creation, full of compassion.

3. The goodness of God is from age to age,
   blessing those who choose to love.
   And justice toward God's children; on all who keep the covenant.

Text: Psalm 103; Jeanne Cotter
Music: Jeanne Cotter
© 1993, GIA Publications, Inc.

59 Psalm 103: The Lord Is Kind and Merciful

Refrain

The Lord is kind and mer-ci-ful, the Lord is kind and mer-ci-ful.

Verses

1. Bless the Lord, O my soul, and all my being bless God's name;
   bless the Lord, and forget not God's benefits.

2. God pardons all your iniquities, and comforts your sorrows,
   redeems your life from destruction and crowns you with kindness.

3. Merciful, merciful, and gracious is our God;
   slow to anger, abounding in kindness.

Text: Psalm 103:1-2, 3-4, 8; para. by Marty Haugen, © 1983, GIA Publications, Inc.; refrain trans. © 1969, ICEL
Music: Marty Haugen, © 1983, GIA Publications, Inc.

Psalm 104: Lord, Send Out Your Spirit 60

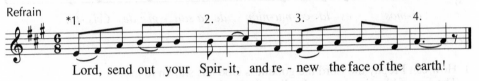

Lord, send out your Spir-it, and re - new the face of the earth!

Verses

1. Bless the Lord, O my soul; O Lord, my God, you are great indeed!
   How manifold are your works, O Lord! The earth is full of your creatures!

2. If you take away their breath, they die and they return to their dust.
   When you send forth your Spirit of life, they are created in your sight!

3. May his glory last for all time; may the Lord be glad in his works.
   Pleasing to him will be my theme; I will be glad in the Lord!

May be sung as a canon.

Text: Psalm 104:1, 24, 29-30, 31, 34; Paul Lisicky, © 1985, GIA Publications, Inc.; refrain trans. © 1969, ICEL
Music: Paul Lisicky, © 1985, GIA Publications, Inc.

61 Psalm 116: Our Blessing-Cup / El Cáliz que Bendecimos

Bilingual Refrain

Our bless-ing - cup is a com-mun - ion with the
Blood of Christ the Lord. *El cá-liz que ben-de-*
ci-mos es la co-mu-nión de la san - gre de Cris-to.

Verses

1. How can I repay the Lord the goodness God has shown to me?
   The cup of blessing I raise; I call upon God's name.

2. Painful to the eyes of God, the death of faithful servants.
   I am your servant, your child; you rescued me from death.

3. Thanks and praise I will offer God, and call upon your name, Lord.
   I will fulfill my vows to the Lord in the presence of God's people.

1. *¿Cómo le pagaré al Señor, mi Dios, todo_el bien que me ha hecho?*
   Alzaré la copa de la salvación, e_invocaré el nombre del Señor.

2. *Al Señor, que penosa es la muerte de sus fieles.*
   Soy tu sirviente, tu hijo: rompiste mis cadenas.

3. *Te_ofreceré mis gracias, Dios, invocando tu nombre.*
   Cumpliré mis promesas al Señor en presencia de todo su pueblo.

Text: Psalm 116:12-13, 15-16bc, 17-18; Tony E. Alonso, © 2003, GIA Publications, Inc.; Spanish refrain trans. © 1970, Conferencia Episcopal Española
Music: Tony E. Alonso, © 2003, GIA Publications, Inc.

Psalm 116: The Name of God   62

Refrain I

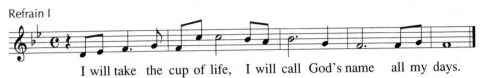

I will take the cup of life, I will call God's name all my days.

Refrain II

Our bless-ing-cup is a com-mun-ion with the Blood of Christ.

Refrain III

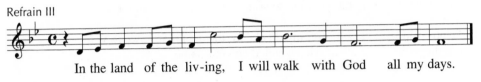

In the land of the liv-ing, I will walk with God all my days.

Verses

1. How can I make a return for the goodness of God?
   This saving cup I will bless and sing, and call the name of God!

2. The dying of those who keep faith is precious to our God.
   I am your servant called from your hands, you have set me free!

3. To you I will offer my thanks and call upon your name.
   You are my promise for all to see. I love your name, O God!

Text: Psalm 116; David Haas, © 1987, GIA Publications, Inc.; refrain II trans. © 1969, ICEL
Music: David Haas, © 1987, GIA Publications, Inc.

63   Psalm 116: Our Blessing-Cup

Refrain

Our bless-ing-cup is a com-mun-ion with the Blood of the Lord.

Verses

1. How can I make a return to the Lord for all God has done for me?
   The cup of salvation I will take up, I will call on the name of the Lord.

2. Precious, indeed, in the sight of the Lord is the death of his faithful ones;
   and I am your servant, your chosen one, for you have set me free.

3. Unto your name I will offer my thanks for the debt that I owe to you.
   In the presence of all who have called on your name,
   in the courts of the house of the Lord.

Text: Psalm 116:12-13, 15-16, 17-19; Marty Haugen
Music: Marty Haugen
© 1983, GIA Publications, Inc.

64   Psalm 118: This Is the Day

Refrain

This is the day the Lord has made; let us re-joice and be glad.

This is the day the Lord has made; let us re-joice and be glad.

Verses

1. Give thanks to the Lord for he is good,
   his mercy endures for ever;
   let the house of Israel say:
   "His mercy endures for ever."

2. The Lord's right hand has struck with power,
   the Lord's right hand is exalted;
   I shall not die, but live
   and declare the works of the Lord.

3. The stone which the builders rejected
   has become the cornerstone.
   By the Lord has this been done;
   it is wonderful in our eyes!

Text: Psalm 118, refrain trans. © 1969, ICEL; verses © Confraternity of Christian Doctrine, alt.
Music: Michael Joncas, b.1951, © 1981, 1982, Jan Michael Joncas Trust. Published by OCP Publications.

Psalm 118: Let Us Rejoice   65

Refrain

This is the   day   the Lord has   made,   let   us re-
Or: Al - le - lu - ia,   al - le - lu - ia!   Al - le -

joice and be   glad;   this is the   day   the Lord has
lu - ia!   Al - le - lu - ia,   al - le - lu -

made,   let   us re - joice and   be   glad!
ia!   Al - le - lu - ia!

Verses

1. Give thanks to the Lord, for God is good; God's mercy endures for ever;
   Let the house of Israel say: "God's mercy endures for ever."

2. The hand of the Lord has struck with power, God's right hand is exalted,
   I shall not die, but live anew, declaring the works of the Lord.

3. The stone which the builders rejected has become the cornerstone,
   the Lord of love and mercy has brought wonder to our eyes!

Text: Psalm 118:1-2, 16-17, 22-23; Marty Haugen, © 1983, GIA Publications, Inc.; refrain trans. © 1969, ICEL
Music: Marty Haugen, © 1983, GIA Publications, Inc.

66 Psalm 121: Our Help Comes from the Lord

Refrain

Our help comes from the Lord, the mak-er of heav-en and earth.

Verses

1. I lift up my eyes to the mountains: from where shall come my help?
   My help shall come from the Lord who made heaven and earth.

2. May God never allow you to stumble! Let God sleep not, your guard.
   Neither sleeping nor slumbering, God, Israel's guard.

3. The Lord is your guard and your shade: and at your right side stands,
   By day the sun shall not smite you nor the moon in the night.

4. The Lord will guard you from evil: God will guard your soul.
   The Lord will guard your going and coming both now and for ever.

5. Glory to the Father, and to the Son, and to the Holy Spirit:
   as it was in the beginning, is now, and will be for ever. Amen.

67 Psalm 121: Our Help Is from the Lord

Refrain

Our help is from the Lord, the mak-er of heav-en, the

mak - er of heav - en and earth.

Verses

1. I lift my eyes to the mountains, from where shall come my help?
   My help shall come from the Lord, the maker of heaven and earth.

2. May our God, ever wakeful, not allow you to fall.
   No, he sleeps not nor slumbers; for Israel God is at guard.

3. God is your guard and protection; by your side God shall stand.
   By day the sun shall not harm you, nor the moon in the night.

4. The Lord will shelter you from evil; God will guard your soul,
   will guard your coming and your going both now and forever more.

Psalm 122: Let Us Go Rejoicing 68

Refrain

Let us go re - joic - ing to the house of the Lord;

Let us go re - joic - ing to the house of the Lord.

Verses

1. I rejoiced when I heard them say: "Let us go to the house of the Lord,"
   and now our feet are standing within your gates, O Jerusalem.

2. Jerusalem is a city built with unity and strength.
   It is there, it is there that the tribes go up, the tribes of the Lord.

3. For Israel's law is to praise God's name and there to give God thanks.
   There are set the judgment thrones for all of David's house.

4. Pray for the peace of Jerusalem! "May those who love you prosper;
   May peace ever reign within your walls, and wealth within your buildings!"

5. For love of my family and love of my friends, I pray that peace be yours.
   For love of the house of the Lord our God I pray for your good.

69 Psalm 126: God Has Done Great Things for Us

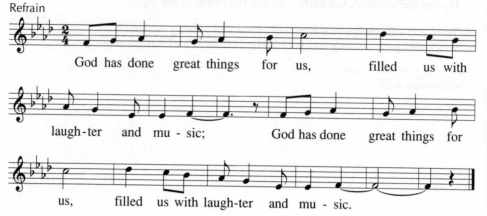

Refrain

God has done great things for us, filled us with laugh-ter and mu - sic; God has done great things for us, filled us with laugh-ter and mu - sic.

Verses

1. When our God led us back to freedom,
   like dreamers we beheld the promised land again;
   our mouths were filled with laughter and rejoicing.

2. We proclaimed to the nations what you had done for us;
   your mighty deeds of love, restoring us to life,
   you lead your people home to you rejoicing.

3. Come restore our fortune, renew us in your love,
   as rivers through the sand, as springs within the desert;
   those who sow in tears shall reap rejoicing.

Text: Psalm 126:1-6; Marty Haugen
Music: Marty Haugen
© 1988, GIA Publications, Inc.

Psalm 128: Blest Are Those Who Love You   70

Refrain I

Blest are those who love you, hap - py those who fol - low you, blest are those who seek you, O God.

Refrain II

May the Lord bless us, May the Lord pro - tect us, all the days, all the days of our life.

Verses

1. Happy all those who fear the Lord, and walk in God's pathway;
   you will find what you long for: the riches of our God.

2. Your spouse shall be like a fruitful vine in the midst of your home,
   your children flourish like olive plants rejoicing at your table.

3. May the blessings of God be yours all the days of your life,
   may the peace and the love of God live always in your heart.

Text: Psalm 128:1-2, 3, 5; Marty Haugen
Music: Marty Haugen; refrain II adapt. by Diana Kodner
© 1987, 1993, GIA Publications, Inc.

71 Psalm 130: With the Lord There Is Mercy

Refrain

With the Lord there is mer-cy, and full-ness of re-demp-tion.

Verses

1. From out of the depths, I cry unto you,
   Lord, hear my voice, come hear my prayer;
   O let your ear be open to my pleading.

2. If you, O Lord, should mark our guilt,
   then who could stand within your sight?
   But in you is found forgiveness for our failings.

3. Just as those who wait for the morning light,
   even more I long for the Lord, my God,
   whose word to me shall ever be my comfort.

Text: Psalm 130:1-2, 3-4, 5-6; Marty Haugen, © 1983, GIA Publications, Inc.; refrain trans. © 1969, ICEL
Music: Marty Haugen, © 1983, GIA Publications, Inc.

72 Psalm 131: My Soul Is Still

Refrain

In you, O Lord, I have found my

peace, I have found my peace.

Verses

1. My heart is not proud, my eyes not above you;
   You fill my soul. I am not filled with great things,
   nor with thoughts beyond me.

2. My soul is still, my soul stays quiet,
   longing for you like a weaned child
   in its mother's arms; so is my soul a child with you.

Text: Psalm 131; verses, David Haas, © 1985, GIA Publications, Inc.; refrain trans. © 1969, ICEL
Music: David Haas, © 1985, GIA Publications, Inc.

Psalm 136: Love Is Never Ending   73

1. We give thanks un - to you, O God of might:
2. In your wis - dom and love you shaped the skies:
3. You have filled all the skies with glo - ry and light:
4. From of old you have led your peo - ple in faith:
5. You de - liv - ered the ones who called un - to you:
6. You have o - pened the sea and brought your peo - ple through:
7. You re - mem - ber your prom - ise age to age:
8. You give food and life to all liv - ing things:

All:
for your love is nev - er end - ing,

Cantor:
We give thanks un - to you, the God of gods:
You spread out the earth up - on the sea:
The sun for the day and moon for night:
You have shown your com - pas - sion, strength and love:
From bond - age to free - dom, you brought them forth:
Brought them in - to a land that flows with life:
You show mer - cy on those of low de - gree:
We give thanks un - to you, the God of all:

All:
for your love is nev - er end - ing.

Text: Psalm 136; Marty Haugen
Music: Marty Haugen
© 1987, GIA Publications, Inc.

74 Psalm 138: The Fragrance of Christ

Refrains I-III

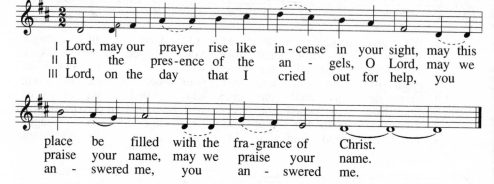

I Lord, may our prayer rise like in-cense in your sight, may this
II In the pres-ence of the an - gels, O Lord, may we
III Lord, on the day that I cried out for help, you

place be filled with the fra-grance of Christ.
praise your name, may we praise your name.
an - swered me, you an - swered me.

Verses

1. I will thank you, Lord, with all of my heart,
   you have heard the words of my mouth.
   In the presence of the angels I will bless you,
   I will adore before your holy temple.

2. I will thank you, Lord, for your faithfulness and love,
   beyond all my hopes and dreams.
   On the day that I called you answered;
   you gave life to the strength of my soul.

3. All who live on earth shall give you thanks
   when they hear the words of your voice.
   And all shall sing of your ways:
   "How great is the glory of God!"

Text: Psalm 138:1-5; David Haas
Music: David Haas
© 1989, GIA Publications, Inc.

75 Psalm 141: Let My Prayer Rise Up

Refrain

Let my prayer rise up like in-cense be - fore you, the

lift-ing up of my hands as an of-fer-ing to you.

Verse 1

Refrain

Verse 2

2. Keep watch with - in me, God; deep in my heart may the

2. Keep watch with - in me, God;

light of your love be burn - ing bright.

deep in my heart may the light of your love be burn - ing

Refrain

Let my prayer rise up like in - cense be -

bright. Let my prayer rise up like

fore you, the lift-ing up of my hands as an

in - cense be - fore you, the lift - ing up of my

of - fer - ing to you.

hands as an of - fer - ing to you.

Verse 3

3. All praise to the God of all— Cre - a - tor of

3. All praise to the

life; all praise be to Christ and the Spir - it of

God of all— Cre - a - tor of life; all praise be to

Refrain

love. Let my prayer rise up like

Christ and the Spir - it of love. Let my prayer rise

in - cense be - fore you, the lift - ing up of my hands as an

up like in - cense be - fore you, the lift - ing up of my

of - fer - ing to you.

hands as an of - fer - ing to you.

Text: Psalm 141; Marty Haugen
Music: *Holden Evening Prayer,* Marty Haugen
© 1990, GIA Publications, Inc.

76 Psalm 145: I Will Praise Your Name

Refrain

I will praise your name, my King and my God.

I will praise your name, my King and my God.

Verses

1. I will give you glory, my God above, and I will bless your name for ever.
   Ev'ry day I will bless and praise your name for ever.

2. The Lord is full of grace and mercy, who is kind and slow to anger.
   God is good in ev'ry way, and full of compassion.

3. Let all your works give you thanks, O Lord,
   and let all the faithful bless you.
   Let them speak of your might, O Lord, the glory of your kingdom.

4. The Lord is faithful in word and deed,
   and always near, his name is holy.
   Lifting up all those who fall, God raises up the lowly.

Text: Psalm 145:1-2, 8-9, 10-11, 13b-14; David Haas
Music: David Haas
© 1983, GIA Publications, Inc.

Psalm 147: Bless the Lord, My Soul 77

Refrain

Bless the Lord, my soul, who heals the bro - ken - heart - ed.

Verses

1. Praise the Lord, O Jerusalem, chant praises to your God.
   The strength of God is your fortress sure, and blessed are your children.

2. All praise to you, O gracious God, your goodness fills the earth.
   You raise anew Jerusalem, and gather all your lost ones.

3. You heal the hurt and broken heart, you bind up ev'ry wound,
   you number all the stars of night and call each one by name.

4. The peace of God shall be your hope, God's finest wheat, your food,
   the word of God fills all the earth, as rapid as the whirlwind.

Text: Psalm 147:12-13, 1-2, 3-4, 14-15; Marty Haugen
Music: Marty Haugen
© 1987, GIA Publications, Inc.

78 Psalm 150: Praise God in This Holy Dwelling

Al-le - lu - ia! Al - le - lu - ia! Al-le - lu - ia!

1. Praise God in this ho - ly dwell - ing; Praise God on the
2. Praise God with the blast of trum - pet; Bring praise now with
3. Praise God with re - sound-ing cym - bals; With cym - bals that
4. Praise God, the al - might - y Fa - ther; Praise Christ, the be -

might - y throne; Prais - ing for all won - der-ful
lyre and harp; Prais - ing with the tim - brel and
crash, give praise; O let ev - 'ry-thing that has
lov - ed Son; Give praise to the Spir - it of

deeds; Sing praise to our Sov - 'reign Maj - es - ty.
dance; With the gen - tle sound of string and reed.
breath, Let all liv - ing crea - tures praise the Lord.
love; For ev - er the Tri - une God be praised.

Al - le - lu - ia! Al - le - lu - ia!

1.-3.
Al - le - lu - ia!

4.
lu - ia!

Text: Psalm 150:1-2, 3-4, 5-6; adapt. by Omer Westendorf
Music: Jan M. Vermulst; arr. by Charles G. Frischmann
© 1964, World Library Publications

Exodus 15: Song of Moses 79

Refrain

Cantor:

I will sing, I will sing to the God who sets me free! I will

sing, I will sing to the God who sets me free! Phar-aoh's

ar - my and his char - i - ots God cast in - to the sea! Phar-aoh's

ar - my and his char - i - ots God cast in - to the sea!

Verses

1. The Lord is my strength, my protection and my shield;
   Pharaoh's army and his chariots God cast into the sea.
   Our God is a warrior whose name is "the Lord,"
   God of might, God of victory!

2. The brave and the mighty, the pride of Pharaoh's army,
   God plunged them to the bottom of the sea like a stone.
   The hand of the Lord is magnificent in power;
   the Lord has crushed our foes!

3. O God who redeems, who delivers us from slavery,
   you set us on the mountain of your holy place.
   Your throne and your temple shall endure for all time;
   your reign shall never end!

Text: Exodus 15; Scott Soper
Music: Scott Soper
© 1997, GIA Publications, Inc.

80 Exodus 15: Song at the Sea

Refrain

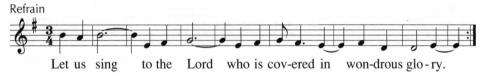

Let us sing   to the   Lord   who is cov-ered in   won-drous glo-ry.

Verses

1. I will sing to the Lord, in glory triumphant;
   horse and rider are thrown to the sea.
   God of strength, of song, of salvation, God of mine, hear these praises.

2. My God is a warrior whose name is "The Lord."
   Pharoah's army is thrown to the sea.
   Your right hand is magnificent in pow'r,
   your right hand has crushed the enemy.

3. In your mercy you led the people you redeemed.
   You brought them to your sacred home.
   There you will plant them on the mountain that is yours.
   The Lord shall reign for ever!

Text: Exodus 15; Niamh O'Kelly-Fischer
Music: Niamh O'Kelly-Fischer
© 1992, GIA Publications, Inc.

81 Isaiah 12: With Joy You Shall Draw Water

Refrain I

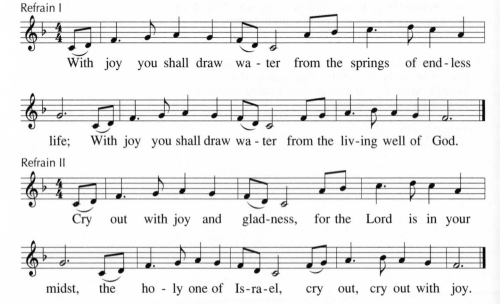

With   joy   you shall draw   wa - ter   from the springs   of end-less

life;   With joy you shall draw wa - ter from the liv-ing well of God.

Refrain II

Cry   out   with joy and   glad-ness,   for the   Lord   is in your

midst,   the   ho - ly one of Is-ra-el,   cry   out, cry out with joy.

Verses

1. God indeed is my Savior, I will never be afraid,
   my strength and courage is the Lord, my Savior and my song.

2. Give thanks and praise the name of God, sing out to all the earth
   the wondrous deeds that God has done, our Savior and our song.

3. Shout with joy, O Zion, for dwelling in your midst
   is the Holy One of Israel, your Savior and your song.

Text: Isaiah 12:2-3, 4, 6; Marty Haugen
Music: Marty Haugen; refrain II adapt. by Diana Kodner
© 1988, 1994, GIA Publications, Inc.

Daniel 3:52-90: Canticle of Daniel   82

Refrain

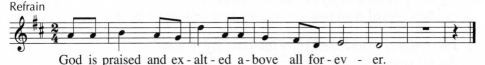

God is praised and ex-alt-ed a-bove all for-ev - er.

Verses

1. Angels of the Lord, *Response*
   you heavens, *Response*
   all waters above the heavens, *Response*
   all you hosts of the Lord, sun and moon,
   stars of heaven, bless the Lord!

2. Every shower and dew, *Response*
   all wind and heat, *Response*
   cold and chill, dew and rain, *Response*
   ice and snow, nights and days,
   lights and darkness and clouds, bless the Lord!

3. Mountains and hills, *Response*
   everything growing from the earth, *Response*
   springs, seas and rivers, *Response*
   all water creatures, all you birds,
   all you beasts, sons of man, bless the Lord!

4. O Israel, *Response*
   priests and servants of the Lord, *Response*
   spirits and souls of the just, *Response*
   holy men, humble of heart,
   Hananiah, Azariah, Mishael, bless the Lord!

Assembly Response

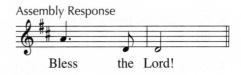

Bless   the Lord!

Text: Daniel 3:52-90; adapt. from the *New American Bible,* © 1970, Confraternity of Christian Doctrine, Inc.
Music: John Angotti; arr. by Paul A. Tate, © 2002, World Library Publications

83 Luke 1:46-55: Holy Is Your Name

Refrain

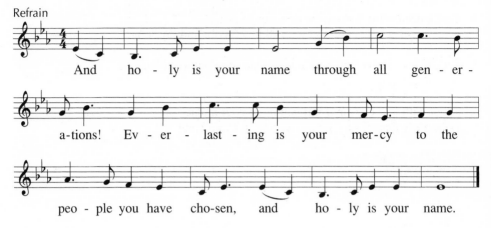

And ho-ly is your name through all gen-er-a-tions! Ev-er-last-ing is your mer-cy to the peo-ple you have cho-sen, and ho-ly is your name.

Verses

1. My soul is filled with joy as I sing to God my savior:
   you have looked upon your servant, you have visited your people.

2. I am lowly as a child, but I know from this day forward
   that my name will be remembered, for all will call me blessed.

3. I proclaim the pow'r of God, you do marvels for your servants;
   though you scatter the proud hearted, and destroy the might of princes.

4. To the hungry you give food, send the rich away empty.
   In your mercy you are mindful of the people you have chosen.

5. In your love you now fulfill what you promised to your people.
   I will praise you Lord, my savior, everlasting is your mercy.

Text: Luke 1:46-55, David Haas
Music: WILD MOUNTAIN THYME, Irregular; Irish traditional; arr. by David Haas
© 1989, GIA Publications, Inc.

84 Luke 1:46-55: Magnificat

Refrain

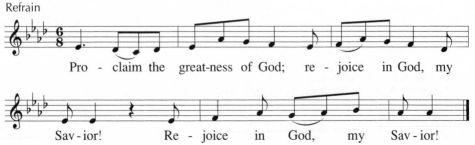

Pro-claim the great-ness of God; re-joice in God, my Sav-ior! Re-joice in God, my Sav-ior!

Verses

1. For he has favored his lowly one, and all shall call me blessed.
   The almighty has done great things for me, and holy is his name.

2. He favors those who fear his name, in ev'ry generation.
   He has shown the might and strength of his arm,
   and scattered the proud of heart.

3. He has cast the mighty from their thrones, and lifted up the lowly.
   He has filled the hungry with all good gifts, and sent the rich away.

4. He has helped his servant Israel, remembering his mercy.
   He promised his mercy to Abraham and his children for evermore.

Text: Luke 1:46-55; James J. Chepponis
Music: James J. Chepponis
© 1980, GIA Publications, Inc.

Luke 2: Nunc Dimittis 85

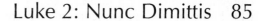

1. Now, O Lord, dis - miss your ser - vants With your word; give
2. Light, en - light - 'ning ev - 'ry peo - ple, Glo - ry of your
3. Child of Mar - y, sign of won - der, By you, man - y

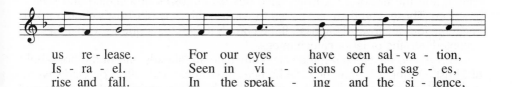

us re - lease. For our eyes have seen sal - va - tion,
Is - ra - el. Seen in vi - sions of the sag - es,
rise and fall. In the speak - ing and the si - lence,

Prom - ised ev - er to in - crease. Lord, dis - miss us, Lord, dis-
Heard in what the proph - ets tell. Lord, dis - miss us, Lord, dis-
Pierce our hearts and break our walls. Lord, dis - miss us, Lord, dis-

miss us; Now let us de - part in peace.
miss us; Now in ev - 'ry spir - it dwell.
miss us; Now, our God, our life, our all.

Text: *Nunc Dimittis*, Sylvia Dunstan, © 1995, GIA Publications, Inc.
Music: PEACETIME, 8 7 8 7 8 7; David Haas, © 2003, GIA Publications, Inc.

Christian Initiation of Adults

86

The passage of an adult into the Christian community takes place over an extended period of time. The members of the local church, the catechists and sponsors, the clergy and the diocesan bishop take part in the journey from inquiry through the catechumenate to baptism, confirmation and eucharist. The candidates are invited by example to pray, reflect on the scriptures, to fast and to join in the community's practice of charity. They are to learn the way of Jesus from the members of the church.

This journey of the candidates and community is marked by liturgical rites; thus the community publicly acknowledges, encourages and strengthens the candidates. The first of these is the rite of becoming catechumens. It concludes the sometimes lengthy period during which those who have come to ask about the way of the church and the life of a Christian have heard the gospel proclaimed and seen it practiced. Those who then feel called to walk in this way of Christ's church ask to begin the journey toward baptism. If the church judges the inquirers ready, they are accepted into the order of catechumens.

Those who have entered the catechumenate are already part of the household of Christ. During this time the catechumens are to hear and reflect on God's word, to learn the teachings and practices of the church, to become gradually accustomed to the ways of prayer and discipline in the church, to observe and to join in the good works of Christians. Ordinarily the catechumens are present on Sunday for the liturgy of the word and may be dismissed after the homily—to continue prayer and study with their catechists—since they cannot join in the eucharist.

Rites of exorcism and blessing may be celebrated during the catechumenate. Through such rites the church prays that the catechumens will be purified, strengthened against all evil and thus eagerly grow in faith and good works. The very presence of the catechumens—at the Sunday liturgy, in these special rites and in everyday life—is itself a source of strength and blessing to the faithful.

Each year as Lent begins, the bishop, with the help of the local pastor and others involved with the catechumens, is to call those catechumens who are judged ready to prepare themselves for baptism at the Easter Vigil. Thus the catechumens become the "elect", the chosen, and for the forty days of Lent they make preparations: praying, fasting, doing good works. All the faithful join them in this. On several Sundays in Lent the rites of scrutiny take place when the assembled church prays over the elect. During Lent also the catechumens may publicly receive the words of the church's creed and of the Lord's Prayer.

Good Friday and Holy Saturday are days of prayer, fasting and preparation for the rites of the Easter Vigil. On the night between Saturday and Sunday, the church assembles to keep vigil and listen to many readings from scripture. Then the catechumens are called forward for baptism and confirmation. These rites are found in the Easter Vigil.

The newly baptized, now called neophytes, take a special place in the Sunday eucharist throughout the fifty days of Eastertime. This is a time for their full incorporation into the local community.

All of these stages of initiation take place in the midst of the community. In various rites, the faithful show the Christian life to the inquirers and catechumens. In turn, the faithful are strengthened and challenged in their faith by the presence of the catechumens.

Those who seek to belong to the Roman Catholic church and who are already baptized may take some part in the catechumenate but they are not baptized again. Rather, they are received into the full communion of the Roman Catholic Church.

ACCEPTANCE INTO THE ORDER OF CATECHUMENS 87

INTRODUCTORY RITES

The presider greets the assembly: candidates, sponsors, members of the parish. The candidates are asked what it is that they seek and each replies. After each candidate has responded, the following may be sung:

88

We stand with you, we pray for you, O ho-ly child of God!

Text: David Haas
Music: David Haas
© 1988, GIA Publications, Inc.

89

We praise you, Lord, we praise you, Lord, we praise you, Lord, and we bless you.

Music: Marty Haugen, © 1995, GIA Publications, Inc.

CANDIDATES' FIRST ACCEPTANCE OF THE GOSPEL

The presider solemnly asks if the candidates are ready to begin walking this way of the gospel. The sponsors and all present are asked if they stand ready to assist the candidates as they strive to know and follow Christ. All respond: **We are.**

SIGNING OF THE CANDIDATES WITH THE CROSS

The sign of the cross marks the candidates for their new way of life. The presider signs each on the forehead saying:

N., receive the cross on your forehead.
It is Christ himself who now strengthens you
with this sign of his love.
Learn now to know him and follow him.

Sponsors and others also sign the candidates. Ears and eyes and other senses may also be signed. The presider prays that the catechumens may share in the saving power of the cross.

One of the following musical settings with assembly acclamations may be used:

90

Priest: Receive the sign of the cross....

Christ will be your strength! Learn to know and fol-low him.

Music: David Haas, © 1988, GIA Publications, Inc.

91

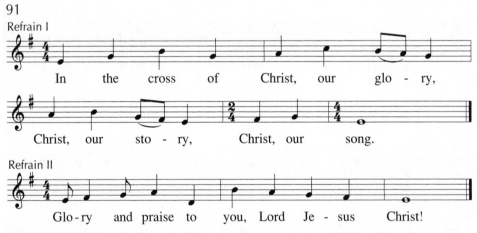

Refrain I

In the cross of Christ, our glo - ry,

Christ, our sto - ry, Christ, our song.

Refrain II

Glo - ry and praise to you, Lord Je - sus Christ!

Text: Adapt. by Marty Haugen
Music: Marty Haugen
© 1995, GIA Publications, Inc.

92 INVITATION TO THE CELEBRATION OF THE WORD OF GOD

The assembly may go into the church for the liturgy of the word singing the following psalm:

Come, my chil - dren, come to me, and

you will know the fear of the Lord.

I will bless the Lord at all times,
God's song is always on my lips.
In the Lord my soul shall make its boast,
the humble will hear and be glad. ℟.

Glory in the Lord with me,
May God's name always be our joy.

God answered me when I cried,
and freed me from my fear. ℟.

Look to God and shine with joy!
May God free your faces from all shame!
God hears the cry of all the poor,
and saves all who live in their fear. ℟.

Text: Psalm 34; adapted by David Haas
Music: David Haas
© 1988, GIA Publications, Inc.

LITURGY OF THE WORD 93

There may be one or more readings from scripture, together with a responsorial psalm. After the homily, a book containing the scriptures may be given to the new catechumens for their study and prayer throughout the time of the catechumenate.

INTERCESSIONS

All join in prayer for the new catechumens.

(Intention) Let us pray to the Lord. Lord, hear our prayer.

Music: Byzantine chant

RITES OF THE CATECHUMENATE 94

DISMISSAL OF THE CATECHUMENS

When the catechumens are present at Mass, they are usually dismissed after the homily. Only when they have been baptized are they able to join the faithful in the reception of the eucharist. After their dismissal, the catechumens remain together and are joined by their catechists or others to pray and reflect on the scripture.

The following may be sung to accompany the dismissal: 95

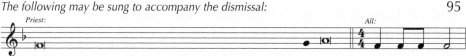

Go in peace, and may the Lord remain with you always. Go now in peace,

go now in peace, Christ will be your way, your truth, your life.

Text: *Rite of Christian Initiation of Adults*, © 1985, ICEL
Music: Lynn Trapp, © 1991, Morning Star Music Publishers

96 *Repeat as needed*

Go in peace, the peace of Christ, and learn the ways of God.

Text: Marty Haugen
Music: Marty Haugen
© 1997, GIA Publications, Inc.

97

May the Word be a lamp for our feet, and a light to guide our path!

Text: David Haas
Music: David Haas
© 1991, GIA Publications, Inc.

CELEBRATIONS OF THE WORD OF GOD

On Sundays, after the catechetical sessions, before the liturgical seasons and at other times the catechumens and others may join for liturgy: song, reading of scripture, psalmody, prayer and silence are normally part of such a service.

MINOR EXORCISMS

At appropriate times during the catechumenate, the catechists or other ministers may lead the community in prayers of exorcism over the catechumens. These prayers acknowledge the struggle against evil and ask that God strengthen the catechumens.

BLESSINGS OF THE CATECHUMENS

Prayers of blessing and the laying on of hands may take place whenever the catechumens gather for instruction of other purposes. Catechists or other ministers ask these blessings over the catechumens.

ANOINTINGS AND PRESENTATIONS

During the catechumenate or during Lent, the candidates may be anointed with the oil of catechumens as a sign of strength given for their struggle to live the gospel. At some point in this time they are publicly presented with the church's treasury of prayer and faith, the Our Father and the Creed.

RITE OF ELECTION OR ENROLLMENT OF NAMES

At the beginning of Lent, it is the responsibility of the bishop to call those who are judged ready to prepare for the sacraments of initiation at Easter. The bishop is to consult first with the pastors, catechists and others. The rite may take place at the cathedral. If the rite takes place in the parish church, the bishop may designate the pastor to act in his place.

This rite is also called the "Enrollment of Names." Each candidate now gives his/her name, or writes it down. When all have been enrolled, the bishop says: "You have been chosen to be initiated into the sacred mysteries at the Easter Vigil." He then speaks to them and to their sponsors about their lenten preparation for baptism.

While or immediately after the candidates have signed their names, a hymn or acclamation (e.g., no. 794) may be sung.

SCRUTINIES

The scrutinies occur on the Third, Fourth and Fifth Sundays of Lent. The elect are called before the community for exorcism and prayer. This rite may conclude with the following song, sung prior to dismissal of the elect:

Refrain

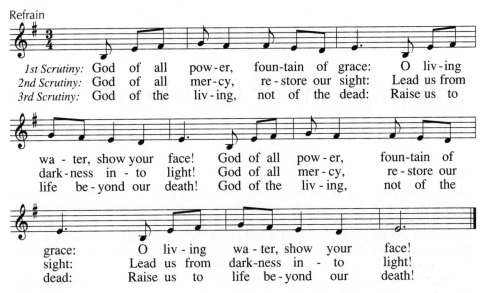

1st Scrutiny: God of all pow-er, foun-tain of grace: O liv-ing wa-ter, show your face! God of all pow-er, foun-tain of grace: O liv-ing wa-ter, show your face!

2nd Scrutiny: God of all mer-cy, re-store our sight: Lead us from dark-ness in-to light! God of all mer-cy, re-store our sight: Lead us from dark-ness in-to light!

3rd Scrutiny: God of the liv-ing, not of the dead: Raise us to life be-yond our death! God of the liv-ing, not of the dead: Raise us to life be-yond our death!

Text: David Haas
Music: David Haas
© 1988, GIA Publications, Inc.

PREPARATORY RITES

Various preparation rites take place during the day on Holy Saturday. These include prayer, recitation of the Creed, and the rite of Ephphetha (opening of ears and mouth).

SACRAMENTS OF INITIATION

The sacraments of initiation take place at the Easter Vigil.

PERIOD OF MYSTAGOGIA

"Mystagogia" refers to the fifty-day period of postbaptismal celebration when the newly baptized are gradually drawn by the community into the fullness of Christian life and prayer. The newly baptized retain a special place in the assembly and are mentioned in the prayers of intercession. A special celebration, on Pentecost or just before, may mark the conclusion of the whole period of initiation.

The Baptism of Children

99
Children are baptized in the faith of the church: of parents, godparents, the local parish, the church throughout the world, the saints. Bringing their children for baptism, the parents profess their commitment to make a home where the gospel is lived. And the godparents and all members of the community promise to support the parents in this. Thus the children enter the waters of baptism and so are joined to this people, all baptized into the death and resurrection of Christ.

Baptism is celebrated above all at the Easter Vigil, but also on other Sundays, for Sunday is the Lord's day, the day when the church gathers to proclaim the paschal mystery. Although baptism may take place at the Sunday Mass, it is always to be celebrated in an assembly of members of the church.

100 RECEPTION OF THE CHILDREN

The parents and godparents are welcomed by all. The priest/deacon asks the names of the children and questions the parents about their own expectations and willingness to take on the responsibilities this baptism brings. The godparents are asked if they are ready to assist the parents to become Christian mothers and fathers.

With joy, then, the priest/deacon, the parents and godparents make the sign of the cross on the child's forehead: "I claim you for Christ our Savior by the sign of his cross."

All then go in procession to the place where the scriptures will be read. The following antiphon, or a hymn, may be sung during this procession:

The assembly repeats each phrase after the cantor.

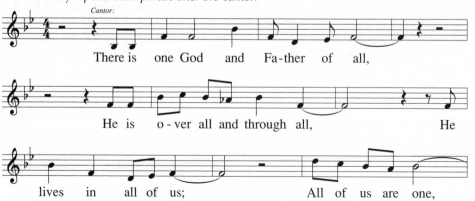

There is one God and Fa-ther of all,
He is o-ver all and through all, He
lives in all of us; All of us are one,

u - nit - ed in Christ   Je - sus.

Text: ICEL, © 1969
Music: Marty Haugen, © 1995, GIA Publications, Inc.

LITURGY OF THE WORD   101

FIRST READINGS

One or more passages from scripture are read. At the conclusion of each:

Reader: The word of the Lord.

Assembly: **Thanks be to God.**

RESPONSORIAL PSALM

The following psalm may follow the first reading:

Refrain

The   Lord   is   my   light   and   my   sal - va - tion.

Text: *Lectionary for Mass,* © 1969, ICEL
Music: Anthony E. Jackson, © 1984

Verses

The Lord is my light and my help;
whom shall I fear?
The Lord is the stronghold of my life:
before whom shall I shrink? ℟.

There is one thing I ask of the Lord,
   for this I long,
to live in the house of the Lord,
   all the days of my life,
to savor the sweetness of the Lord,
to behold his temple. ℟.

I am sure I shall see the Lord's goodness
in the land of the living.
Hope in him, hold firm and take heart.
Hope in the Lord! ℟.

Text: Psalm 27:1, 4, 13-14, © 1963, The Grail, GIA Publications, Inc., agent
Music: Cyril Baker, © The Antilles Episcopal Conference

GOSPEL   102

Before the gospel reading, this acclamation is sung:

Cantor, then all:

Al - le - lu - ia,   al - le - lu - ia,   al - le - lu - ia.

Music: Chant Mode VI; acc. by Richard Proulx, © 1985, GIA Publications, Inc.

During Lent:

Cantor, then all:

Praise to you, Lord Je - sus Christ, king of end-less glo-ry!

Text: ICEL, © 1969
Music: Frank Schoen, © 1970, GIA Publications, Inc.

Deacon (or priest): The Lord be with you.
  Assembly: **And also with you.**
    Deacon: A reading from the holy gospel according to N.
  Assembly: **Glory to you, Lord.**

After the reading:

    Deacon: The gospel of the Lord.
  Assembly: **Praise to you, Lord Jesus Christ.**

103   GENERAL INTERCESSIONS

All join in prayer for the church, the needs of the world, the poor, the children to be baptized and their parents.

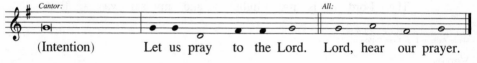

Cantor: *All:*

(Intention)   Let us pray   to the Lord.   Lord, hear our prayer.

Music: Byzantine chant

This prayer concludes with the litany of the saints which may include the patron saints of the children and of the local church.

104

Cantor: *All:*

1. Holy Mary, Mother of   God,   pray for us.
2. Saint John the   Bap - tist,   pray for us.
3. Saint   Jo - seph,   pray for us.
4. Saint Peter and Saint Paul,   pray for us.

The names of other saints may be added here. The litany concludes:

5. All you saints of   God,   pray for us.

105   PRAYER OF EXORCISM AND ANOINTING

The priest/deacon stands before the parents with their infants and prays that God deliver these children from the power of evil. The children may be anointed with the oil of catechumens, an anointing which makes them strong for their struggle against evil in their lives or the priest/deacon may lay hands on each child. The priest/deacon lays hands on each child to show the love and concern the Church has for them. If there is a procession to the baptistry, the following may be sung:

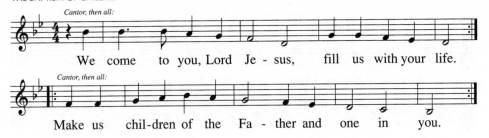

Cantor, then all:

We come to you, Lord Je - sus, fill us with your life.

Cantor, then all:

Make us chil-dren of the Fa - ther and one in you.

Text: ICEL, © 1969
Music: Ronald Arnatt, © 1984, GIA Publications, Inc.

SACRAMENT OF BAPTISM 106

BLESSING AND INVOCATION OF GOD OVER BAPTISMAL WATER
When all are gathered at the font, the priest/deacon leads a blessing of the water, unless the baptismal water has already been blessed.

RENUNCIATION OF SIN AND PROFESSION OF FAITH
The priest/deacon then questions the parents and godparents, and they make a renunciation of sin and evil and profess their faith. The assembly listens to their responses. The priest/deacon then invites all to give their assent to this profession of faith:

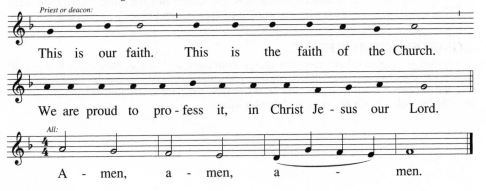

Priest or deacon:

This is our faith. This is the faith of the Church.

We are proud to pro - fess it, in Christ Je - sus our Lord.

All:

A - men, a - men, a - men.

Text: ICEL, © 1969
Music: Danish Amen

BAPTISM 107
One by one, the infants are brought to the font by their parents. There the parents express their desire to have their child baptized in the faith of the church which they have professed. The infant is then immersed in the water three times (or water is poured over the infant's head three times) as the priest/deacon says: "N., I baptize you in the name of the Father, and of the Son, and of the Holy Spirit." All may respond to each baptism with an acclamation.

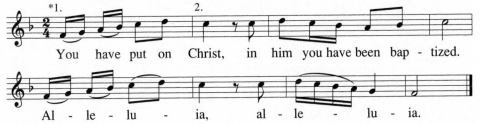

*1.   2.

You have put on Christ, in him you have been bap - tized.

Al - le - lu - ia, al - le - lu - ia.

*May be sung in canon.
Text: ICEL, © 1969
Music: Howard Hughes, SM, © 1977, ICEL

108

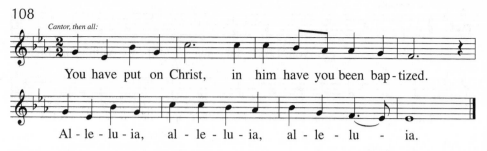

Cantor, then all:

You have put on Christ, in him have you been bap-tized.

Al - le - lu - ia, al - le - lu - ia, al - le - lu - ia.

Text: ICEL, © 1969
Music: J. William Greene, © 1998, GIA Publications, Inc.

109 ANOINTING WITH CHRISM

The priest/deacon anoints each child on the crown of the head with holy chrism, a mixture of oil and perfume. The word "Christ" means "anointed." The baptized child has been "Christ-ed" and the sweet smell of the anointing reminds all of this.

CLOTHING WITH THE BAPTISMAL GARMENT AND GIVING OF THE CANDLE

The infants are then clothed in baptismal garments and a candle for each of the newly baptized is lighted from the paschal candle.

Optional | *The priest/deacon may touch the ears and mouth of each child: "May Jesus soon touch your ears to receive his word, and your mouth to proclaim his faith."*

CONCLUSION AND BLESSING

If baptism is celebrated at Mass, the liturgy continues with the eucharist. Otherwise, all process to the altar, carrying lighted candles. The above acclamation may be sung again during this procession. All then pray the Lord's Prayer, the parents are blessed and the liturgy concludes with a hymn of praise and thanksgiving.

Reconciliation of Several Penitents

110

The sacrament of penance, also called the sacrament of reconciliation, may be celebrated with one penitent or with many. The latter form, the communal penance service, is a gathering of a few or a large number of Christians. Together they listen to the scriptures, sing psalms and hymns, pray, individually confess their sins and receive absolution, then praise God whose mercy and love are greater than our evil. In the rite of penance, the members of the church confront the struggle that was entered at baptism. There has been failure, evil done and good undone, but the penitent church comes again and again to name and renounce its sins and to return to the way of the Lord.

INTRODUCTORY RITES   111

An appropriate hymn or psalm may be sung.

GREETING

The priest and people greet each other in these or other words:

> *Priest:* Grace, mercy, and peace be with you
> from God the Father and Christ Jesus our Savior.
> *Assembly:* **And also with you.**

OPENING PRAYER

After silent prayer, the priest concludes the gathering rite with a solemn prayer.

CELEBRATION OF THE WORD OF GOD   112

FIRST READINGS

One or more passages from scripture are read. At the conclusion of each:

> *Reader:* The word of the Lord.
> *Assembly:* **Thanks be to God.**

RESPONSORIAL PSALM

The following psalm may follow the first reading:

With the Lord there is mer-cy, and full-ness of re-demp-tion.

Out of the depths I cry to you, O Lord,
Lord, hear my voice!
O let your ears be attentive
to the voice of my pleading. ℟.

If you, O Lord, should mark our guilt,
Lord, who would survive?
But with you is found forgiveness:
for this we revere you. ℟.

My soul is waiting for the Lord,
I count on his word.
My soul is longing for the Lord
more than watchman for daybreak. ℟.

Because with the Lord there is mercy
and fullness of redemption,
Israel indeed he will redeem
from all its iniquity. ℟.

Text: Psalm 130:1-2, 3-4, 5-6, 7-8; © 1963, The Grail, GIA Publications, Inc., agent; refrain trans. © 1969, ICEL
Music: Michel Guimont, © 1995, GIA Publications, Inc.

113 GOSPEL

Before the gospel reading, this acclamation is sung:

Cantor, then all:

Al-le-lu-ia, al-le-lu-ia, al-le-lu-ia.

Music: Chant Mode VI; acc. by Richard Proulx, © 1985, GIA Publications, Inc.

During Lent:

Cantor, then all:

Praise to you, Lord Je-sus Christ, king of end-less glo-ry!

Text: ICEL, © 1969
Music: Frank Schoen, © 1970, GIA Publications, Inc.

Deacon (or priest): The Lord be with you.
Assembly: **And also with you.**
Deacon: A reading from the holy gospel according to N.
Assembly: **Glory to you, Lord.**

After the reading:

Deacon: The gospel of the Lord.
Assembly: **Praise to you, Lord Jesus Christ.**

HOMILY

EXAMINATION OF CONSCIENCE
In silence or through some other manner all reflect on their lives with sorrow for their sins.

SACRAMENT OF PENANCE 114

GENERAL CONFESSION OF SINS
Kneeling (or with another posture that expresses sorrow,) all join in confession.
This form may be used:

I confess to almighty God,
and to you, my brothers and sisters,
that I have sinned through my own fault
in my thoughts and in my words,
in what I have done,
and in what I have failed to do;
and I ask blessed Mary, ever virgin,
all the angels and saints,
and you, my brothers and sisters,
to pray for me to the Lord our God.

115

Standing, all join in a litany using one of the following responses, or a song asking God's mercy. The Lord's Prayer is then recited or sung (see no. 150 and 164).

A **We pray you, hear us.**

B **Lord, be merciful to me, a sinner.**

C **Lord, have mercy.**

INDIVIDUAL CONFESSION AND ABSOLUTION 116
One by one the penitents approach the priest confessors. All confess their sins, accept some fitting act of satisfaction and the counsel of the confessor. Then the priest extends his hands over the penitent's head and speaks the prayer of absolution, concluding: "Through the ministry of the church may God give you pardon and peace, and I absolve you from your sins in the name of the Father, and of the Son, and of the Holy Spirit." The penitent responds, "Amen." (Note: On those occasions when general absolution is permitted, the rest of the rite remains the same.)

PROCLAMATION OF PRAISE FOR GOD'S MERCY
The priest invites all to give thanks and to show by their lives—and in the life of the whole community—the grace of repentance. A psalm, canticle or hymn may be sung to proclaim God's mercy.

CONCLUDING PRAYER OF THANKSGIVING
This prayer is spoken by the priest.

BLESSING AND DISMISSAL
The priest blesses all present and the deacon or other minister dismisses the assembly.
All respond: **Thanks be to God.**

Funeral Mass

117

The rites which surround the death of a Christian extend from the Viaticum (last communion) and final prayers before death through the wake service and funeral Mass to the burial of the body or ashes. In all of this the community affirms its faith in the communion of saints and the resurrection of the dead. The family and friends are helped in their time of sorrow with prayer and song. Thus they express present grief even as they hold to the church's lasting hope. Following is the rite of the funeral Mass.

INTRODUCTORY RITES

118 GREETING

The priest greets the assembly at the door, using these or similar words.

> *Priest:* The grace and peace of God our Father and the Lord Jesus Christ be with you.
> *Assembly:* **And also with you.**

The body is sprinkled with holy water.

SONG

As the procession enters the church, an appropriate song is sung.

The Mass continues as usual with the Opening Prayer, no. 139.

119 FINAL COMMENDATION

Following the prayer after Communion, the commendation begins with an invitation to silent prayer.

120 SONG OF FAREWELL

The following or another appropriate responsory or song may be sung.

Refrain

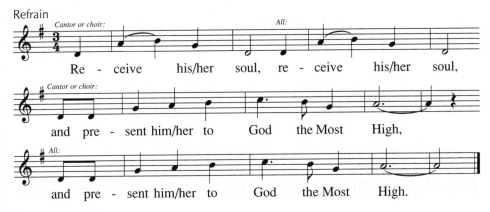

Re - ceive his/her soul, re - ceive his/her soul,

and pre - sent him/her to God the Most High,

and pre - sent him/her to God the Most High.

Verses .

1. Saints of God, come to his/her aid!
   Hasten to meet him/her, angels of the Lord!

2. May Christ, who called you, take you to himself;
   may angels lead you to the bosom of Abraham.

3. Eternal rest grant unto him/her, O Lord, and let
   perpetual light shine upon him/her.

Text: *Order of Christian Funerals*, © 1985, ICEL
Music: Steven R. Janco, © 1990, GIA Publications, Inc.

PRAYER OF COMMENDATION   121

At the conclusion of the prayer all respond: **Amen.**

PROCESSION TO THE PLACE OF COMMITTAL

The deacon or priest says: In peace let us take our brother/sister to his/her place of rest.

SONG   122

*As the assembly leaves the church, the following or another appropriate responsory or song
may be sung.*

May the an - gels lead you in - to par - a - dise; may the

mar - tyrs come to wel-come you and take you to the ho - ly

cit - y, the new and e - ter-nal Je - ru - sa - lem.

Text: *Order of Christian Funerals*, © 1985, ICEL
Music: Steven R. Janco, © 1990, GIA Publications, Inc.

Holy Communion Outside Mass

123
When for good reason communion cannot be received at Mass, the faithful may share in the paschal mystery through the liturgy of the word and the reception of holy communion.

INTRODUCTORY RITES
An appropriate hymn or psalm may be sung.

124   GREETING
If the minister is a priest or deacon, the usual form of greeting is used:

Assembly: **And also with you.**

If the minister is not a priest or deacon, another form of greeting may be used:

Assembly: **Blessed be God forever.**

PENITENTIAL RITE
The minister invites silent reflection and repentance. After some silence:

Assembly: **I confess to almighty God,**
       and to you, my brothers and sisters,
       that I have sinned through my own fault
       in my thoughts and in my words,
       in what I have done,
       and in what I have failed to do;
       and I ask blessed Mary, ever virgin,
       all the angels and saints,
       and you, my brothers and sisters,
       to pray for me to the Lord our God.

The forms found at no. 136 may also be used.

CELEBRATION OF THE WORD OF GOD
125

FIRST READINGS
One or more passages from scripture are read. At the conclusion of each:

Reader: The word of the Lord.
Assembly: **Thanks be to God.**

RESPONSORIAL PSALM
An appropriate psalm may follow the first reading.

GOSPEL
126

Before the gospel reading, the alleluia or Lenten acclamation is sung.

[*Deacon (or priest):* The Lord be with you.
        Assembly: **And also with you.**]
            Reader: A reading from the holy gospel according to N.
        Assembly: **Glory to you, Lord.**

After the reading:

        Reader: The gospel of the Lord.
        Assembly: **Praise to you, Lord Jesus Christ.**

GENERAL INTERCESSIONS
127

The assembly joins in prayer for the needs of the world, of the poor, and of the church.

HOLY COMMUNION
128

The minister invites all to join in the Lord's Prayer, then to exchange a sign of peace. The minister then raises the eucharistic bread and all respond to the invitation.

Assembly: **Lord, I am not worthy to receive you,**
        but only say the word and I shall be healed.

A psalm or hymn may be sung during communion. Afterwards, there may be a period of silence or the singing of a psalm or hymn. The minister then recites a concluding prayer.

CONCLUDING RITE
All are blessed and dismissed.

Presiding minister: Go in the peace of Christ.
        Assembly: **Thanks be to God.**

Eucharistic Exposition and Benediction

129

"Exposition of the holy eucharist . . . is intended to acknowledge Christ's marvelous presence in the sacrament. Exposition invites us to the spiritual union with him that culminates in sacramental communion. Thus it fosters very well the worship which is due to Christ in spirit and in truth.

This kind of exposition must clearly express the cult of the blessed sacrament in its relationship to the Mass. The plan of the exposition should carefully avoid anything which might somehow obscure the principal desire of Christ in instituting the eucharist, namely, to be with us as food, medicine, and comfort" (Holy Communion and Worship of the Eucharist outside of Mass, #82).

130 **EXPOSITION**

As the priest or deacon prepares the holy eucharist for adoration, the following or another suitable song is sung:

1. O Sav - ing Vic - tim, o - p'ning wide The
2. To your great name be end - less praise, Im -
1. O sa - lu - tá - ris hó - sti - a, Quae
2. U - ni tri - nó - que Dó - mi - no Sit

gate of heav'n to us be - low! Our foes press on from
mor - tal God-head, One in Three; O grant us end - less
cae - li pan - dis ó - sti - um: Bel - la pre - munt ho -
sem - pi - tér - na gló - ri - a: Qui vi - tam si - ne

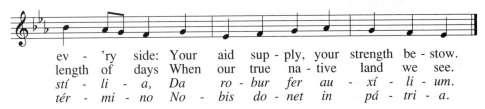

ev - 'ry   side: Your   aid   sup - ply,   your   strength be - stow.
length of   days   When   our   true   na - tive   land   we   see.
stí - li - a,   Da   ro - bur fer   au - xí - li - um.
tér - mi - no   No -   bis   do - net   in   pá - tri - a.

Text: Thomas Aquinas, 1227-1275; tr. by Edward Caswall, 1814-1878, alt.
Music: DUGUET, LM; Dieu donne Duguet, d.1767

ADORATION   131

During the adoration there are prayers, songs, Scripture readings, and possibly a homily to develop a better understanding of the eucharistic mystery. Silent prayer is also encouraged. If time allows, the Liturgy of the Hours may be celebrated here.

BENEDICTION   132

As the priest or deacon incenses the Blessed Sacrament, the following or another appropriate hymn or song may be sung:

1. Come   a - dore this   won-drous pres - ence, Bow   to   Christ the
2. Glo - ry   be   to   God   the   Fa - ther, Praise to   his   co -
1. *Tan - tum er - go   Sa - cra - mén - tum   Ve - ne - ré - mur*
2. *Ge - ni - tó - ri,   Ge - ni - tó - que   Laus   et   ju - bi -*

source of grace.   Here   is   kept the   an - cient prom - ise
e - qual Son,   Ad - o - ra - tion   to   the   Spir - it,
cér - nu - i: Et   an - tí - quum   do - cu - mén - tum
lá - ti - o,   Sa - lus, ho - nor,   vir - tus   quo - que

Of   God's earth - ly   dwell - ing - place. Sight is   blind be -
Bond of   love,   in   God - head one.   Blest be   God   by
No - vo   ce - dat   rí - tu - i: Prae - stet fi - des
Sit   et   be - ne - dí - cti - o: Pro - ce - dén - ti

fore God's glo - ry,   Faith a - lone may   see   his face.
all   cre - a - tion   Joy - ous - ly   while   a - ges run.
sup - ple - mén - tum   Sén - su - um   de - fé - ctu - i.
ab   u - tró - que   Com - par sit   lau - dá - ti - o.

Text: Thomas Aquinas, 1227-1274; tr. by James Quinn, SJ, © 1969. Used by permission of Selah Publishing Co., Inc.
Music: ST. THOMAS, 8 7 8 7 8 7; John F. Wade, 1711-1786

After a prayer, the priest or deacon blesses the assembly with the Blessed Sacrament.

133 **REPOSITION**

As the priest or deacon replaces the Sacrament in the tabernacle, the assembly sings or says the following acclamations:

Blessed be God.
Blessed be his holy name.
Blessed be Jesus Christ, true God and true man.
Blessed be the name of Jesus.
Blessed be his most sacred heart.
Blessed be his most precious blood.
Blessed be Jesus in the most holy sacrament of the altar.
Blessed be the Holy Spirit, Consoler.
Blessed be the great Mother of God, Mary most holy.
Blessed be her holy and immaculate conception.
Blessed be her glorious assumption.
Blessed be the name of Mary, virgin and mother.
Blessed be Saint Joseph, her most chaste spouse.
Blessed be God in his angels and in his saints.

The Order of Mass

134

Each church gathers on the Lord's Day to listen to the Scriptures, to offer prayers, to give thanks and praise to God while recalling God's gifts in creation and saving deeds in Jesus, and to share in holy communion.

In these rites of word and eucharist, the Church keeps Sunday as the Lord's Day, the day of creation and resurrection, the "eighth day" when the fullness of God's kingdom is anticipated. The Mass or eucharistic celebration of the Christian community has rites of gathering, of word, of eucharist, of dismissal. All those who gather constitute the assembly. One member of this assembly who has been ordained to the presbyterate or episcopate, the priesthood, leads the opening and closing prayers and the eucharistic prayer, and presides over the whole assembly. A member ordained to the diaconate may assist, read the gospel, and preach. Other members of the assembly are chosen and trained for various ministries: These are the readers, servers, ushers, musicians, communion ministers. All of these assist the assembly. It is the assembly itself, all those present, that does the liturgy.

The Order of Mass which follows is familiar to all who regularly join in this assembly. It is learned through repetition. This Order of Mass leaves many decisions to the local community and others are determined by the various seasons of the liturgical year.

INTRODUCTORY RITES

The rites which precede the liturgy of the word assist the assembly to gather as a community. They prepare that community to listen to the Scriptures and to celebrate the eucharist together. The procession and entrance song are ways of expressing the unity and spirit of the assembly.

GREETING

All make the sign of the cross.

  Priest: In the name of the Father, and of the Son, and of the Holy Spirit.
  Assembly: **Amen.**

After the sign of the cross one of the greetings is given.

A

Priest: The grace of our Lord Jesus Christ and the love of God
and the fellowship of the Holy Spirit be with you all.

Assembly: **And also with you.**

B

Priest: The grace and peace of God our Father
and the Lord Jesus Christ be with you.

Assembly: **Blessed be God, the Father of our Lord Jesus Christ.**
or: And also with you.

C

Priest: The Lord be with you. (*Bishop:* Peace be with you.)

Assembly: **And also with you.**

135 BLESSING AND SPRINKLING OF HOLY WATER

On Sundays, especially during the season of Easter, instead of the penitential rite below, the blessing and sprinkling of holy water may be done. The following or another appropriate song is sung as the water is sprinkled.

Refrain

If we have died to our-selves in Je-sus, then we shall a - rise to

new life in him. Al - le - lu - ia, al - le-lu - ia!

Verses

1. We are fire and wa-ter, we are sym - bol and
2. In the wa - ter we seek him, in the well-spring of
3. In the fire we seek him, in the hun - gers and
4. In our dy - ing and ris - ing, we shall fol - low where
5. Flow-ing out of the des-ert, roll - ing down from the
6. Rain-ing down from the heav-ens, spring-ing up from the
7. Gift of love and of mer-cy, giv - en free - ly to

sign of grace, we are the mys - t'ry,
all that lives, all who are thirst - y,
pains we bear, hope for the hope - less,
he has gone, pil - grims and lov - ers,
moun - tain side, up from with - in you,
dri - est earth, sim - ple and ho - ly,
all who thirst, gen - tle and yield - ing,

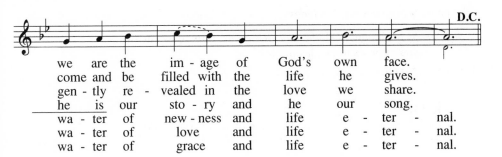

we	are	the	im - age	of	God's	own	face.
come and	be		filled with	the	life	he	gives.
gen - tly	re -		vealed in	the	love	we	share.
he	is	our	sto - ry	and	he	our	song.
wa - ter	of		new - ness	and	life	e - ter - nal.
wa - ter	of		love	and	life	e - ter - nal.
wa - ter	of		grace	and	life	e - ter - nal.

Text: *Mass of Creation*, Marty Haugen
Music: *Mass of Creation*, Marty Haugen
© 1984, GIA Publications, Inc.

PENITENTIAL RITE   136

The priest invites all to be mindful of their sins and of the great mercy of God. After a time of silence, one of the following forms is used.

A *Assembly:* **I confess to almighty God,
and to you, my brothers and sisters,
that I have sinned through my own fault
in my thoughts and in my words,
in what I have done,
and in what I have failed to do;
and I ask blessed Mary, ever virgin,
all the angels and saints,
and you, my brothers and sisters,
to pray for me to the Lord our God.**

B *Priest:* Lord, we have sinned against you: Lord, have mercy.

Assembly: **Lord, have mercy.**

Priest: Lord, show us your mercy and love.

Assembly: **And grant us your salvation.**

C *The priest or another minister makes a series of invocations according to the following pattern.*

Priest: (Invocation)
Lord, have mercy.

Assembly: **Lord, have mercy.**

Priest: (Invocation)
Christ, have mercy.

Assembly: **Christ, have mercy.**

Priest: (Invocation)
Lord, have mercy.

Assembly: **Lord, have mercy.**

The penitential rite always concludes:

> *Priest:* May almighty God have mercy on us, forgive us our sins,
> and bring us to everlasting life.

Assembly: **Amen.**

137 KYRIE

Unless form C of the penitential rite has been used, the Kyrie follows.

Refrain

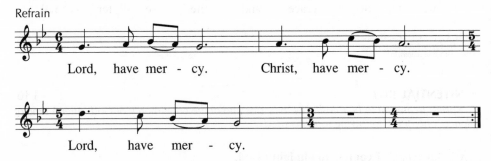

Music: *Mass of Creation,* Marty Haugen, © 1984, GIA Publications, Inc.

138 GLORIA

The Gloria is omitted during Advent, Lent, and most weekdays.

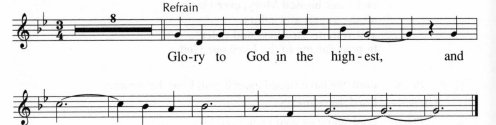

Verses

1. Lord God, heavenly King, almighty God and Father,
   we worship you, we give you thanks,
   we praise you for your glory.

2. Lord Jesus Christ, only Son of the Father,
   Lord God, Lamb of God,
   you take away the sin of the world: have mercy on us;
   you are seated at the right hand of the Father:
   receive our prayer.

3. For you alone are the Holy One,
   you alone are the Lord,
   you alone are the Most High, Jesus Christ,
   with the Holy Spirit,
   in the glory of God, the Father. Amen! Amen!

Music: *Mass of Creation*, Marty Haugen, © 1984, GIA Publications, Inc.

OPENING PRAYER   139

After the invitation from the priest, all pray for a while. The introductory rites conclude with the proper opening prayer and the Amen of the assembly.

LITURGY OF THE WORD   140

When the Church assembles, the book containing the Scriptures (Lectionary) is opened and all listen as the readers and deacon (or priest) read from the places assigned. The first reading is normally from the Hebrew Scriptures (Old Testament), the second from the letters of the New Testament, and the third from the Book of Gospels. Over a three-year cycle, the Church reads through the letters and gospels and a portion of the Hebrew Scriptures. During the Sundays of Ordinary Time, the letters and gospels are read in order, each Sunday continuing near the place where the previous Sunday's readings ended. During Advent/Christmas and Lent/Easter, the readings are those which are traditional and appropriate to these seasons.

The Church listens to and—through the weeks and years—is shaped by the Scriptures. Those who have gathered for the Sunday liturgy are to give their full attention to the words of the reader. A time of silence and reflection follows each of the two readings. After the first reading, this reflection continues in the singing of the psalm. A homily, bringing together the Scriptures and the life of the community, follows the gospel. The liturgy of the word concludes with the creed, the dismissal of the catechumens and the prayers of intercession. In the latter, the assembly continues its constant work of recalling and praying for the universal Church and all those in need.

This reading and hearing of the word—simple things that they are—are the foundation of the liturgical celebration. The public reading of the Scriptures and the rituals which surround this—silence and psalm and acclamation, posture and gesture, preaching and litany of intercession—gather the Church generation after generation. They gather and sustain and gradually make of us the image of Christ.

READING I

In conclusion:

   Reader: The word of the Lord.
   Assembly: **Thanks be to God.**

After a period of silence, the responsorial psalm is sung.

READING II

In conclusion:

   Reader: The word of the Lord.
   Assembly: **Thanks be to God.**

A time of silence follows the reading.

141   GOSPEL

Before the gospel, an acclamation is sung.

Cantor:

1, 5. Praise the God of all cre - a - tion, God of
2. Tree of life and end-less wis - dom, be our
3. Liv - ing wa - ter, we are thirst - ing for the
4. Come, O Spir - it, kin - dle fire in the

mer - cy and com - pas - sion:
root, our growth and glo - ry: Al - le - lu - ia! Al-le -
life that you have prom - ised:
hearts of all your peo - ple:

lu - ia! Praise the Word of truth and life!

Text: *Mass of Creation,* Marty Haugen
Music: *Mass of Creation,* Marty Haugen
© 1984, GIA Publications, Inc.

During Lent one of the following acclamations replaces the alleluia.

A

Praise to you, Lord Je - sus Christ, king of end-less glo-ry!

Text: ICEL, © 1969
Music: *Mass of Creation,* Marty Haugen, © 1984, GIA Publications, Inc.

Or:

B   **Praise and honor to you, Lord Jesus Christ!**

C   **Glory and praise to you, Lord Jesus Christ!**

D   **Glory to you, Word of God, Lord Jesus Christ!**

Deacon (or priest): The Lord be with you.
   Assembly: **And also with you.**
      Deacon: A reading from the holy gospel according to N.
   Assembly: **Glory to you, Lord.**

After the reading:

Deacon: The gospel of the Lord.
Assembly: **Praise to you, Lord Jesus Christ.**

HOMILY

PROFESSION OF FAITH   142

We believe in one God,
the Father, the Almighty,
maker of heaven and earth,
of all that is seen and unseen.

We believe in one Lord, Jesus Christ,
the only Son of God,
eternally begotten of the Father,
God from God, Light from Light,
true God from true God,
begotten, not made, one in Being with the Father.
Through him all things were made.
For us men and for our salvation he came down from heaven:

All bow at the following words up to: and became man.

by the power of the Holy Spirit
he was born of the Virgin Mary, and became man.
For our sake he was crucified under Pontius Pilate;
he suffered, died, and was buried.
On the third day he rose again
in fulfillment of the Scriptures;
he ascended into heaven
and is seated at the right hand of the Father.
He will come again in glory to judge the living and the dead,
and his kingdom will have no end.

We believe in the Holy Spirit, the Lord, the giver of life,
who proceeds from the Father and the Son.
With the Father and the Son he is worshiped and glorified.
He has spoken through the Prophets.
We believe in one holy catholic and apostolic Church.
We acknowledge one baptism for the forgiveness of sins.
We look for the resurrection of the dead,
and the life of the world to come. Amen.

143 *At Masses with children, the Apostles' Creed may be used:*

We believe in God, the Father almighty,
    creator of heaven and earth.

We believe in Jesus Christ, his only Son, our Lord.
    He was conceived by the power of the Holy Spirit
        and born of the Virgin Mary.
    He suffered under Pontius Pilate,
        was crucified, died, and was buried.
    He descended to the dead.
    On the third day he arose again.
    He ascended into heaven,
        and is seated at the right hand of the Father.
    He will come again to judge the living and the dead.

We believe in the Holy Spirit,
    the holy catholic Church,
    the communion of saints,
    the forgiveness of sins,
    the resurrection of the body,
    and the life everlasting. Amen.

144 GENERAL INTERCESSIONS

The people respond to each petition as follows, or according to local practice.

Music: *Mass of Creation*, Marty Haugen, © 1984, GIA Publications, Inc.

LITURGY OF THE EUCHARIST 145

To celebrate the eucharist means to give God thanks and praise. When the table has been prepared with the bread and wine, the assembly joins the priest in remembering the gracious gifts of God in creation and God's saving deeds. The center of this is the paschal mystery, the death of our Lord Jesus Christ which destroyed the power of death and his rising which brings us life. That mystery into which we were baptized we proclaim each Sunday at the eucharist. It is the very shape of Christian life. We find this in the simple bread and wine which stir our remembering and draw forth our prayer of thanksgiving. "Fruit of the earth and work of human hands," the bread and wine become our holy communion in the body and blood of the Lord. We eat and drink and so proclaim that we belong to one another and to the Lord.

The members of the assembly quietly prepare themselves even as the table is prepared. The priest then invites all to lift up their hearts and join in the eucharistic prayer. All do this by giving their full attention and by singing the acclamations from the "Holy, holy" to the great "Amen." Then the assembly joins in the Lord's Prayer, the sign of peace and the "Lamb of God" litany which accompanies the breaking of bread. Ministers of communion assist the assembly to share the body and blood of Christ. A time of silence and prayer concludes the liturgy of the eucharist.

PREPARATION OF THE ALTAR AND THE GIFTS

Bread and wine are brought to the table and the deacon or priest prepares these gifts. If there is no music, the prayers may be said aloud, and all may respond: **"Blessed be God for ever."** *The priest then invites all to pray.*

Assembly: **May the Lord accept the sacrifice at your hands**
for the praise and glory of his name,
for our good, and the good of all his Church.

The priest says the prayer over the gifts and all respond: **Amen.**

EUCHARISTIC PRAYER 146

The central prayer of the Mass begins with this greeting and invitation between priest and assembly.

The Lord be with you. And al - so with you. Lift up your hearts.

We lift them up to the Lord. Let us give thanks to the Lord, our God.

It is right to give him thanks and praise.

Music: *Mass of Creation*, Marty Haugen, © 1984, GIA Publications, Inc.

147 *The Sanctus acclamation is sung to conclude the introduction to the eucharistic prayer.*

Ho - ly, ho - ly, ho - ly Lord, God of pow-er, God of might, heav - en and earth are full of your glo - ry. Ho - san - na in the high - est. Bless - ed is he who comes in the name of the Lord. Ho - san - na in the high - est, ho - san - na in the high - est.

Music: *Mass of Creation,* Marty Haugen, © 1984, GIA Publications, Inc.

148-A *One of the following acclamations follows the priest's invitation: "Let us proclaim the mystery of faith."*

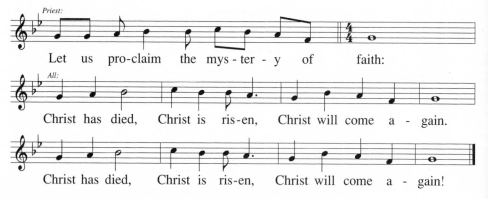

Priest: Let us pro-claim the mys - ter - y of faith:

All: Christ has died, Christ is ris-en, Christ will come a - gain.

Christ has died, Christ is ris-en, Christ will come a - gain!

Text: ICEL, © 1973
Music: *Mass of Creation,* Marty Haugen, © 1984, GIA Publications, Inc.

148-B

Text: ICEL, © 1973
Music: *Mass of Creation*, Marty Haugen, © 1990, GIA Publications, Inc.

148-C

Priest: Let us pro-claim the mys-ter-y of faith:

All: When we eat this bread, when we drink this cup, we pro-claim your death, Lord Je-sus, un-til you come in glo-ry.

Text: ICEL, © 1973
Music: *Mass of Creation*, Marty Haugen, © 1993, GIA Publications, Inc.

148-D

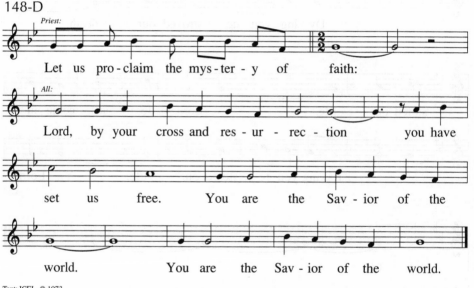

Priest: Let us pro-claim the mys-ter-y of faith:

All: Lord, by your cross and res-ur-rec-tion you have set us free. You are the Sav-ior of the world. You are the Sav-ior of the world.

Text: ICEL, © 1973
Music: *Mass of Creation*, Marty Haugen, © 1993, GIA Publications, Inc.

149 *The eucharistic prayer concludes:*

Priest: Through him, with him, in him, in the unity of the Holy Spirit, all glory and honor is yours, almighty Father, for ever and ever.

A - men, a - men, a - men!

A - men, a - men, a - men!

Music: *Mass of Creation*, Marty Haugen, © 1984, GIA Publications, Inc.

COMMUNION RITE 150

The priest invites all to join in the Lord's Prayer.

Our Fa - ther, who art in heav - en,

hal - low - ed be thy name; thy king - dom come; thy

will be done on earth as it is in heav - en.

Give us this day our dai - ly bread; and for -

give us our tres - pass - es as we for - give those who

tres - pass a - gainst us; and lead us not in - to temp -

ta - tion, but de - liv - er us from e - vil.

Priest: Deliver us, Lord. . . for the coming of our Savior, Jesus Christ.

All:

For the king - dom, the pow - er, and the glo - ry are yours,

now and for ev - er - more. A - men.

Music: *Mass of Creation*, Marty Haugen, © 1984, GIA Publications, Inc.

151 *Following the prayer "Lord, Jesus Christ," the priest invites all to exchange the sign of peace.*

> *Priest:* The peace of the Lord be with you always.
> *Assembly:* **And also with you.**

All exchange a sign of peace.

152 *Then the eucharistic bread is solemnly broken and the consecrated bread and wine are prepared for holy communion. The litany "Lamb of God" is sung during the breaking of the bread.*

1. Je-sus, Lamb of
2. Je-sus, Bread of
3. Je-sus, Prince of

God,
Life, you take a-way the sins of the world: have
Peace,

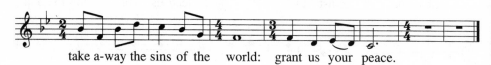

mer-cy on us. Je-sus, Lamb of God; you

take a-way the sins of the world: grant us your peace.

Music: *Mass of Creation*, Marty Haugen, © 1984, GIA Publications, Inc.

153 *The priest then invites all to share in holy communion.*

> *Priest:* This is the Lamb of God...his supper.
> *Assembly:* **Lord, I am not worthy to receive you,**
> **but only say the word and I shall be healed.**

> *Minister of communion:* The body (blood) of Christ.
> *Communicant:* **Amen.**

A song or psalm is ordinarily sung during communion. After communion, a time of silence is observed or a song of thanksgiving is sung. The rite concludes with the prayer after communion to which all respond: **Amen.**

CONCLUDING RITE

The liturgy of word and eucharist ends very simply. There may be announcements of events and concerns for the community, then the priest gives a blessing and the assembly is dismissed.

GREETING AND BLESSING

Priest: The Lord be with you.
Assembly: **And also with you.**

Optional | *When the bishop blesses the people he adds the following:*

Bishop: Blessed be the name of the Lord.
Assembly: **Now and for ever.**

Bishop: Our help is in the name of the Lord.
Assembly: **Who made heaven and earth.**

The blessing may be in a simple or solemn form. All respond to the blessing or to each part of the blessing: **Amen.**

DISMISSAL

The deacon or priest then dismisses the assembly:

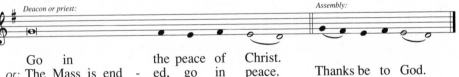

Go in   the peace of   Christ.   Thanks be to God.
or: The Mass is end - ed, go in peace.
or: Go in peace to love and serve the Lord.

EASTER DISMISSAL

The deacon or priest then dismisses the assembly:

Go in the peace of Christ, al-le-lu - ia, al-le - lu - ia.
Thanks be to God, al-le-lu - ia, al-le - lu - ia.

Composite Setting

155 SPRINGS OF WATER

Refrain

Springs of wa-ter, bless the Lord! Give him glo-ry and praise for ev-er!

Verses

Cantor:

1. O - ceans of earth, sing glo-ry to God! Praise to the one who
2. Riv - ers and lakes, sing glo-ry to God! Praise, all you ponds and
3. Brooks of the hills, sing glo-ry to God! Praise to the source of
4. Show - ers and springs, sing glo-ry to God! Praise, all you liv - ing

formed you! Sound from your depths a hymn that tells the
bogs! Rich with the life that God cre - ates, now
life! Danc - ing with joy from peak to val - ley,
wa - ters! Show - er the earth with life and good-ness,

won - ders God has done!
let your song be heard! Oh Bless-ed be God for
laugh-ing and clear your song!
show - er the grace of God!

All:

ev - er! Bless - ed be God for ev - er!

D.C.

Text: Refrain trans. © 1973, ICEL; additional text by Marty Haugen, © 1994, GIA Publications, Inc.
Music: Marty Haugen, © 1994, GIA Publications, Inc.

KYRIE ELEISON 156

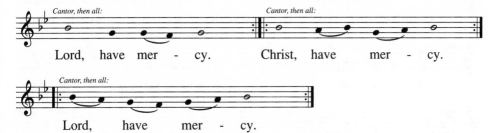

Lord, have mer - cy. Christ, have mer - cy.

Lord, have mer - cy.

Music: *Litany of the Saints;* adapt. by Richard Proulx, © 1971, GIA Publications, Inc.

Or:

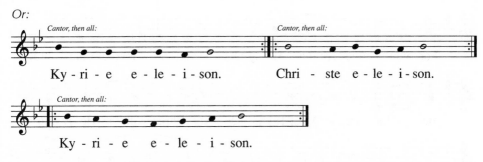

Ky - ri - e e - le - i - son. Chri - ste e - le - i - son.

Ky - ri - e e - le - i - son.

Music: *Litany of the Saints;* adapt. by Richard Proulx, © 1971, GIA Publications, Inc.

GLORIA 157

Glo - ry to God in the high - est, and peace to his peo - ple on

earth. Lord God, heav - en - ly King, al -

might - y God and Fa - ther, we wor - ship you, we

give you thanks, we praise you for your glo - ry.

Lord Je - sus Christ, on - ly Son of the Fa - ther, Lord God,

Lamb of God, you take a-way the sin of the world: have mer-cy on us; you are seat-ed at the right hand of the Fa-ther: re - ceive our prayer.

All:
For you a-lone are the Ho-ly One, you a - lone are the Lord, you a - lone are the Most High, Je - sus Christ, with the Ho-ly Spir-it, in the glo-ry of God the Fa-ther. A - men.

Music: *A New Mass for Congregations,* Carroll T. Andrews, © 1970, GIA Publications, Inc.

158 GOSPEL ACCLAMATION

Cantor, then all:
Al - le - lu - ia, al - le - lu - ia, al - le - lu - ia.

Music: Chant Mode VI; acc. by Richard Proulx, © 1985, GIA Publications, Inc.

Lenten Acclamation

Cantor, then all:
Praise to you, Lord Je - sus Christ, king of end-less glo-ry!

Text: ICEL, © 1969
Music: Frank Schoen, © 1970, GIA Publications, Inc.

GENERAL INTERCESSIONS 159

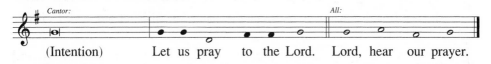

Cantor: All:

(Intention) Let us pray to the Lord. Lord, hear our prayer.

Music: Byzantine chant

PREFACE DIALOG 160

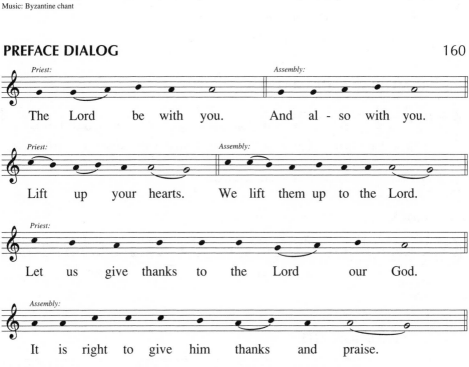

Priest: Assembly:

The Lord be with you. And al - so with you.

Priest: Assembly:

Lift up your hearts. We lift them up to the Lord.

Priest:

Let us give thanks to the Lord our God.

Assembly:

It is right to give him thanks and praise.

Music: Sacramentary, 1974

SANCTUS 161

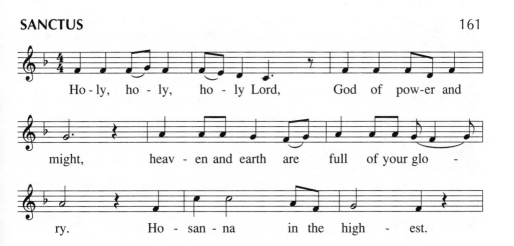

Ho - ly, ho - ly, ho - ly Lord, God of pow-er and

might, heav - en and earth are full of your glo -

ry. Ho - san - na in the high - est.

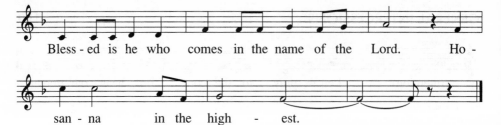

Bless - ed is he who comes in the name of the Lord. Ho - san - na in the high - est.

Music: *People's Mass,* Jan Vermulst, 1925-1994, acc. by Richard Proulx, © 1970, World Library Publications

162 MEMORIAL ACCLAMATION

Christ has died, Christ is ris - en, Christ will come a - gain.

Text: ICEL, © 1973
Music: *Danish Amen Mass,* David Kraehenbuehl; © 1970, World Library Publications

163 AMEN

A - men, a - men, a - men.

Music: Danish Amen

164 COMMUNION RITE

Our Fa - ther, who art in heav - en, hal - lowed be thy name;

thy king - dom come; thy will be done on earth as it

is in heav - en. Give us this day our dai - ly bread;

and for - give us our tres - pass - es as we for - give

those who tres - pass a - gainst us; and lead us not

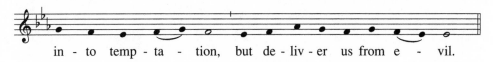

in - to temp - ta - tion, but de - liv - er us from e - vil.

Priest: Deliver us, Lord…
for the coming of our Savior, Jesus Christ.

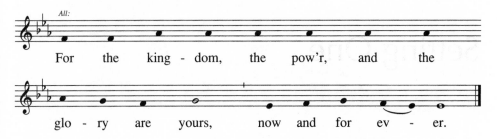

For the king - dom, the pow'r, and the

glo - ry are yours, now and for ev - er.

Music: Traditional chant, adapt. by Robert Snow, 1964; acc. by Robert J. Batastini, © 1975, 1993, GIA Publications, Inc.

AGNUS DEI 165

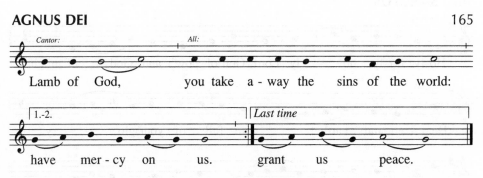

Lamb of God, you take a - way the sins of the world:

|1.-2.| |Last time|

have mer - cy on us. grant us peace.

Music: Agnus Dei XVIII, Vatican Edition; acc. by Robert J. Batastini, © 1993, GIA Publications, Inc.

DISMISSAL 166-A

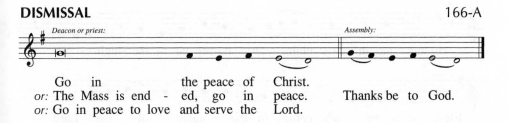

Go in the peace of Christ.
or: The Mass is end - ed, go in peace. Thanks be to God.
or: Go in peace to love and serve the Lord.

EASTER DISMISSAL 166-B

Go in the peace of Christ, al - le - lu - ia, al - le - lu - ia.
Thanks be to God, al - le - lu - ia, al - le - lu - ia.

Setting One

MISSA EMMANUEL

167 SANCTUS

Ho-ly, ho-ly, ho - ly Lord, God of pow'r and God of might.

Heav - en and earth are full of your glo - ry.

Ho-san - na in the high - est, ho-san-na in the high - est.

Ho-san - na in the high - est, ho-san-na in the high - est.

Bless - ed is he who comes in the name of the Lord.

Ho - san - na in the high - est, ho-san-na in the

high - est. Ho - san - na in the high -

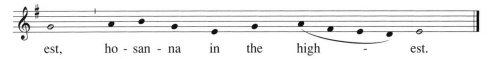

est,   ho - san - na   in   the   high   -   est.

Music: *Missa Emmanuel*, Richard Proulx, © 1991, GIA Publications, Inc.

MEMORIAL ACCLAMATION   168

Christ has died, Christ is ris - en, Christ will come a - gain.

Text: ICEL, © 1973
Music: *Missa Emmanuel*, Richard Proulx, © 1991, 2002, GIA Publications, Inc.

AMEN   169

A - men,   a - men,   a - men,   a - men.

Music: *Missa Emmanuel*, Richard Proulx, © 1991, 2002, GIA Publications, Inc.

AGNUS DEI   170

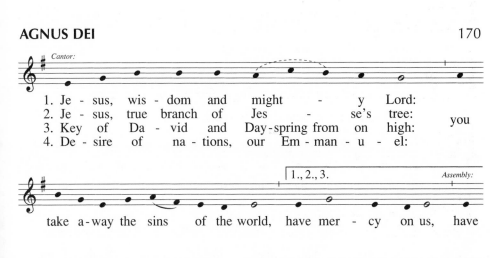

1. Je - sus, wis - dom and might - y Lord:
2. Je - sus, true branch of Jes - se's tree: you
3. Key of Da - vid and Day-spring from on high:
4. De - sire of na - tions, our Em - man - u - el:

1., 2., 3.   *Assembly:*

take a - way the sins of the world, have mer - cy on us, have

4.   *Assembly:*

mer - cy on us.   grant us peace,   grant us peace.

Music: *Missa Emmanuel*, Richard Proulx, © 1991, GIA Publications, Inc.

Setting Two

CORPUS CHRISTI MASS

171 SANCTUS

Cantor, then all:

Ho - ly, ho - ly, ho - ly Lord, God of pow'r and might.

Cantor:

Heav'n and earth are full of your glo - ry.

Ho - san - na in the high - est, in the high - est.

All:

Ho - san - na in the high-est, in the high - est.

Cantor:

Blessed is he who comes in the name of the Lord.

Cantor, then all:

Last time

Ho - san - na in the high - est, in the high - est.

Music: *Corpus Christi Mass, Adoro te devote*, setting by Richard Proulx, © 1992, GIA Publications, Inc.

MEMORIAL ACCLAMATION 172

Cantor, then all:

Christ has died, Christ is ris - en, Christ will come a - gain.

Text: ICEL, © 1973
Music: *Corpus Christi Mass, Adoro te devote,* setting by Richard Proulx, © 1992, GIA Publications, Inc.

AMEN 173

Cantor, then all:

A - men, a - men, a - men.

Music: *Corpus Christi Mass, Adoro te devote,* setting by Richard Proulx, © 1992, GIA Publications, Inc.

AGNUS DEI 174

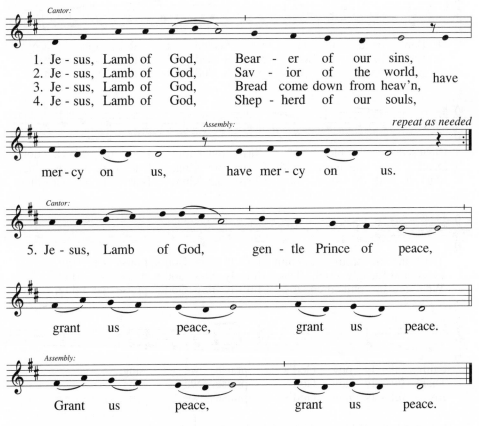

Cantor:

1. Je - sus, Lamb of God, Bear - er of our sins,
2. Je - sus, Lamb of God, Sav - ior of the world,
3. Je - sus, Lamb of God, Bread come down from heav'n,
4. Je - sus, Lamb of God, Shep - herd of our souls, have

Assembly: *repeat as needed*

mer - cy on us, have mer - cy on us.

Cantor:

5. Je - sus, Lamb of God, gen - tle Prince of peace,

grant us peace, grant us peace.

Assembly:

Grant us peace, grant us peace.

Music: *Corpus Christi Mass, Adoro te devote,* setting by Richard Proulx, © 1992, GIA Publications, Inc.

Setting Three

MASS OF THE ANGELS AND SAINTS

175 SPRINKLING RITE

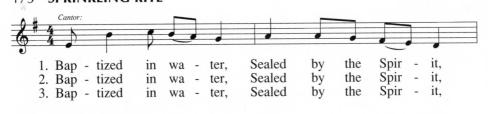

Cantor:

1. Bap - tized in wa - ter, Sealed by the Spir - it,
2. Bap - tized in wa - ter, Sealed by the Spir - it,
3. Bap - tized in wa - ter, Sealed by the Spir - it,

Cleansed by the blood of Christ our King: Heirs of sal - va - tion,
Dead in the tomb with Christ our King: One with his ris - ing,
Marked with the sign of Christ our King: Born of one Fa - ther,

Trust - ing his prom - ise; Faith - ful - ly now God's praise we sing.
Freed and for - giv - en, Thank - ful - ly now God's praise we sing.
We are his chil - dren, Joy - ful - ly now God's praise we sing.

All:

Faith - ful - ly now God's praise we sing.
Thank - ful - ly now God's praise we sing.
Joy - ful - ly now God's praise we sing.

Text: Michael Saward, b.1932, © 1982, Jubilate Hymns, Ltd. (admin. by Hope Publishing Co.)
Music: *Mass of the Angels and Saints*, Steven R. Janco, © 1996, GIA Publications, Inc.

KYRIE ELEISON 176

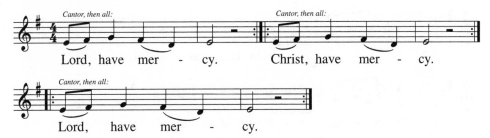

Cantor, then all:

Lord, have mer - cy. Christ, have mer - cy.

Cantor, then all:

Lord, have mer - cy.

Music: *Mass of the Angels and Saints,* Steven R. Janco, © 1996, GIA Publications, Inc.

GLORIA 177

Refrain

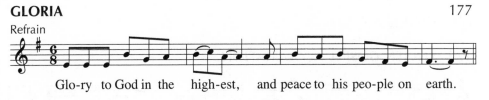

Glo-ry to God in the high-est, and peace to his peo-ple on earth.

Verses

1. Lord God, heavenly King, almighty God and Father,
   we worship you, we give you thanks, we praise you for your glory. *(To refrain)*

2. Lord Jesus Christ, only Son of the Father, Lord God, Lamb of God,
   you take away the sin of the world: have mercy on us;
   you are seated at the right hand of the Father: receive our prayer. *(To refrain)*

3. For you alone are the Holy One, you alone are the Lord,
   you alone are the Most High, Jesus Christ,
   with the Holy Spirit, in the glory of God the Father. *(To refrain)*

Cantor, then all:

A - men.

Music: *Mass of the Angels and Saints,* Steven R. Janco, © 1996, GIA Publications, Inc.

178 ALLELUIA

Al - le - lu - ia, al - le - lu - ia, al - le - lu - ia.

Al - le - lu - ia, al - le - lu - ia, al - le - lu - ia.

Optional Verse Response

After first phrase:

After second phrase:

D.C.

Al - le - lu - ia.   Al - le - lu - ia.

Music: *Mass of the Angels and Saints*, Steven R. Janco, © 1996, GIA Publications, Inc.

179 LENTEN GOSPEL ACCLAMATION

Glo - ry, praise and hon - or to you, Lord Je - sus Christ.

Music: *Mass of the Angels and Saints*, Steven R. Janco, © 1996, GIA Publications, Inc.

180 GENERAL INTERCESSIONS

Cantor: *All:*

We pray to the Lord: Lord, hear our prayer.

Alternate Responses

180-A

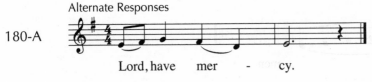

Lord, have mer - cy.

180-B

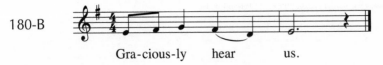

Gra - cious - ly hear us.

Music: *Mass of the Angels and Saints*, Steven R. Janco, © 1996, GIA Publications, Inc.

PREFACE DIALOG

Priest: The Lord be with you. *All:* And al - so with you.

Priest: Lift up your hearts. *All:* We lift them up to the Lord.

Priest: Let us give thanks to the Lord our God.

All: It is right to give him thanks and praise.

Music: *Mass of the Angels and Saints,* Steven R. Janco, © 1996, GIA Publications, Inc.

SANCTUS

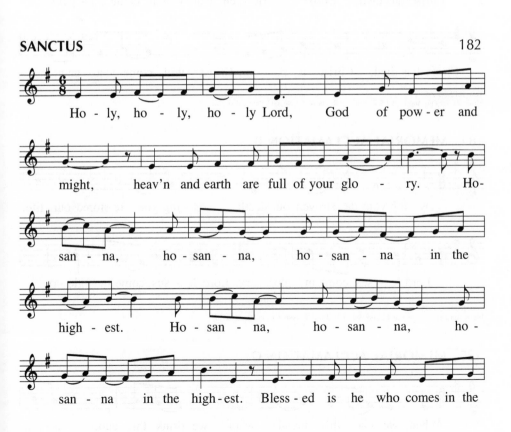

Ho - ly, ho - ly, ho - ly Lord, God of pow - er and

might, heav'n and earth are full of your glo - ry. Ho-

san - na, ho - san - na, ho - san - na in the

high - est. Ho - san - na, ho - san - na, ho -

san - na in the high - est. Bless - ed is he who comes in the

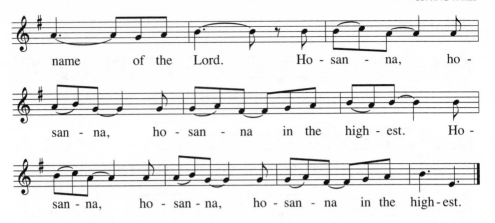

name of the Lord. Ho - san - na, ho -

san - na, ho - san - na in the high - est. Ho -

san - na, ho - san - na, ho - san - na in the high - est.

Music: *Mass of the Angels and Saints,* Steven R. Janco, © 1996, GIA Publications, Inc.

183 MEMORIAL ACCLAMATION A

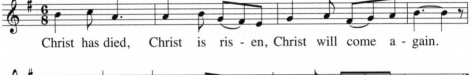

Christ has died, Christ is ris - en, Christ will come a - gain.

Christ has died, Christ is ris - en, Christ will come a - gain.

Text: ICEL, © 1973
Music: *Mass of the Angels and Saints,* Steven R. Janco, © 1996, GIA Publications, Inc.

184 MEMORIAL ACCLAMATION B

Dy - ing you de - stroyed our death, ris - ing you re-stored our life.

Lord Je - sus, come in glo - ry. Lord Je - sus, come in glo - ry.

Text: ICEL, © 1973
Music: *Mass of the Angels and Saints,* Steven R. Janco, © 1996, GIA Publications, Inc.

185 MEMORIAL ACCLAMATION C

When we eat this bread, when we drink this cup, we pro-

claim your death, Lord Je - sus, un - til you come in glo - ry.

Text: ICEL, © 1973
Music: *Mass of the Angels and Saints*, Steven R. Janco, © 1996, GIA Publications, Inc.

MEMORIAL ACCLAMATION D   186

Lord, by your cross and res - ur - rec - tion you have set us free.

You are the Sav - ior of the world, the Sav - ior of the world.

Text: ICEL, © 1973
Music: *Mass of the Angels and Saints*, Steven R. Janco, © 1996, GIA Publications, Inc.

AMEN   187

A - men, a - men, a - men.

A - men, a - men, a - men.

Music: *Mass of the Angels and Saints*, Steven R. Janco, © 1996, GIA Publications, Inc.

AGNUS DEI   188

Cantor, then all: *Repeat ad lib.*

Have mer - cy on us.

Cantor: *All:*

Grant us peace. Grant us peace.

Music: *Mass of the Angels and Saints*, Steven R. Janco, © 1996, GIA Publications, Inc.

Setting Four

BENEATH THE TREE OF LIFE

189 SPRINKLING RITE

Refrain*

Springs of wa - ter, bless the Lord, Sing your glo-ry and praise for-ev-er. Al-le - lu - ia! Sing your glo - ry and praise!

*Refrain may be sung continously under verses.

Music: *Beneath the Tree of Life*; Marty Haugen, © 2000, 2001, GIA Publications, Inc.

190 GLORIA

Refrain

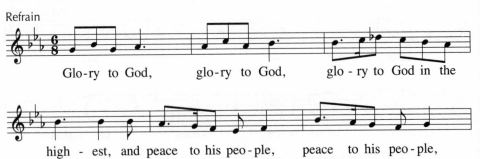

Glo-ry to God, glo-ry to God, glo - ry to God in the high - est, and peace to his peo-ple, peace to his peo-ple,

peace   to   his   peo - ple   on   earth.

Verses

1. Lord God, heavenly King, almighty God and Father,
    we worship you, we give you thanks,
    we praise you for your glory.

2. Lord Jesus Christ, only Son of the Father,
    Lord God, Lamb of God,
    you take away the sin of the world: have mercy on us;
    you are seated at the right hand of the Father:
    receive our prayer.

3. For you alone are the Holy One,
    you alone are the Lord,
    you alone are the Most High, Jesus Christ,
    with the Holy Spirit,
    in the glory of God, the Father.

Music: *Beneath the Tree of Life*, Marty Haugen, © 2000, 2001, GIA Publications, Inc.

ALLELUIA   191

Al-le-lu-ia,   Al-le-lu-ia,   Al - le-lu - ia,

Al - le-lu-ia,   Al - le-lu-ia,   Al - le-lu - ia,

Music: *Beneath the Tree of Life*, Marty Haugen, © 2000, 2001, GIA Publications, Inc.

192 **SANCTUS**

Ho - ly, ho - ly, ho - ly Lord, God of pow-er and might,

heav-en and earth are full of your glo - ry. Ho - san-na, ho -

san-na, ho - san-na in the high - est. Bless-ed is he,

bless-ed is he who comes in the name of the Lord. Ho -

san - na, ho - san - na, ho - san - na in the

high - est, ho - san - na in the high - est!

Music: *Beneath the Tree of Life*, Marty Haugen, © 2000, 2001, GIA Publications, Inc.

193 **MEMORIAL ACCLAMATION**

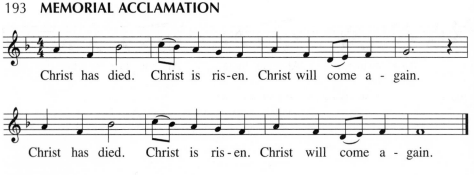

Christ has died. Christ is ris-en. Christ will come a - gain.

Christ has died. Christ is ris-en. Christ will come a - gain.

Text: ICEL, © 1973
Music: *Beneath the Tree of Life*, Marty Haugen, © 2000, 2001, GIA Publications, Inc.

AMEN 194

A - men, A - men, A - men!

Music: *Beneath the Tree of Life*, Marty Haugen, © 2000, 2001, GIA Publications, Inc.

AGNUS DEI 195

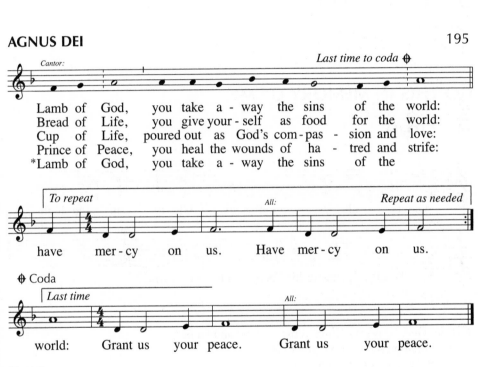

Cantor:

Last time to coda ⊕

Lamb of God, you take a - way the sins of the world:
Bread of Life, you give your - self as food for the world:
Cup of Life, poured out as God's com - pas - sion and love:
Prince of Peace, you heal the wounds of ha - tred and strife:
*Lamb of God, you take a - way the sins of the

To repeat

All:

Repeat as needed

have mer - cy on us. Have mer - cy on us.

⊕ Coda

Last time

All:

world: Grant us your peace. Grant us your peace.

*Last time

Music: *Beneath the Tree of Life*, Marty Haugen, © 2000, 2001, GIA Publications, Inc.

Setting Five

DO THIS IN MEMORY OF ME

196 GLORIA

Refrain

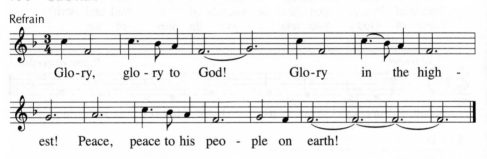

Glo-ry,   glo-ry to God!   Glo-ry   in   the   high -
est!   Peace,   peace to his peo - ple on earth!

Verses

1. Lord God, heavenly King, almighty God and Father,
   we worship you, we give you thanks,
   we praise you for your glory.

2. Lord Jesus Christ, only Son of the Father,
   Lord God, Lamb of God,
   you take away the sin of the world: have mercy on us;
   you are seated at the right hand of the Father:
   receive our prayer.

3. For you alone are the Holy One,
   you alone are the Lord,
   you alone are the Most High, Jesus Christ,
   with the Holy Spirit,
   in the glory of God the Father. Amen!

Music: *Do This in Memory of Me*, David Haas, © 2003, GIA Publications, Inc.

ALLELUIA   197

Al-le - lu - ia,   al - le - lu - ia!

Al-le - lu - ia!   Al-le - lu - ia!

Music: *Do This in Memory of Me*, David Haas, © 2003, GIA Publications, Inc.

SANCTUS   198

Ho - ly, ho - ly, ho - ly, Lord,   God   of

pow - er and   might,   heav - en and earth   are   full   of your

glo - ry.   Ho - san - na,   ho - san - na

in   the   high - est.   Bless-ed   is

he   who comes   in the   name of the   Lord.   Ho - san -

na,   ho - san - na   in   the   high - est.

Music: *Do This in Memory of Me*, David Haas, © 2003, GIA Publications, Inc.

199 MEMORIAL ACCLAMATION

Christ has died. Christ is ris - en.

Christ will come, Christ will come a - gain.

Text: ICEL, © 1973
Music: *Do This in Memory of Me*, David Haas, © 2003, GIA Publications, Inc.

200 AMEN

A - men, A - men, Al - le - lu - ia!

A - men, A - men!

Music: *Do This in Memory of Me*, David Haas, © 2003, GIA Publications, Inc.

201 AGNUS DEI

Cantor: Assembly:

Lamb of God, you take a - way the sins of the

1., 2.

world: have mer - cy on us.

Final ending

world: grant us your peace, grant us your peace.

Music: *Do This in Memory of Me*, David Haas, © 2003, GIA Publications, Inc.

Setting Six

A COMMUNITY MASS

KYRIE

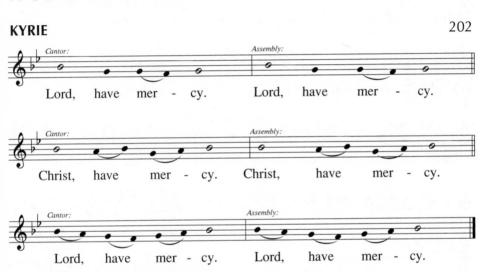

Cantor: Lord, have mer - cy. *Assembly:* Lord, have mer - cy.

Cantor: Christ, have mer - cy. *Assembly:* Christ, have mer - cy.

Cantor: Lord, have mer - cy. *Assembly:* Lord, have mer - cy.

203 **GLORIA**

Glo - ry to God in the high-est, and peace to his peo-ple on earth. Lord God, heav-en-ly King, al - might - y God and Fa-ther, We wor - ship you, we give you thanks, we praise you for your glo-ry.

Lord Je-sus Christ, on-ly Son of the Fa-ther, Lord, God, Lamb of God, you take a - way the sin of the world: have mer - cy on us; You are seat - ed at the right hand of the Fa-ther: re - ceive our pray'r, re - ceive, re - ceive our pray'r.

For you a-lone are the Ho-ly One, you a - lone are the Lord, you a - lone are the Most High, Je-sus Christ with the Ho - ly

Spir - it in the glo - ry of God the Fa - ther.

A - men. A - men.

Music: *A Community Mass*, Richard Proulx, © 1971, 1977, GIA Publications, Inc.

SANCTUS 204

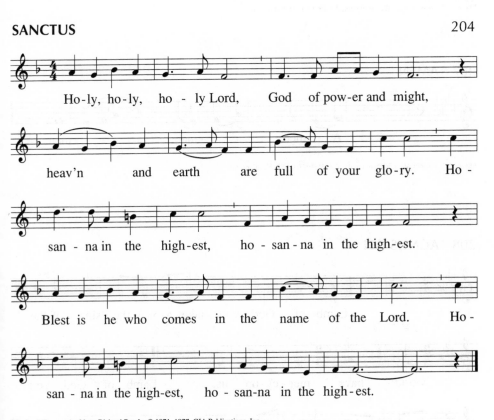

Ho-ly, ho-ly, ho - ly Lord, God of pow-er and might,

heav'n and earth are full of your glo-ry. Ho -

san - na in the high-est, ho - san - na in the high-est.

Blest is he who comes in the name of the Lord. Ho -

san - na in the high-est, ho - san-na in the high - est.

Music: *A Community Mass*, Richard Proulx, © 1971, 1977, GIA Publications, Inc.

MEMORIAL ACCLAMATION A 205

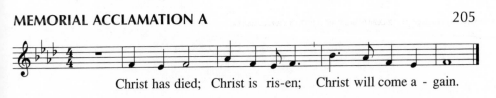

Christ has died; Christ is ris-en; Christ will come a - gain.

Text: ICEL, © 1973
Music: *A Community Mass*, Richard Proulx, © 1971, 1977, GIA Publications, Inc.

206 MEMORIAL ACCLAMATION C

When we eat this bread and drink this cup, we pro-

claim your death, Lord Je-sus, un-til you come in glo-ry.

Text: ICEL, © 1973
Music: *A Community Mass,* Richard Proulx, © 1988, GIA Publications, Inc.

207 AMEN

A - men, a - men, a - men.

Music: *A Community Mass,* Richard Proulx, © 1971, 1977, GIA Publications, Inc.

208 AGNUS DEI

Lamb of God, you take a-way the sins of the

world: have mer-cy on us. Lamb of God, you

take a-way the sins of the world: grant us peace.

Music: *A Community Mass,* Richard Proulx, © 1971, 1977, GIA Publications, Inc.

Setting Seven

MASS OF REMEMBRANCE

KYRIE

209

Ky - ri - e   e - le - i - son,   Chri - ste   e - le - i - son,

Ky - ri - e   e - le - i - son.

Music: *Mass of Remembrance*, Marty Haugen, © 1987, GIA Publications, Inc.

210 GLORIA

Refrain

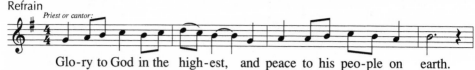

Glo-ry to God in the high-est, and peace to his peo-ple on earth.

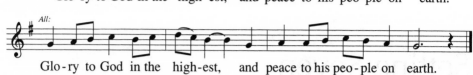

Glo-ry to God in the high-est, and peace to his peo-ple on earth.

Verses

Choir: Lord God, heavenly King, almighty God and Father,
we worship you, we give you thanks,
we praise you for your glory.
All sing entire refrain

Lord Jesus Christ, only Son of the Father,
Lord God, Lamb of God, you take away the sin of the world:
have mercy on us;
you are seated at the right hand of the Father:
receive our prayer.
All sing entire refrain

For you alone are the Holy One, you alone are the Lord,
you alone are the Most High, Jesus Christ,
with the Holy Spirit, in the glory of God the Father. Amen.
All sing entire refrain

Music: *Mass of Remembrance*, Marty Haugen, © 1987, GIA Publications, Inc.

211 ALLELUIA

Al - le - lu - ia, al - le - lu - ia, al - le - lu - ia!

Music: *Mass of Remembrance*, Marty Haugen, © 1987, GIA Publications, Inc.

212 PREFACE DIALOG

The Lord be with you. And al - so with

Priest: Lift up your hearts.
Assembly: We lift them up to the Lord.
Priest: Let us give thanks to the Lord our God.
Assembly: It is right to give him thanks and praise.

Music: *Mass of Remembrance*, Marty Haugen, © 1987, GIA Publications, Inc.

EUCHARISTIC ACCLAMATION IA (OPTIONAL)*   213

*As in the Eucharistic Prayers for Masses with Children.

Praise, thanks and glo-ry be to you, O God!

Music: *Mass of Remembrance*, Marty Haugen, © 1987, GIA Publications, Inc.

SANCTUS   214

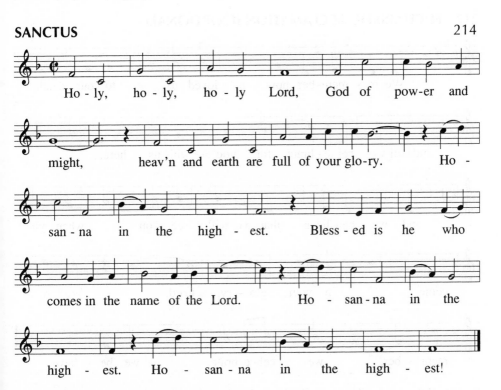

Ho-ly, ho-ly, ho-ly Lord, God of pow-er and might, heav'n and earth are full of your glo-ry. Ho-san-na in the high-est. Bless-ed is he who comes in the name of the Lord. Ho-san-na in the high-est. Ho-san-na in the high-est!

Music: *Mass of Remembrance*, Marty Haugen, © 1987, GIA Publications, Inc.

215 EUCHARISTIC ACCLAMATION IB (OPTIONAL)

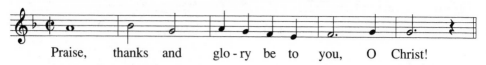

Praise, thanks and glo-ry be to you, O Christ!

Music: *Mass of Remembrance*, Marty Haugen, © 1987, GIA Publications, Inc.

216 MEMORIAL ACCLAMATION

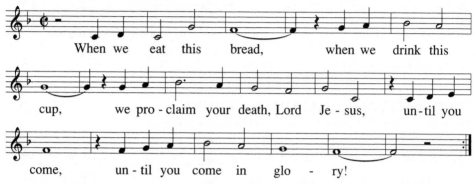

When we eat this bread, when we drink this cup, we pro-claim your death, Lord Je-sus, un-til you come, un-til you come in glo - ry!

Text: ICEL, © 1973
Music: *Mass of Remembrance*, Marty Haugen, © 1987, GIA Publications, Inc.

217 EUCHARISTIC ACCLAMATION II (OPTIONAL)

We re - mem-ber how you loved us to your death, and still we cel-e-brate, for you are with us here; and we be-lieve that we will see you when you come in your glo - ry, Lord. We re - mem - ber, we cel-e-brate, we be - lieve.

Music: *Mass of Remembrance*, Marty Haugen, © 1987, GIA Publications, Inc.

EUCHARISTIC ACCLAMATION III (OPTIONAL) 218

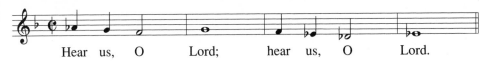

Hear us, O Lord; hear us, O Lord.

Music: *Mass of Remembrance*, Marty Haugen, © 1987, GIA Publications, Inc.

AMEN 219

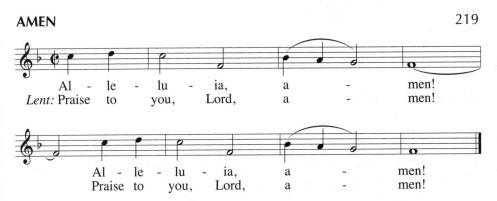

Al - le - lu - ia, a - men!
Lent: Praise to you, Lord, a - men!

Al - le - lu - ia, a - men!
Praise to you, Lord, a - men!

Music: *Mass of Remembrance*, Marty Haugen, © 1987, GIA Publications, Inc.

AGNUS DEI 220

Cantors: *All:* To repeat

1. *Lamb of God,
2. Prince of Peace, you take a-way the sins of the world: have mer-cy on
3. Bread of Life,

Last time

us. world: grant us peace, grant us peace.

**"Lamb of God" is sung the first and last times. Alternate intervening invocations
include: Ancient Cup, Bread of Peace, Wine of Hope, Lord of lords.*

Music: *Mass of Remembrance*, Marty Haugen, © 1987, GIA Publications, Inc.

Setting Eight

MASS OF LIGHT

221 KYRIE

GLORIA

222

Refrain

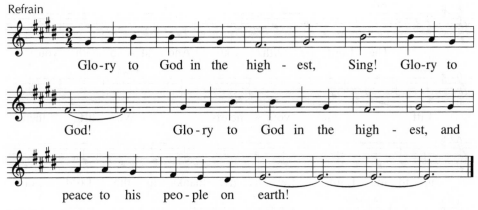

Glo-ry to God in the high - est, Sing! Glo-ry to

God! Glo-ry to God in the high - est, and

peace to his peo-ple on earth!

Verses

1. Lord God, heavenly King, almighty God and Father,
   we worship you, we give you thanks, we praise you for your glory.

2. Lord Jesus Christ, only Son of the Father, Lord God, Lamb of God,
   you take away the sin of the world: have mercy on us;
   you are seated at the right hand of the Father: receive our prayer.

3. For you alone are the Holy One, you alone are the Lord,
   the Most High, Jesus Christ, with the Holy Spirit, in the glory of God the Father.

Music: *Mass of Light*, David Haas, © 1988, GIA Publications, Inc.

ALLELUIA

223

Cantor or choir, then all:

Al - le - lu - ia! Al - le - lu - ia! Al - le - lu - ia!

Music: *Mass of Light*, David Haas, © 1988, GIA Publications, Inc.

LENTEN GOSPEL ACCLAMATION

224

Cantor or choir, then all:

Glo-ry to you, O Word of God, Lord Je - sus Christ!

Text: ICEL, © 1969
Music: *Mass of Light*, David Haas, © 1988, GIA Publications, Inc.

225 **PREFACE DIALOG**

Music: *Mass of Light*, David Haas, © 1988, GIA Publications, Inc.

226 **SANCTUS**

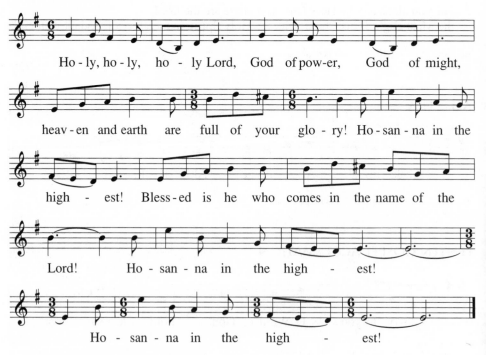

Music: *Mass of Light*, David Haas, © 1988, GIA Publications, Inc.

EUCHARISTIC ACCLAMATION I (OPTIONAL)* 227
As in the Eucharistic Prayers for Masses with Children.

Ho - san - na in the high - est!

Music: *Mass of Light,* David Haas, © 1988, GIA Publications, Inc.

MEMORIAL ACCLAMATION 228

Dy - ing you de - stroyed our death, ris - ing you re - stored our life.

Lord Je - sus come! Lord Je - sus come in glo - ry!

Text: ICEL, © 1973
Music: *Mass of Light,* David Haas, © 1988, GIA Publications, Inc.

EUCHARISTIC ACCLAMATION II (OPTIONAL) 229

Hear us, hear us. Hear us, hear us.

Music: *Mass of Light,* David Haas, © 1988, GIA Publications, Inc.

AMEN 230

A - men, a - men! A - men, a - men!

Music: *Mass of Light,* David Haas, © 1988, GIA Publications, Inc.

231 AGNUS DEI

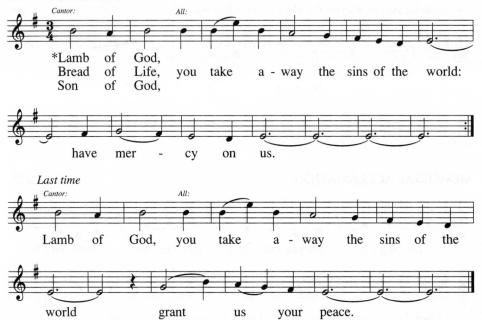

*Lamb of God,
Bread of Life, you take a - way the sins of the world:
Son of God,

have mer - cy on us.

Last time

Lamb of God, you take a - way the sins of the

world grant us your peace.

"Lamb of God" is sung the first and last times. Alternate intervening invocations include: "Saving Cup," "Hope for all," "Prince of Peace," "Wine of Peace," etc.

Music: *Mass of Light*, David Haas, © 1988, GIA Publications, Inc.

Setting Nine

JUBILATION MASS

KYRIE

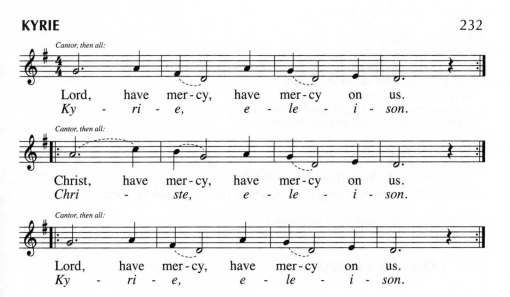

Cantor, then all:

Lord, have mer-cy, have mer-cy on us.
Ky - ri - e, e - le - i - son.

Cantor, then all:

Christ, have mer-cy, have mer-cy on us.
Chri - ste, e - le - i - son.

Cantor, then all:

Lord, have mer-cy, have mer-cy on us.
Ky - ri - e, e - le - i - son.

Music: *Jubilation Mass*, James J. Chepponis, © 1999, GIA Publications, Inc.

233 GLORIA

Refrain

Glo-ri-a!   Glo-ri-a!   Glo-ry to God in the high-est!

Glo-ri-a!   Glo - ri-a! And peace to his peo-ple on   earth!

Verses

1. Lord God, heavenly King,
   almighty God and Father,
   we worship you,
   we give you thanks,
   we praise you for your glory.

2. Lord Jesus Christ,
   only Son of the Father,
   Lord God, Lamb of God,
   you take away the sin of the world:
   have mercy upon us;
   you are seated at the right hand of the Father:
   receive our prayer, receive our prayer.

3. For you alone are the Holy One,
   you alone are the Lord,
   you alone are the Most High, Jesus Christ,
   with the Holy Spirit, in the glory of God the Father, of God the Father.

Music: *Jubilation Mass,* James J. Chepponis, © 1999, GIA Publications, Inc.

234 GOSPEL ACCLAMATION

Refrain

Al - le - lu - ia,   al-le - lu - ia,   al - le-lu - ia!
Lent: Glo-ry to you,   Word of God,   Lord   Je - sus   Christ.

Al - le - lu - ia,   al - le - lu - ia,   al - le-lu - ia!
Glo-ry to you,   Word of God,   Lord   Je - sus Christ!

Text: ICEL, © 1969
Music: *Jubilation Mass,* James J. Chepponis, © 1999, GIA Publications, Inc.

SANCTUS 235

Music: *Jubilation Mass,* James J. Chepponis, © 1999, GIA Publications, Inc.

MEMORIAL ACCLAMATION A 236

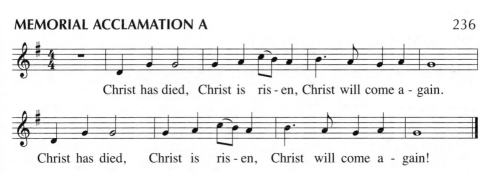

Text: ICEL, © 1973
Music: *Jubilation Mass,* James J. Chepponis, © 1999, GIA Publications, Inc.

237 MEMORIAL ACCLAMATION B

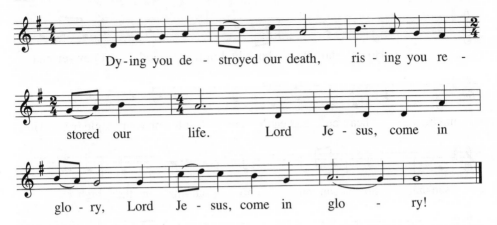

Dy-ing you de - stroyed our death, ris - ing you re - stored our life. Lord Je - sus, come in glo - ry, Lord Je - sus, come in glo - ry!

Text: ICEL, © 1973
Music: *Jubilation Mass*, James J. Chepponis, © 1999, GIA Publications, Inc.

238 MEMORIAL ACCLAMATION C

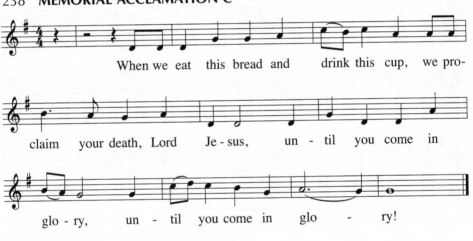

When we eat this bread and drink this cup, we pro-claim your death, Lord Je - sus, un - til you come in glo - ry, un - til you come in glo - ry!

Text: ICEL, © 1973
Music: *Jubilation Mass*, James J. Chepponis, © 1999, GIA Publications, Inc.

239 MEMORIAL ACCLAMATION D

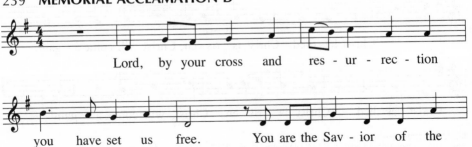

Lord, by your cross and res - ur - rec - tion you have set us free. You are the Sav - ior of the

world, the Sav - ior of the world!

Text: ICEL, © 1973
Music: *Jubilation Mass*, James J. Chepponis, © 1999, GIA Publications, Inc.

AMEN   240

A - men, A - men, A -

men. A - men, A - men, A - men!

Music: *Jubilation Mass*, James J. Chepponis, © 1999, GIA Publications, Inc.

AGNUS DEI   241

Cantor: *All:*

Lamb of God, you take a-way the sins of the

To repeat   Last time

world, have mer-cy on us.   world, grant us peace.

Music: *Jubilation Mass*, James J. Chepponis, © 1999, GIA Publications, Inc.

Setting Ten

BLACK MOUNTAIN LITURGY

242 KYRIE

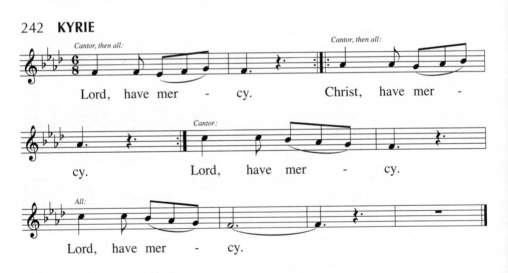

Cantor, then all:

Lord, have mer - cy.

Cantor, then all:

Christ, have mer - cy.

Cantor:

Lord, have mer - cy.

All:

Lord, have mer - cy.

Music: *Black Mountain Liturgy*, Sally Ann Morris, © 2003, GIA Publications, Inc.

243 GLORIA

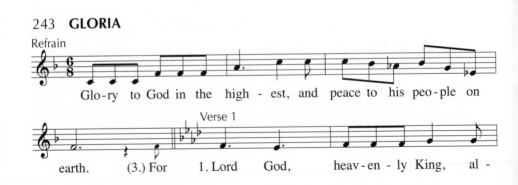

Refrain

Glo-ry to God in the high - est, and peace to his peo-ple on

Verse 1

earth. (3.) For 1. Lord God, heav-en - ly King, al -

might - y God and Fa - ther, we wor - ship you,

*opt. **D.C.**

we give you thanks, we praise you for your glo - ry.

Verse 2

2. Lord Je - sus Christ, on - ly Son of the Fa - ther, Lord God, Lamb of

God, you take a - way the sin of the world: have

mer - cy on us; you are seat - ed at the right hand

opt. **D.C.**

of the Fa - ther: re - ceive our prayer. (3. For)

Verse 3

you a - lone are the Ho - ly One, you a - lone are the

Lord, you a - lone are the Most High, Je - sus

Christ, with the Ho - ly Spir - it, in the

opt. **D.C.**

glo - ry of God the Fa - ther. A - men.

May be sung with or without refrains.

Music: *Black Mountain Liturgy*, Sally Ann Morris, © 2003, GIA Publications, Inc.

244 GOSPEL ACCLAMATION

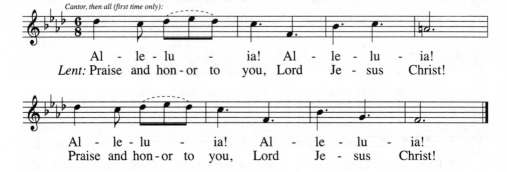

Cantor, then all (first time only):

Al - le - lu - ia! Al - le - lu - ia!
Lent: Praise and hon - or to you, Lord Je - sus Christ!

Al - le - lu - ia! Al - le - lu - ia!
Praise and hon - or to you, Lord Je - sus Christ!

Text: ICEL, © 1969
Music: *Black Mountain Liturgy,* Sally Ann Morris, © 2003, GIA Publications, Inc.

245 SANCTUS

Ho - ly, ho - ly, ho - ly Lord, God of

pow - er, God of might, heav - en and earth are

full of your glo - ry. Ho - san - na in the high -

est. Bless - ed is he who comes in the name of the

Lord. Ho - san - na in the

high - est, ho - san - na in the high - est.

Music: *Black Mountain Liturgy,* Sally Ann Morris, © 2003, GIA Publications, Inc.

MEMORIAL ACCLAMATION

246

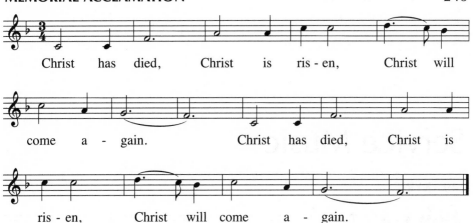

Christ has died, Christ is ris - en, Christ will come a - gain. Christ has died, Christ is ris - en, Christ will come a - gain.

Text: ICEL, © 1973
Music: *Black Mountain Liturgy*, Sally Ann Morris, © 2003, GIA Publications, Inc.

AMEN

247

A - men, a - men. A - men, a - men.

Music: *Black Mountain Liturgy*, Sally Ann Morris, © 2003, GIA Publications, Inc.

AGNUS DEI

248

Cantor: / All: Lamb of God, you take a - way the sins of the world: have mer-cy on us. Cantor: Lamb of God, All: you take a - way the sins of the world: grant us peace. Grant us peace.

Music: *Black Mountain Liturgy*, Sally Ann Morris, © 2003, GIA Publications, Inc.

Service Music

249 KYRIE

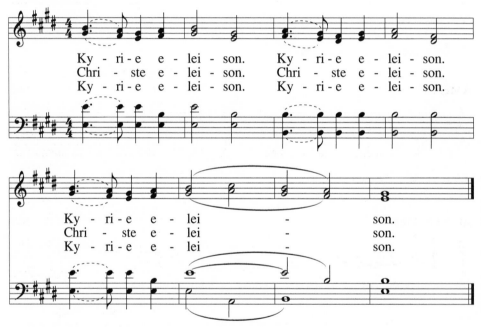

Ky - ri - e e - lei - son. Ky - ri - e e - lei - son.
Chri - ste e - lei - son. Chri - ste e - lei - son.
Ky - ri - e e - lei - son. Ky - ri - e e - lei - son.

Ky - ri - e e - lei - son.
Chri - ste e - lei - son.
Ky - ri - e e - lei - son.

Music: Russian Orthodox; arr. by John L. Bell, © 1990, Iona Community, GIA Publications, Inc., agent

250 GLORIA

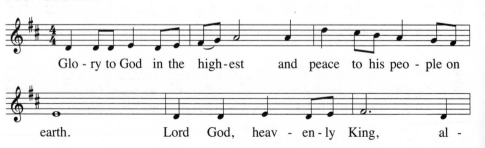

Glo - ry to God in the high-est and peace to his peo - ple on earth. Lord God, heav - en - ly King, al -

might - y God and Fa-ther, we wor - ship you, we give you thanks, we praise you for your glo - ry. Lord Je-sus Christ, on - ly Son of the Fa - ther, Lord God, Lamb of God, you take a - way the sin of the world: have mer - cy on us; you are seat - ed at the right hand of the Fa - ther: re - ceive our prayer. For you a - lone are the Ho - ly One, you a - lone are the Lord, you a - lone are the Most High, Je - sus Christ, with the Ho - ly Spir - it, in the glo - ry of God the Fa - ther. A - men, a - men, a - men.

251 GLORIA

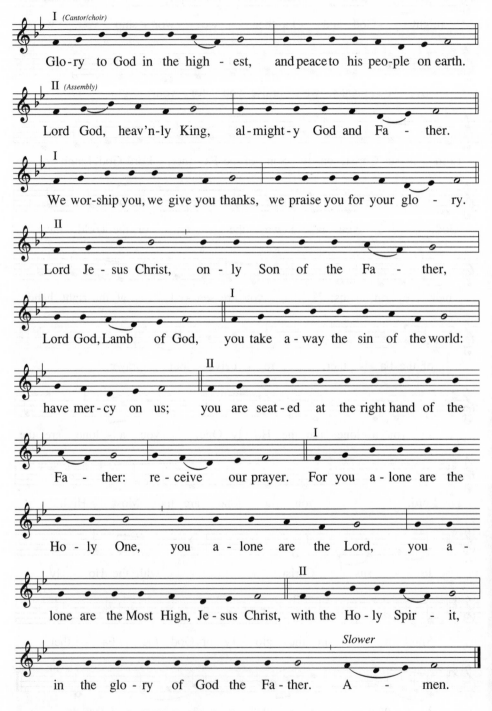

I *(Cantor/choir)*

Glo-ry to God in the high - est, and peace to his peo-ple on earth.

II *(Assembly)*

Lord God, heav'n-ly King, al-might-y God and Fa - ther.

I

We wor-ship you, we give you thanks, we praise you for your glo - ry.

II

Lord Je - sus Christ, on - ly Son of the Fa - ther,

I

Lord God, Lamb of God, you take a - way the sin of the world:

II

have mer - cy on us; you are seat - ed at the right hand of the

I

Fa - ther: re - ceive our prayer. For you a - lone are the

Ho - ly One, you a - lone are the Lord, you a -

II

lone are the Most High, Je - sus Christ, with the Ho - ly Spir - it,

Slower

in the glo - ry of God the Fa - ther. A - men.

Music: *Congregational Mass;* John Lee, © 1970, GIA Publications, Inc.

GLORIA

Refrain

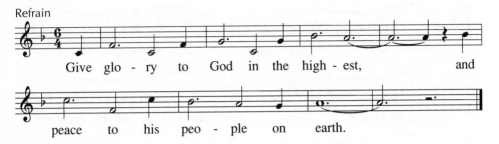

Give glo - ry to God in the high - est, and peace to his peo - ple on earth.

Verses

1. Lord God, heavenly King,
   almighty God and Father,
   we worship you,
   we give you thanks,
   we praise you for your glory.

2. Lord Jesus Christ,
   only Son of the Father,
   Lord God, Lamb of God,
   you take away the sin of the world:
   have mercy upon us;
   you are seated at the right hand of the Father:
   receive our prayer.

3. You alone are the Holy One,
   you alone are the Lord,
   you alone are the Most High, Jesus Christ,
   with the Holy Spirit, in the glory of God the Father.

Music: John B. Foley, S.J., © 1978, John B. Foley, S J and OCP Publications

GLORIA

Canon—*4 voices*

Glo - ri - a, glo - ri - a, in ex - cel - sis De - o!

Glo - ri - a, glo - ri - a, al - le - lu - ia, al - le - lu - ia!

Music: Jacques Berthier, © 1979, 1988, Les Presses de Taizé, GIA Publications, Inc., agent

254 **GLORIA**

All:

Glo-ry to God in the high-est, and peace to his peo-ple on earth.

Glo-ry to God in the high-est, and peace to his peo-ple on earth.

Choir (or cantor):

Lord God, heav-en-ly King, al-might-y God and Fa - ther.

All:

Glo-ry to God in the high-est, and peace to his peo-ple on earth.

Choir:

We wor-ship you, we give you thanks, we praise you for your

All:

glo - ry. Glo-ry to God in the high-est, and

Choir:

peace to his peo-ple on earth. Lord Je-sus Christ, on-ly

All:

Son of the Fa-ther. Glo-ry to God in the high-est, and

Choir:

peace to his peo-ple on earth. Lord God, Lamb of God,

you take a-way the sin of the world; have mer-cy on us;

you are seat-ed at the right hand of the Fa-ther:

Music: *Mass of the Bells;* Alexander Peloquin, © 1972, 1973, GIA Publications, Inc.

255 GLORIA

mi-se-ré-re no - bis. Quó - ni - am tu so - lus San - ctus.

Tu so-lus Dó - mi - nus. Tu so-lus Al - tís - si-mus,

Je - su Chri - ste. Cum San - cto Spí - ri - tu,

in gló-ri-a De - i Pa - tris. A - men.

Music: Vatican Edition VIII, acc. by Richard Proulx, © 1995, GIA Publications, Inc.

GLORIA

256

Refrain

Glo - ry to God in the high - est, and

peace to his peo - ple on earth.

Verses

1. Lord God, heavenly King, almighty God and Father.

2. We worship you, we give you thanks,
   we praise you, we praise you for your glory.

3. Lord Jesus Christ, only Son of the Father,
   Lord God, Lamb of God, you take away the sin of the world:
   have mercy on us; you are seated at the right hand of the Father:
   receive, receive our prayer.

4. For you alone are the Holy One, you alone are the Lord,
   you alone are the Most High, Jesus Christ,
   with the Holy Spirit in the glory of God the Father.

Music: *Melodic Gloria*, James J. Chepponis, © 1986, GIA Publications, Inc.

257 GLORIA

Refrain

Glo-ry to God, glo-ry to God, glo-ry to God in the high - est heav - en. Glo-ry to God, glo-ry to God, peace to his peo-ple, his peo-ple on earth.

Verses

1. Lord God, heavenly King, almighty God and Father,
   we worship you, we give you thanks,
   we praise you for your glory.

2. Lord Jesus Christ, only Son of the Father,
   Lord God, Lamb of God,
   you take away the sin of the world: have mercy on us;
   you are seated at the right hand of the Father:
   receive our prayer.

3. For you alone are the Holy One,
   you alone are the Lord,
   you alone are the Most High, Jesus Christ,
   with the Holy Spirit,
   in the glory, the glory, the glory of God the Father.

Music: *Mass of the Celtic Saints*, Liam Lawton; arr. by John McCann, © 1998, GIA Publications, Inc.

258 CHILDREN'S DISMISSAL FOR LITURGY OF THE WORD

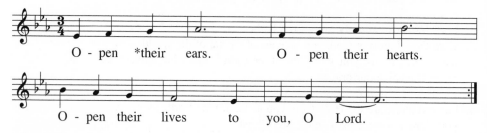

O - pen *their ears. O - pen their hearts. O - pen their lives to you, O Lord.

Or "our"

Text: Francis Patrick O'Brien
Music: Francis Patrick O'Brien
© 2003, GIA Publications, Inc.

CHILDREN'S DISMISSAL FOR LITURGY OF THE WORD 259

Go and lis-ten to the Word of God. Go and lis-ten to the

Word of God. God has the words of ev-er-last-ing life.

God has the words of ev-er-last-ing life.

Text: Robert J. Batastini
Music: Robert J. Batastini
© 2003, GIA Publications, Inc.

ALLELUIA 260

Al - le - lu - ia! Al - le - lu - ia!

Al - le - lu - ia! Al - le - lu - ia!

Music: Norah Duncan IV, © 1987, GIA Publications, Inc.

HALLE, HALLE, HALLE 261

Hal-le, hal-le, hal-le - lu - jah! Hal-le, hal-le, hal-

le - lu - ia! Hal-le, hal-le, hal-le -

lu - jah! Hal-le-lu-jah! Hal-le-lu - jah!

Music: Traditional Caribbean, arr. by John L. Bell, © 1990, Iona Community, GIA Publications, Inc., agent; verses and acc. by Marty Haugen, © 1993,
    GIA Publications, Inc.

262 ALLELUIA

Al - le - lu - ia! Al-le-lu - ia! Al - le -lu - ia!
Al - le - lu - ia! Al - le - lu - ia! Al-le-lu - ia!
Al - le - lu - ia! Al - le - lu - ia!

Music: David Haas, © 1986, 1997, GIA Publications, Inc.

263 ALLELUIA

Al - le - lu - ia, al - le - lu-ia, al-le - lu - ia.
Al - le - lu - ia, al - le - lu - ia, al - le - lu - ia!

Music: Alleluia 7; Jacques Berthier, © 1984, Les Presses de Taizé, GIA Publications, Inc., agent

264 ALLELUIA

Al-le-lu - ia, al-le-lu-ia, al - le-lu-ia, al-le - lu - ia!

Music: Alleluia 17; Jacques Berthier, © 1998, Les Presses de Taizé, GIA Publications, Inc., agent

265 ALLELUIA

Al-le-lu - i-a, al-le-lu - i-a, al-le-lu - i - a!

Music: Alleluia 18; Jacques Berthier, © 1998, Les Presses de Taizé, GIA Publications, Inc., agent

CELTIC ALLELUIA

266

Al - le - lu - ia, al - le - lu - ia!

Al - le - lu - ia, al - le - lu - ia!

Text: Fintan O'Carroll and Christopher Walker
Music: Fintan O'Carroll and Christopher Walker
© 1985, Fintan O'Carroll and Christopher Walker. Published by OCP Publications.

ALLELUIA

267

Cantor:
Al - le-lu - ia, al - le-lu - ia!

Assembly:
Al - le-lu - ia, al - le-lu - ia!

Cantor:
Al - le-lu - ia, al - le-lu - ia!

Assembly:
Al - le-lu - ia, al - le-lu - ia!

Cantor:
Al - le-lu - ia, al - le-lu - ia!

Assembly:
Al - le-lu - ia, al - le-lu - ia!

Cantor:
Al - le-lu - ia, al - le-lu - ia!

Assembly:
Al - le-lu - ia, al - le-lu - ia!

Music: *Joyful Alleluia;* Howard Hughes, SM, © 1973, 1979, GIA Publications, Inc.

268 ALLELUIA

Al-le-lu-ia, al-le-lu - ia. Al-le-lu-ia, al-le-lu - ia.

Music: Based on VENI EMMANUEL, Stephen Pishner, © 2000, GIA Publications, Inc.

269 ALLELUIA

Al - le - lu - ia. Al - le - lu - ia. Al - le - lu - ia.

Al - le - lu - ia. Al - le - lu - ia. Al - le - lu - ia.

Music: *Alleluia in C*, Howard Hughes, SM, © 1973, 1982, GIA Publications, Inc.

270 ALLELUIA

Al - le - lu - ia, al - le - lu - ia, al - le - lu - ia.

Music: A. Gregory Murray, OSB, © 1958, The Grail, GIA Publications, Inc., agent

271 HONDURAS ALLELUIA

¡A-le - lu-ya, a-le-lu - ya! ¡A-le - lu-ya, a-le-lu - ya! ¡A-le -

lu-ya, a-le-lu - ya! ¡El Se - ñor re-su-ci-tó! ¡A-le -

Music: *The Honduras Alleluia*, Rob Glover, © 1997, GIA Publications, Inc.

ALLELUIA / ALELUYA 272

Music: *Mass for the Life of the World,* David Haas, arr. by Rob Glover, © 1993, GIA Publications, Inc.

ALLELUIA 273

Music: Liam Lawton, © 1995, Veritas Publications/Liam Lawton, GIA Publications, Inc., agent

LENTEN GOSPEL ACCLAMATION 274

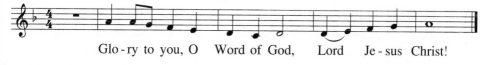

Text: ICEL, © 1969
Music: Richard Proulx, © 1975, GIA Publications, Inc.

275 **LENTEN GOSPEL ACCLAMATION**

Praise and hon - or to you, O Lord, O Lord.

Praise and hon - or to you, Lord Je - sus Christ.

Text: ICEL, © 1969
Music: Based on WONDROUS LOVE, Stephen Pishner, © 1998, GIA Publications, Inc.

276 **LENTEN GOSPEL ACCLAMATION**

Praise to you, Lord Je - sus, king of end - less glo - ry,

Sav - ior of the world, Sav - ior of the world.

Text: Marty Haugen
Music: Marty Haugen
© 1983, GIA Publications, Inc.

277 **GENERAL INTERCESSIONS**

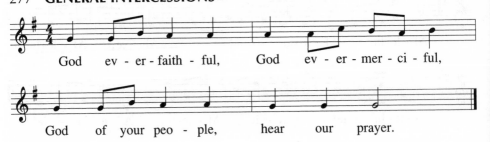

God ev - er - faith - ful, God ev - er - mer - ci - ful,

God of your peo - ple, hear our prayer.

Text: Michael Joncas
Music: Michael Joncas
© 1990, GIA Publications, Inc.

278 **GENERAL INTERCESSIONS**

Ky - ri - e, Ky - ri - e, e - le - i - son.

Music: Jacques Berthier, © 1980, Les Presses de Taizé, GIA Publications, Inc., agent

GENERAL INTERCESSIONS 279

Ky-ri-e e - le-i-son, Ky-ri-e e - le-i-son.

Music: Jacques Berthier, © 1998, Les Presses de Taizé, GIA Publications, Inc., agent

GENERAL INTERCESSIONS 280

Ky-ri-e, Ky-ri-e, Ky-ri-e e - lei-son. lei - son.

Music: Jacques Berthier, © 1998, Les Presses de Taizé, GIA Publications, Inc., agent

GENERAL INTERCESSIONS 281

Response
Cantor, then all (first time only):

O, Lord, hear our prayer. Lord, hear us.

O, Lord, hear our prayer.

Petitions
All:

O, Lord, hear our prayer.

All: D.C.

O, Lord, hear our prayer.

Music: Mass of the Nations, Donna Peña, © 2000, GIA Publications, Inc.

GENERAL INTERCESSIONS 282

Gra-cious Lord, hear us we pray.

Music: Ronald F. Krisman, © 1977, GIA Publications, Inc.

283-A GENERAL INTERCESSIONS–ADVENT

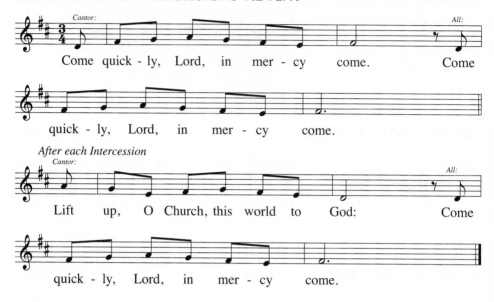

Come quick - ly, Lord, in mer - cy come. Come

quick - ly, Lord, in mer - cy come.

After each Intercession

Lift up, O Church, this world to God: Come

quick - ly, Lord, in mer - cy come.

Text: Gabe Huck
Music: Based on CONDITOR ALME SIDERUM; adapt. and arr. by Tony Alonso
© 2004, GIA Publications, Inc.

283-B GENERAL INTERCESSIONS–CHRISTMAS

Child of Mar - y, hear our prayer.

Child of Mar - y, hear our prayer.

After each Intercession

All cre - a - tion, raise your voic - es:

Child of Mar - y, hear our prayer.

Text: Gabe Huck
Music: Based on DIVINUM MYSTERIUM; adapt. and arr. by Tony E. Alonso
© 2004, GIA Publications, Inc.

GENERAL INTERCESSIONS–LENT

283-C

Cantor, then all:

Hear, O Lord, en - fold us in your mer - cy.

After each Intercession

Cantor: *All:*

Cry out for God's mer-cy: Hear, O Lord, en - fold us in your mer-cy.

Text: Gabe Huck
Music: Based on PARCE DOMINE; adapt. and arr. by Tony Alonso
© 2004, GIA Publications, Inc.

GENERAL INTERCESSIONS–EASTER

283-D

Cantor or choir, then all:

Hear us, Sav - ior, hear our prayer.

Text: Gabe Huck
Music: Tony Alonso
© 2004, GIA Publications, Inc.

GENERAL INTERCESSIONS

284

Hear our prayer, Lord. Hear our prayer,
Se - ñor, ó - ye-nos. Ó - ye - nos,

Lord, hear our prayer.
Se - ñor, ó - ye - nos.

Music: Tony E. Alonso, © 2001, GIA Publications, Inc.

285 GENERAL INTERCESSIONS

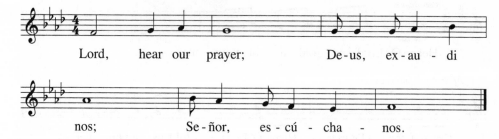

Lord, hear our prayer; De-us, ex-au-di nos; Se-ñor, es-cú-cha-nos.

Music: Michael Hay, © 1994, World Library Publications

286 PREFACE DIALOG–EUCHARISTIC PRAYER FOR CHILDREN

Priest: The Lord be with you. *Assembly:* And al-so with you. *Priest:* Lift up your hearts.

Assembly: We lift them up to the Lord. *Priest:* Let us give thanks to the Lord, our God.

Assembly: It is right to give him thanks and praise.

Music: *Mass of Creation*, Marty Haugen, © 1984, GIA Publications, Inc.

287 CHILDREN'S ACCLAMATION 1

Ho-san-na in the high-est, ho-san-na in the high-est!

Music: Eucharistic Prayer for Children, *Mass of Creation*, Marty Haugen, adapt. by Rob Glover, © 1989, GIA Publications, Inc.

SANCTUS

Ho - ly, ho - ly, ho - ly Lord,
God of pow-er, God of might, heav - en and
earth are full of your glo - ry. Ho -
san - na in the high - est. Bless - ed is
he who comes in the name of the Lord.
Ho - san - na in the high - est, ho -
san - na in the high - est.

Music: *Mass of Creation*, Marty Haugen, © 1984, GIA Publications, Inc.

CHILDREN'S ACCLAMATION 2

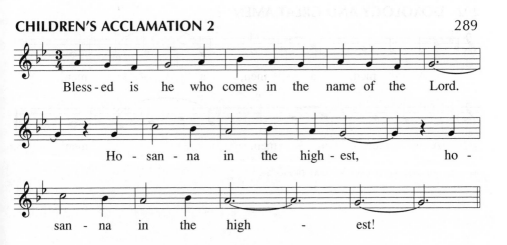

Bless - ed is he who comes in the name of the Lord.
Ho - san - na in the high - est, ho -
san - na in the high - est!

Music: Eucharistic Prayer for Children, *Mass of Creation*, Marty Haugen, adapt. by Rob Glover, © 1989, GIA Publications, Inc.

290 CHILDREN'S ACCLAMATION 3

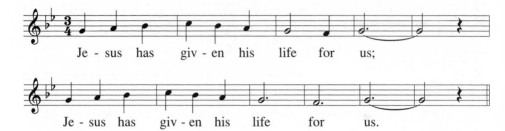

Je - sus has giv - en his life for us;

Je - sus has giv - en his life for us.

Text: ICEL, © 1975
Music: Eucharistic Prayer for Children, *Mass of Creation*, Marty Haugen, adapt. by Rob Glover, © 1989, GIA Publications, Inc.

291 CHILDREN'S ACCLAMATION 4

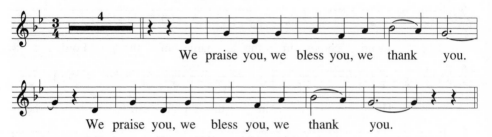

We praise you, we bless you, we thank you.

We praise you, we bless you, we thank you.

Text: ICEL, © 1975
Music: Eucharistic Prayer for Children, *Mass of Creation*, Marty Haugen, adapt. by Rob Glover, © 1989, GIA Publications, Inc.

292 DOXOLOGY AND GREAT AMEN

A - men, a - men, a - men!

A - men, a - men, a - men!

Music: *Mass of Creation*, Marty Haugen, © 1984, GIA Publications, Inc.

SANCTUS–LAND OF REST 293

Ho - ly, ho - ly, ho - ly Lord, God of pow-er and might, heav - en and earth are full of your glo - ry. Ho - san - na in the high - est. Bless - ed is he who comes in the name of the Lord. Ho - san - na in the high - est, ho - san - na in the high - est.

Music: *Land of Rest,* adapt. by Marcia Pruner, © 1980, Church Pension Fund; acc. by Richard Proulx, © 1986, GIA Publications, Inc.

MEMORIAL ACCLAMATION 294

*Christ has died, Christ is ris-en, Christ will come a-gain.

Christ has died, Christ is ris-en, Christ will come a-gain.

For a shorter version of this acclamation, sing the first two measures and the last two measures.

Text: ICEL, © 1973
Music: *Land of Rest,* adapt. by Richard Proulx, © 1986, GIA Publications, Inc.

AMEN 295

A - men, a - men, a - men.

Music: *Land of Rest,* adapt. by Richard Proulx, © 1986, GIA Publications, Inc.

296 SANCTUS–MASS FOR BENILDE-ST. MARGARET

Ho - ly, ho - ly, ho - ly Lord, God of pow'r and might, heav'n and earth are full of your glo - ry. Ho - san-na, ho - san-na, ho - san-na in the high-est! Ho - san-na, ho - san-na, ho - san-na in the high-est. Bless - ed, bless-ed is he who comes in the name of the Lord. Ho - san-na, ho - san-na, ho - san-na in the high-est! Ho - san-na, ho - san - na, ho - san - na in the high - est!

Music: *Mass for Benilde–St. Margaret*, Michael Mahler, © 2004, GIA Publications, Inc.

297 MEMORIAL ACCLAMATION

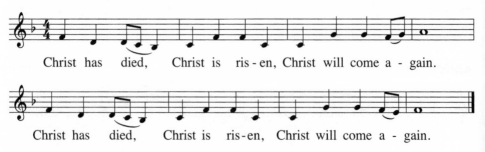

Christ has died, Christ is ris - en, Christ will come a - gain.

Christ has died, Christ is ris-en, Christ will come a - gain.

Text: ICEL, © 1973
Music: *Mass for Benilde–St. Margaret*, Michael Mahler, © 2004, GIA Publications, Inc.

AMEN

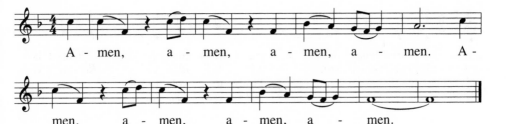

A - men,   a - men,   a - men,   a - men.   A -

men,   a - men,   a - men,   a - men.

Music: *Mass for Benilde–St. Margaret*, Michael Mahler, © 2004, GIA Publications, Inc.

SANCTUS–MASS FOR THE LIFE OF THE WORLD

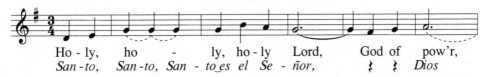

Ho - ly,   ho - ly, ho - ly   Lord,   God of   pow'r,
San - to,   San - to, San - to_es el Se - ñor,   Dios

God of   might,   heav - en   and   earth   are
del   U - ni - ver - so.   Lle - nos es - tán el   cie - lo   y la

full   of   your   glo - ry,   Ho - san - na   in   the
tie - rra   de   tu   glo - ria.   ¡Ho - san - na   en   el

high - est! Blest is   he   who   comes   in the
cie - lo!   Ben - di - to   el que   vie - ne   en

name   of   the   Lord.   Ho - san -
nom - bre   del   Se - ñor.   ¡Ho - san -

na!   Ho - san - na   in   the   high - est!
na!   ¡Ho - san - na   en   el   cie - lo!

Text: Spanish adapt. by Ronald F. Krisman, © 2004, GIA Publications, Inc.
Music: *Mass for the Life of the World*, David Haas, arr. by Rob Glover, © 1993, GIA Publications, Inc.

300 MEMORIAL ACCLAMATION

Christ has	died.	Al - le - lu - ia!	Christ is
Cris - to	*mu - rió.*	*¡A - le - lu - ya!*	*Re - su - ci -*
		Praise to you, Lord!	
		¡Glo - ria a Cris - to!	

ris - en.	Al - le - lu - ia!	Christ will come	a -
tó!	*¡A - le - lu - ya!*	*Cris - to de nue - vo*	*ven -*
	Praise to you, Lord!		
	¡Glo - ria al Se - ñor!		

gain.	Al - le - lu - ia!	Al - le - lu - ia!
drá.	*¡A - le - lu - ya!*	*¡A - le - lu - ya!*
	Praise to you, Lord!	Praise to you, Lord!
	¡Glo - ria a Cris - to!	*¡Glo - ria al Se - ñor!*

English Text: ICEL, © 1973; Spanish adapt. by Ronald F. Krisman, © 2004, GIA Publications, Inc.
Music: *Mass for the Life of the World*, David Haas, arr. by Rob Glover, © 1993, GIA Publications, Inc.

301 AMEN

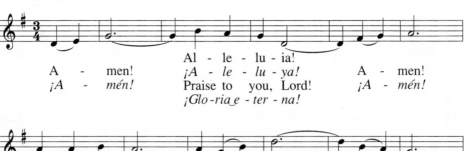

		Al - le - lu - ia!		
A -	men!	*¡A - le - lu - ya!*	A -	men!
¡A -	*mén!*	Praise to you, Lord!	*¡A -*	*mén!*
		¡Glo - ria e - ter - na!		

Al - le - lu - ia!			A -	men!	A -	men!
¡A - le - lu - ya!						
Praise to you, Lord!			*¡A -*	*mén!*	*¡A -*	*mén!*
¡Glo - ria al Se - ñor!						

Al - le - lu - ia!
¡A - le - lu - ya!   A -   men!
Praise to you, Lord!   ¡A -   men!
¡Glo - ria e - ter - na!

Text: Spanish adapt. by Ronald F. Krisman, © 2004, GIA Publications, Inc.
Music: *Mass for the Life of the World,* David Haas, arr. by Rob Glover, © 1993, GIA Publications, Inc.

AGNUS DEI   302

*Lamb   of   God,   you   take a - way   the
Cor - de - ro de   Dios,   que   qui - tas   el   pe -

sins of the world: have   mer - cy   on   us.
ca - do del mun - do,   ten   pie - dad   de no - so - tros.

Last time:

Lamb   of   God,   you   take a - way   the   sins   of the
Cor - de - ro de   Dios,   que   qui - tas   el   pe   -   ca - do del

world: grant   us   your   peace.
mun - do,   da   -   nos   la   paz.

*Other invocations may be used: King of kings, Prince of Peace, Bread of Life, Ancient Cup,
Pan de Vida (Bread of Life), Copa de Promesa (Cup of Promise), Sangre de la Cruz,
(Blood of the Cross), Mi Redentor (My Redeemer), etc.

Music: *Mass for the Life of the World,* David Haas, © 1987, 1993, GIA Publications, Inc.

303 SANCTUS–MASS OF PLENTY

Ho - ly, ho - ly, ho - ly Lord, God of pow-er and might, heav-en and earth, heav-en and earth are full of your glo - ry. Ho - san - na in the high - est, ho - san - na in the high - est.

Bless-ed is he, bless-ed is he who comes in the name of the Lord.

Ho - san - na in the high - est, ho - san - na in the high - est. Ho - san - na in the high - est, ho - san - na in the high - est.

This section may be used as an additional acclamation with the Children's Eucharistic Prayer.

Music: *Mass of Plenty*, Rob Glover, © 2000, GIA Publications, Inc.

MEMORIAL ACCLAMATION 304

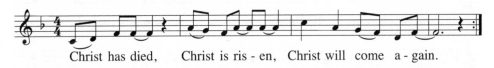

Christ has died, Christ is ris - en, Christ will come a - gain.

Text: ICEL, © 1973
Music: *Mass of Plenty*, Rob Glover, © 2000, GIA Publications, Inc.

AMEN 305

A - men, al - le - lu - ia, a -

men, al - le - lu - ia! A - men, al - le -

lu - ia, a - men, al - le - lu - ia!

Music: *Mass of Plenty*, Rob Glover, © 2000, GIA Publications, Inc.

SANCTUS–DEUTSCHE MESSE 306

Ho - ly, ho - ly, ho - ly Lord, God of pow'r and

might. Ho - ly, ho - ly, ho - ly Lord,

God of pow'r and might. Heav - en and earth are

full, full of your glo - ry. Ho -

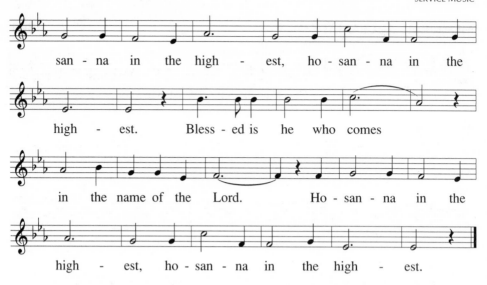

san - na in the high - est, ho - san - na in the high - est. Bless - ed is he who comes in the name of the Lord. Ho - san - na in the high - est, ho - san - na in the high - est.

Music: *Deutsche Messe*, Franz Schubert, 1797-1828; adapt. by Richard Proulx, © 1985, 1989, GIA Publications, Inc.

307 MEMORIAL ACCLAMATION

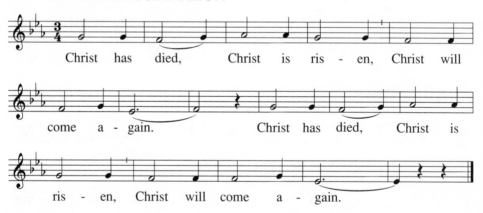

Christ has died, Christ is ris - en, Christ will come a - gain. Christ has died, Christ is ris - en, Christ will come a - gain.

Text: ICEL, © 1973
Music: *Deutsche Messe*, Franz Schubert, 1797-1828; adapt. by Richard Proulx, © 1985, 1995, GIA Publications, Inc.

308 AMEN

A - men, A - men, A - men, A-men, A - men.

Music: *Deutsche Messe*, Franz Schubert, 1797-1828, adapt. by Richard Proulx, © 1985, 1989, GIA Publications, Inc.

SANCTUS–SANTO

English*

Ho - ly, ho - ly, ho - ly Lord, God of pow'r and might,

Spanish*

San - to, San - to, San - to es el Se - ñor, Dios del U - ni - ver - so.

heav - en and earth are full of your glo - ry. Ho - san - na in the

Lle - nos es - tán el cie-lo y la tie-rra de tu glo -

high - est. Bless - ed is he who comes in the name of the

ria. Ben - di - to el que vie - ne en nom - bre del Se -

Lord. Ho - san - na in the high - est, ho - san - na in the high - est.

ñor. Ho - san - na en el cie - lo, ho - san - na en el cie - lo.

*For a bilingual version, sing the words in italics.

Music: *Santo*; Argentine folk melody; adapt. by Marty Haugen, © 2001, GIA Publications, Inc.

310 MEMORIAL ACCLAMATION

English*

Dy - ing you de-stroyed our death,

Spanish*

A - nun - cia - mos tu muer - te, Se - ñor, pro-cla -

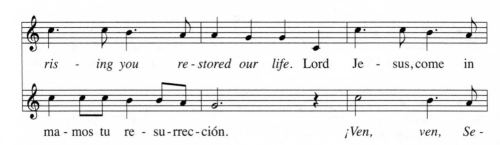

ris - ing you re-stored our life. Lord Je - sus, come in

ma - mos tu re - su-rrec-ción. ¡Ven, ven, Se -

glo - ry, Lord Je - sus, come in glo - ry.

ñor Je - sús! ¡Ven, Se - ñor Je - sús!

*For a bilingual version, sing the words in italics.

English text: ICEL, © 1973
Music: *Santo*; Argentine folk melody; adapt. by Marty Haugen, © 2001, GIA Publications, Inc.

311 AMEN

English

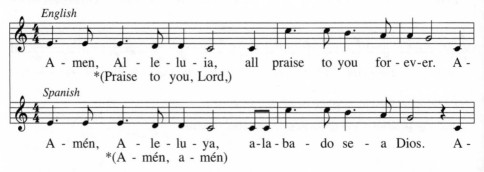

A - men, Al - le - lu - ia, all praise to you for - ev-er. A -
*(Praise to you, Lord,)

Spanish

A - mén, A - le - lu - ya, a-la-ba - do se - a Dios. A -
*(A - mén, a - mén)

*During Lent

men, A-men, to you, O God, now and ev - er-more.

mén, A-mén a tí, O Dios, a - ho - ra y pa - ra siem-pre.

Music: *Santo;* Argentine folk melody; adapt. by Marty Haugen, © 2001, GIA Publications, Inc.

AGNUS DEI

312

English

Cantor:

*Lamb of God,
Bread of Life, you take a - way the sin of the
Sav - ing Cup,

To repeat   *All:*

world: have mer-cy on us, have mer - cy on us.

Last time   *All:*

world: grant us your peace, grant us your peace.

Spanish

Cantor:

*Cor - de-ro de Dios,
Pan de Vi - da, que qui - tas el pe - ca-do del
San - ta Co-pa,

To repeat   *All:*

mun-do, ten pie-dad de no - so-tros, ten pie-dad de no-

Cantor: *Last time*

so-tros. (Cor-) mun-do, da-nos la paz, da - nos la paz.

**"Lamb of God/Cordero de Dios"* first and last times.

Music: *Santo;* Argentine folk melody; adapt. by Marty Haugen, © 2001, GIA Publications, Inc.

313 SANCTUS–ST. LOUIS JESUITS MASS

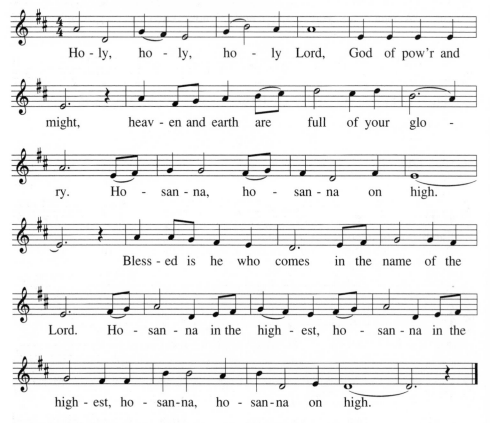

Ho - ly, ho - ly, ho - ly Lord, God of pow'r and might, heav - en and earth are full of your glo - ry. Ho - san - na, ho - san - na on high. Bless - ed is he who comes in the name of the Lord. Ho - san - na in the high - est, ho - san - na in the high - est, ho - san - na, ho - san - na on high.

Music: *St. Louis Jesuits Mass;* Robert J. Dufford, SJ and Daniel L. Schutte, © 1973, Robert J. Dufford, SJ and Daniel L. Schutte; acc. by Diana Kodner
Published by OCP Publications.

314 MEMORIAL ACCLAMATION

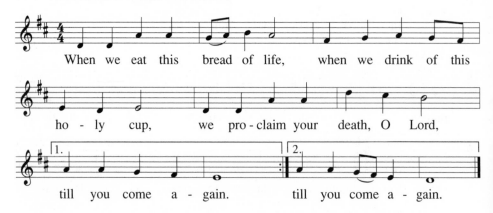

When we eat this bread of life, when we drink of this ho - ly cup, we pro - claim your death, O Lord,

1. till you come a - gain. 2. till you come a - gain.

Text: ICEL, © 1973
Music: *St. Louis Jesuits Mass;* Robert J. Dufford, SJ and Daniel L. Schutte, © 1973, 1979, Robert J. Dufford, SJ and Daniel L. Schutte
Published by OCP Publications

AMEN
315

A - men, al-le-lu - ia, for ev-er and ev-er, for ev-er, al-le-lu - ia, for ev-er and ev-er. A-men.

Music: *St. Louis Jesuits Mass;* Robert J. Dufford, SJ and Daniel L. Schutte, © 1973, Robert J. Dufford, SJ and Daniel L. Schutte
Published by OCP Publications

SANCTUS
316

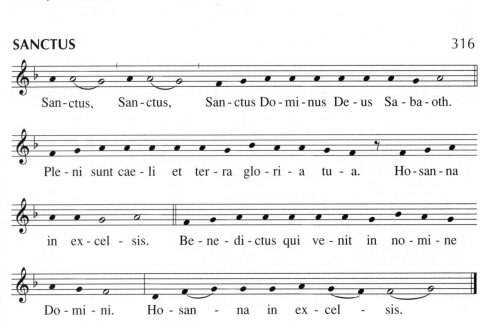

San-ctus, San-ctus, San-ctus Do-mi-nus De-us Sa-ba-oth.

Ple-ni sunt cae-li et ter-ra glo-ri-a tu-a. Ho-san-na

in ex-cel-sis. Be-ne-di-ctus qui ve-nit in no-mi-ne

Do-mi-ni. Ho-san-na in ex-cel-sis.

Music: *Sanctus XVIII, Vatican Edition;* acc. by Gerard Farrell, OSB, © 1986, GIA Publications, Inc.

MEMORIAL ACCLAMATION
316-A

Mor-tem tu-am an-nun-ti-á-mus, Dó-mi-ne, et re-sur-

re-cti-ó-nem con-fi-té-mur, do-nec vé-ni-as.

Music: Vatican Edition; acc. by Richard Proulx, © 1995, GIA Publications, Inc.

316-B AMEN

After the doxology: *Assembly:*

per o - mni - a   sae - cu - la   sae-cu - lo - rum.   A - men.

317 AGNUS DEI

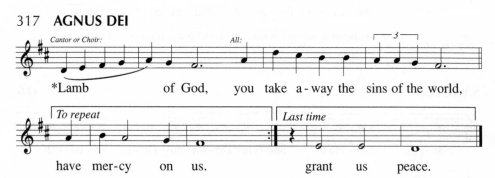

Cantor or Choir: *All:*   3

*Lamb   of God,   you take a - way the sins of the world,

| To repeat | Last time |

have mer-cy   on us.   grant   us   peace.

Alternates: 1. Emmanuel, 2. Prince of peace, 3. Son of God, 4. Word made flesh,
5. Paschal Lamb, 6. Bread of Life, 7. Lord Jesus Christ, 8. Lord of Love,
9. Christ the Lord, 10. King of kings.

Music: *Holy Cross Mass*, David Clark Isele, © 1979, GIA Publications, Inc.

318 AGNUS DEI

*Cantor:**

**O Lamb of   God,   you take a - way

| Repeat as needed |

the sins of the world: have mer - cy on us.

| Last time |

Grant   us   peace,   grant   us   peace.

The assembly echoes each phrase of the cantor at the interval of one measure.

**Alternates: 1. O Morning Star, 2. O Word of God, 3. Emmanuel, 4. O Word made flesh,*
5. O Tree of Life, 6. O Risen Lord, 7. O Cornerstone, 8. O Spring of Life, 9. O Bread of Life,
10. O Cup of Joy, 11. O Prince of Peace

Music: Ralph R. Stewart, © 1999, GIA Publications, Inc.; acc. by Robert J. Batastini, © 2003, GIA Publications, Inc.

AGNUS DEI 319

First Invocation

Je-sus, Lamb of God, you take a-way the sins of the world:

have mer - cy, have mer - cy on us.

Invocations

1. Bread of life and sav - ing cup,
2. King of kings and Lord of lords, you take a - way the
3. Lov - ing Sav - ior, Prince of peace,

sins of the world: have mer-cy, have mer-cy on us.

Last Invocation

Je - sus, Lamb of God, you take a-way the sins of the world:

have mer - cy, and grant us your peace.

Music: *The Psallite Mass*, Michael Joncas, © 1988, GIA Publications, Inc.

AGNUS DEI 320

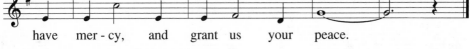

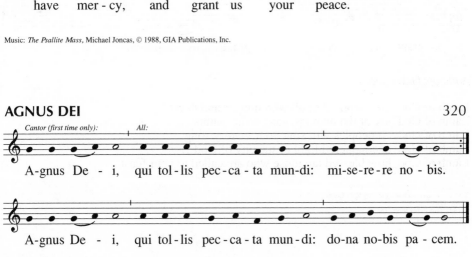

A-gnus De - i, qui tol-lis pec-ca-ta mun-di: mi-se-re-re no - bis.

A-gnus De - i, qui tol-lis pec-ca-ta mun-di: do-na no-bis pa - cem.

Music: *Agnus Dei XVIII, Vatican Edition;* acc. by Robert J. Batastini, © 1993, GIA Publications, Inc.

321 LAMB OF GOD: MAY WE BE ONE

Cantor(s):

1. Lamb of God, you
2. Lamb of God, un -
3. Lamb of God, de -
4. Lamb of God, whose
5. Lamb of God, our
6. Lamb of God, our

take a - way the sins of the world:
blem - ished of - f'ring made for our sin:
stroyed that all who eat might be healed:
blood will save your peo - ple from death:
com - mon mem - 'ry, cov - e - nant feast:
free - dom won, re - mem - bered for ev - er:

All:

have mer - cy on us, have mer - cy on us.

Last time
Cantor(s):

Lamb of God, you take a-way the sins of the world,

All:

grant us peace, grant us peace.

Additional invocations:

Lamb of God, the shepherd of all who hunger and thirst...
Lamb of God, joy of the martyrs, song of the saints...
Lamb of God, all peoples will sing your victory song...
Lamb of God, unconquered light of the city of God...
Lamb of God, how blessed are those who are called to your feast...

Text: *Agnus Dei;* additional text by Rory Cooney
Music: Gary Daigle
© 1993, GIA Publications, Inc.

MAY WE BE ONE (COMMUNION HYMN)

Refrain

When we eat this bread and drink this cup, we pro-claim your death, Lord Je - sus. So as we share this feast may we be - come, heal-ing and light and peace. May we be one. (To verses) one. (Last time)

Verses

A - men, a - men.

A - men, a - men. A - men, a -

men. A - men, a - men.

D.C.

Text: Rory Cooney, b.1952
Tune: Gary Daigle, b.1957
© 1993, GIA Publications, Inc.

323 O Come, O Come, Emmanuel

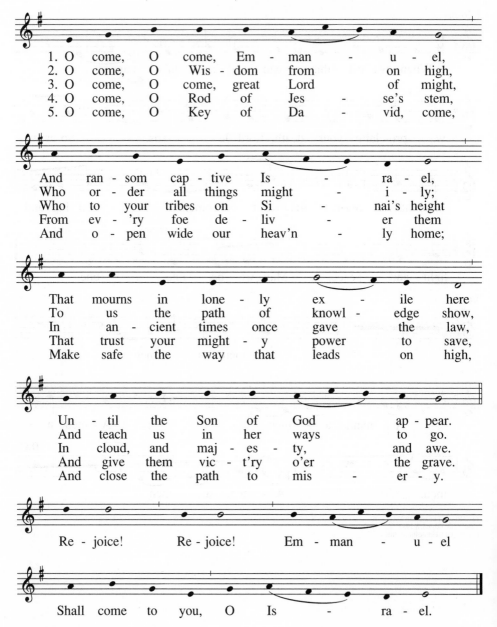

1. O come, O come, Emmanuel,
2. O come, O Wisdom from on high,
3. O come, O come, great Lord of might,
4. O come, O Rod of Jesse's stem,
5. O come, O Key of David, come,

And ransom captive Israel,
Who order all things mightily;
Who to your tribes on Sinai's height
From ev'ry foe deliver them
And open wide our heav'nly home;

That mourns in lonely exile here
To us the path of knowledge show,
In ancient times once gave the law,
That trust your mighty power to save,
Make safe the way that leads on high,

Until the Son of God appear.
And teach us in her ways to go.
In cloud, and majesty,
And give them vic - t'ry o'er the grave.
And close the path to misery.

Re - joice! Re - joice! Emmanuel

Shall come to you, O Israel.

6. O come, O Dayspring from on high
And cheer us by your drawing nigh;
Disperse the gloomy clouds of night,
And death's dark shadow put to flight.

7. O come, Desire of nations, bind
In one the hearts of humankind;
O bid our sad divisions cease,
And be for us our King of Peace.

Text: *Veni, veni Emmanuel;* Latin 9th C.; tr. by John M. Neale, 1818-1866, alt.
Tune: VENI VENI EMMANUEL, LM with refrain; Mode I; adapt. by Thomas Helmore, 1811-1890; acc. by Richard Proulx, b.1937, © 1975, GIA Publications, Inc.

Maranatha, Lord Messiah 324

Verses

Cantor or choir:

1. Gra - cious God of Wis - dom, who hears your peo - ple's
2. Might - y Voice of Si - nai, whom Mos - es heard in
3. Fra - grant Bud of Jes - se, whose bloom - ing Kings re -
4. Da - vid's Key of Heav - en, un - lock us from our
5. Blaz - ing Sun of Jus - tice, the flame of East - ern
6. Sov - ereign of all Na - tions, our cor - ner-stone of
7. Je - sus, be God with us, Em - man - u - el fore -

cry, teach us ways of pru - dence, O
awe, Ad - o - nai, now lead us with
vere, root your words with - in us, God's
sins. Freed from er - ror's pris - on, our
dawn, scat - ter cling - ing shad - ows, that
trust, de - liv - er, in your mer - cy, your
told. Feed us like a shep - herd, in

All:

Breath of God Most High.
ho - ly arm and law.
words for all to hear.
life in you be - gins. Ma-ra-
gloom of death be gone.
crea - tures made from dust.
safe - ly gath - ered fold.

Refrain

na - tha, Lord Mes - si - ah, long a - wait - ed from a -

far. Come and make your home a - mong us. Let us

| 1.-6. | *To verses* | *Last time* |

see your birth - ing star. star.

Text: Based on the "O" Antiphons; Kathy Powell, b.1942
Tune: Kathy Powell, b.1942
© 1999, GIA Publications, Inc.

325 Walk in the Reign

Refrain

Close as to - mor - row the sun shall ap - pear.

Free-dom is com-ing and heal-ing is near. And I shall be

with you in laugh-ter and pain to stand in the wind and

walk in the reign, to walk in the reign.

Verses

1. In days to come the des - ert shall bloom.
2. Com-fort each oth-er, for pain soon must end. A
3. A cur - tain of fear is be - ing torn down.
4. The streets of So - we-to, the docks at G - dansk, Ti -

Riv - ers will run there, soon, ver - y soon. So
day comes when li - on and lamb shall be friends. The
Pris - ons are o - pened; the lost have been found. So
en - an - men Square, the slums of The Bronx, When

what shall we fear, though death do its
sight - less shall see then, the speech - less sing
go tell the seek-er what we've seen and
we stand to - geth-er to stand a - gainst

worst? The word of our God is the
songs. The name of our God is the
heard: The name of our God is the
hell, The name of this peo - ple is

last   shall   be   first,   the   last   shall   be   first.
right - er   of   wrongs,   the   right - er   of   wrongs.
keep - er   of   word,   the   keep - er   of   word.
"Em - man - u - el,"   is   "Em - man - u - el."

Text: Rory Cooney, b.1952
Tune: Rory Cooney, b.1952
© 1990, GIA Publications, Inc.

Lead Us to Your Light   326

Refrain

Lead us to   your   light,   lead us out   of   dark - ness.

Lead us to   your   light.   Come, Je - sus,   come.

Verses

1. Lord,   we a - wait   your   com - ing   to   our   world;
2. Lord,   you are hope   and   heal - ing   for our   world;
3. Come,   O   come,   O   come, Em - man - u -   el.
4. Rouse   us from sleep,   wake us   from our   slum - ber,
5. Child   of the light   and   love be - yond all   tell - ing,

bring   us   the   gift   of   sal - va - tion.
come,   now,   and   bring   us   your   good news.
Come with us   on   earth   here   to   dwell.
ban -   ish   the   dark - ness   of   night.
fill   our hearts with won - der   and   praise.

Text: Carol E. Browning, b.1956
Tune: Carol E. Browning, b.1956
© 2001, GIA Publications, Inc.

327 When the King Shall Come Again

1. When the King shall come a - gain All his pow'r re -
2. In the des - ert trees take root Fresh from his cre -
3. Strength-en fee - ble hands and knees, Faint - ing hearts, be
4. There God's high - way shall be seen Where no roar - ing

veal - ing, Splen - dor shall an - nounce his reign,
a - tion; Plants and flow'rs and sweet - est fruit
cheer - ful! God who comes for such as these
li - on, Noth - ing e - vil or un - clean

Life and joy and heal - ing; Earth no
Join the cel - e - bra - tion; Riv - ers
Seeks and saves the fear - ful; Deaf ears,
Walks the road to Zi - on: Ran - somed

long - er in de - cay, Hope no more frus - trat - ed;
spring up from the earth, Bar - ren lands a - dorn - ing;
hear the si - lent tongues Sing a - way their weep - ing;
peo - ple home-ward bound All your prais - es voic - ing,

This is God's re - demp - tion day
Val - leys, this is your new birth,
Blind eyes, see the life - less ones
See your Lord with glo - ry crowned,

Long - ing - ly a - wait - ed.
Moun - tains, greet the morn - ing!
Walk - ing, run - ning, leap - ing.
Share in his re - joic - ing!

Text: Isaiah 35; Christopher Idle, b.1938, © 1982, Jubilate Hymns, Ltd. (Administered by Hope Publishing Co.)
Tune: GAUDEAMUS PARITER, 7 6 7 6 D; Johann Horn, c. 1495-1547

Come, Light of the World 328

1. Come, light of the world, light up our lives, Lord.
2. Come, strength of our days, strength-en our lives, Lord.
3. Come, joy for the world, fill us with glad - ness.
4. Come, hope of the world, com - fort your peo - ple.
5. Come, Spir - it of God, be with us now, Lord.

Come, light of the world, light up our
Come, strength of our days, strength - en our
Come, joy for the world, glad - den our
Come, hope of the world, com - fort our
Come, Spir - it of God, fill us with

hearts. Dis - pel all our dark - ness,
hearts. Come, fill us with cour - age
hearts. Come, bring us to - geth - er
hearts. Come, heal all our sor - row
truth. En - light - en our lives, Lord,

re - move all our blind-ness, Come, light of the
to fol - low you al - ways. Come, strength of our
with sing - ing and laugh - ter. Come, joy for the
with love and com - pas - sion. Come, hope of the
with ra - diance and pow - er. Come, Spir - it of

world, be light for our eyes.
days, be strength for our minds.
world, bring warmth to our lives.
world, bring peace to us all.
God, in - spire all we do.

Text: Paul Inwood, b.1947
Tune: Paul Inwood, b.1947

329   Advent Alleluia

Refrain

Cantor, then all (first time only):

Hal - le - lu - ia, hal - le - lu - ia,
hal - le - lu - ia, hal - le - lu - ia!

Verses

1. Lord, show us your mercy and love,
   and grant us your salvation.

2. Prepare the way of the Lord, make straight his paths:
   all people shall see the salvation of God.

3. The Spirit of the Lord is upon me,
   he sent me to bring good news to the poor.

4. A virgin will give birth to a Son; a virgin will give birth to a Son;
   his name will be Emmanuel: God is with us.

5. I am the servant of the Lord:
   may his will for me be done.

Text: *Lectionary for Mass*, © 1969, 1981, ICEL
Tune: Michael Joncas, b.1951, © 1988, GIA Publications, Inc.

330   Prepare the Way of the Lord

Canon

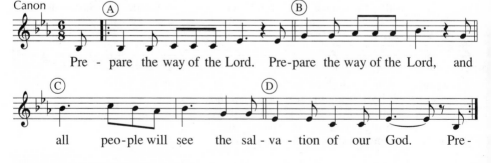

Pre - pare the way of the Lord. Pre-pare the way of the Lord, and
all peo-ple will see the sal - va - tion of our God. Pre-

Text: Luke 3:4,6; Taizé Community, 1984
Tune: Jacques Berthier, 1923-1994
© 1984, Les Presses de Taizé, GIA Publications, Inc., agent

Comfort, Comfort, O My People   331

1. Com - fort, com - fort, O my peo - ple, Speak of peace, now
2. Hark, the voice of one who's cry - ing In the des - ert
3. O make straight what long was crook - ed, Make the rough - er

says our God; Com - fort those who sit in dark - ness,
far and near, Bid - ding all to full re - pent - ance
plac - es plain; Let your hearts be true and hum - ble,

Mourn - ing 'neath their sor - row's load. Speak un - to Je -
Since the king - dom now is here. O that warn - ing
As be - fits his ho - ly reign. For the glo - ry

ru - sa - lem Of the peace that waits for them;
cry o - bey! Now pre - pare for God a way;
of the Lord Now o'er earth is shed a - broad;

Tell of all the sins I cov - er, And that war - fare now is o - ver.
Let the val - leys rise to meet him And the hills bow down to greet him.
And all flesh shall see the to - ken That his word is nev - er bro - ken.

Text: Isaiah 40:1-8; *Tröstet, tröstet, meine Lieben*; Johann Olearius, 1611-1684; tr. by Catherine Winkworth, 1827-1878, alt.
Tune: GENEVA 42, 8 7 8 7 77 88; *Genevan Psalter*, 1551; harm. adapt. from Claude Goudimel, 1505-1572

332 Like a Shepherd

Text: Isaiah 40:9ff, Ezekiel 34:11, Matthew 11:28ff; Bob Dufford, SJ, b.1943
Tune: Bob Dufford, SJ, b.1943; acc. by Sr. Theophane Hytrek, OSF, 1915-1992, alt.
© 1976, Robert J. Dufford, SJ, and OCP Publications

O Come, Divine Messiah 333

1. O come, Di - vine Mes - si - ah, The
2. O come De - sired of na - tions, Whom
3. O come in peace and meek - ness, For

world in si - lence waits the day When hope shall sing its
priest and proph - et long fore-told, Will break the cap - tive
low - ly will your cra - dle be: Though clothed in hu - man

tri - umph, And sad - ness flee a - way.
fet - ters, Re - deem the long - lost fold.
weak - ness We shall your God - head see.

Dear Sav - ior, haste! Come, come to earth. Dis - pel the

night and show your face, And bid us hail the dawn of

grace. O come, Di - vine Mes - si - ah, The

world in si - lence waits the day When hope shall sing its

tri - umph, And sad - ness flee a - way.

Text: *Venez, divin Messie;* Abbé Simon-Joseph Pellegrin, 1663-1745; tr. by S. Mary of St. Philip, 1877
Tune: VENEZ, DIVIN MESSIE, 7 8 7 6 with refrain; French Noël, 16th C.; harm. by Healey Willan, 1880-1968, © 1958, The Basilian Fathers,
assigned to Ralph Jusko Publications, Inc.

334 Creator of the Stars of Night

Verses

1. Cre - a - tor of the stars of night, Your
2. In sor - row that the an - cient curse Should
3. When this old world drew on toward night, You
4. At your great Name, O Je - sus, now All
5. Come in your ho - ly might, we pray, Re -
6. To God Cre - a - tor, God the Son, And

peo - ple's ev - er - last - ing light, O
doom to death a u - ni - verse, You
came; but not in splen - dor bright, Not
knees must bend, all hearts must bow: All
deem us for e - ter - nal day; De -
God the Spir - it, Three - in - One, Praise,

Christ, Re - deem - er of us all, We
came, O Sav - ior, to set free Your
as a mon - arch, but the child Of
things on earth with one ac - cord, Like
fend us while we dwell be - low From
hon - or, might, and glo - ry be From

To next verse

pray you hear us when we call.
own in glo - rious lib - er - ty.
Mar - y, blame - less moth - er mild.
those in heav'n, shall call you Lord.
all as - saults of our dread foe.
age to age e - ter - nal - ly.

To refrain   Refrain

Come, O Lord, and bring your light, O ra - diant

Hymn may be sung without refrain.

star and heart's de - light. O God-with-us, Em-man-u -

Last time

el, with your love, the dark dis - pel.

Text: *Conditor alme siderum*, Latin 9th. C.; tr. *The Hymnal 1982*, © 1985, The Church Pension Fund;
  refrain, Carol E. Browning, b.1956, © 2003, GIA Publications, Inc.
Tune: CONDITOR ALME SIDERUM, LM; Mode IV; acc. and refrain music by Carol E. Browning, b.1956, © 2003, GIA Publications, Inc.

Maranatha, Come   335

Refrain

Ma - ra-na - tha, come, come, Lord Je - sus.

Ma - ra-na - tha, come, come, O God.

Verses

1. Wis - dom of God, guid - ing cre - a - tion,
2. O sa - cred Lord, come in your glo - ry;
3. From Jes - se's stem raise up your peo - ple.
4. O roy - al power, O key of Da - vid,
5. O ra - diant dawn, O sun of jus - tice,
6. Rul - er of all, joy of our long - ing,
7. Sav - ior of all, hope of the na - tions,

D.C.

lead us in ways that are faith - ful to your name.
stretch forth your hand and we shall be free.
Let noth - ing keep you from com - ing to our aid.
o - pen the heav - ens and lead us in - to life.
shine on your peo - ple in dark - ness and in death.
come save the peo - ple you fash - ion from the dust.
bring us to free - dom, E - man - u - el.

Text: Based on the "O" Antiphons; Francis Patrick O'Brien, b.1958
Tune: Francis Patrick O'Brien, b.1958
© 1996, GIA Publications, Inc.

336 My Soul in Stillness Waits

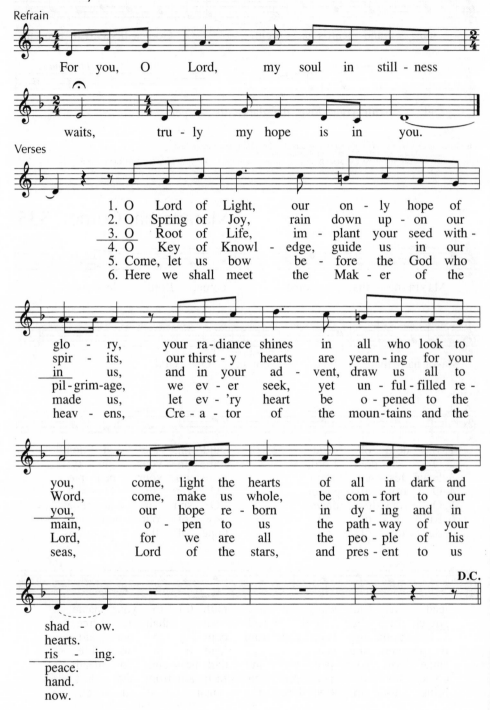

Refrain

For you, O Lord, my soul in still - ness waits, tru - ly my hope is in you.

Verses

1. O Lord of Light, our on - ly hope of
2. O Spring of Joy, rain down up - on our
3. O Root of Life, im - plant your seed with -
4. O Key of Knowl - edge, guide us in our
5. Come, let us bow be - fore the God who
6. Here we shall meet the Mak - er of the

glo - ry, your ra - diance shines in all who look to
spir - its, our thirst - y hearts are yearn - ing for your
in us, and in your ad - vent, draw us all to
pil - grim-age, we ev - er seek, yet un - ful - filled re -
made us, let ev - 'ry heart be o - pened to the
heav - ens, Cre - a - tor of the moun-tains and the

you, come, light the hearts of all in dark and
Word, come, make us whole, be com - fort to our
you, our hope re - born in dy - ing and in
main, o - pen to us the path - way of your
Lord, for we are all the peo - ple of his
seas, Lord of the stars, and pres - ent to us

D.C.

shad - ow.
hearts.
ris - ing.
peace.
hand.
now.

Text: Psalm 95 and "O" Antiphons; Marty Haugen, b.1950
Tune: Marty Haugen, b.1950
© 1982, GIA Publications, Inc.

People, Look East   337

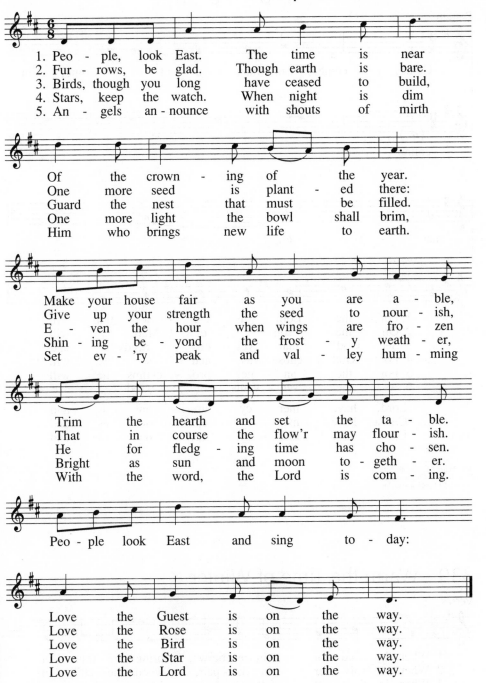

1. Peo - ple, look East. The time   is   near
2. Fur - rows, be   glad. Though earth is   bare.
3. Birds, though you long   have   ceased to   build,
4. Stars, keep the   watch. When night is   dim
5. An - gels an - nounce with shouts of   mirth

Of   the   crown - ing   of   the   year.
One   more   seed   is   plant - ed   there:
Guard   the   nest   that   must   be   filled.
One   more   light   the   bowl   shall   brim,
Him   who   brings   new   life   to   earth.

Make   your   house   fair   as   you   are   a - ble,
Give   up   your   strength the   seed   to   nour - ish,
E -   ven   the   hour   when   wings   are   fro - zen
Shin - ing   be - yond   the   frost - y   weath - er,
Set   ev - 'ry   peak   and   val   - ley   hum - ming

Trim   the   hearth and   set   the   ta   -   ble.
That   in   course the   flow'r may   flour - ish.
He   for   fledg - ing   time   has   cho   - sen.
Bright as   sun   and   moon   to - geth -   er.
With   the   word,   the   Lord   is   com   - ing.

Peo - ple   look   East   and   sing   to - day:

Love   the   Guest   is   on   the   way.
Love   the   Rose   is   on   the   way.
Love   the   Bird   is   on   the   way.
Love   the   Star   is   on   the   way.
Love   the   Lord   is   on   the   way.

Text: Eleanor Farjeon, 1881-1965, © David Higham Assoc. Ltd.
Tune: BESANÇON, 87 98 87; French traditional; harm. by Martin Shaw, 1875-1958, © Oxford University Press

338 Advent Gathering Song

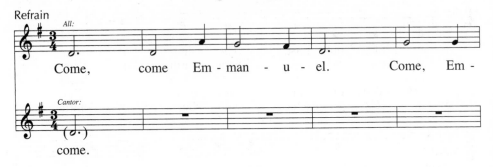

Refrain

All:

Come,   come Em - man - u - el.   Come,   Em -

Cantor:

come.

man - u - el.

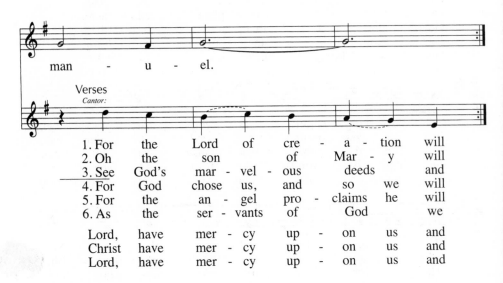

Verses

Cantor:

1. For	the	Lord	of	cre	-	a	-	tion	will
2. Oh	the	son		of		Mar	-	y	will
3. See	God's	mar	- vel -	ous		deeds		and
4. For	God	chose	us,	and		so		we	will
5. For	the	an	- gel	pro	-	claims		he	will
6. As	the	ser	- vants	of		God		we

Lord,	have	mer	- cy	up	-	on	us	and
Christ	have	mer	- cy	up	-	on	us	and
Lord,	have	mer	- cy	up	-	on	us	and

Text: James J. Chepponis, b.1956
Tune: James J. Chepponis, b.1956
© 1995, GIA Publications, Inc.

339 Warm the Time of Winter

Verses

1. When the wind	of	win - ter blows,	bring - ing times	of
2. When we shiv - er		in des - pair,	when the chill	of
3. When in days	of	fall - en snow,	change con - founds	or

sol - i - tude,   fill the si - lent,   ic - y night;
death comes near,   hold us, Spir - it,   calm our fear,
love burns low,   from the ash - es   may there rise

Refrain

be our hearts' com - pas - sion.
while the eve - ning deep - ens.   Ho - ly Light,
phoe - nix of our grow - ing.

warm our night;   warm the time of win - ter.   Ho - ly Light,

warm our night;   warm the time of win - ter.

Text: Ruth Duck, b.1947, © 1992, GIA Publications, Inc.
Tune: Lori True, b.1961, © 2000, GIA Publications, Inc.

Wait for the Lord   340

Wait for the Lord, whose day is near.

Wait for the Lord: be strong, take heart!

Text: Isaiah 40, Philippians 4, Matthew 6:33, 7:7; Taizé Community, 1984
Tune: Jacques Berthier, 1923-1994
© 1984, Les Presses de Taizé, GIA Publications, Inc., agent

341 Lift Up Your Heads

1. Lift up your heads, e - ter - nal gates, Al - le - lu -
2. But not in arms or bat - tle dress, Al - le - lu -
3. God brings a new face to the brave, Al - le - lu -
4. God's match - less and ma - jes - tic strength, Al - le - lu -

ia! See how the King of glo - ry waits,
ia! God comes, a child a - midst dis - tress,
ia! God re - de - fines who best can save:
ia! In all its height, depth, breadth, and length,

Al - le - lu - ia! The Lord of Hosts is draw - ing
Al - le - lu - ia! No might - y ar - mies shield the
Al - le - lu - ia! Not those whose pow'r re - lies on
Al - le - lu - ia! Now is re - vealed, its pow'r to

near, The Sav - ior of the world is here.
way, On - ly coarse lin - en, wool, and hay.
threat, Ter - ror or tor - ture, de - struc-tion or debt.
prove, By Christ pro - test - ing "God is love!"

Al-le-lu - ia! Al-le-lu - ia! Al - le - lu - ia!

Text: George Weissel, 1590-1635; tr. Catherine Winkworth, 1827-1878; adapt. by John L. Bell, b.1949, © 2001, Iona Community, GIA Publications, Inc., agent
Tune: CH THREE, 8 8 8 8 with alleluias; John L. Bell, b.1949, © 2001, Iona Community, GIA Publications, Inc., agent

Find Us Ready 342

Refrain

Find us read-y, Lord, not stand-ing still. Find us work-ing and lov-ing and do-ing your will. Find us read-y, Lord, faith-ful in love, build-ing the king-dom that's here and a-bove, build-ing the king-dom of mer-cy and love.

Verses

1. We must wait for the Lord for we know not the time.
   So here and today we gather and pray,
   discovering love in our midst.

2. We must make straight the path, God's love revealed.
   With sin cast aside, God's mercy alive,
   fear not for here is your God.

3. Lifting up those bowed down, we prepare for our God.
   Rejoice in the Lord, for hope has been born
   in hearts where our God finds a home.

Text: Tom Booth, b.1961
Tune: Tom Booth, b.1961; acc. by Ed Bolduc
© 1993, Tom Booth. Published by OCP Publications

343 A Voice Cries Out

Verse 1

1. Con-sole my peo-ple, the ones dear to me: speak to the heart of Je - ru-sa-lem: the time of your mourn-ing is end - ed now, the Lord of life will come.

𝄉 Refrain

A voice cries out in the wil - der - ness: Pre - pare a way for the Lord! A voice cries out in the wil - der - ness: Make straight a high-way for God!

Verse 2

2. Ev - 'ry val - ley is made a plain, ev - 'ry moun-tain is lev - eled the glo - ry of God shall

D.S.

then be re - vealed, and the na-tions will sing in praise.

Verse 3

3. A voice shouts: "Cry!" O what shall I cry? All flesh is like

grass and its flow-ers: the grass may with-er, the

D.S.

flow-er may fade, but the Word of the Lord is for - ev-er.

Verse 4

4. Zi - on, shout from the moun - tain top, lift up your

voice O Je - ru-sa-lem, and say to the peo-ple of

D.S.

God's own land, "Be-hold, be - hold your God!"

Verse 5

5. The Lord will ap - pear as a shep-herd, hold-ing his

lambs in his arms, keep-ing his flock so

D.S.

close to his heart lead-ing them all, old and young.

Text: Isaiah 40:1-11; Michael Joncas, b.1951
Tune: Michael Joncas, b.1951
© 1981, 1982, Jan Michael Joncas Trust. Published by OCP Publications.

344 On Jordan's Bank

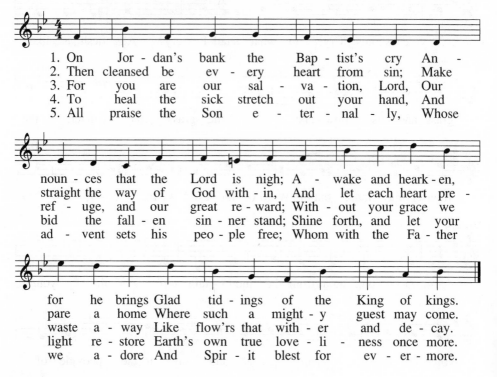

1. On   Jor - dan's   bank   the   Bap - tist's   cry   An -
2. Then cleansed be   ev - ery   heart   from   sin;   Make
3. For   you   are   our   sal - va - tion,   Lord,   Our
4. To   heal   the   sick   stretch   out   your   hand,   And
5. All   praise   the   Son   e - ter - nal - ly,   Whose

noun - ces   that   the   Lord   is   nigh; A - wake and heark - en,
straight the   way   of   God   with - in,   And   let   each heart pre -
ref - uge,   and   our   great re - ward; With - out   your   grace   we
bid   the   fall - en   sin - ner stand; Shine   forth,   and   let   your
ad - vent   sets   his   peo - ple free;   Whom with   the   Fa - ther

for   he   brings Glad   tid - ings   of   the   King   of   kings.
pare   a   home Where   such   a   might - y   guest   may   come.
waste   a - way   Like   flow'rs that   with - er   and   de - cay.
light   re - store Earth's   own   true   love - li - ness   once   more.
we   a - dore   And   Spir - it   blest   for   ev - er - more.

Text: *Jordanis oras praevia;* Charles Coffin, 1676-1749; tr. by John Chandler, 1806-1876
Tune: WINCHESTER NEW, LM; adapt. from *Musikalisches Handbuch,* Hamburg, 1690

345 Come, O Long Expected Jesus

1. Come,   O   long   ex - pect - ed   Je - sus,
2. Is - rael's strength   and   con - so - la - tion,
3. Born   your   peo - ple   to   de - liv - er;
4. By   your   own   e - ter - nal   Spir - it

Born   to   set   your   peo - ple free;   From   our   fears   and
You,   the   hope   of   all   the earth, Dear   de - sire   of
Born   a   child   and   yet   a   king!   Born   to   reign   in
Rule   in   all   our   hearts a - lone;   By   your   all   suf -

sins re - lease us; Free us from cap - tiv - i - ty.
ev - 'ry na - tion, Come, and save us by your birth.
us for ev - er, Now your grac - ious king - dom bring.
fi - cient mer - it Raise us to your glo - rious throne.

Text: Haggai 2:7; Charles Wesley, 1707-1788, alt.
Tune: STUTTGART, 8 7 8 7; *Psalmodia Sacra,* 1715; adapt. and harm. by William Henry Havergal, 1793-1870, alt.

People of the Night   346

1. We are your peo - ple of the night,
2. For in our win - ter we are dead,
3. You wait for us, you are our choice,
4. Give us new faith, give us the joy,

We long to see your new - born light,
Lead us in hope to see a - head   The
The liv - ing word; the sav - ing voice.
As we a - wait your Son, the Lord.

Dis - tant glim - mer; ris - ing from a - far.
spring-time and the gift that is to come.
Break the si - lence, lis - ten to our call.
In our pres - ence, child born of your breath,

We a - wait you, ho - ly morn - ing star.
Come and save us, be God's on - ly Son.
Be our an - swer, new life for us all.
Sav - ior broth - er; life that shat - ters death.

Text: David Haas, b.1957
Tune: SHEPHERD'S SONG, 88 99; David Haas, b.1957
© 1983, GIA Publications, Inc.

347 The King Shall Come When Morning Dawns

1. The King shall come when morn - ing dawns And
2. Not, as of old, a lit - tle child, To
3. The King shall come when morn - ing dawns And
4. And let the end - less bliss be - gin, By
5. The King shall come when morn - ing dawns And

light tri - um - phant breaks. When beau - ty gilds the
suf - fer and to die, But crowned with glo - ry
earth's dark night is past; O haste the ris - ing
wea - ry saints fore - told, When right shall tri - umph
light and beau - ty brings. Hail, Christ, the Lord! Your

east - ern hills And life to joy a - wakes.
like the sun That lights the morn - ing sky.
of that morn Whose day shall ev - er last.
o - ver wrong, And truth shall be ex - tolled.
peo - ple pray: Come quick - ly, King of kings.

Text: John Brownlie, 1857-1925
Tune: MORNING SONG, CM; John Wyeth, 1770-1858; arr. by Robert J. Batastini, b.1942, © 1994, GIA Publications, Inc.

348 Savior of the Nations, Come

1. Sav - ior of the na - tions, come; Show the glo - ry
2. Not by hu - man flesh and blood, By the Spir - it
3. Won - drous birth! O won - drous child Of the Vir - gin
4. God Cre - a - tor is his source, Back to God he
5. Now your low - ly man - ger bright Hal - lows night with

of the Son! Mar - vel now, O heav'n and earth,
of our God Was the word of God made flesh—
un - de - filed! Might - y God and man in one,
runs his course, Down to death and hell de - scends,
new - born light; Let no night this light sub - due,

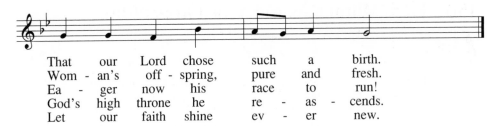

That   our   Lord   chose   such   a   birth.
Wom - an's off - spring, pure and fresh.
Ea - ger   now   his   race   to   run!
God's high throne he   re - as - cends.
Let   our   faith shine   ev - er   new.

Text: *Veni, Redemptor gentium*; ascr. to St. Ambrose, 340-397; tr. sts. 1-3a, William Reynolds, 1812-1876; sts. 3b-5, Martin L. Seltz, 1909-1967, alt.
Tune: NUN KOMM DER HEIDEN HEILAND, 77 77; *Geystliche gesangk Buchleyn,* Wittenberg, 1524

God of All People   349

1. God   of   all   plac - es: pres - ent,   un - seen;
2. God   of   all   dream - ing,   near   and   yet   far.
3. God   of   all   peo - ple,   dust   and   the   clay.

Voice   in   our   si - lence,   song   in   our   midst.
Vi - sion   un - heard of,   wake   us   to   rest.
Breath   of   a   new wind,   fire   in   our   hearts.

We   are   your   peo - ple,   know - ing,   un - sure.
We   are   your   pres - ence,   sent   forth   a - fraid.
Light   born   of   heav - en,   peace   on   the   earth.

Come,   Lord   Je - sus,   come!
Come,   Lord   Je - sus,   come!
Come,   Lord   Je - sus,   come!

Text: David Haas, b.1957
Tune: KINGDOM, 9 9 9 5; David Haas, b.1957
© 1988, GIA Publications, Inc.

350 Each Winter As the Year Grows Older

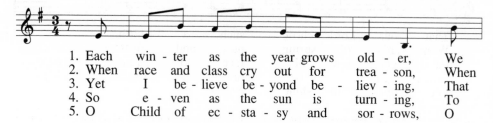

1. Each win - ter as the year grows old - er, We
2. When race and class cry out for trea - son, When
3. Yet I be - lieve be - yond be - liev - ing, That
4. So e - ven as the sun is turn - ing, To
5. O Child of ec - sta - sy and sor - rows, O

each grow old - er too. The chill sets in a
si - rens call for war, They o - ver - shout the
life can spring from death; That growth can flow - er
jour - ney to the north, The liv - ing flame, in
Prince of peace and pain, Bright - en to - day's world

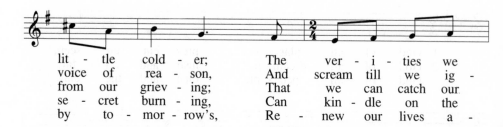

lit - tle cold - er; The ver - i - ties we
voice of rea - son, And scream till we ig -
from our griev - ing; That we can catch our
se - cret burn - ing, Can kin - dle on the
by to - mor - row's, Re - new our lives a -

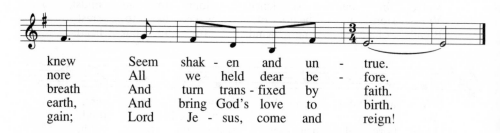

knew Seem shak - en and un - true.
nore All we held dear be - fore.
breath And turn trans - fixed by faith.
earth, And bring God's love to birth.
gain; Lord Je - sus, come and reign!

Text: William Gay, fl. 1969, © 1971, United Church Press
Tune: CAROL OF HOPE, 9 6 9 66; Annabeth Gay, b.1925, © 1971, United Church Press; acc. by Marty Haugen, b.1950, alt.,
  © 1987, GIA Publications, Inc.

Awake! Awake, and Greet the New Morn 351

1. A - wake! a - wake, and greet the new morn, For
2. To us, to all in sor - row and fear, Em -
3. In dark - est night his com - ing shall be, When
4. Re - joice, re - joice, take heart in the night, Though

an - gels her - ald its dawn - ing, Sing out your joy, for
man - u-el comes a - sing - ing, His hum - ble song is
all the world is de - spair - ing, As morn - ing light so
dark the win - ter and cheer - less, The ris - ing sun shall

now* he is born, Be - hold! the Child of our long - ing.
qui - et and near, Yet fills the earth with its ring - ing;
qui - et and free, So warm and gen - tle and car - ing.
crown you with light, Be strong and lov - ing and fear - less;

Come as a ba - by weak and poor, To bring all hearts to -
Mu - sic to heal the bro - ken soul And hymns of lov - ing
Then shall the mute break forth in song, The lame shall leap in
Love be our song and love our prayer, And love, our end - less

geth - er, He o - pens wide the heav'n - ly door And
kind - ness, The thun - der of his an - thems roll To
won - der, The weak be raised a - bove the strong, And
sto - ry, May God fill ev - 'ry day we share, And

lives now in - side us for ev - er.
shat - ter all ha - tred and blind - ness.
weap - ons be bro - ken a - sun - der.
bring us at last in - to glo - ry.

*During Advent: "soon"

Text: Marty Haugen, b.1950
Tune: REJOICE, REJOICE, 9 8 9 8 8 7 8 9; Marty Haugen, b.1950
© 1983, GIA Publications, Inc.

352 Gift of God

Refrain

Christmas: Gift of God, O Em-man-u-el. Gift of God, O Em-
Advent: Come to us, O Em-man-u-el. Come to us, O Em-

Last time   Christmas Verses
Cantor:

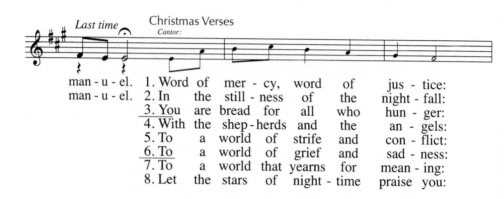

man-u-el. 1. Word of mer - cy, word of jus - tice:
man-u-el. 2. In the still - ness of the night - fall:
    3. You are bread for all who hun - ger:
    4. With the shep - herds and the an - gels:
    5. To a world of strife and con - flict:
    6. To a world of grief and sad - ness:
    7. To a world that yearns for mean - ing:
    8. Let the stars of night - time praise you:

All: Cantor:

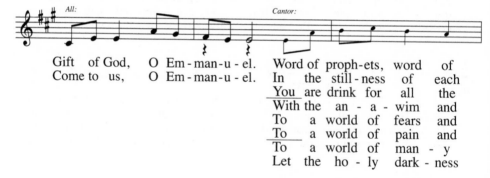

Gift of God, O Em - man-u-el. Word of proph-ets, word of
Come to us, O Em - man-u-el. In the still-ness of each
             You are drink for all the
             With the an - a - wim and
             To a world of fears and
             To a world of pain and
             To a world of man - y
             Let the ho - ly dark - ness

All: Cantor:

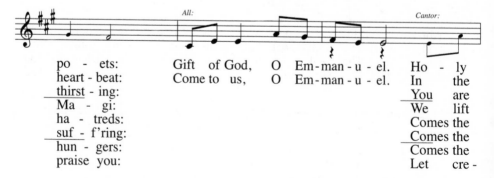

po - ets: Gift of God, O Em-man-u - el. Ho - ly
heart - beat: Come to us, O Em-man-u - el. In the
thirst - ing: You are
Ma - gi: We lift
ha - treds: Comes the
suf - f'ring: Comes the
hun - gers: Comes the
praise you: Let cre -

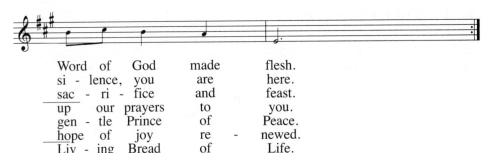

Word	of	God	made	flesh.
si -	lence,	you	are	here.
sac -	ri -	fice	and	feast.
up	our	prayers	to	you.
gen -	tle	Prince	of	Peace.
hope	of	joy	re -	newed.
Liv -	ing	Bread	of	Life.
a -	tion	join	in	song.

Advent Verses

1. Come, O Wisdom, breathe within us:
   Come, O mighty tender Teacher:
   Come, and show us how to live.

2. Come, O Lord, of ancient Israel:
   You who lead us through the desert:
   Come, and set your people free.

3. Come, O Root of Jesse's lineage:
   Come, O ruler of all nations:
   Come, and be our Savior sure.

4. Come, O Holy Key of David:
   Come, and open hearts to knowledge:
   Come, and break the chains of death.

5. Come, O Radiant Sun of Justice:
   Come, and shine on those in darkness:
   All who dwell in shades of death.

6. Come, O Light of all the nations:
   Come, bright Morning Star of new hope:
   Come, and shine among us here.

7. Come, O Living Flame of Freedom:
   Living hope of our redemption:
   Come, and lead us to new life.

Text: Marty Haugen, b.1950
Tune: Marty Haugen, b.1950
© 2000, GIA Publications, Inc.

353 Joy to the World

1. Joy to the world! the Lord is come: Let
2. Joy to the world! the Sav - ior reigns: Let
3. No more let sin and sor - rows grow, Nor
4. He rules the world with truth and grace, And

[⌢]

earth re - ceive her King; Let ev - 'ry
us, our songs em - ploy; While fields and
thorns in - fest the ground; He comes to
makes the na - tions prove The glo - ries

heart pre - pare him room, And
floods, rocks, hills and plains Re -
make his bless - ings flow Far
of his right - eous - ness, And

heav'n and na - ture sing, And heav'n and na - ture
peat the sound - ing joy, Re - peat the sound - ing
as the curse is found, Far as the curse is
won - ders of his love, And won - ders of his

sing, And heav'n, and heav'n and na - ture sing.
joy, Re - peat, re - peat the sound-ing joy.
found, Far as, far as the curse is found.
love, And won - ders, won - ders of his love.

Text: Psalm 98; Isaac Watts, 1674-1748
Tune: ANTIOCH, CM; arr. from George F. Handel, 1685-1759, in T. Hawkes' *Collection of Tunes*, 1833

Carol at the Manger 354

1. Ho - ly Child with - in the man - ger, Long a -
2. Once a - gain we tell the sto - ry— How your
3. Ho - ly Child with - in the man - ger, Lead us

go yet ev - er near; Come as friend to ev - 'ry
love for us was shown, When the Im - age of your
ev - er in your way, So we see in ev - 'ry

stran - ger, Come as hope for ev - 'ry fear. As you
glo - ry Wore an im - age like our own. Come, en -
stran - ger How you come to us to - day. In our

lived to heal the bro - ken, Greet the
light - en with your wis - dom, Come, and
lives and in our liv - ing Give us

out - cast, free the bound, As you taught us love un -
fill us with your grace, May the fire of your com -
strength to live as you, That our hearts might be for -

spo - ken, Teach us now where you are found.
pas - sion Kin - dle ev - 'ry land and race.
giv - ing And our spir - its strong and true.

Text: Marty Haugen, b.1950
Tune: JOYOUS LIGHT, 8 7 8 7 D; Marty Haugen, b.1950
© 1987, GIA Publications, Inc.

355 Star-Child / Niño: Es Astro

Verses

1. Star - Child, earth - Child, Go - be-tween of
2. Street child, beat child, No place left to
3. Grown child, old child, Mem - 'ry full of
4. Spared child, spoiled child, Hav - ing, want-ing
5. Hope - for peace Child, God's stu - pen-dous

1. *Ni - ño: es as - tro, Me - dia-dor de*
2. *Ni - ño a - bu - sa - do, Po - bre y sin ho -*
3. *Ni - ño: ha cre - ci - do; ¡Cuán-to ha de a - ño -*
4. *Ni - ño e - xi - gen - te, Tie - ne y quie - re*
5. *Es es - pe - ran - za, es Ni - ño del Se -*

God, Love Child, Christ Child, Heav - en's light-ning rod:
go, Hurt child, used child No one wants to know:
years, Sad child, lost child, Sto - ry told in tears:
more, Wise child, faith child Know-ing joy in store:
sign, Down-to - earth Child, Star of stars that shine:

Dios; Ni - ño Cris - to, De los cie - los luz.
gar; Ni - ño he - ri - do, No le van a a - mar.
rar! Ni - ño tris - te, Llo - ra su pe - sar.
más; Ni - ño sa - bio, Go - za de la paz.
ñor; Ni - ño hu - ma - no, As - tro de ful - gor.

Refrain

This year, this year let the day ar -
Oh Dios, da - le en es - ta Na - vi -

rive When Christ - mas comes for ev - 'ry - one,
dad Un dí - a de fe - li - ci - dad

ev - 'ry - one a - live.
a la hu - ma - ni - dad.

Text: Shirley Erena Murray, b.1931; Spanish tr. by Raquel Gutiérrez-Achón and George Lockwood, © 1994, 1997, Hope Publishing Co.
Tune: NOAH'S SONG, 4 5 4 5 with refrain; Ronald F. Krisman, b.1946, © 2003, GIA Publications, Inc.

Hark! The Herald Angels Sing 356

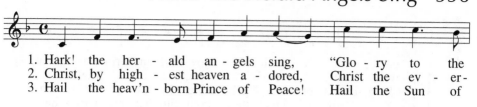

1. Hark! the her - ald an - gels sing, "Glo - ry to the
2. Christ, by high - est heaven a - dored, Christ the ev - er -
3. Hail the heav'n - born Prince of Peace! Hail the Sun of

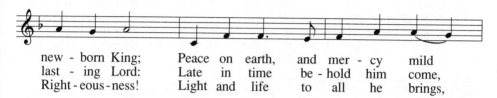

new - born King; Peace on earth, and mer - cy mild
last - ing Lord: Late in time be - hold him come,
Right - eous - ness! Light and life to all he brings,

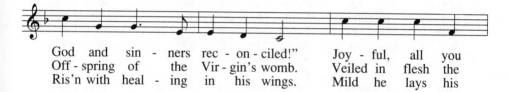

God and sin - ners rec - on - ciled!" Joy - ful, all you
Off - spring of the Vir - gin's womb. Veiled in flesh the
Ris'n with heal - ing in his wings. Mild he lays his

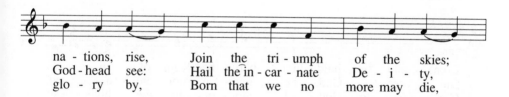

na - tions, rise, Join the tri - umph of the skies;
God - head see: Hail the in - car - nate De - i - ty,
glo - ry by, Born that we no more may die,

With the an - gel - ic host pro - claim, "Christ is born in Beth - le - hem!"
Pleased as man with us to dwell, Je - sus, our Em - man - u - el.
Born to raise us from the earth, Born to give us sec - ond birth.

Hark! the her - ald an - gels sing, "Glo - ry to the new - born King!"

Text: Charles Wesley, 1707-1788, alt.
Tune: MENDELSSOHN, 77 77 D with refrain; Felix Mendelssohn, 1809-1847

357 O Come, All Ye Faithful / Adeste Fideles

1. O come, all ye faith-ful, joy-ful and tri-um-phant, O
2. God of___ God,___ Light___ of___ Light,___
3. Sing, choirs of an-gels, sing in ex-ul-ta-tion,
4. Yea, Lord, we greet thee, born this hap-py morn-ing,

1. Ad-é-ste fi-dé-les, laé-ti, tri-um-phán-tes, Ve-
2. De-um de De-o, Lu-men de Lú-mi-ne
3. Can-tet nunc i-o, cho-rus an-ge-lo-rum,
4. Er-go qui na-tus Di-e ho-di-ér-na,

come ye, O come ye to Beth-le-hem;
Lo! He comes forth from the Vir-gin's womb.
Sing, all ye cit-i-zens of heav'n a-bove!
Je-sus, to thee be all glo-ry giv'n;

ní-te, ve-ní-te in Béth-le-hem.
Ge-stant pu-él-lae ví-sce-ra.
Can-tet nunc au-la cae-lés-ti-um.
Je-su___ ti-bi sit gló-ri-a.

Come and be-hold him, born the King of an-gels;
Our ver-y God, be-got-ten not cre-a-ted,
Glo-ry to God, all glo-ry in the high-est;
Word of the Fa-ther, now in flesh ap-pear-ing;

Na-tum vi-dé-te, Re-gem an-ge-ló-rum.
De-um ve-rum, Gé-ni-tum, non fa-ctum.
Gló-ri-a, gló-ria, in ex-cél-sis De-o.
Pa-tris ae-ter-nae ver-bum ca-ro fa-ctum.

O come, let us a-dore him, O come, let us a-dore him,
Ve-ní-te a-do-ré-mus, ve-ní-te a-do-ré-mus,

O come, let us a-dore him, Christ, the Lord!
ve-ní-te a-do-ré-mus Dó-mi-num.

Text: *Adeste fideles;* John F. Wade, c.1711-1786; tr. by Frederick Oakeley, 1802-1880, alt.
Tune: ADESTE FIDELES, Irregular with refrain; John F. Wade, c.1711-1786

Wood of the Cradle   358

Verses

1. Wood of the cra - dle, wood of the cross,
2. Shep - herds lie sleep - ing, deep in their dreams;
3. Star in the heav - ens bear - ing new light,
4. Come, all who hun - ger, come, all who thirst;

bear - ing a life - time of joy and of loss,
an - gels a - wak - en them: "What could this mean?
guid - ing the sag - es and a - ges this night:
Come, all who seek him, God's joy on the earth.

who is your loved one? Who could he be,
Whom do you her - ald? Whom must we find? A
Where will you lead us? Where can he be, the
Find him a shel - ter, bright, safe, and warm;

born in a man - ger to die on a tree?
child in a man - ger? Our God born in time?"
child born of mys - t'ry who died on a tree?
see in all peo - ple his love be - ing born.

Refrain

This, this is Je - sus the Lord, here in the bod - y and

blood out - poured. Come, come, walk in his ways. Kneel at the

man - ger and rise from the grave.

Text: Francis Patrick O'Brien, b.1958
Tune: Francis Patrick O'Brien, b.1958
© 2002, GIA Publications, Inc.

359   O Little Town of Bethlehem

1. O lit - tle town of Beth - le - hem, How
2. For Christ is born of Mar - y, And
3. How si - lent - ly, how si - lent - ly, The
4. O ho - ly Child of Beth - le - hem! De -

still we see thee lie! A - bove thy deep and
gath - ered all a - bove, While mor - tals sleep, the
won - drous gift is giv'n! So God im - parts to
scend to us we pray; Cast out our sin and

dream - less sleep The si - lent stars go by;
an - gels keep Their watch of won - d'ring love.
hu - man hearts The bless - ings of his heav'n.
en - ter in, Be born in us to - day.

Yet in the dark streets shin - eth The ev - er -
O morn - ing stars, to - geth - er Pro - claim the
No ear may hear his com - ing, But in this
We hear the Christ - mas an - gels The great glad

last - ing Light; The hopes and fears of
ho - ly birth! And prais - es sing to
world of sin, Where meek souls will re -
tid - ings tell; O come to us, a -

all the years Are met in thee to - night.
God the King, And peace to all on earth.
ceive him, still The dear Christ en - ters in.
bide with us, Our Lord Em - man - u - el!

Text: Phillips Brooks, 1835-1893
Tune: ST. LOUIS, 8 6 8 6 7 6 8 6; Lewis H. Redner, 1831-1908

Nativity Carol 360

Verses

1. Si - lent,   in the chill of mid - night,
2. "Fear not,"   said an - gel - ic voic - es;
3. Je - sus,   Lord of all cre - a - tion,

star - light   shines up - on a low - ly man - ger.
"tid - ings   of a won - drous love we bring you.
sleep now   close be - side your moth - er, Mar - y.

Won - der,   won - der of the a - ges;
Go   now,   find him in a man - ger;
Bring us   light a - mid the dark - ness,

heav - en breaks forth on the earth.
vis - it God's home on the earth."
prom - ise of life with - out end.

Refrain

For a child is born, the world re - joic - es! Shep-herds and

an - gels pro - claim his birth. This is Je - sus the Lord, our

Sav - ior and broth - er, bear - ing God's peace to the earth.

Text: Francis Patrick O'Brien, b.1958
Tune: Francis Patrick O'Brien, b.1958
© 1992, GIA Publications, Inc.

361 Angels We Have Heard on High

1. An - gels we have heard on high
2. Shep-herds, why this ju - bi - lee?
3. Come to Beth - le - hem and see
4. See him in a man - ger laid,

Sweet - ly sing - ing
Why your joy - ous
Him whose birth the
Whom the choirs of

o'er the plains, And the moun - tains in re - ply
strains pro - long? Say what may the tid - ings be,
an - gels sing; Come a - dore, on bend - ed knee,
an - gels praise; Mar - y, Jo - seph, lend your aid,

Ech - o back their joy - ous strains.
Which in - spire your heav'n - ly song.
Christ, the Lord, the new - born King.
While our hearts in love we raise.

Glo - - - ri - a

in ex - cel - sis De - o, Glo - -

- - ri - a in ex - cel - sis De - o.

Text: *Les anges dans nos campagnes;* French, c. 18th C.; tr. from *Crown of Jesus Music,* London, 1862
Tune: GLORIA, 7 7 7 7 with refrain; French traditional

Sing Alleluia 362

Verses

1. Dark is the night and deep are the shad - ows,
2. Who would be - lieve that here in a man - ger
3. Great is the joy of Mar - y, his moth - er;
4. Hope for the poor, re - lease for the cap - tive,

Qui - et the ba - by bathed in lan - tern light;
God comes a - mong us as a ti - ny child?
Great is the joy of Jo - seph by her side.
Love for the out - cast, light for wea - ry eyes;

Hushed are the sounds of cat - tle and shep - herds;
See in his eyes the glo - ry of heav - en;
Great is the joy of all those in dark - ness,
Word that brings life, em - brac - ing hu - man - i - ty,

Sweet is the mu - sic the an - gels bring this night.
Hear in his laugh-ter the joy of God on high.
Here lies the Sav - ior so soon to die and rise.
Je - sus, com-pan - ion, be born in - to our lives.

Refrain

Sing Al - le - lu - ia, sing Al - le - lu - ia.

Wel - come the Sav - ior, the prom-ise of new life.

Sing Al - le - lu - ia, sing Al - le - lu - ia.

All of cre - a - tion sing this night.

Text: Francis Patrick O'Brien, b.1958
Tune: Francis Patrick O'Brien, b.1958
© 1996, GIA Publications, Inc.

363 Go Tell It on the Mountain

Refrain

Go tell it on the moun-tain, O-ver the hills and ev - 'ry-where;

Go tell it on the moun - tain That Je - sus Christ is born!

Verses

1. While shep - herds kept their watch - ing O'er
2. The shep - herds feared and trem - bled When
3. Down in a low - ly man - ger The

si - lent flocks by night, Be - hold through - out the
lo! a - bove the earth Rang out the an - gel
hum - ble Christ was born, And God sent us sal -

D.C.

heav - ens There shone a ho - ly light.
cho - rus That hailed our Sav - ior's birth.
va - tion That bless - ed Christ - mas morn.

Text: African-American spiritual; adapt. by John W. Work, Jr., 1871-1925, © Mrs. John W. Work, III
Tune: GO TELL IT ON THE MOUNTAIN, 7 6 7 6 with refrain; African-American spiritual; harm. by Robert J. Batastini, b.1942, © 1995, GIA
    Publications, Inc.

364 He Came Down

He came down that we may have *love; He

*Substitute peace, joy, hope, life, etc.

came down that we may have love; He came down that we may have love, Hal-le-lu-jah for ev-er-more.

Cantor: Why did he come?

Text: Cameroon traditional
Tune: Cameroon traditional; transcribed and arr. by John L. Bell, b.1949, © 1990, Iona Community, GIA Publications, Inc., agent

Away in a Manger 365

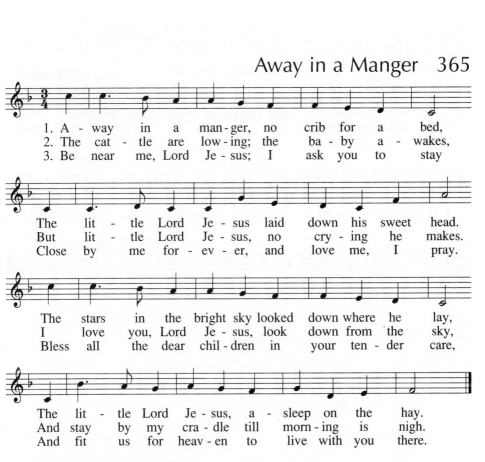

1. A - way in a man - ger, no crib for a bed,
2. The cat - tle are low - ing; the ba - by a - wakes,
3. Be near me, Lord Je - sus; I ask you to stay

The lit - tle Lord Je - sus laid down his sweet head.
But lit - tle Lord Je - sus, no cry - ing he makes.
Close by me for - ev - er, and love me, I pray.

The stars in the bright sky looked down where he lay,
I love you, Lord Je - sus, look down from the sky,
Bless all the dear chil - dren in your ten - der care,

The lit - tle Lord Je - sus, a - sleep on the hay.
And stay by my cra - dle till morn - ing is nigh.
And fit us for heav - en to live with you there.

Text: St. 1-2, anonymous, st. 3, John T. McFarland, 1851-1913
Tune: MUELLER, 11 11 11 11; James R. Murray, 1841-1905; harm. by Robert J. Batastini, b. 1942, © 1994, GIA Publications, Inc.

366 God Rest You Merry, Gentlemen

1. God rest you mer - ry, gen - tle-men, Let noth-ing you dis -may,
2. In Beth - le - hem in Ju - dah This bless-ed babe was born,
3. From God our great Cre - a - tor A bless-ed an - gel came,
4. The shep-herds at those tid - ings Re - joic-ed much in mind,
5. Now to the Lord sing prais - es, All you with - in this place,

For Je - sus Christ our Sav - ior Was born up - on this day,
And laid with - in a man - ger Up - on this bless - ed morn:
And un - to cer - tain shep - herds Brought tid - ings of the same,
And left their flocks a - feed - ing In tem - pest, storm, and wind,
And with true love and char - i - ty Each oth - er now em -brace;

To save us all from Sa - tan's power When we were gone a - stray.
For which his moth - er Mar - y Did noth-ing take in scorn.
How that in Beth - le - hem was born The Son of God by name.
And went to Beth - le - hem straight-way, The bless - ed babe to find.
This ho - ly tide of Christ - mas All oth - ers shall re - place.

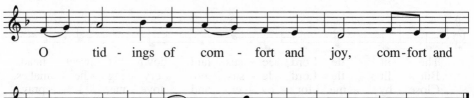

O tid - ings of com - fort and joy, com -fort and

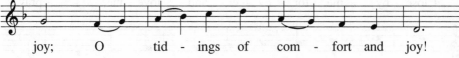

joy; O tid - ings of com - fort and joy!

Text: English carol, 18th C.
Tune: GOD REST YOU MERRY, 8 6 8 6 8 6 with refrain; English 18th C.; harm. by John Stainer, 1840-1901

Good Christian Friends, Rejoice   367

1. Good Chris - tian friends, re - joice With heart and
2. Good Chris - tian friends, re - joice With heart and
3. Good Chris - tian friends, re - joice With heart and

soul and voice; O give heed to what we say:
soul and voice; Now you hear of end - less bliss:
soul and voice; Now you need not fear the grave:

Je - sus Christ is born to - day! Ox and ass be -
Je - sus Christ was born for this! He has o - pened
Je - sus Christ was born to save! Calls you one and

fore him bow, And he is in the man - ger now.
heav - en's door, And we are blest for ev - er - more.
calls you all To gain his ev - er - last - ing hall.

Christ is born to - day! Christ is born to - day!
Christ was born for this! Christ was born for this!
Christ was born to save! Christ was born to save!

Text: *In dulci jubilo;* Latin and German, 14th C.; tr. by John M. Neal, 1818-1866
Tune: IN DULCI JUBILO, 66 77 78 55; Klug's *Geistliche Lieder,* Wittenberg, 1535; harm. by Robert L. Pearsall, 1795-1856

368 Child of Mercy

Refrain

Child of mer - cy, child of peace, Je-sus, Bread of life,
food to fill our long - ing. Child of jus-tice, child of light,
Je-sus, sav - ing cup, Em-man-u - el, God with us.

Verses

1. All who walk in dark - ness have seen a great light, to
2. ' A child is born to us, a son is giv - en us, up -
3. ' We name him: "Won-der, coun-s'lor, he - ro, might-y God," The
4. We pro-claim good news to you, great tid - ings of joy: To

D.C.

those who dwell in fear, a light has shone!
on his shoul - der glo - ry rests!
Ho - ly One for ev - er: Prince of peace!
you is born a sav - ior: Christ the Lord!

Text: Isaiah 9:1, 5; David Haas, b.1957
Tune: David Haas, b.1957
© 1991, GIA Publications, Inc.

369 Angels, from the Realms of Glory

1. An - gels, from the realms of glo - ry, Wing your flight o'er
2. Shep - herds, in the fields a - bid - ing, Watch-ing o'er your
3. Sag - es, leave your con - tem-pla-tions, Bright - er vi - sions
4. Though an in - fant now we view him, He shall fill his

all the earth; You who sang cre - a - tion's sto - ry,
flocks by night, God on earth is now re - sid - ing,
beam a - far; Seek the great De - sire of na - tions,
heav'n-ly throne, Gath - er all the na - tions to him;

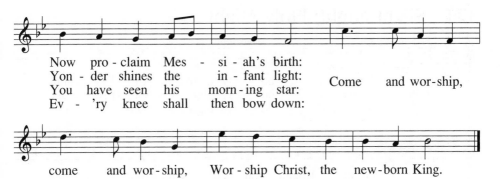

Now pro - claim Mes - si - ah's birth:
Yon - der shines the in - fant light:
You have seen his morn - ing star: Come   and wor-ship,
Ev - 'ry knee shall then bow down:

come   and wor-ship,   Wor - ship Christ, the   new-born King.

Text: Sts. 1-3, James Montgomery, 1771-1854; st. 4, *Christmas Box*, 1825
Tune: REGENT SQUARE, 8 7 8 7 8 7; Henry Smart, 1813-1879

Song of the Stable   370

1. Chill of the night - fall,   Lamps in the win-dows,
2. Si - lence of mid - night,   Voic - es of an - gels,
3. Splen - dor of star - light,   High on the hill - side,
4. Glo - ry of day - break!   Sor - rows and shad-ows,

Let - ting their light fall Clear on the snow;
Sing - ing to bid night Yield to the dawn;
Faint is the far light Burn - ing be - low;
Sud - den - ly they break Forth in - to morn;

Bit - ter De - cem - ber Bids us re - mem - ber
Dark - ness is end - ed, Sin - ners be - friend-ed,
Kneel - ing be - fore him Shep - herds a - dore him,
Sing out and tell now All shall be well now;

Christ in the sta - ble Long, long a - go.
Where in the sta - ble Je - sus is born.
Christ in the sta - ble Long, long a - go.
For in the sta - ble Je - sus is born!

Text: *Chill of the Nightfall*, Timothy Dudley-Smith, b.1926, © 1980, Hope Publishing Co.
Tune: PRIOR LAKE, 5 5 5 4 D; David Haas, b.1957, © 1985, GIA Publications, Inc.

371 Silent Night, Holy Night

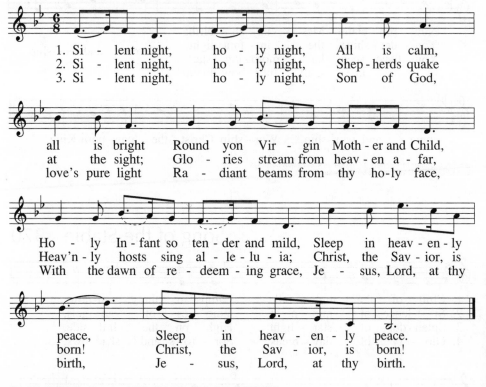

1. Si - lent night, ho - ly night, All is calm,
2. Si - lent night, ho - ly night, Shep - herds quake
3. Si - lent night, ho - ly night, Son of God,

all is bright Round yon Vir - gin Moth - er and Child,
at the sight; Glo - ries stream from heav - en a - far,
love's pure light Ra - diant beams from thy ho-ly face,

Ho - ly In - fant so ten - der and mild, Sleep in heav - en - ly
Heav'n - ly hosts sing al - le - lu - ia; Christ, the Sav - ior, is
With the dawn of re - deem - ing grace, Je - sus, Lord, at thy

peace, Sleep in heav - en - ly peace.
born! Christ, the Sav - ior, is born!
birth, Je - sus, Lord, at thy birth.

Text: *Stille Nacht, heilige Nacht;* Joseph Mohr, 1792-1849; tr. John F. Young, 1820-1885
Tune: STILLE NACHT, 66 89 66; Franz X. Gruber, 1787-1863

372 Night of Silence

1. Cold are the peo - ple, win - ter of life, We
2. Voice in the dis - tance, call in the night, On
3. Spir - it a - mong us, shine like the star, Your

trem - ble in shad - ows this cold end - less night,
wind you en - fold us, you speak of the light,
light that guides shep - herds and kings from a - far,

Fro - zen in the snow lie ros - es sleep - ing,
Gen - tle on the ear you whis - per soft - ly,
Shim - mer in the sky so emp - ty, lone - ly,

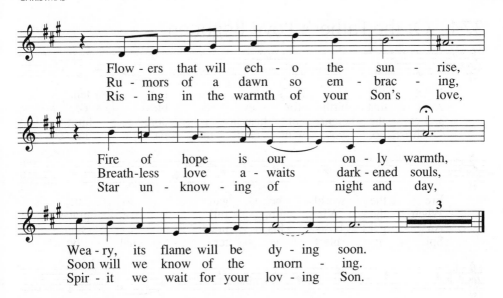

Flow - ers that will ech - o the sun - rise,
Ru - mors of a dawn so em - brac - ing,
Ris - ing in the warmth of your Son's love,

Fire of hope is our on - ly warmth,
Breath-less love a - waits dark - ened souls,
Star un - know - ing of night and day,

Wea - ry, its flame will be dy - ing soon.
Soon will we know of the morn - ing.
Spir - it we wait for your lov - ing Son.

Text: Daniel Kantor, b.1960
Tune: Daniel Kantor, b.1960
© 1984, GIA Publications, Inc.

Lo, How a Rose E'er Blooming 373

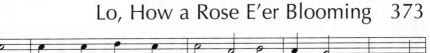

1. Lo, how a Rose e'er bloom-ing From ten - der stem hath
2. I - sa - iah 'twas for - told it, The Rose I have in
3. O Flower, whose fra - grance ten - der With sweet-ness fills the

sprung! Of Jes - se's lin - eage com - ing As seers of
mind, With Mar - y we be - hold it, The Vir - gin
air, Dis - pel in glo - rious splen - dor The dark - ness

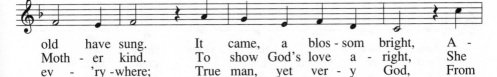

old have sung. It came, a blos - som bright, A -
Moth - er kind. To show God's love a - right, She
ev - 'ry -where; True man, yet ver - y God, From

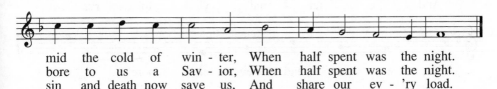

mid the cold of win - ter, When half spent was the night.
bore to us a Sav - ior, When half spent was the night.
sin and death now save us, And share our ev - 'ry load.

Text: Isaiah 11:1; *Es ist ein' Ros' entsprungen; Speier Gesangbuch,* 1599; tr. sts. 1-2 by Theodore Baker, 1851-1934; st. 3, *The Hymnal, 1940*
Tune: ES IST EIN' ROS' ENSTSPRUNGEN, 7 6 7 6 6 7 6; *Geistliche Kirchengesang,* Cologne, 1599; harm. by Michael Praetorius, 1571-1621

374 Of the Father's Love Begotten

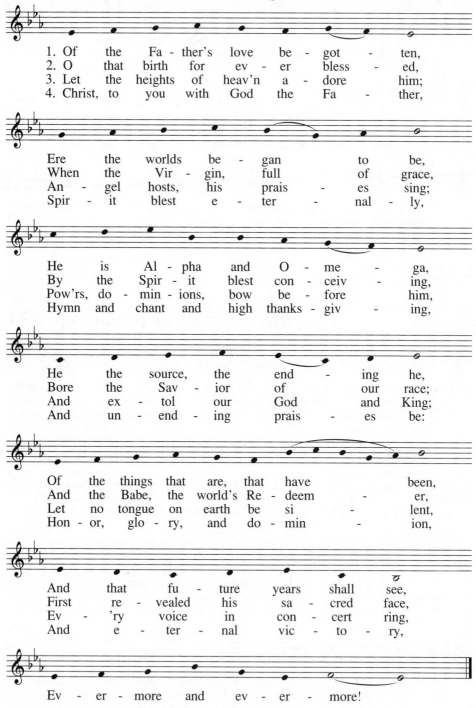

1. Of the Fa - ther's love be - got - ten,
2. O that birth for ev - er bless - ed,
3. Let the heights of heav'n a - dore him;
4. Christ, to you with God the Fa - ther,

Ere the worlds be - gan to be,
When the Vir - gin, full of grace,
An - gel hosts, his prais - es sing;
Spir - it blest e - ter - nal - ly,

He is Al - pha and O - me - ga,
By the Spir - it blest con - ceiv - ing,
Pow'rs, do - min - ions, bow be - fore him,
Hymn and chant and high thanks - giv - ing,

He the source, the end - ing he,
Bore the Sav - ior of our race;
And ex - tol our God and King;
And un - end - ing prais - es be:

Of the things that are, that have been,
And the Babe, the world's Re - deem - er,
Let no tongue on earth be si - lent,
Hon - or, glo - ry, and do - min - ion,

And that fu - ture years shall see,
First re - vealed his sa - cred face,
Ev - 'ry voice in con - cert ring,
And e - ter - nal vic - to - ry,

Ev - er - more and ev - er - more!

Text: *Corde natus ex Parentis*; Aurelius Prudentius, 348-413; tr. by John M. Neale, 1818-1866 and Henry W. Baker, 1821-1877
Tune: DIVINUM MYSTERIUM, 8 7 8 7 8 7 7; 12th C.; Mode V; acc. by Richard Proulx, b.1937, © 1985, GIA Publications, Inc.

Rise Up, Shepherd, and Follow 375

Verses

Leader:

1. There's a star in the East on Christ-mas morn,
2. If you take good heed to the an - gel's words,

All:

Rise up, shep - herd, and fol - low, It will
Rise up, shep - herd, and fol - low, You'll for -

Leader:

lead to the place where the Christ was born,
get your flocks, you'll for - get your herds,

All:

Rise up, shep - herd, and fol - low.
Rise up, shep - herd, and fol - low.

Refrain

Fol - low, fol - low, Rise up, shep-herd, and

fol - low, Fol - low the Star of Beth - le - hem,

Rise up, shep - herd, and fol - low.

Text: Traditional
Tune: African-American spiritual

376 Where the Promise Shines

1. When a star is shin-ing o - ver east - ern
2. Where the world is wait-ing for an un-known
3. Lead us on, O Day-star, in the qui - et

hills, When the air is si - lent,
day, Where a voice for-got-ten
night; Guide us through the shad - ow

and the clam-or stills, When the night is
cries, "Pre - pare the way!" Where an earth - ly
with your gen - tle light; Show us in a

wait-ing, and the old hopes rise,
pow - er makes the heart turn cold,
man - ger our re - demp-tion's sign;

Then the time has rip - ened and the heart grows
There the gifts are of - fered— in - cense, myrrh, and
Bring us to a morn-ing where the prom - ise

wise.
gold. Lead us on, lead us on,
shines.

to a morn-ing where the prom - ise shines.

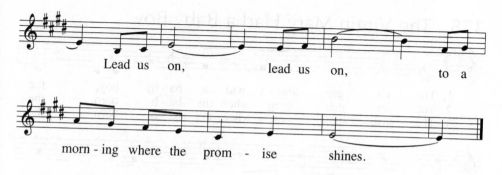

Lead us on, lead us on, to a

morn - ing where the prom - ise shines.

Text: Sylvia G. Dunstan, 1955-1993, © 1995, GIA Publications, Inc.
Tune: Bob Moore, b.1962, © 2003, GIA Publications, Inc.

Infant Holy, Infant Lowly 377

1. In - fant ho - ly, In - fant low - ly, For his bed a
2. Flocks were sleep - ing: Shep-herds keep - ing Vi - gil till the

cat - tle stall; Ox - en low - ing, Lit - tle know - ing
morn-ing new. Saw the glo - ry, Heard the sto - ry,

Christ the babe is Lord of all. Swift are wing - ing
Tid - ings of a gos - pel true. Thus re - joic - ing,

An - gels sing - ing, No - els ring - ing, Tid - ings bring - ing:
Free from sor - row, Prais-es voic - ing Greet the mor - row:

Christ the babe is Lord of all.
Christ the babe was born for you.

Text: Polish carol; para. by Edith M. G. Reed, 1885-1933
Tune: W ZLOBIE LEZY, 44 7 44 7 4444 7; Polish carol; harm. by A. E. Rusbridge, 1917-1969, © Bristol Churches Housing Assoc. Ltd.

The Virgin Mary Had a Baby Boy

1. The vir - gin Mar - y had a ba - by boy, the
2. The an - gels sang when the ba - by born, the
3. The wise men saw where the ba - by born, the

vir - gin Mar - y had a ba - by boy, the
an - gels sang when the ba - by born, the
wise men saw where the ba - by born, the

vir - gin Mar - y had a ba - by boy, and they
an - gels sang when the ba - by born, and they
wise men went where the ba - by born, and they

say that his name was Je - sus.
say that his name was Je - sus.
say that his name was Je - sus.

He come from the glo - ry, he come from the

glo - rious king - dom. Oh, yes! be - liev - er!

Oh, yes! be - liev - er! He come from the

glo - ry, he come from the glo - rious king - dom.

Text: West Indian carol, © 1945, Boosey and Co., Ltd.
Tune: West Indian carol, © 1945, Boosey and Co., Ltd.; acc. by Robert J. Batastini, b.1942, © 1993, GIA Publications, Inc.

It Came upon the Midnight Clear   379

1. It came up-on the mid - night clear, That
2. Still through the clo - ven skies they come, With
3. Yet with the woes of sin and strife, The
4. For, lo, the days are has - tening on, By

glo - rious song of old, From an - gels bend - ing
peace - ful wings un - furled, And still their heav'n - ly
world has suf - fered long; Be - neath the heav'n - ly
proph - ets seen of old, When with the ev - er -

near the earth To touch their harps of gold: "Peace
mu - sic floats O'er all the wea - ry world: A -
hymn have rolled Two thou - sand years of wrong; And
cir - cling years Shall come the time fore - told, When

on the earth, good will to all From
bove its sad and low - ly plains They
war - ring hu - man - kind hears not The
peace shall o - ver all the earth Its

heaven's all gra - cious King"; The world in sol - emn
bend on hov - 'ring wing, And ev - er o'er its
tid - ings which they bring; O hush the noise and
an - cient splen - dors fling, And all the world give

still - ness lay, To hear the an - gels sing.
Ba - bel sounds The bless - ed an - gels sing.
cease your strife And hear the an - gels sing.
back the song Which now the an - gels sing.

Text: Edmund H. Sears, 1810-1876, alt.
Tune: CAROL, CMD; Richard S. Willis, 1819-1900

380 Once in Royal David's City

1. Once in roy - al Da - vid's cit - y Stood a
2. He came down to earth from heav - en Who is
3. And through all his won - drous child - hood He would
4. For he is our child - hood's pat - tern, Day by
5. And our eyes at last shall see him, Through his

low - ly cat - tle shed, Where a moth - er laid her
God and Lord of all, And his shel - ter was a
hon - or and o - bey, Love and watch the low - ly
day like us he grew; He was lit - tle, weak, and
own re - deem - ing love; For that child so dear and

ba - by In a man - ger for his bed. Mar - y
sta - ble, And his cra - dle was a stall. With the
maid - en In whose gen - tle arms he lay. Chris - tian
help - less, Tears and smiles like us he knew: And he
gen - tle Is our Lord in heav'n a - bove: And he

was that moth - er mild, Je - sus
poor and mean and low - ly Lived on
chil - dren all should be Kind, o -
feels for all our sad - ness, And he
leads his chil - dren on To the

Christ her lit - tle Child.
earth our Sav - ior ho - ly.
be - dient, good as he.
shares in all our glad - ness.
place where he has gone.

Text: Cecil Frances Alexander, 1818-1895
Tune: IRBY, 8 7 8 7 77; Henry J. Gauntlett, 1805-1876; harm. by Arthur H. Mann, 1850-1929. © 1957, Novello and Co. Ltd.

The Aye Carol 381

1. Who is the ba - by an hour or two old
2. Who is the wom - an with child at her breast,
3. Who is the man who looks on at the door,
4. Who are the peo - ple come in from the street,
5. Will you come with me, ev'n though I feel shy,

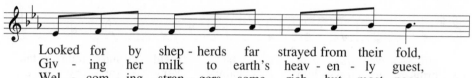

Looked for by shep - herds far strayed from their fold,
Giv - ing her milk to earth's heav - en - ly guest,
Wel - com - ing stran - gers, some rich but most poor,
Some to bring pres - ents and some just to meet,
Come to his cra - dle and come to his cry,

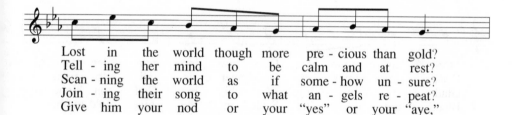

Lost in the world though more pre - cious than gold?
Tell - ing her mind to be calm and at rest?
Scan - ning the world as if some - how un - sure?
Join - ing their song to what an - gels re - peat?
Give him your nod or your "yes" or your "aye,"

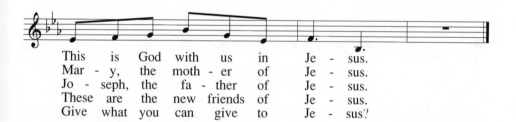

This is God with us in Je - sus.
Mar - y, the moth - er of Je - sus.
Jo - seph, the fa - ther of Je - sus.
These are the new friends of Je - sus.
Give what you can give to Je - sus?

Text: John L. Bell, b.1949
Tune: AYE CAROL, 10 10 10 8; John L. Bell, b.1949
© 1987, Iona Community, GIA Publications, Inc., agent

382 We Three Kings of Orient Are

1. We three kings of O - ri - ent are,
2. Born a babe on Beth - le - hem's plain,
3. Frank - in - cense to of - fer have I;
4. Myrrh is mine: its bit - ter per - fume
5. Glo - rious now be - hold him rise,

Bear - ing gifts we trav - erse a - far Field and foun - tain, Moor and moun - tain, Fol - low - ing yon - der star.
Gold we bring to crown him a - gain; King for - ev - er, Ceas - ing nev - er, O - ver us all to reign.
In - cense owns a De - i - ty nigh, Prayer and prais - ing Glad - ly rais - ing, Wor - ship - ing God on high.
Breathes a life of gath - 'ring gloom; Sor - rowing, sigh - ing, Bleed - ing, dy - ing, Sealed in the stone cold tomb.
King and God and sac - ri - fice: Heav'n sings, "Hal - le - lu - jah!" "Hal - le - lu - jah!" earth re - plies.

O star of won - der, star of night, Star with roy - al beau - ty bright, West - ward lead - ing, still pro - ceed - ing, Guide us to the per - fect Light.

Text: Matthew 2:1-11; John H. Hopkins, Jr., 1820-1891
Tune: KINGS OF ORIENT, 88 44 6 with refrain; John H. Hopkins, Jr., 1820-1891

Songs of Thankfulness and Praise 383

1. Songs of thank-ful-ness and praise, Je - sus, Lord, to
2. Man - i - fest at Jor - dan's stream, Proph - et, Priest, and
3. Man - i - fest in mak - ing whole Pal - sied limbs and
4. Grant us grace to see you, Lord, Mir - rored in your

you we raise, Man - i - fest - ed by the star
King su - preme; And at Ca - na, wed - ding guest,
faint - ing soul; Man - i - fest in val - iant fight,
ho - ly word; May we im - i - tate you now,

To the sag - es from a - far; Branch of roy - al
In your God - head man - i - fest; Man - i - fest in
Quell - ing all the dev - il's might; Man - i - fest in
And on us your grace en - dow; That we like to

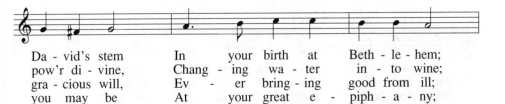

Da - vid's stem In your birth at Beth - le - hem;
pow'r di - vine, Chang - ing wa - ter in - to wine;
gra - cious will, Ev - er bring - ing good from ill;
you may be At your great e - piph - a - ny;

An - thems be to you ad-drest, God in flesh made man-i-fest.
An - thems be to you ad-drest, God in flesh made man-i-fest.
An - thems be to you ad-drest, God in flesh made man-i-fest.
And may praise you ev - er blest, God in flesh made man-i-fest.

Text: Christopher Wordsworth, 1807-1885
Tune: SALZBURG, 77 77 D; Jakob Hintze, 1622-1702, alt.; harm. by J.S. Bach, 1685-1750

384 As with Gladness Men of Old

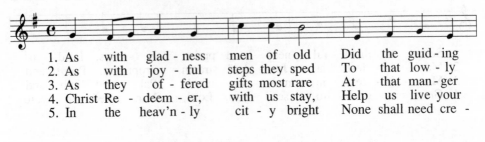

1. As with glad - ness men of old Did the guid - ing
2. As with joy - ful steps they sped To that low - ly
3. As they of - fered gifts most rare At that man - ger
4. Christ Re - deem - er, with us stay, Help us live your
5. In the heav'n - ly cit - y bright None shall need cre -

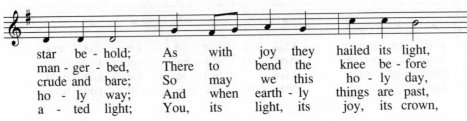

star be - hold; As with joy they hailed its light,
man - ger - bed, There to bend the knee be - fore
crude and bare; So may we this ho - ly day,
ho - ly way; And when earth - ly things are past,
a - ted light; You, its light, its joy, its crown,

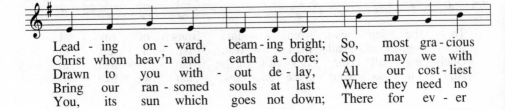

Lead - ing on - ward, beam - ing bright; So, most gra - cious
Christ whom heav'n and earth a - dore; So may we with
Drawn to you with - out de - lay, All our cost - liest
Bring our ran - somed souls at last Where they need no
You, its sun which goes not down; There for ev - er

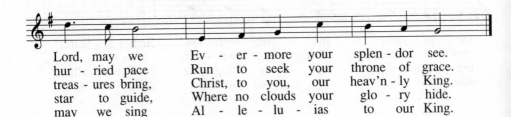

Lord, may we Ev - er - more your splen - dor see.
hur - ried pace Run to seek your throne of grace.
treas - ures bring, Christ, to you, our heav'n - ly King.
star to guide, Where no clouds your glo - ry hide.
may we sing Al - le - lu - ias to our King.

Text: William C. Dix, 1837-1898
Tune: DIX, 77 77 77; arr. from Conrad Kocher, 1786-1872, by William H. Monk, 1823-1889

Lord, Today 385

Refrain

Lord, to-day we have seen your glo-ry, dawn
fol-lows the night. We, your peo-ple who walked in
dark-ness now have seen a great light.

Verses

1. A child is born, a Son giv-en
2. The Lord is king, the na-tions re-
3. O Beth-le-hem, you are from of
4. The days will come, the Lord prom-ised
5. New light has dawned up-on all the

us, on him do-min-ion shall rest.
joice, let all God's peo-ple be glad. The
old, too small a-mong Ju-dah's clans.
us, when God would raise up a shoot
just, glad-ness for up-right of heart. Re-

His name shall be Won-der-ful God,
heav-ens pro-claim jus-tice for all.
From you shall come a rul-er this day,
to rule the land, reign as a king,
joice in the Lord, you faith-ful ones.

Coun-sel-or, Prince of Peace.
Glo-ry has filled the land.
shep-herd to guide the land.
whose name is Lord the Just.
Give thanks to God's great name.

Text: Mike Balhoff, b.1946
Tune: Darryl Ducote, b.1945, Gary Daigle, b.1957
© 1978, Damean Music. Distributed by GIA Publications, Inc.

386 Epiphany Carol

1. Ev - 'ry na - tion sees the glo - ry Of a
2. Ev - 'ry tongue shall sing the prais - es Of his
3. Once a - gain may we dis - cov - er Word made
4. Gath - er, God, the world to - geth - er In the

star that pierced the night. As we tell the won-drous
birth in deep - est night. He is heal - ing for the
flesh sent from a - bove. In our neigh - bor, sis - ter,
bright - ness of your day. Fill our hearts with joy for -

sto - ry We are bathed in ra - diant light.
a - ges; He is Christ, our God's de - light.
broth - er, In the lone - ly and un - loved.
ev - er; Help us walk the ho - ly way.

Star sent forth from high-est heav - en, Danc-ing
He pro - claims with - in his be - ing All our
May we touch him, may we hold him, May we
May your jus - tice rule the na - tions; May all

light of God's de - sign, Shine up - on the gift that's
hopes, our great de - sires. He shall die to rise, re -
cra - dle him with care As we learn to love each
peo - ple live as one. Now we see our true sal -

giv - en: Word made flesh now born in time.
deem - ing All who fol - low with their lives.
oth - er, Bring-ing hope from out de - spair.
va - tion In the glo - ry of your Son.

Text: Francis Patrick O'Brien, b.1958, © 2002, GIA Publications, Inc.
Tune: BEACH SPRING, 8 7 8 7 D; *The Sacred Harp*, 1844; harm. by Ronald A. Nelson, b.1927, © 1978, *Lutheran Book of Worship*

What Child Is This   387

1. What child is this, who, laid to rest, On
2. Why lies he in such mean es - tate Where
3. So bring him in - cense, gold and myrrh, Come

Mar - y's lap is sleep - ing? Whom an - gels greet with
ox and ass are feed - ing? Good Chris - tian, fear; for
peas - ant, king to own him; The King of kings sal -

an - thems sweet, While shep - herds watch are keep - ing?
sin - ners here The si - lent Word is plead - ing.
va - tion brings, Let lov - ing hearts en - throne him.

This, this is Christ the King, Whom shep-herds guard and an - gels sing;

Haste, haste to bring him laud, The babe, the son of Mar - y.

Text: William C. Dix, 1827-1898
Tune: GREENSLEEVES, 8 7 8 7 with refrain; English melody, 16th C.; harm. by John Stainer, 1840-1901

388 The First Nowell

1. The first Now - ell, the an - gel did say, Was to
2. They look - ed up and saw a star Shin - ing
3. And by the light of that same star Three
4. This star drew nigh to the north - west, O'er
5. Then en - tered in those wise men three, Full
6. Then let us all with one ac - cord Sing

cer - tain poor shep-herds in fields as they lay; In
in the east, be - yond them far, And
wise men came from coun - try far; To
Beth - le - hem it took its rest; And
rev - 'rent - ly up - on their knee, And
prais - es to our heav - 'nly Lord; Who

fields where they lay keep-ing their sheep, On a
to the earth it gave great light, And
seek for a king was their in - tent, And to
there it did both stop and stay, Right
of - fered there, in his pres - ence, Their
with the Fa - ther we a - dore And

cold win - ter's night that was so deep.
so it con - tin - ued both day and night.
fol - low the star where - ev - er it went.
o - ver the place where Je - sus lay.
gold and myrrh and frank - in - cense.
Spir - it blest for ev - er - more.

Now - ell, Now - ell, Now - ell, Now - ell,

Born is the King of Is - ra - el.

Text: English Carol, 17th C.
Tune: THE FIRST NOWELL, Irregular; English Melody; harm. from *Christmas Carols New and Old*, 1871

What Star Is This   389

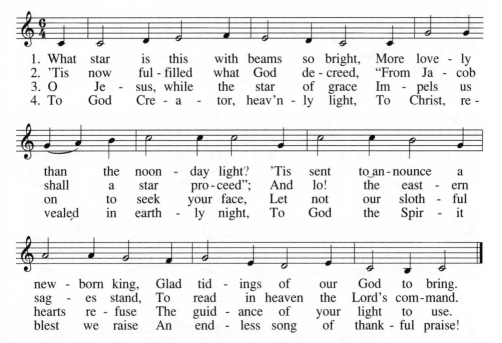

1. What star is this with beams so bright, More love - ly
2. 'Tis now ful - filled what God de - creed, "From Ja - cob
3. O Je - sus, while the star of grace Im - pels us
4. To God Cre - a - tor, heav'n - ly light, To Christ, re -

than the noon - day light? 'Tis sent to an - nounce a
shall a star pro - ceed"; And lo! the east - ern
on to seek your face, Let not our sloth - ful
vealed in earth - ly night, To God the Spir - it

new - born king, Glad tid - ings of our God to bring.
sag - es stand, To read in heaven the Lord's com - mand.
hearts re - fuse The guid - ance of your light to use.
blest we raise An end - less song of thank - ful praise!

Text: *Quem stella sole pulchrior,* Charles Coffin, 1676-1749; tr. by John Chandler, 1806-1876, alt.
Tune: PUER NOBIS, LM; adapt. by Michael Praetorius, 1571-1621

390   When John Baptized by Jordan's River

1. When John bap - tized by Jor - dan's riv - er
2. There as the Lord, bap - tized and pray - ing,
3. O Son of Man, our na - ture shar - ing,

In faith and hope the peo - ple came, That John and
Rose from the stream, the sin - less one, A voice was
In whose o - be - dience all are blest, Sav - ior, our

Jor - dan might de - liv - er Their trou - bled
heard from heav - en say - ing, "This is my
sins and sor - rows bear - ing, Hear us and

souls from sin and shame. They came to seek a
own be - lov - ed Son." There as the Fa - ther's
grant us this re - quest: Dai - ly to grow, by

new be - gin - ning, The hu - man spir - it's age - less
word was spo - ken, Not in the pow'r of wind and
grace de - fend - ed, Filled with the Spir - it from a -

quest, Re - pent - ance, and an end of
flame, But of his love and peace the
bove; In Christ bap - tized, be - loved, be -

sin - ning, Re - nounc - ing ev - 'ry wrong con - fessed.
to - ken, Seen as a dove, the Spir - it came.
friend - ed, Chil - dren of God in peace and love.

Text: Timothy Dudley-Smith, b.1926, © 1984, Hope Publishing Co.
Tune: RENDEZ À DIEU, 9 8 9 8 D; Louis Bourgeois, c.1510-1561

Remember You Are Dust 391

Additional verse tropes for the season of Lent:

Seek the God of compassion…
Live in kindness and mercy…
Trust in God and be faithful…
Praise the God of salvation…
Let us bow down in worship…

Text: Joel 2:12-18, 2 Corinthians 5:20–6:2; Paul A. Tate, b.1968, © 2003, GIA Publications, Inc.; refrain from the *Sacramentary,* © 1973, ICEL
Tune: Paul A. Tate, b.1968, © 2003, GIA Publications, Inc.

392 Dust and Ashes

Verses

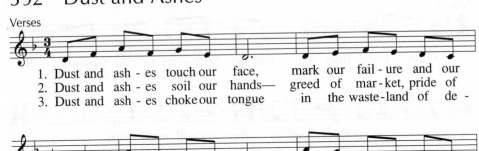

1. Dust and ash-es touch our face, mark our fail-ure and our
2. Dust and ash-es soil our hands— greed of mar-ket, pride of
3. Dust and ash-es choke our tongue in the waste-land of de-

fall-ing. Ho-ly Spir-it, come, walk with us to-mor-row,
na-tion. Ho-ly Spir-it, come, walk with us to-mor-row,
pres-sion. Ho-ly Spir-it, come, walk with us to-mor-row,

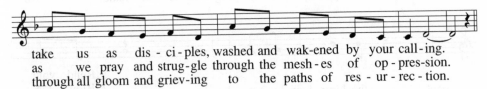

take us as dis-ci-ples, washed and wak-ened by your call-ing.
as we pray and strug-gle through the mesh-es of op-pres-sion.
through all gloom and griev-ing to the paths of res-ur-rec-tion.

Refrain

Take us by the hand and lead us, lead us through the des-ert sands,

bring us liv-ing wa-ter, Ho-ly Spir-it, come.

Text: Brian Wren, b.1936, © 1989, Hope Publishing Co.
Tune: David Haas, b.1957, © 1991, GIA Publications, Inc.

Crucem Tuam / O Lord, Your Cross   393

Ostinato Refrain

Cru - cem tu - am a - do - ra - mus Do - mi -
O   Lord,   your   cross,   we   a - dore and glo - ri -

ne, res - ur - re - cti - o - nem tu - am lau - da - mus Do - mi -
fy,   for your ho - ly res - ur - rec - tion,   we praise you Lord of

ne.   Lau - da - mus et glo - ri - fi - ca - mus.
life.   We praise   you   and we glo - ri - fy   you.

Res - ur - re - cti - o - nem tu - am lau - da - mus Do - mi - ne.
For your ho - ly res - ur - rec - tion, we praise you Lord of   life.

Text: Taizé Community, 1991
Tune: Jacques Berthier, 1923-1994

394 Somebody's Knockin' at Your Door

Some-bod - y's knock-in' at your door; Some-bod - y's
knock-in' at your door; O sin - ner, why don't you
an - swer? Some-bod - y's knock-in' at your door.

Solo:
1. Knocks like Je - sus,
2. Can't you hear him?
3. Je - sus calls you,
4. Can't you trust him?

All:
Some-bod - y's knock-in' at your door.

Solo:
Knocks like Je - sus,
Can't you hear him?
Je - sus calls you,
Can't you trust him?

All:
Some-bod - y's knock-in' at your door.

O sin - ner, why don't you an - swer?

Some-bod - y's knock-in' at your door.

Text: African-American spiritual
Tune: SOMEBODY'S KNOCKIN', Irregular; African-American spiritual; harm. by Richard Proulx, b.1937, © 1986, GIA Publications, Inc.

Seek the Lord   395

Refrain

Seek the Lord while he may be found;
call to him while he is still near.

Verses 1, 2

1. To-day is the day and now the pro-per hour
2. As high as the sky is a-bove the earth,

to for-sake our sin - ful lives and turn to the Lord.
so high a - bove our ways, the ways of the Lord.

Verse 3

3. Find-ing the Lord, let us cling to him. His

words, his ways lead us to life.

Verse 4

4. Some day we'll live in the house of God;

gaze on his face and praise his name.

Text: Isaiah 55:6-9; Roc O'Connor, SJ, b.1949
Tune: Roc O'Connor, SJ, b.1949; arr. by Peter Felice, alt.
© 1976, Robert F. O'Connor, SJ, and OCP Publications

396 The Cross of Jesus

1. Come, O God, re - new your peo - ple,
2. Deep with - in cre - ate a new heart;
3. In the dark - ness that sur - rounds us
4. Call us forth to walk in jus - tice.

We who long to see your face.
Melt a - way the win - ter chill.
We have lost you from our sight.
Res - cue us from sin and grave.

Strength - en hearts that have grown fee - ble;
Help us now to make a new start,
E - ven though your love has found us,
Through the pow - er of your Spir - it,

Fill our lives with truth and grace.
Help us now to know your will.
We em - brace the powers of night.
Breathe in us the breath that saves.

On - ly you can win our free - dom;
Washed in wa - ters of for - giv - ness,
Scat - ter now our deep - est dark - ness.
Strength - en us in our com - mun - ion,

On - ly you can bring us peace.
Cleansed in wa - ters of new birth,
Guide our hearts in - to the light.
One in Word and cup and bread.

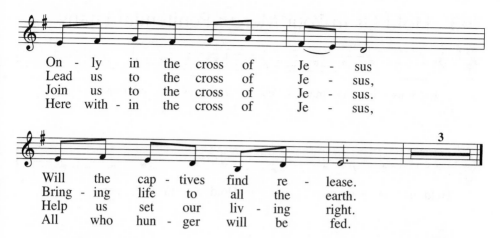

On - ly in the cross of Je - sus
Lead us to the cross of Je - sus,
Join us to the cross of Je - sus.
Here with - in the cross of Je - sus,

Will the cap - tives find re - lease.
Bring - ing life to all the earth.
Help us set our liv - ing right.
All who hun - ger will be fed.

Text: Francis Patrick O'Brien, b.1958
Tune: Francis Patrick O'Brien, b.1958
© 1996, GIA Publications, Inc.

The Glory of These Forty Days   397

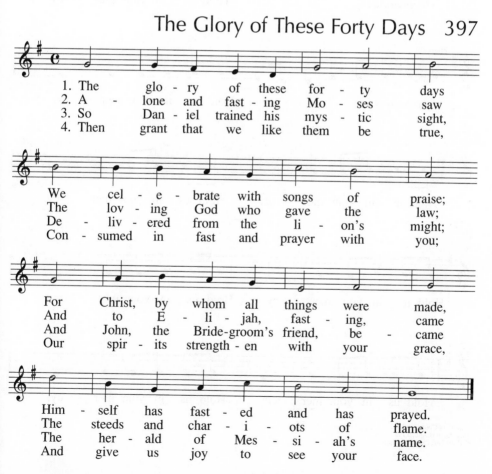

1. The glo - ry of these for - ty days
2. A - lone and fast - ing Mo - ses saw
3. So Dan - iel trained his mys - tic sight,
4. Then grant that we like them be true,

We cel - e - brate with songs of praise;
The lov - ing God who gave the law;
De - liv - ered from the li - on's might;
Con - sumed in fast and prayer with you;

For Christ, by whom all things were made,
And to E - li - jah, fast - ing, came
And John, the Bride-groom's friend, be - came
Our spir - its strength - en with your grace,

Him - self has fast - ed and has prayed.
The steeds and char - i - ots of flame.
The her - ald of Mes - si - ah's name.
And give us joy to see your face.

Text: *Clarum decus jejunii;* Gregory the Great, c. 540-604; tr. by Maurice F. Bell, 1862-1947, © Oxford University Press
Tune: OLD HUNDREDTH, LM; Louis Bourgeois, c.1510-1561

398 Hold Us in Your Mercy: Penitential Litany

Hold us in your mer - cy. Hold us in your mer - cy.

Hold us in your mer - cy. Hold us in your mer - cy.

(Invocation) Hold us in your mer - cy.

(Invocation) Hold us in your mer - cy.

Hold us in your mer - cy. Hold us in your mer - cy.

Hold us in your mer - cy. Hold us in your mer - cy.

Hold us in your mer - cy. Hold us in your mer - cy.

Text: Rory Cooney, b. 1952
Tune: Gary Daigle, b. 1957
© 1993, GIA Publications, Inc.

Jerusalem, My Destiny 399

Refrain

I have fixed my eyes on your hills, Je - ru - sa - lem, my des - ti - ny! Though I can - not see the end for me, I can - not turn a - way. We have set our hearts for the way; this jour - ney is our des - ti - ny. Let no - one walk a - lone. The jour - ney makes us one.

Verses

1. Oth - er spir - its, less - er gods, have court - ed me with lies.
2. See, I leave the past be - hind; a new land calls to me.
3. In my thirst, you let me drink the wa - ters of your life.
4. All the worlds I have not seen you o - pen to my view.
5. To the tombs I went to mourn the hope I thought was gone.

D.C.

Here a - mong you I have found a truth which bids me rise.
Here a - mong you now I find a glimpse of what might be.
Here a - mong you I have met the sav - ior, Je - sus Christ.
Here a - mong you I have found a vi - sion, bright and new.
Here a - mong you I a - woke to un - ex - pect - ed dawn.

Text: Rory Cooney, b.1952
Tune: Rory Cooney, b.1952
© 1990, GIA Publications, Inc.

400 Adoramus Te Christe

Canon Refrain

A - do - ra - mus te Chri - ste, a - do - ra - mus te Chri - ste, a - do - ra - mus te Chri - ste, a - do - ra - mus Chri - ste.

Verses

1. A - do - ra - mus te Chri - ste, et be - ne - di - ci - mus ti - bi, 2. Qui - a per san - ctam Cru - cem tu - am re - de - mi - sti mun - dum.

Text: Antiphon from Good Friday Liturgy; *We adore you, O Christ, and we bless you, because by your holy cross you have redeemed the world.*
Tune: Marty Haugen, b.1950, © 1984, GIA Publications, Inc.

401 Tree of Life

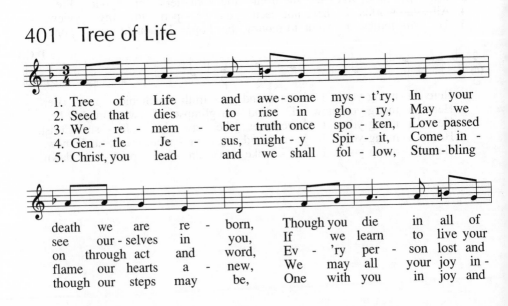

1. Tree of Life and awe-some mys - t'ry, In your death we are re - born, Though you die in all of
2. Seed that dies to rise in glo - ry, May we see our-selves in you, If we learn to live your
3. We re - mem - ber truth once spo - ken, Love passed on through act and word, Ev - 'ry per - son lost and
4. Gen - tle Je - sus, might - y Spir - it, Come in - flame our hearts a - new, We may all your joy in -
5. Christ, you lead and we shall fol - low, Stum - bling though our steps may be, One with you in joy and

his - t'ry,   Still   you   rise with   ev - 'ry   morn,   Still   you
sto - ry   We   may   die   to   rise   a - new,   We   may
bro - ken   Wears the   bod - y   of   our   Lord,   Wears the
her - it   If   we   bear the   cross   with   you,   If   we
sor - row,   We   the   riv - er,   you   the   sea,   We   the

rise   with   ev - 'ry   morn.
die   to   rise   a - new.
bod - y   of   our   Lord.
bear   the cross   with   you.
riv - er,   you   the   sea.

Lenten Verses

General: Light of life beyond conceiving, Mighty Spirit of our Lord;
Give new strength to our believing, Give us faith to live your word.

1st Sunday: From the dawning of creation, You have loved us as your own;
Stay with us through all temptation, Make us turn to you alone.

2nd Sunday: In our call to be a blessing, May we be a blessing true;
May we live and die confessing Christ as Lord of all we do.

3rd Sunday: Living Water of salvation, Be the fountain of each soul;
Springing up in new creation, Flow in us and make us whole.

4th Sunday: Give us eyes to see you clearly, Make us children of your light;
Give us hearts to live more nearly As your gospel shining bright.

5th Sunday: God of all our fear and sorrow, God who lives beyond our death;
Hold us close through each tomorrow, Love as near as every breath.

402 From Ashes to the Living Font

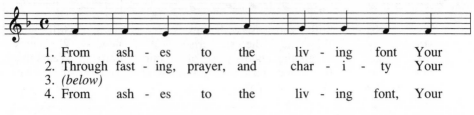

1. From ash - es to the liv - ing font Your
2. Through fast - ing, prayer, and char - i - ty Your
3. *(below)*
4. From ash - es to the liv - ing font, Your

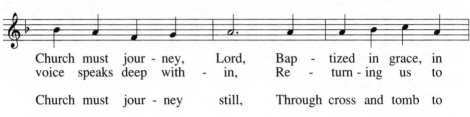

Church must jour - ney, Lord, Bap - tized in grace, in
voice speaks deep with - in, Re - turn - ing us to

Church must jour - ney still, Through cross and tomb to

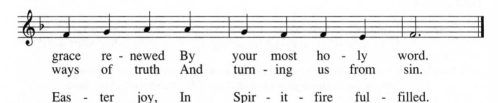

grace re - newed By your most ho - ly word.
ways of truth And turn - ing us from sin.

Eas - ter joy, In Spir - it - fire ful - filled.

Sundays I & II

3. From desert to the mountaintop
   In Christ our way we see,
   So, tempered by temptation's might
   We might transfigured be.

Sunday IV

3. We sit beside the road and plead,
   "Come, save us, David's son!"
   Now with your vision heal our eyes,
   The world's true Light alone.

Sunday III

3. For thirsting hearts let waters flow
   Our fainting souls revive;
   And at the well your waters give
   Our everlasting life.

Sunday V

3. Our graves split open, bring us back,
   Your promise to proclaim;
   To darkened tombs call out, "Arise!"
   And glorify your name.

Text: Alan J. Hommerding, b.1956, © 1994, World Library Publications, Inc.
Tune: ST. FLAVIAN, CM; *John's Day Psalter,* 1562; harm. based on the original *faux-bourdon* setting

Jesus, the Lord 403

Refrain

Je - sus. Je - sus. Let all cre-a - tion bend the knee to the Lord.

Verse 1

1. In him we live, we move and have our be - ing; in him the Christ, in him the King. Je - sus, the Lord.

Verses 2, 3

2. Though Son, he did not cling to god - li - ness; but emp - tied him - self, be - came a slave!
3. He lived o - be - dient - ly his Fa - ther's will ac - cept - ing his death, death on a tree! Je - sus, the Lord.

Text: *Jesus Prayer,* Philippians 2:5-11; Acts 17:28; Roc O'Connor, SJ, b.1949
Tune: Roc O'Connor, SJ, b.1949; arr. by Rick Modlin, b.1966
© 1981, 1994, Robert F. O'Connor, SJ, and OCP Publications

404 Stations of the Cross

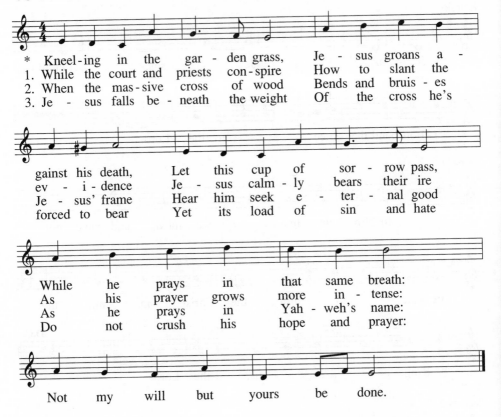

```
*   Kneel-ing  in   the    gar - den grass,   Je - sus  groans  a -
1.  While  the  court and  priests  con-spire   How  to   slant  the
2.  When   the  mas-sive  cross   of  wood   Bends and  bruis - es
3.  Je -  sus  falls be - neath  the weight   Of   the   cross  he's

    gainst his death,   Let   this  cup   of   sor - row pass,
    ev - i - dence     Je - sus  calm - ly   bears  their  ire
    Je - sus' frame    Hear  him  seek   e - ter - nal good
    forced to  bear    Yet   its  load  of   sin   and hate

    While   he    prays   in    that  same  breath:
    As      his   prayer grows more  in - tense:
    As      he    prays   in    Yah - weh's name:
    Do      not   crush   his   hope  and  prayer:

    Not    my    will   but   yours  be   done.
```

This stanza begins the devotions. Stanzas 1-14 accompany each station.

1. Jesus is condemned to death

2. Jesus carries his Cross

3. Jesus falls the first time

4. **Jesus meets his afflicted mother**
   Jesus reads in Mary's eyes
   all the sorrow mothers bear,
   and he prays his friend supplies
   grace to strengthen her own prayer:
   Not my will but yours be done.

5. **Simon of Cyrene helps Jesus to carry his Cross**
   We with Simon of Cyrene
   help the Savior bear the cross.
   Step by step we slowly glean
   what true faith and prayer will cost:
   Not my will but yours be done.

6. **Veronica wipes the face of Jesus**
Seek the courage and the grace
that Veronica displays
when she wipes the bleeding face
of the one who bravely prays:
Not my will but yours be done.

7. **Jesus falls the second time**
Jesus trips and falls again
as he struggles through the street
where the mob's unceasing din
mocks the prayer his lips repeat:
Not my will but yours be done.

8. **Jesus meets the women of Jerusalem**
Christ directs the women's tears
toward the coming judgment day
when God weighs our faithless years
with our willingness to pray:
Not my will but yours be done.

9. **Jesus falls a third time**
Jesus stumbles one last time
nearly broken by the load
yet by prayer finds strength to climb
Calvary's final stretch of road:
Not my will but yours be done.

10. **Jesus is stripped of his clothes**
Naked to the sun and clouds
and the jeers and gawking stare
of the soldiers and the crowds
Christ continues with his prayer:
Not my will but yours be done.

11. **Jesus is nailed to the Cross**
While the soldiers throw their dice
they ignore their victim's groans,
lost to them the sacrifice
and the prayer that Jesus moans:
Not my will but yours be done.

12. **Jesus dies on the Cross**
Jesus gives one loud last cry
at the moment of his death
while his prayer moves heaven's sky
with his final, parting breath:
Not my will but yours be done.

13. **The body of Jesus is taken
down from the Cross**
As they take the body down
and they wrap it in a sheet
in their hearts they hear the sound
that his lips no more repeat:
Not my will but yours be done.

14. **Jesus is laid in the tomb**
Quiet is the hollowed cave.
Peace and tears and grief descend.
Mourners offer at the grave
what they learned from Christ their friend:
Not my will but yours be done.

Text: Thomas H. Troeger, b.1945, © 1993, Oxford University Press
Tune: VIA CRUCIS, 77 77 with refrain; William P. Rowan, b.1951, © 1995, GIA Publications, Inc.

405 Hosea

Verses

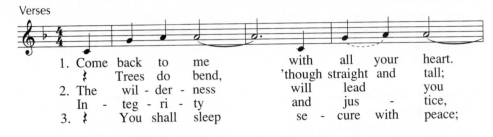

1. Come back to me with all your heart.
   { Trees do bend, 'though straight and tall;
2. The wil - der - ness will lead you
   In - teg - ri - ty and jus - tice,
3. { You shall sleep se - cure with peace;

Don't let fear keep us a - part.
so must we to oth - ers' call. *(To refrain)*
to your heart where I will speak.
With ten - der - ness, { you shall know. *(To refrain)*
faith - ful - ness will be your joy. *(To refrain)*

Refrain

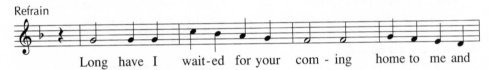

Long have I wait-ed for your com - ing home to me and

liv - ing deep - ly our new life.

Text: Hosea 6:1, 3:3, 2:16, 21; Joel 2:12; Weston Priory, Gregory Norbet, OSB, b.1940
Tune: Gregory Norbet, OSB, b.1940; arr. by Mary David Callahan, OSB, b.1923
© 1972, 1980, The Benedictine Foundation of the State of Vermont, Inc.

406 Jesus Walked This Lonesome Valley

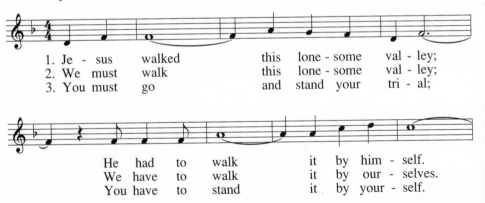

1. Je - sus walked this lone - some val - ley;
2. We must walk this lone - some val - ley;
3. You must go and stand your tri - al;

He had to walk it by him - self.
We have to walk it by our - selves.
You have to stand it by your - self.

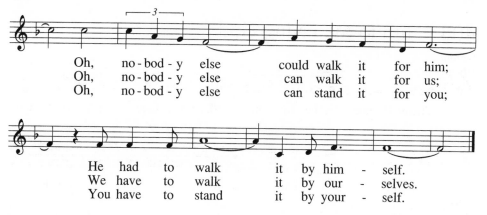

Oh,   no-bod-y   else   could walk   it   for   him;
Oh,   no-bod-y   else   can walk   it   for   us;
Oh,   no-bod-y   else   can stand   it   for   you;

He   had   to   walk   it   by   him - self.
We   have   to   walk   it   by   our - selves.
You   have   to   stand   it   by   your - self.

Text: American Folk Hymn
Tune: LONESOME VALLEY, 8 8 10 8; American folk hymn; harm. by Richard Proulx, b.1937, © 1975, GIA Publications, Inc.

Again We Keep This Solemn Fast   407

1. A - gain   we   keep   this   sol - emn   fast
2. The   law   and   proph - ets   from   of   old
3. More   spar - ing,   there - fore,   let   us   make
4. Let   us   a - void   each   harm - ful   way
5. We   pray,   O   bless - ed   Three   in   One,

A   gift   of   faith   from   a - ges   past,
In   fig - ured   ways   this   Lent   fore - told,
The   words   we   speak,   the   food   we   take,
That   lures   the   care - less   mind   a - stray;
Our   God   while   end - less   a - ges   run,

This   Lent   which   binds   us   lov - ing - ly
Which   Christ,   all   a - ges'   Lord   and   Guide,
Our   sleep,   our   laugh - ter,   ev - 'ry   sense;
By   watch - ful   prayer   our   spir - its   free
That   this,   our   Lent   of   for - ty   days,

To   faith   and   hope   and   char - i - ty.
In   these   last   days   has   sanc - ti - fied.
Learn   peace   through   ho - ly   pen - i - tence.
From   schem - ing   of   the   En - e - my.
May   bring   us   growth   and   give   you   praise.

Text: *Ex more docti mystico*; ascr. to Gregory the Great, c. 540-604, tr. by Peter J. Scagnelli, b. 1949, ©
Tune: OLD HUNDREDTH, LM; Louis Bourgeois, c.1510-1561

408 Turn to the Living God

Refrain

Turn, turn to the liv-ing God, the God of heal-ing and com-fort, and with de-light, God will turn to you. With de-light, God will turn to you.

Verse 1

1. For now is the time of ful-fill-ment. The reign of our God is at hand. Re-form your life, turn from sin and be-lieve this glo-rious news.

D.C.

Verse 2

2. Come, and re-turn to the Lord. All you wea-ry, bring your griev-ing hearts. With kind-ness and mer-cy God's com-pas-sion will fill your hearts with love.

D.C.

Verse 3

3. Have mer-cy, O Lord, on your peo-ple. In your good-ness wipe a-way our guilt. Wash us clean, free us, to be-come your liv-ing song of praise.

D.C.

Verse 4

4. Come, sing with joy to the Lord. Lis-ten with an o-pen heart. Hear God's voice and fol-low; our good shep-herd is guid-ing the way.

D.C.

Text: Lori True, b.1961
Tune: Lori True, b.1961
© 2003, GIA Publications, Inc.

Lord Jesus Christ 409

Ostinato Refrain

Lord Je-sus Christ, Son of the liv-ing God, have mer-cy on me, a sin-ner, have mer-cy.

Text: *The Jesus Prayer*; verses, Psalm 51 and Agnus Dei, adapt. by Carol E. Browning, b.1956
Tune: Carol E. Browning, b.1956; acc. by Kathy McGrath
© 2003, GIA Publications, Inc.

410 Return to God

Refrain

Re-turn to God with all your heart, the source of grace and

mer-cy; come seek the ten-der faith-ful-ness of God.

Verses

1. Now the time of grace has come,
the day of salvation;
come and learn now the way of our God.

2. I will take your heart of stone
and place a heart within you,
a heart of compassion and love.

3. If you break the chains of oppression,
if you set the pris'ner free;
if you share your bread with the hungry,
give protection to the lost;
give a shelter to the homeless,
clothe the naked in your midst,
then your light shall break forth like the dawn.

Text: Marty Haugen, b.1950
Tune: Marty Haugen, b.1950
© 1990, 1991, GIA Publications, Inc.

411 Forty Days and Forty Nights

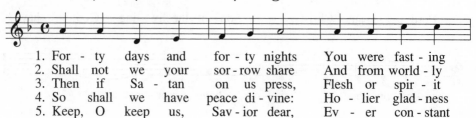

1. For - ty days and for - ty nights You were fast - ing
2. Shall not we your sor - row share And from world - ly
3. Then if Sa - tan on us press, Flesh or spir - it
4. So shall we have peace di - vine: Ho - lier glad - ness
5. Keep, O keep us, Sav - ior dear, Ev - er con - stant

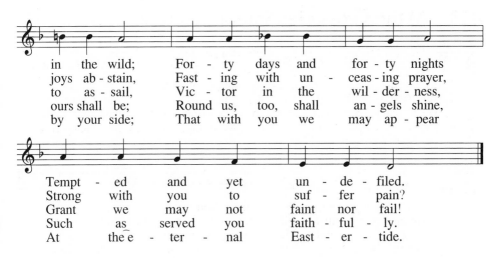

in the wild;   For - ty   days   and   for - ty   nights
joys ab - stain,   Fast - ing   with   un - ceas - ing   prayer,
to   as - sail,   Vic - tor   in   the   wil - der - ness,
ours shall be;   Round us,   too,   shall   an - gels shine,
by your side;   That   with   you   we   may ap - pear

Tempt - ed   and   yet   un - de - filed.
Strong   with   you   to   suf - fer   pain?
Grant   we   may   not   faint   nor   fail!
Such   as   served   you   faith - ful - ly.
At   the e - ter - nal   East - er - tide.

Text: George H. Smyttan, 1822-1870, alt.
Tune: HEINLEIN, 7 7 7 7; attr. to Martin Herbst, 1654-1681, *Nürnbergisches Gesangbuch*, 1676

Parce Domine 412

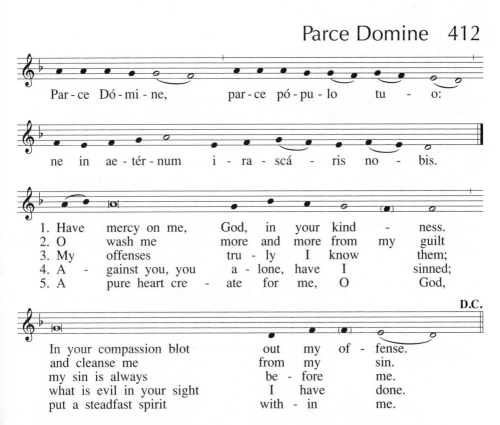

Par - ce Dó - mi - ne,   par - ce pó - pu - lo   tu - o:

ne in ae - tér - num   i - ra - scá - ris no - bis.

1. Have   mercy on me,   God,   in   your   kind - ness.
2. O   wash me   more and   more from   my   guilt
3. My   offenses   tru - ly   I   know   them;
4. A - gainst you, you   a - lone, have   I   sinned;
5. A   pure heart cre - ate   for   me,   O   God,

D.C.

In your compassion blot   out   my   of - fense.
and cleanse me   from   my   sin.
my sin is always   be - fore   me.
what is evil in your sight   I   have   done.
put a steadfast spirit   with - in   me.

Text: *Spare your people, Lord, lest you be angry for ever*, Joel 2:17, Psalm 51:3-6, 12; tr. The Grail, © 1963, The Grail, GIA Publications, Inc., agent
Tune: PARCE DOMINE, Irregular; Mode I with Tonus Peregrinus; acc. by Robert LeBlanc, OSB, b.1948, © 1986, GIA Publications, Inc.

413 At the Cross Her Station Keeping

1. At   the   cross her   sta - tion keep-ing, Mar - y   stood in
2. While she wait - ed   in   her   an-guish, See - ing Christ in
3. With what pain and   des - o - la - tion, With   what no - ble
4. Ev - er   pa - tient   in   her yearn-ing, Though her   tear - filled

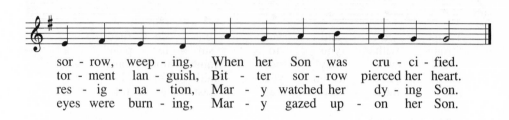

sor - row,   weep - ing,   When her   Son   was   cru - ci - fied.
tor - ment   lan - guish,   Bit - ter   sor - row   pierced her heart.
res - ig - na - tion,   Mar - y   watched her   dy - ing Son.
eyes were   burn - ing,   Mar - y   gazed   up - on   her Son.

5. Who, that sorrow contemplating,
   On that passion meditating,
   Would not share the Virgin's grief?

6. Christ she saw, for our salvation,
   Scourged with cruel acclamation,
   Bruised and beaten by the rod.

7. Christ she saw with life-blood failing,
   All her anguish unavailing,
   Saw him breathe his very last.

8. Mary, fount of love's devotion,
   Let me share with true emotion
   All the sorrow you endured.

9. Virgin, ever interceding,
   Hear me in my fervent pleading:
   Fire me with your love of Christ.

10. Mother, may this prayer be granted:
    That Christ's love may be implanted
    In the depths of my poor soul.

11. At the cross, your sorrow sharing,
    All your grief and torment bearing,
    Let me stand and mourn with you.

12. Fairest maid of all creation,
    Queen of hope and consolation,
    Let me feel your grief sublime.

13. Virgin, in your love befriend me,
    At the Judgment Day defend me.
    Help me by your constant prayer.

14. Savior, when my life shall leave me,
    Through your mother's prayers receive me
    With the fruits of victory.

15. Let me to your love be taken,
    Let my soul in death awaken
    To the joys of Paradise.

Text: *Stabat mater dolorosa;* Jacopone da Todi, 1230-1306; trans. by Anthony G. Petti, 1932-1985, © 1971, Faber Music, Ltd.
Tune: STABAT MATER, 88 7; *Mainz Gesangbuch,* 1661; harm. by Richard Proulx, b.1937, © 1986, GIA Publications, Inc.

Change Our Hearts 414

Refrain

Change our hearts this time, Your word says it can be. Change our minds, this time, Your life could make us free. We are the peo - ple Your call set a - part, Lord, this time change our hearts.

Verses

1. Brought by your hand to the edge of our dreams.
2. Now as we watch you stretch out your hands,
3. Show us the way that leads to your side,

One foot in par - a - dise, one in the waste.
of - 'fring a - bun - dan - ces, full - ness of joy.
o - ver the moun - tains and sands of the soul.

Drawn by your prom - is - es, still we are
Your milk and hon - ey seem dis - tant, un -
Be for us man - na, wa - ter from

D.C.

lured by the shad - ows and the chains we leave be - hind. But
real, when we have bread and wa - ter in our hands. But
stone, light which says we nev - er walk a - lone. And

Text: Rory Cooney, b.1952
Tune: Rory Cooney, b.1952
© 1984, North American Liturgy Resources. Published by OCP Publications.

415 Return to the Lord

Refrain

Cantor:

Re - turn, re - turn to the Lord, your God.

Assembly:

Re - turn, re - turn to the Lord, your God.

Verse 1

1. Who is gra - cious and mer - ci - ful, and slow to an - ger, a - bound - ing in love. Re -

Verse 2

2. Re - turn with all your heart, with fast - ing and weep-ing, rend your hearts, and re - turn to God. Re -

Verse 3

3. Have mer - cy, O God, in your good-ness, cleanse me from my sin. Re -

Verse 4

4. Cre - ate in me a clean heart, re - new your

D.S.

spir-it, keep me in your pres - ence. Re -

Verse 5

5. Give back to me, the joy of your sal - va-tion, sus -

D.S.

tain your spir - it with - in me. Re -

Text: David Haas, b.1957
Tune: David Haas, b.1957
© 2003, GIA Publications, Inc.

Lord, Who throughout These Forty Days   416

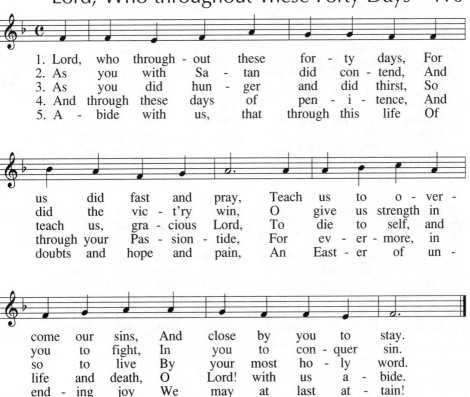

1. Lord, who through - out these for - ty days, For
2. As you with Sa - tan did con - tend, And
3. As you did hun - ger and did thirst, So
4. And through these days of pen - i - tence, And
5. A - bide with us, that through this life Of

us did fast and pray, Teach us to o - ver -
did the vic - t'ry win, O give us strength in
teach us, gra - cious Lord, To die to self, and
through your Pas - sion - tide, For ev - er - more, in
doubts and hope and pain, An East - er of un -

come our sins, And close by you to stay.
you to fight, In you to con - quer sin.
so to live By your most ho - ly word.
life and death, O Lord! with us a - bide.
end - ing joy We may at last at - tain!

Text: Claudia F. Hernaman, 1838-1898, alt.
Tune: ST. FLAVIAN, CM; *John's Day Psalter,* 1562; harm. based on the original *faux-bourdon* setting

417 Mercy, O God

Refrain

Mer-cy, O God, have mer-cy on us.

Send down your mer-cy to set us free.

Mer-cy, O God, have mer-cy on us.

Send down your mer-cy to set us free.

Verses

1. Gath - er the peo - ple, the chil - dren, the el - ders;
2. Now is the hour, the day of sal - va - tion;
3. Long is the jour - ney and steep are the moun - tains,
4. Wash us a - new in your life - giv - ing wa - ter;
5. Once lost in dark-ness you did not for - sake us, but
6. Wake, O sleep - er, a - wake from your slum - ber;

1. come now and gath - er be - fore the Lord.
2. now is the time to re - turn to God.
3. come now and guide us, O gra - cious God.
4. come quench the thirst of our yearn - ing hearts.
5. called us your chil - dren and gave us light.
6. rise from the chains of the dark, cold tomb.

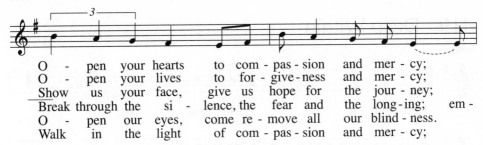

O - pen your hearts   to com - pas - sion and mer - cy;
O - pen your lives   to for - give - ness and mer - cy;
Show us your face,   give us hope for   the jour - ney;
Break through the si - lence, the fear and the long-ing; em -
O - pen our eyes,   come re - move all   our blind - ness.
Walk in the light of com - pas - sion and mer - cy;

D.C.

O - pen your hearts   to the Lord.
O - pen your lives   to the Lord.
Lead us to walk   in your love.
brace us with un - end - ing love.
O - pen our eyes   to your love.
walk in the light   of the Lord.

Text: Francis Patrick O'Brien, b.1958
Tune: Francis Patrick O'Brien, b.1958
© 2001, GIA Publications, Inc.

Kyrie   418

Ostinato I

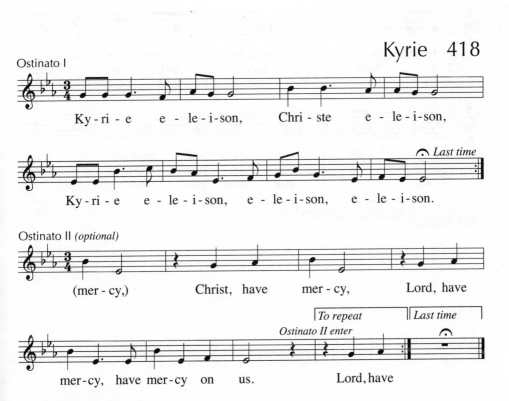

Ky - ri - e   e - le - i - son,   Chri - ste   e - le - i - son,

Last time

Ky - ri - e   e - le - i - son,   e - le - i - son,   e - le - i - son.

Ostinato II *(optional)*

(mer - cy,)   Christ, have   mer - cy,   Lord, have

To repeat | *Last time*

Ostinato II enter

mer - cy, have mer - cy on   us.   Lord, have

Text: Marty Haugen, b.1950
Tune: Marty Haugen, b.1950
© 2001, GIA Publications, Inc.

LENT

419 Deep Within

Refrain

Deep with - in   I will plant my law,

not on stone,   but in your heart.

Fol - low me,   I will bring you back,   you will

be my own,   and I   will be   your   God.

Verses

1. I will give you a new heart, a new spir - it with -
2. ♪ Seek my face, and see your
3. Re - turn to me, with all your

D.C.

in you, for I will be your strength.
God, ♪ for I will be your hope.
heart, ♪ and I will bring you back.

Text: Jeremiah 31:33, Ezekiel 36:26, Joel 2:12; David Haas, b.1957
Tune: David Haas, b.1957; acc. by Jeanne Cotter, b.1964
© 1987, GIA Publications, Inc.

Palm Sunday Processional 420

Cantor:

1. When they heard that Je - sus was com - ing,
2. Spread their cloaks and branch - es be - fore him,
3. Blest is he, like Da - vid be - fore him.
4. Guid - ing cloud and pil - lar of fire,
5. Word of God, and first - born of peo - ple,
6. Vi - sion blest, and hope for the fu - ture,
7. Won - drous bread, and stream in the des - ert,
8. Eye of God, who see to the heart of us,
9. Ris - ing sun, the light of the world,
10. Friend in death, who weep for our dy - ing,
11. Friend in death, who wake us to new life,

Assembly:

Sing ho - san - na to the cho - sen one!

Cantor:

All the peo - ple went out to meet him.
Chil - dren sang with palm branch-es wav - ing.
Blest is he, God's bless - ing up - on him.
Sa - tan's foe and friend of the sin - ner.
Prom - ise kept, the crown of cre - a - tion.
God's be - lov - ed, ra - diant with glo - ry.
Ho - ly thirst, and God's liv - ing wa - ter.
Heal - ing touch, the sight for our blind - ness.
Word of life, who give us your Spir - it.
Friend in death, who roll back the stone for us.
Friend in life, we sing glad ho - san - nas.

Assembly:

Sing ho - san - na to the cho - sen one! Sing ho - san - na,

sing ho - san - na, sing ho - san - na to the cho - sen one!

Text: Rory Cooney, b.1952
Tune: Rory Cooney, b.1952
© 1999, GIA Publications, Inc.

421 All Glory, Laud, and Honor

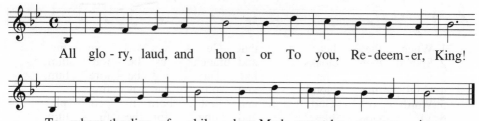

All glo-ry, laud, and hon-or To you, Re-deem-er, King!

To whom the lips of chil-dren Made sweet ho-san-nas ring.

1. You are the King of Is-ra-el, And Da-vid's roy-al Son,
2. The com-pa-ny of an-gels Are prais-ing you on high;
3. The peo-ple of the He-brews With palms be-fore you went:
4. To you be-fore your pas-sion They sang their hymns of praise:
5. Their prais-es you ac-cept-ed, Ac-cept the prayers we bring,

D.C.

Now in the Lord's Name com-ing, Our King and Bless-ed One.
And mor-tals, joined with all things Cre-a-ted, make re-ply.
Our praise and prayers and an-thems Be-fore you we pre-sent.
To you, now high ex-alt-ed, Our mel-o-dy we raise.
Great source of love and good-ness, Our Sav-ior and our King.

Text: *Gloria, laus et honor;* Theodulph of Orleans, c.760-821; tr. by John M. Neale, 1818-1866, alt.
Tune: ST. THEODULPH, 7 6 7 6 D; Melchior Teschner, 1584-1635

422 Jesus, Remember Me

Ostinato Refrain

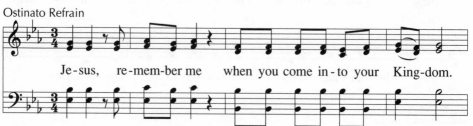

Je-sus, re-mem-ber me when you come in-to your King-dom.

Text: Luke 23:42; Taizé Community, 1981
Tune: Jacques Berthier, 1923-1994
© 1981, Les Presses de Taizé, GIA Publications, Inc., agent

Hosanna 423

Refrain

Ho - san - na, ho - san - na! Ho - san - na in the high - est!

Verses

Cantor:

1. Bless - ed is he, bless - ed is he; Ho -
2. Chil - dren of Je - ru - sa - lem; Ho -
3. Sing your praise, sing your praise: Ho -

All: Cantor:

san - na! Ho - san - na! He who comes in the
san - na! Ho - san - na! Chil - dren, wel - come
san - na! Ho - san - na! Hail the dawn of e -

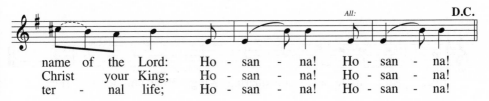

All: D.C.

name of the Lord: Ho - san - na! Ho - san - na!
Christ your King; Ho - san - na! Ho - san - na!
ter - nal life; Ho - san - na! Ho - san - na!

Text: Scott Soper, b.1961
Tune: Scott Soper, b.1961
© 1997, GIA Publications, Inc.

424 Ride On, Jesus, Ride

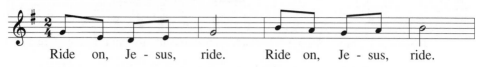

Ride on, Je - sus, ride. Ride on, Je - sus, ride.

Ride on, Je - sus, con - quering King, Ride on, Je - sus ride.

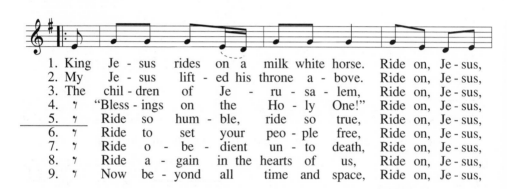

1. King Je - sus rides on a milk white horse. Ride on, Je - sus,
2. My Je - sus lift - ed his throne a - bove. Ride on, Je - sus,
3. The chil - dren of Je - ru - sa - lem, Ride on, Je - sus,
4. ⁊ "Bless - ings on the Ho - ly One!" Ride on, Je - sus,
5. ⁊ Ride so hum - ble, ride so true, Ride on, Je - sus,
6. ⁊ Ride to set your peo - ple free, Ride on, Je - sus,
7. ⁊ Ride o - be - dient un - to death, Ride on, Je - sus,
8. ⁊ Ride a - gain in the hearts of us, Ride on, Je - sus,
9. ⁊ Now be - yond all time and space, Ride on, Je - sus,

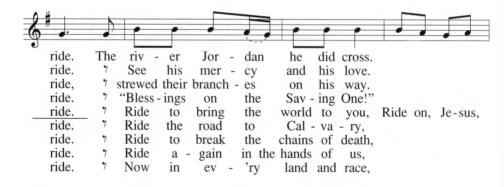

ride. The riv - er Jor - dan he did cross.
ride. ⁊ See his mer - cy and his love.
ride, ⁊ strewed their branch - es on his way.
ride. ⁊ "Bless - ings on the Sav - ing One!"
ride. ⁊ Ride to bring the world to you, Ride on, Je - sus,
ride. ⁊ Ride the road to Cal - va - ry,
ride. ⁊ Ride to break the chains of death,
ride. ⁊ Ride a - gain in the hands of us,
ride. ⁊ Now in ev - 'ry land and race,

ride. Ride on, Je-sus, con - quering King. Ride on, Je - sus ride.

Text: African-American spiritual; verses 3-9, Marty Haugen, b.1950, © 1991, GIA Publications, Inc.
Tune: African-American spiritual; harm. by Barbara Jackson Martin, © 1987, GIA Publications, Inc.

Hosanna 425

Refrain

Ho - san-na, Ho - san-na, Ho - san-na in the high-est!

Ho - san-na, Ho - san-na, Ho - san-na in the high-est!

Verses

1. Chil - dren of Je - ru - sa - lem shout - ing prais - es
2. En - ter - ing Je - ru - sa - lem crowds of peo - ple
3. O - pen wide the sa - cred door the king of glo - ry
4. Bless - ed Christ, who comes in pow'r, saves us all from
5. Earth and sea and sky a - bove glo - ry in this
6. Ev - 'ry tongue on earth con - fess, Je - sus, rich in
7. Spir - it of the liv - ing God, pour - ing forth e -

fol - lowed him. "This is he who comes to save,
cov - ered him. "Ho - san - na to the cho - sen One!
rides once more. Sing ho - san - nas, shout his name,
Sa - tan's hour. Grasp - ing not Di - vin - i - ty he
sav - ing love. Bless - ed, rich in mer - cy be
ho - li - ness, comes to be our sav - ing Lord;
ter - nal love, help us praise the bless - ed One,

D.C.

he our ran - som from the grave."
Blessed is he, God's on - ly Son!
to the world God's love pro - claim.
wins our free - dom on a tree.
he who sets all peo - ple free.
in his name be God a - dored.
praise un - til our life is done.

Text: Francis Patrick O'Brien, b.1958
Tune: Francis Patrick O'Brien, b.1958
© 2001, GIA Publications, Inc.

426 Hail Our Savior's Glorious Body / Pange Lingua

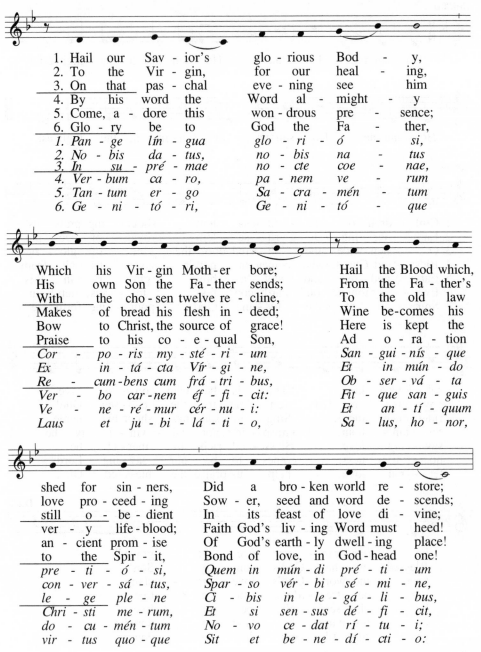

1. Hail our Sav - ior's glo - rious Bod - y,
2. To the Vir - gin, for our heal - ing,
3. On that pas - chal eve - ning see him
4. By his word the Word al - might - y
5. Come, a - dore this won - drous pre - sence;
6. Glo - ry be to God the Fa - ther,

1. Pan - ge lín - gua glo - ri - ó - si,
2. No - bis da - tus, no - bis na - tus
3. In su - pré - mae no - cte coe - nae,
4. Ver - bum ca - ro, pa - nem ve - rum
5. Tan - tum er - go Sa - cra - mén - tum
6. Ge - ni - tó - ri, Ge - ni - tó - que

Which his Vir - gin Moth-er bore; Hail the Blood which,
His own Son the Fa - ther sends; From the Fa - ther's
With the cho - sen twelve re - cline, To the old law
Makes of bread his flesh in - deed; Wine be-comes his
Bow to Christ, the source of grace! Here is kept the
Praise to his co - e - qual Son, Ad - o - ra - tion

Cor - po - ris my - sté - ri - um San - gui - nís - que
Ex - in - tá - cta Vír - gi - ne, Et in mún - do
Re - cum-bens cum frá - tri - bus, Ob - ser - vá - ta
Ver - bo car-nem éf - fi - cit: Fit - que san - guis
Ve - ne - ré - mur cér - nu - i: Et an - tí - quum
Laus et ju - bi - lá - ti - o, Sa - lus, ho - nor,

shed for sin - ners, Did a bro - ken world re - store;
love pro - ceed - ing Sow - er, seed and word de - scends;
still o - be - dient In its feast of love di - vine;
ver - y life - blood; Faith God's liv - ing Word must heed!
an - cient prom - ise Of God's earth - ly dwell - ing place!
to the Spir - it, Bond of love, in God-head one!

pre - ti - ó - si, Quem in mún - di pré - ti - um
con - ver - sá - tus, Spar - so vér - bi sé - mi - ne,
le - ge ple - ne Ci - bis in le - gá - li - bus,
Chri - sti me - rum, Et si sen - sus dé - fi - cit,
do - cu - mén - tum No - vo ce - dat rí - tu - i;
vir - tus quo - que Sit et be - ne - dí - cti - o:

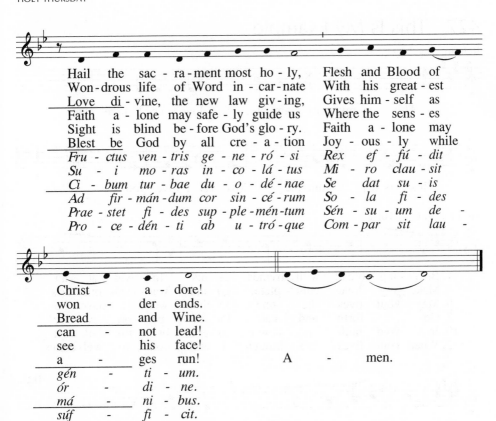

Hail	the	sac - ra-ment most ho - ly,	Flesh and Blood of
Won-drous	life	of Word in - car-nate	With his great - est
Love	di - vine,	the new law giv-ing,	Gives him - self as
Faith	a - lone	may safe - ly guide us	Where the sens - es
Sight	is	blind be - fore God's glo - ry.	Faith a - lone may
Blest	be	God by all cre - a - tion	Joy - ous - ly while
Fru - ctus	*ven - tris*	*ge - ne - ró - si*	*Rex ef - fú - dit*
Su - i	*mo - ras*	*in - co - lá - tus*	*Mi - ro clau - sit*
Ci - bum	*tur - bae*	*du - o - dé - nae*	*Se dat su - is*
Ad fir - mán - dum		*cor sin - cé - rum*	*So - la fi - des*
Prae - stet	*fi - des*	*sup - ple - mén - tum*	*Sén - su - um de -*
Pro - ce - dén - ti		*ab u - tró - que*	*Com - par sit lau -*

Christ	a - dore!		
won - der	ends.		
Bread and	Wine.		
can - not	lead!		
see his	face!		
a - ges	run!	A - men.	
gén - ti - um.			
ór - di - ne.			
má - ni - bus.			
súf - fi - cit.			
fé - ctu - i.			
dá - ti - o.		A - men.	

Text: *Pange lingua*, Thomas Aquinas, 1227-1274; tr. by James Quinn, SJ, b.1919, © 1969; Used by permission of Selah Publishing Co., Inc.
Tune: Mode III; acc. by Eugene Lapierre, © 1964, GIA Publications, Inc.

427　This Is My Example

Refrain

This　is my　ex - am-ple,　love　as I love　you.

This　is my ex - am-ple,　love　as I love you.

Verses 1, 4, 6, 7, 10, 12

1. Break - ing　bread　with　friends　as　his　life　was　at　an
4. Make　my　love　com - plete,　go　and　wash each　oth - er's
6. May　your　lives　be　one　in　this　work　I　have　be -
7. Go　forth　and　care　for　all　peo - ple　ev - 'ry -
10. In　your　faith　is　pow'r　to em - brace the　dark - est
12. When your　lives　are　through　I　will　come　to　wel-come

D.C.

end,　7　Je - sus　knelt　to　wash　their　feet.
feet;　what　I　have　done　so　you　must　do.
gun;　7　come and　fol - low　where　I　lead.
where.　7　Find　your strength　with - in　my　love.
hour;　go with - out　fear　to　heal　and　serve.
you.　7　We　will　be　for - ev - er　one.

Verses 2, 5, 8, 11

2. In　a　time　to　come　you will　know what　I　have
5. To　the　poor　and　weak,　be　the　com - fort　that they
8. Speak my　words　of　peace. To　the　cap - tives, bring　re -
11. This　my　life　I　give;　I must　die　that　you	may

D.C.

done;　7　let me wash　you,　let　me　serve.
seek;　let　my	ex - am - ple	be	your	guide.
lease.　7　Go	em-brace	them	in	my	name.
live.　All	this	I	do	for	love	of	you.

Verses 3 and 9

3. Si-mon Pe-ter said, "Wash my hands, my feet, my
9. If my love you bear to the peo-ple ev-'ry-

head!" Je-sus looked on him with love.
where all will know that you are mine.

Text: Francis Patrick O'Brien, b.1958
Tune: Francis Patrick O'Brien, b.1958
© 2001, GIA Publications, Inc.

Prepare a Room for Me 428

To be sung in alternating verses by cantor and congregation.

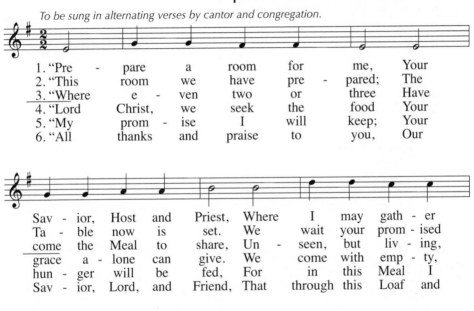

1. "Pre - pare a room for me, Your
2. "This room we have pre - pared; The
3. "Where e - ven two or three Have
4. "Lord Christ, we seek the food Your
5. "My prom - ise I will keep; Your
6. "All thanks and praise to you, Our

Sav - ior, Host and Priest, Where I may gath - er
Ta - ble now is set. We wait your prom - ised
come the Meal to share, Un - seen, but liv - ing,
grace a - lone can give. We come with emp - ty,
hun - ger will be fed, For in this Meal I
Sav - ior, Lord, and Friend, That through this Loaf and

you, my friends, To cel - e - brate the feast."
pres - ence, Lord, Where we once more are met."
lov - ing still, I sure - ly will be there!"
hun - g'ring hearts That we may eat and live."
of - fer you My - self, the liv - ing Bread!"
Cup you share Your love that has no end!"

Text: Herman G. Stuempfle, Jr., b.1923, © 2000, GIA Publications, Inc.
Tune: SOUTHWELL, SM; Damon's *Psalmes*, alt.

429 Jesu, Jesu

Refrain

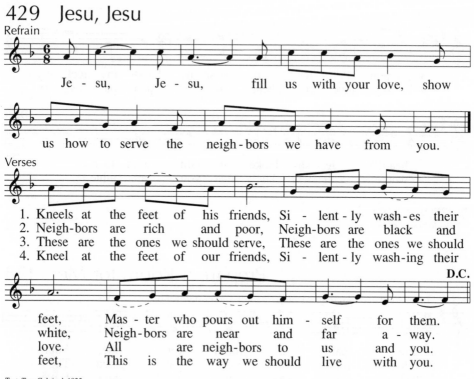

Je - su, Je - su, fill us with your love, show us how to serve the neigh - bors we have from you.

Verses

1. Kneels at the feet of his friends, Si - lent - ly wash - es their
2. Neigh - bors are rich and poor, Neigh - bors are black and
3. These are the ones we should serve, These are the ones we should
4. Kneel at the feet of our friends, Si - lent - ly wash - ing their

D.C.

feet, Mas - ter who pours out him - self for them.
white, Neigh - bors are near and far a - way.
love. All are neigh - bors to us and you.
feet, This is the way we should live with you.

Text: Tom Colvin, b.1925
Tune: CHEREPONI, Irregular; Ghana folk song; adapt. Tom Colvin, b.1925; acc. by Jane M. Marshall, b.1924
© 1969, and arr. © 1982, Hope Publishing Co.

430 Ubi Caritas

Refrain

U - bi ca - ri - tas et a - mor,
Live in char - i - ty and stead - fast love,

u - bi ca - ri - tas De - us i - bi est.
live in char - i - ty; God will dwell with you.

Text: 1 Corinthians 13:2-8; *Where charity and love are found, God is there;* Taizé Community, 1978
Tune: Jacques Berthier, 1923-1994
© 1979, Les Presses de Taizé, GIA Publications, Inc., agent

So You Must Do 431

Refrain

Je - sus, our teach - er and our Lord, stooped to

wash the feet of his dis - ci - ples, and he told them, "This is an ex -

Last time to Coda

am - ple; just as I have done, so you must do."

Verses

1. When Je - sus had gath - ered with those he loved, as a
2. With tow - el and ba - sin he washed their feet, so that
3. He asked, "Do you know what I have done? I give
4. "As I, your teach - er, have washed your feet, so must
5. "A new com - mand - ment I give to you, that you

D.C.

hum - ble ser - vant he knelt at their feet.
they might share in his pas - sion and death.
you a wit - ness of what you must do."
you be will - ing to serve in my name."
love each oth - er as I have loved you."

Coda

done, so you must do." And he told them, "This is an ex -

am - ple; just as I have done, so you must do."

Text: John 13:1-15, adapt. by Marty Haugen, b.1950
Tune: Marty Haugen, b.1950
© 1998, GIA Publications, Inc.

432 Song of the Lord's Command

Refrain

Do you know what I have done for you, you who call me your teach-er and your Lord? If I have washed your feet, so you must do as I have done for you.

Verses

1. What I am doing now you do not know,
   but after a time has gone by, you will understand.

2. Don't you understand what I must do?
   If you would be mine, then I must bend to wash your feet.

3. I have given to you an example;
   what I have done for you, you must do for one another.

4. There is no greater love than this:
   than to lay down your life for a friend.

5. Go, and live in my love.
   You will live in my love if you keep my commands.

6. Go, and love as I have shown you.
   Love one another as I have loved you.

7. You did not choose me, I chose you;
   I chose you to go forth and bear fruit that will endure.

Text: John 13:1-15, 15:12-14, 16; David Haas, b.1957
Tune: David Haas, b.1957
© 1997, GIA Publications, Inc.

Stay Here and Keep Watch 433

Ostinato Refrain

Stay here and keep watch with me. The hour has come. Stay here and keep watch with me. Watch and pray.

Text: from Matthew 26; Taizé Community
Tune: Jacques Berthier, 1923-1994
© 1984, Les Presses de Taizé, GIA Publications, Inc., agent

434 Song of the Lord's Supper

1. We re-mem-ber one who loved us well,
2. We re-mem-ber how he spoke of you,
3. On the night be-fore he suf-fered death,
4. As they sat at ta-ble he took bread,
5. Now we take these gifts of field and vine,

Shared our life, its joy and sor-row, Walked a-mong us as the
Taught us to be-lieve your prom-ise, Showed us all what you are
Je-sus gath-ered his dis-ci-ples, Knelt be-fore them as a
Blest it, broke it, gave it free-ly: "Take this bread and eat it,
Bless and share them in his mem-'ry: Bread of life and cup of

least of all, Gave him-self in-to our keep-ing.
real-ly like— Faith-ful, ten-der, God of peo-ple:
ser-vant might, Washed their feet and bid them wel-come:
all of you; Take and eat, this is my bod-y."
cov-e-nant, King-dom-feast in pledge and prom-ise.

He is light that dawns for blind-ed eyes,
Not a God to break the wound-ed heart,
"Do you know what I have done for you,
Then he took the cup and passed it round:
When we eat this bread and drink this cup

He is hope for the de-spair-ing; All on earth can find a
Not the thun-der of the might-y, But a God that wel-comes
I who am your Lord and Mas-ter? If I bend to you and
"Take and drink, this is my life-blood, Shed for you and for all
We pro-claim the death of Je-sus, Taste his pres-ence, liv-ing

place with him, Saint and sin-ner at his ta-ble.
sin-ners home, Meets the low-ly with com-pas-sion.
wash your feet, So must you for one an-oth-er."
hu-man-kind, Shed that sins may be for-giv-en."
in our midst, Look for him to come in glo-ry.

Text: Michael Joncas, b.1951
Tune: Michael Joncas, b.1951
© 1988, GIA Publications, Inc.

O Sacred Head Surrounded 435

1. O Sa - cred Head sur-round - ed By crown of pierc - ing
2. I see your strength and vig - or All fad - ing in the
3. In this, your bit - ter pas - sion, Good Shep-herd, think of

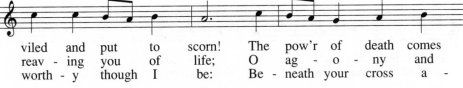

thorn! O bleed - ing Head, so wound - ed, Re -
strife, And death with cru - el rig - or, Be -
me With your most sweet com - pas - sion, Un -

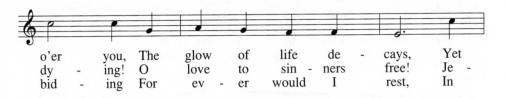

viled and put to scorn! The pow'r of death comes
reav - ing you of life; O ag - o - ny and
worth - y though I be: Be - neath your cross a -

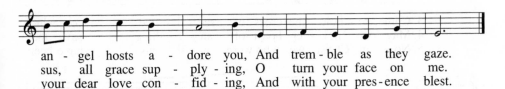

o'er you, The glow of life de - cays, Yet
dy - ing! O love to sin - ners free! Je -
bid - ing For ev - er would I rest, In

an - gel hosts a - dore you, And trem - ble as they gaze.
sus, all grace sup - ply - ing, O turn your face on me.
your dear love con - fid - ing, And with your pres - ence blest.

Text: *Salve caput cruentatum;* ascr. to Bernard of Clairvaux, 1091-1153; tr. by Henry Baker, 1821-1877
Tune: PASSION CHORALE, 7 6 7 6 D; Hans Leo Hassler, 1564-1612; harm. by J. S. Bach, 1685-1750

436 In the Cross of Christ

Refrain

In the cross of Christ, our glo - ry, Christ, our sto - ry,

Christ, our song, Christ, our song.

Verses 1, 2

1. Let your mind and heart be one with Christ who
2. He was pierced for our in - iq - ui - ties, and

emp - tied him - self, for us be - came a slave, ac -
crushed for our sins. He died to make us whole, and

D.C.

cept - ing death up - on the cross.
by his suf - f'ring we are healed.

Verses 3-5

3. Come, be - hold the cross of sac - ri - fice on which
4. May we nev - er boast of an - y - thing save the
5. Now in Christ, we who were a - li - ens have been

Je - sus died— the Sav - ior of us all— to
cross of Christ, by which we die to sin and
rec - on - ciled; as mem - bers of God's house, we

D.C.

save a lost and bro - ken world.
rise to life in Je - sus Christ.
live as God's own dwell - ing place.

Text: Philippians 2:5-8, Ephesians 2:12-13, Galatians 6:14; adapt. by Marty Haugen, b.1950
Tune: Marty Haugen, b.1950
© 1997, GIA Publications, Inc.

Behold the Wood 437

Refrain

Be - hold, be - hold the wood of the cross, on which is hung our sal - va - tion. O come, let us a - dore.

Verses

1. Un - less a grain of wheat shall fall up -
2. And when my hour of glo - ry comes as
3. For there can be no great - er love
4. My Fa - ther, if it be your plan, this
5. For sure - ly he has borne our tears, is
6. My bod - y now is torn with pain, my

on the ground and die, it shall re - main but a
all was meant to be, you shall see me
shown up - on this land than in the one who
cup might pass me by, yet let it hap - pen
wound - ed by our sin, and yet he o - pens
friends have left and gone. O lov - ing Fa - ther,

D.C.

sin - gle grain and not give life.
lift - ed up up - on a tree.
came to die that we might live.
as you will if I must die.
not his mouth that we might live.
take my life in - to your hands.

Text: John 12; Dan Schutte, b.1947
Tune: Dan Schutte, b.1947
© 1976, Daniel L. Schutte and OCP Publications

438 Were You There

1. Were you there when they cru - ci - fied my Lord?
2. Were you there when they nailed him to the tree?
3. Were you there when they pierced him in the side?
4. Were you there when the sun re - fused to shine?
5. Were you there when they laid him in the tomb?
6. Were you there when they rolled the stone a - way?

Were you there when they cru - ci - fied my Lord?
Were you there when they nailed him to the tree?
Were you there when they pierced him in the side?
Were you there when the sun re - fused to shine?
Were you there when they laid him in the tomb?
Were you there when they rolled the stone a - way?

Oh! Some-times it caus - es me to

trem - ble, trem - ble, trem - ble, Were you

there when they cru - ci - fied my Lord?
there when they nailed him to the tree?
there when they pierced him in the side?
there when the sun re - fused to shine?
there when they laid him in the tomb?
there when they rolled the stone a - way?

Text: African-American spiritual
Tune: WERE YOU THERE, 10 10 with refrain; African-American spiritual; harm. by Robert J. Batastini, b.1942, © 1987, GIA Publications, Inc.

Christ the Lord Is Risen Today 439

1. Christ the Lord is ris'n to - day, Al - le -
2. Lives a - gain our glo - rious King; Al - le -
3. Love's re - deem - ing work is done, Al - le -
4. Soar we now where Christ has led, Al - le -

lu - ia! All on earth with an - gels say,
lu - ia! Where, O death, is now your sting?
lu - ia! Fought the fight, the bat - tle won.
lu - ia! Fol - l'wing our ex - alt - ed head;

Al - le - lu - ia! Raise your joys and
Al - le - lu - ia! Once he died our
Al - le - lu - ia! Death in vain for -
Al - le - lu - ia! Made like him, like

tri - umphs high, Al - le - lu - ia!
souls to save, Al - le - lu - ia!
bids him rise; Al - le - lu - ia!
him we rise, Al - le - lu - ia!

Sing, O heav'ns, and earth re - ply,
Where your vic - to - ry, O grave?
Christ has o - pened par - a - dise.
Ours the cross, the grave, the skies.

Al - le - lu - ia!

Text: Charles Wesley, 1707-1788
Tune: LLANFAIR, 77 77 with alleluias; Robert Williams, 1781-1821

440 Alleluia! Alleluia! Let the Holy Anthem Rise

1. Al - le - lu - ia! Al - le - lu - ia! Let the
2. Al - le - lu - ia! Al - le - lu - ia! He en -
3. Al - le - lu - ia! Al - le - lu - ia! Like the
4. Al - le - lu - ia! Al - le - lu - ia! He has
5. Al - le - lu - ia! Al - le - lu - ia! Bless - ed

ho - ly an - them rise, And the choirs of heav-en
dured the knot - ted whips, And the jeer - ing of the
sun from out the wave He has ris - en up in
burst our pris - on bars; He has lift - ed up the
Je - sus, make us rise From the life of this cor -

chant it In the tem - ple of the skies; Let the
rab - ble, And the scorn of mock-ing lips, And the
tri - umph From the dark - ness of the grave. He's the
por - tals Of our home be - yond the stars; He has
rup - tion To the life that nev - er dies. May we

moun - tains skip with glad - ness And the
ter - rors of the gib - bet Up - on
splen - dor of the na - tions; He's the
won for us our free - dom— 'Neath his
share with you your glo - ry When the

joy - ful val - leys ring With ho - san - nas in the
which he would be slain, But his death was on - ly
lamp of end - less day; He's the ver - y Lord of
feet our foes are trod; He has pur - chased back our
days of time are past, And the dead shall be a -

high - est   To   our   Sav   -   ior   and   our   King!
slum - ber;   He   is   ris   -   en   up   a - gain!
glo - ry   Who is   ris   -   en   up   to - day!
birth - right   To   the   king   -   dom   of   our   God!
wak - ened   By   the   trum   -   pet's   might - y   blast!

Text: Edward Caswall, 1814-1878
Tune: HOLY ANTHEM, 8 7 8 7 D; traditional melody; harm. by Jerry R. Brubaker, b.1946, © 1975, Romda Ltd.

Earth, Earth, Awake!   441

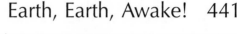

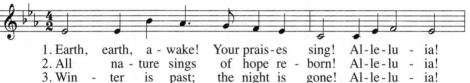

1. Earth,   earth,   a - wake!   Your prais-es   sing!   Al-le-lu - ia!
2. All   na - ture sings   of hope re - born!   Al-le-lu - ia!
3. Win - ter   is   past;   the night is   gone!   Al-le-lu - ia!
4. Praise   we   the   Fa - ther, Spir-it,   Son!   Al-le-lu - ia!

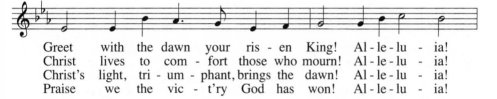

Greet   with   the dawn   your ris - en   King!   Al-le-lu - ia!
Christ   lives   to com - fort those who mourn!   Al-le-lu - ia!
Christ's   light,   tri - um - phant, brings the dawn!   Al-le-lu - ia!
Praise   we   the   vic - t'ry God has   won!   Al-le-lu - ia!

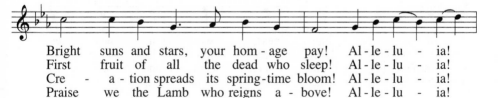

Bright   suns and stars,   your hom - age   pay!   Al-le-lu - ia!
First   fruit of all   the dead who sleep!   Al-le-lu - ia!
Cre - a - tion spreads its spring-time bloom!   Al-le-lu - ia!
Praise   we   the Lamb   who reigns a - bove!   Al-le-lu - ia!

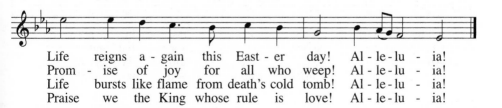

Life   reigns a - gain   this East - er   day!   Al-le-lu - ia!
Prom - ise   of joy   for   all who weep!   Al-le-lu - ia!
Life   bursts like flame from death's cold tomb!   Al-le-lu - ia!
Praise   we   the King whose rule   is   love!   Al-le-lu - ia!

Text: Herman G. Stuempfle, Jr., b.1923
Tune: STUEMPFLE, LM with alleluias; Sally Ann Morris, b.1952
© 1996, GIA Publications, Inc.

442 Sing with All the Saints in Glory

1. Sing with all the saints in glo - ry,
Sing the res - ur -
rec - tion song!
Death and sor - row, earth's dark sto - ry,
To the for - mer days be - long.
All a - round the clouds are break - ing,
Soon the storms of time shall cease;
In God's like - ness, we a - wak - en,
Know - ing ev - er - last - ing peace.

2. O what glo - ry, far ex - ceed - ing
All that eye has yet per - ceived!
Ho - liest hearts for a - ges plead - ing,
Nev - er that full joy con - ceived.
God has prom - ised, Christ pre - pares it,
There on high our wel - come waits;
Ev - 'ry hum - ble spir - it shares it,
Christ has passed the e - ter - nal gates.

3. Life e - ter - nal! heav'n re - joic - es:
Je - sus lives who once was dead;
Shout with joy, O death - less voic - es!
Child of God, lift up your head!
Pa - tri - archs from dis - tant a - ges,
Saints all long - ing for their heav'n,
Proph - ets, psalm - ists, seers, and sag - es,
All a - wait the glo - ry giv'n.

4. Life e - ter - nal! O what won - ders
Crowd on faith; what joy un - known,
When, a - midst earth's clos - ing thun - ders,
Saints shall stand be - fore the throne!
O to en - ter that bright por - tal,
See that glow - ing fir - ma - ment,
Know, with you, O God im - mor - tal,
Je - sus Christ whom you have sent!

Text: 1 Corinthians 15:20; William J. Irons, 1812-1883, alt.
Tune: HYMN TO JOY, 8 7 8 7 D; arr. from Ludwig van Beethoven, 1770-1827, by Edward Hodges, 1796-1867

Resucitó 443

Refrain

Re - su - ci - tó, re - su - ci - tó, re - su - ci -
A - le - lu - ya, a - le - lu - ya, a - le - lu -

To verses | *Final ending*

tó, a - le - lu - ya. A - le - lu - ya.
ya, re - su - ci - tó.

Verses

1. La muer - te ¿dón - de_es - tá la
2. Gra - cias se - an da - das al
3. A - le - grí - a, a - le - grí - a_her -
4. Si con Él mo - ri - mos, y con Él vi -
1. And death now, van - ished is the
2. The king - dom, praise to God, the
3. Our glad - ness, bliss - ful in our
4. With him then, die and live with

muer - te? ¿Dón - de_es - tá mi
Pa - dre que nos pa - só_a su
ma - nos, que si hoy nos que -
vi - mos, y con Él can -
fear now, ban - ished are my
king - dom! Raised up to the
glad - ness, this will be our
him then, rise and sing our

D.C.

muer - te? ¿Dón - de su vic - to - ria?
rei - no dón - de se vi - ve de_a - mor.
re - mos es que re - su - ci - tó.
ta - mos. y ¡A - le - lu - ya!
tears now, death has passed a - way.
king - dom, we shall live in love.
glad - ness, that he is a - live.
hymn then, sing al - le - lu - ia.

Text: Kiko Argüello, © 1972, Ediciones Musical PAX, U.S. agent: OCP Publications; trans. © 1988, OCP Publications
Tune: Kiko Argüello, © 1972, Ediciones Musical PAX, U.S. agent: OCP Publications; acc. by Diana Kodner

444 Sequence for Easter

1. Chris-tians, praise the pas-chal vic-tim! Of-fer thank-ful sac-ri-fice!
1. *Ví - cti - mae Pa-schá-li lau-des im-mó-lent Chri-sti - á - ni.*

2. Christ the Lamb has saved the sheep, Christ the just one paid the
3. Death and life fought bit-ter-ly For this won-drous vic-to-
2. *A - gnus ré - de - mit ó - ves: Chri-stus ín - no-cens Pá-*
3. *Mors et vi - ta du-él - lo con - fli - xé - re mi-rán-*

price, Re-con-cil-ing sin-ners to the Fa-ther.
ry; The Lord of life who died reigns glo-ri-fied!
tri re-con-ci - li - á - vit pec-ca-tó-res.
do: dux vi - tae mór-tu-us re-gnat vi-vus.

4. O Mar-y, come and say what you saw at break of day.
6. Bright an-gels tes-ti-fied, Shroud and grave clothes side by side!
4. *Dic no-bis Ma-rí-a, quid vi-dí-sti in vi-a?*
6. *An - gé-li-cos te-stes, su-dá-ri-um, et ve-stes.*

5. "The emp-ty tomb of my liv-ing Lord! I saw Christ Je-sus ri-
7. "Yes, Christ my hope rose glo-ri-ous-ly. He goes be-fore you in-
5. *Se - púl-crum Chri-sti vi-vén-tis, et gló-ri-am vi-di*
7. *Sur - ré-xit Chri-stus spes me - a: prae-cé-det su-os in*

sen and a - dored! 8. Share the good news, sing joy-ful-ly
to Ga-li - lee." 8. *Scí - mus Chrí-stum sur-re-xís-se*
re - sur-gén - tis.
Ga-li - láe - am.

His death is vic-to-ry! Lord Je-sus, Vic-tor King, Show us mer-cy.
a mór-tu-is ve-re: tu no-bis vi-ctor Rex, mi-se-ré - re.

Text: Sequence for Easter, ascr. to Wipo of Burgundy, d.1048; tr. by Peter J. Scagnelli, b.1949, © 1983
Tune: Mode I; acc. by Richard Proulx, b.1937, © 1975, GIA Publications, Inc.

On the Journey to Emmaus   445

1. On the jour - ney to Em - ma - us with our
2. And our hearts burned with - in us as we
3. And that eve - ning at the ta - ble as he
4. On our jour - ney to Em - ma - us, in our

hearts cold as stone— The One who would
talked on the way, How all that was
blessed and broke bread, We saw it was
stor - ies and feast, With Je - sus we

save us had left us a - lone. Then a
prom - ised was ours on that day. So we
Je - sus a - ris'n from the dead; Though he
claim that the great - est is least: And his

stran - ger walks with us and, to our sur - prise, He
begged him, "Stay with us and grant us your word." We
van - ished be - fore us we knew he was near— The
words burn with - in us— let none be ig - nored— Who

o - pens our stor - ies and he o - pens our eyes.
wel - comed the stran - ger and we wel - comed the Lord.
life in our dy - ing and the hope in our fear.
wel - comes the stran - ger shall wel - come the Lord.

Text: Luke 24:13-35; Marty Haugen. b.1950
Tune: COLUMCILLE, Irregular; Gaelic, arr. by Marty Haugen, b.1950
© 1995, GIA Publications, Inc.

446 O Sons and Daughters

Al - le - lu - ia, al - le - lu - ia, al - le - lu - ia.

1. O sons and daugh - ters, let us sing!
2. That East - er morn, at break of day,
3. An an - gel clad in white they see,
4. That night the a - pos - tles met in fear;
5. When Thom - as, first the tid - ings heard,
6. "My wound - ed side, O Thom - as, see;

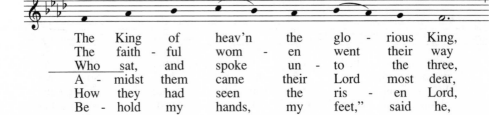

The King of heav'n the glo - rious King,
The faith - ful wom - en went their way
Who sat, and spoke un - to the three,
A - midst them came their Lord most dear,
How they had seen the ris - en Lord,
Be - hold my hands, my feet," said he,

D.C.

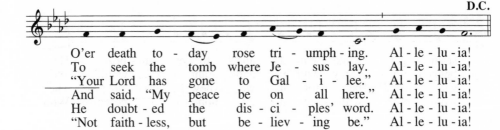

O'er death to - day rose tri - umph - ing. Al - le - lu - ia!
To seek the tomb where Je - sus lay. Al - le - lu - ia!
"Your Lord has gone to Gal - i - lee." Al - le - lu - ia!
And said, "My peace be on all here." Al - le - lu - ia!
He doubt - ed the dis - ci - ples' word. Al - le - lu - ia!
"Not faith - less, but be - liev - ing be." Al - le - lu - ia!

7. No longer Thomas then denied,
   He saw the feet, the hands, the side;
   "You are my Lord and God," he cried. Alleluia!

8. How blest are they who have not seen,
   And yet whose faith has constant been,
   For they eternal life shall win. Alleluia!

9. On this most holy day of days,
   To God your hearts and voices raise,
   In laud, and jubilee and praise. Alleluia!

Text: *O filii et filiae;* Jean Tisserand, d.1494; tr. by John M. Neale, 1818-1866, alt.
Tune: O FILII ET FILIAE, 888 with alleluias; Mode II; acc. by Richard Proulx, b.1937, © 1975, GIA Publications, Inc.

Easter Alleluia 447

Refrain

Al-le-lu-ia, al - le - lu-ia, al-le-lu - ia!

Verses

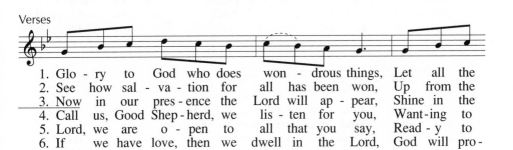

1. Glo - ry to God who does won - drous things, Let all the
2. See how sal - va - tion for all has been won, Up from the
3. Now in our pres - ence the Lord will ap - pear, Shine in the
4. Call us, Good Shep - herd, we lis - ten for you, Want-ing to
5. Lord, we are o - pen to all that you say, Read - y to
6. If we have love, then we dwell in the Lord, God will pro -

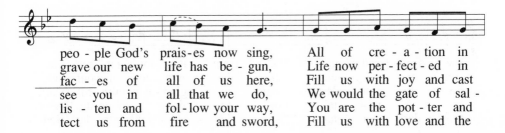

peo - ple God's prais-es now sing, All of cre - a - tion in
grave our new life has be - gun, Life now per - fect - ed in
fac - es of all of us here, Fill us with joy and cast
see you in all that we do, We would the gate of sal -
lis - ten and fol-low your way, You are the pot - ter and
tect us from fire and sword, Fill us with love and the

D.C.

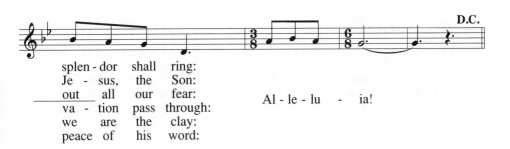

splen - dor shall ring:
Je - sus, the Son:
out all our fear: Al - le - lu - ia!
va - tion pass through:
we are the clay:
peace of his word:

Text: Marty Haugen, b.1950
Tune: O FILII ET FILIAE; 10 10 10 with alleluias; adapt. by Marty Haugen, b.1950
© 1986, GIA Publications, Inc.

448 Come, Ye Faithful, Raise the Strain

1. Come, ye faith-ful raise the strain Of tri-um-phant glad-ness; God has brought his Is-ra-el In-to joy from sad-ness; Loosed from Phar-aoh's bit-ter yoke Ja-cob's sons and daugh-ters; Led them with un-moist-ened foot Through the Red Sea wa-ters.

2. 'Tis the spring of souls to-day; Christ has burst the pris-on, And from three days' sleep in death As a sun has ris-en; All the win-ter of our sins, Long and dark is fly-ing From his light, to whom we give Laud and praise un-dy-ing.

3. Now the queen of sea-sons, bright With the day of splen-dor, With the roy-al feast of feasts, Comes its joy to ren-der; Comes to glad-den faith-ful hearts Who with true af-fec-tion Wel-come in un-wea-ried strains Je-sus' res-ur-rec-tion.

4. Nei-ther could the gates of death, Nor the tomb's dark por-tal, Nor the watch-ers, nor the seal Hold him as a mor-tal; Who, tri-um-phant, burst the bars Of the tomb's dark por-tal; For to-day a-mong the Twelve Christ ap-peared be-stow-ing Last-ing peace which ev-er-more Pass-es hu-man know-ing.

5. "Al-le-lu-ia!" now we cry To our King im-mor-tal, Who, tri-um-phant, burst the bars Of the tomb's dark por-tal; "Al-le-lu-ia!" with the Son, God the Fa-ther prais-ing; "Al-le-lu-ia!" yet a-gain To the Spir-it rais-ing.

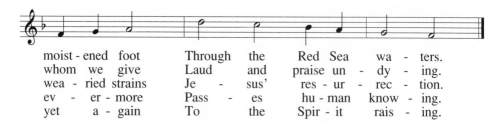

Text: Exodus 15; Ασωμεν παντεζ λαοι; John of Damascus, c.675-c.749; tr. by John M. Neale, 1818-1886, alt.
Tune: GAUDEAMUS PARITER, 7 6 7 6 D; Johann Horn, c.1495-1547

Christ Is Risen! Shout Hosanna! 449

1. Christ is ris - en! Shout Ho - san - na! Cel - e - brate this
2. Christ is ris - en! Raise your spir - its From the cav - erns
3. Christ is ris - en! Earth and heav - en Nev - er - more shall

day of days! Christ is ris - en! Hush in won - der:
of des - pair. Walk with glad - ness in the morn - ing.
be the same. Break the bread of new cre - a - tion

All cre - a - tion is a - mazed. In the des - ert
See what love can do and dare. Drink the wine of
Where the world is still in pain. Tell its grim, de -

all sur - round - ing, See, a spread - ing tree has grown.
res - ur - rec - tion, Not a ser - vant, but a friend.
mon - ic cho - rus: "Christ is ris - en! Get you gone!"

Heal - ing leaves of grace a - bound - ing
Je - sus is our strong com - pan - ion.
God the First and Last is with us.

Bring a taste of love un - known.
Joy and peace shall nev - er end.
Sing Ho - san - na ev - 'ry one!

Text: Brian Wren, b.1936, © 1986, Hope Publishing Co.
Tune: HOSANNA, 8 7 8 7 D; David Haas, b.1957, © 1991, GIA Publications, Inc.

450 All Things New

Refrain

Sing a new song! Re - joice! The dawn is break-ing,

the earth is wak-ing, its dreams come true. And do you

hear the voice, dark-ness sur - pris - ing, sing in its

ris - ing: "See, I am mak - ing all things new!"

Verses

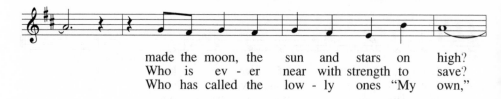

1. Whom shall we live for? Whose might - y hand
2. Who found us wan - der-ers, and made us in - to one?
3. Who is known to ev - 'ry heart and called by man - y names?

made the moon, the sun and stars on high?
Who is ev - er near with strength to save?
Who has called the low - ly ones "My own,"

Who made a way for us through
Whose love a - dopt - ed us as
Breathes a dream of jus - tice in - to

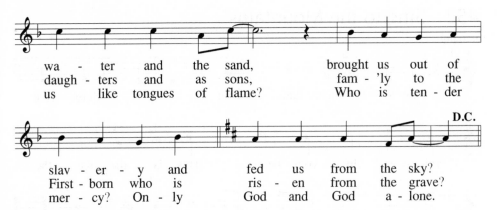

wa - ter and the sand, brought us out of
daugh - ters and as sons, fam - 'ly to the
us like tongues of flame? Who is ten - der

D.C.

slav - er - y and fed us from the sky?
First - born who is ris - en from the grave?
mer - cy? On - ly God and God a - lone.

Text: Rory Cooney, b. 1952
Tune: Rory Cooney, b. 1952
© 1993, GIA Publications, Inc.

Goodness Is Stronger Than Evil 451

Good-ness is strong-er than e - vil; love is strong-er than

hate; light is strong-er than dark - ness;

life is strong-er than death. Vic-'try is ours, vic-t'ry is

ours through him who loved us. Vic-'try is

ours, vic-t'ry is ours through him who loved us.

Text: Desmond Tutu, b.1931, ©; adapt. by John L. Bell, b.1949
Tune: GOODNESS IS STRONGER, Irregular; John L. Bell, b.1949, © 1996, Iona Community, GIA Publications, Inc., agent

452 Sing to the Mountains

Refrain

Sing to the moun-tains, sing to the sea. Raise your voic-es, lift your hearts. This is the day the Lord has made. Let all the earth re-joice.

Verse 1

1. I will give thanks to you, my Lord. You have an-swered my plea. You have saved my soul from death. You are my strength and my song.

D.C.

Verse 2

2. Ho-ly, ho-ly, ho-ly Lord, heav-en and earth are full of your glo - ry.

D.C.

Verse 3

3. This is the day that the Lord has made. Let us be glad and re-joice. Death has lost and

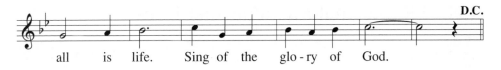

D.C.

all is life. Sing of the glo - ry of God.

Text: Psalm 118; Bob Dufford, SJ, b.1943
Tune: Bob Dufford, SJ, b.1943; acc. by Randall DeBruyn
© 1975, Robert J. Dufford, SJ, and OCP Publications

This Is a Day of New Beginnings 453

Refrain

Christ is a-live, and goes be-fore us to show and share what

love can do. This is a day of new be-gin-nings; our God is mak-ing

all things new, our God is mak - ing all things new.

Verses

1. This is a day of new be-gin-nings, time to re-mem - ber,
2. For by the life and death of Je - sus, love's might-y Spir - it,
3. Then let us, with the Spir - it's dar - ing, step from the past, and

and move on, time to be-lieve what love is bring-ing,
now as then, can make for us a world of dif - f'rence
leave be - hind our dis - a - point - ment, guilt, and griev-ing,

D.C.

lay - ing to rest the pain that's gone.
as faith and hope are born a - gain.
seek-ing new paths, and sure to find.

Text: Brian Wren, b.1936, © 1975, 1995, Hope Publishing Co.
Tune: Lori True, b.1961, © 2003, GIA Publications, Inc.

454   I Know That My Redeemer Lives

1. I know that my Re - deem - er lives;
2. He lives, to bless me with his love;
3. He lives, and grants me dai - ly breath;
4. He lives, all glo - ry to his name;

What joy the blest as - sur - ance gives!
He lives, to plead for me a - bove;
He lives, and I shall con - quer death;
He lives, my Sav - ior still the same;

He lives, he lives, who once was dead;
He lives, my hun - gry soul to feed;
He lives, my man - sion to pre - pare;
What joy the blest as - sur - ance gives;

He lives, my ev - er - last - ing Head!
He lives, to help in time of need.
He lives, to bring me safe - ly there.
I know that my Re - deem - er lives!

Text: Samuel Medley, 1738-1799
Tune: DUKE STREET, LM; John Hatton, c.1710-1793

455   Surrexit Christus

Ostinato Refrain

(hum)   Sur - re - xit Chri - stus, al - le - lu - ia!

(hum) Can - ta - te Do - mi - no, al - le - lu - ia!

Text: *Christ is risen, sing to the Lord;* Daniel 3; Taizé Community, 1984
Tune: Jacques Berthier, 1923-1994
© 1984, Les Presses de Taizé, GIA Publications, Inc., agent

Now the Green Blade Rises   456

1. Now the green blade ris - es from the bur - ied grain,
2. In the grave they laid him, love by ha - tred slain,
3. Forth he came at East - er, like the ris - en grain,
4. When our hearts are win - try, griev - ing, or in pain,

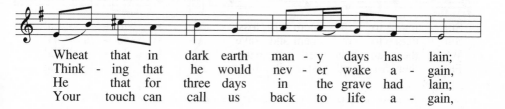

Wheat that in dark earth man - y days has lain;
Think - ing that he would nev - er wake a - gain,
He that for three days in the grave had lain;
Your touch can call us back to life a - gain,

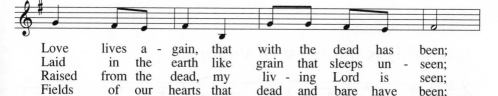

Love lives a - gain, that with the dead has been;
Laid in the earth like grain that sleeps un - seen;
Raised from the dead, my liv - ing Lord is seen;
Fields of our hearts that dead and bare have been;

Love is come a - gain like wheat a - ris - ing green.

Text: John M.C. Crum, 1872-1958, *Oxford Book of Carols,* © Oxford University Press
Tune: NOEL NOUVELET, 11 10 10 11; French Carol; acc. by Marty Haugen, b.1950, © 1987, GIA Publications, Inc.

457 Jesus Christ Is Risen Today

1. Je - sus Christ is ris'n to - day, Al - le - lu - ia!
2. Hymns of praise then let us sing, Al - le - lu - ia!
3. But the pains which he en - dured, Al - le - lu - ia!
4. Sing we to our God a - bove, Al - le - lu - ia!

Our tri - um - phant ho - ly day, Al - le - lu - ia!
Un - to Christ, our heav'n - ly King, Al - le - lu - ia!
Our sal - va - tion have pro - cured; Al - le - lu - ia!
Praise e - ter - nal as his love; Al - le - lu - ia!

Who did once up - on the cross, Al - le - lu - ia!
Who en - dured the cross and grave, Al - le - lu - ia!
Now a - bove the sky he's King, Al - le - lu - ia!
Praise him, now his might con - fess, Al - le - lu - ia!

Suf - fer to re - deem our loss. Al - le - lu - ia!
Sin - ners to re - deem and save. Al - le - lu - ia!
Where the an - gels ev - er sing. Al - le - lu - ia!
Fa - ther, Son, and Spir - it blest. Al - le - lu - ia!

Text: St. 1, *Surrexit Christus hodie,* Latin, 14th C.; para. in *Lyra Davidica,* 1708, alt.; st. 2, 3, *The Compleat Psalmodist,* c.1750, alt.; st. 4, Charles
Wesley, 1707-1788
Tune: EASTER HYMN, 77 77 with alleluias; *Lyra Davidica,* 1708

458 This Is the Feast of Victory

This is the feast of vic - to - ry for our God. Al - le -

To verses | Last time

lu - ia, al - le - lu - ia, al - le - lu - ia. lu - ia.

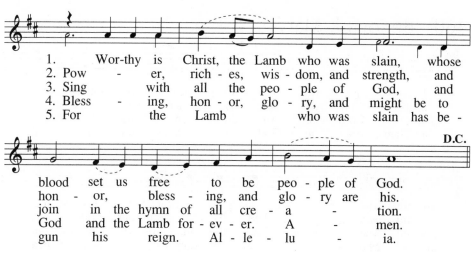

1. Wor-thy is Christ, the Lamb who was slain, whose
2. Pow - er, rich - es, wis - dom, and strength, and
3. Sing with all the peo - ple of God, and
4. Bless - ing, hon - or, glo - ry, and might be to
5. For the Lamb who was slain has be -

blood set us free to be peo - ple of God.
hon - or, bless - ing, and glo - ry are his.
join in the hymn of all cre - a - tion.
God and the Lamb for - ev - er. A - men.
gun his reign. Al - le - lu - ia.

Text: Based on Revelation 5, © 1978, *Lutheran Book of Worship*
Tune: FESTIVAL CANTICLE, Irregular; Richard Hillert, b.1923, © 1975, 1988, Richard Hillert

The Strife Is O'er 459

Al - le - lu - ia! Al - le - lu - ia! Al - le - lu - ia!

1. The strife is o'er, the bat - tle done; Now is the
2. Death's might - iest pow'rs have done their worst, And Je - sus
3. He closed the yawn - ing gates of hell; The bars from
4. On the third morn he rose a - gain, Glo - rious in

Vic - tor's tri - umph won; Now be the song of
has his foes dis - persed; Let shouts of praise and
heav'n's high por - tals fell; Let hymns of praise his
maj - es - ty to reign; O let us swell the

praise be - gun: Al - le - lu - ia!
joy out - burst: Al - le - lu - ia!
tri - umph tell: Al - le - lu - ia!
joy - ful strain: Al - le - lu - ia!

Text: *Finita iam sunt praelia;* Latin, 12th C.; tr. by Francis Pott, 1832-1909, alt.
Tune: VICTORY, 888 with alleluias; Giovanni da Palestrina, 1525-1594; adapt. by William H. Monk, 1823-1889

460 Be Joyful, Mary

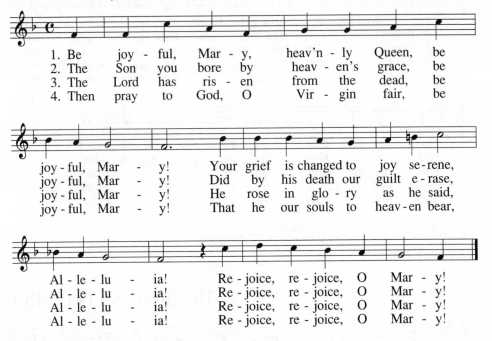

1. Be joy - ful, Mar - y, heav'n - ly Queen, be
2. The Son you bore by heav - en's grace, be
3. The Lord has ris - en from the dead, be
4. Then pray to God, O Vir - gin fair, be

joy - ful, Mar - y! Your grief is changed to joy se - rene,
joy - ful, Mar - y! Did by his death our guilt e - rase,
joy - ful, Mar - y! He rose in glo - ry as he said,
joy - ful, Mar - y! That he our souls to heav - en bear,

Al - le - lu - ia! Re - joice, re - joice, O Mar - y!
Al - le - lu - ia! Re - joice, re - joice, O Mar - y!
Al - le - lu - ia! Re - joice, re - joice, O Mar - y!
Al - le - lu - ia! Re - joice, re - joice, O Mar - y!

Text: *Regina caeli, jubila;* Latin, 17th C.; tr. anon. in *Psallite,* 1901
Tune: REGINA CAELI, 8 5 8 4 7; Leisentritt's *Gesangbuch,* 1584, alt.

461 That Easter Day with Joy Was Bright

1. That East - er day with joy was bright, The sun shone
2. His ris - en flesh with ra - diance glowed; His wound - ed
3. O Je - sus, King of gen - tle - ness, Who with your
4. O Lord of all, with us a - bide In this our
5. All praise, to you, O ris - en Lord, Now both by

out with fair - er light, When to their long - ing
hands and feet he showed; Those scars their sol - emn
grace our hearts pos - sess, That we may give you
joy - ful East - er - tide; From ev - 'ry weap - on
heaven and earth a - dored; To God the Fa - ther

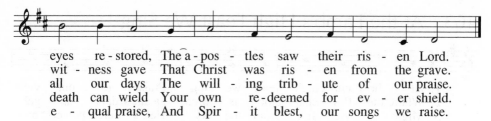

eyes re-stored, The a-pos-tles saw their ris-en Lord.
wit-ness gave That Christ was ris-en from the grave.
all our days The will-ing trib-ute of our praise.
death can wield Your own re-deemed for ev-er shield.
e-qual praise, And Spir-it blest, our songs we raise.

Text: *Claro paschali gaudio;* Latin 5th C.; tr. by John M. Neale, 1818-1866, alt.
Tune: PUER NOBIS, LM; adapt. by Michael Praetorius, 1571-1621

Alleluia No. 1   462

Refrain

Al-le-lu-ia, al-le-lu-ia, give thanks to the ris-en Lord.

Al-le-lu-ia, al-le-lu-ia, give praise to his Name.

Verses

1. Je-sus is Lord of all the earth.
2. Spread the good news o'er all the earth:
3. We have been cru-ci-fied with Christ.
4. God has pro-claimed his gra-cious gift:
5. Come, let us praise the liv-ing God,

D.C.

He is the King of cre-a-tion.
Je-sus has died and has ris-en.
Now we shall live for ev-er.
Life e-ter-nal for all who be-lieve.
Joy-ful-ly sing to our Sav-ior.

Text: Donald Fishel, b.1950, © 1973, Word of God Music
Tune: ALLELUIA NO. 1, 8 8 with refrain; Donald Fishel, b.1950, © 1973, Word of God Music; descant harm. by Betty Pulkingham, b.1929,
Charles Mallory, b.1953, and George Mims, b.1938, © 1979, Celebration

463 At the Lamb's High Feast We Sing

1. At the Lamb's high feast we sing Praise to our vic-
to - rious King. Who has washed us in the tide
Flow - ing from his pierc - ed side; Praise we him, whose
love di - vine Gives his sa - cred Blood for wine,
Gives his Bod - y for the feast,
Christ the vic - tim, Christ the priest.

2. Where the Pas - chal blood is poured, Death's dark an - gel
sheathes his sword; Is - rael's hosts tri - umph - ant go
Through the wave that drowns the foe. Praise we Christ, whose
blood was shed, Pas - chal vic - tim, Pas - chal bread;
With sin - cer - i - ty and love
Eat we man - na from a - bove.

3. Might - y vic - tim from the sky, Hell's fierce powers be -
neath you lie; You have con - quered in the fight,
You have brought us life and light: Now no more can
death ap - pall, Now no more the grave en - thrall;
You have o - pened par - a - dise,
And in you your saints shall rise.

4. East - er tri - umph, East - er joy, This a - lone can
sin de - stroy; From sin's power, Lord, set us free
New - born souls in you to be. Fa - ther, who the
crown shall give, Sav - ior, by whose death we live,
Spir - it, guide through all our days,
Three in One, your name we praise.

Text: *Ad regias agni dapes;* Latin, 4th C.; tr. by Robert Campbell, 1814-1868
Tune: SALZBURG, 77 77 D; Jakob Hintze, 1622-1702; harm. by J.S. Bach, 1685-1750

The Tomb Is Empty   464

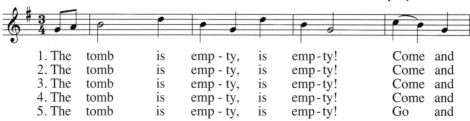

1. The tomb is emp - ty, is emp - ty! Come and
2. The tomb is emp - ty, is emp - ty! Come and
3. The tomb is emp - ty, is emp - ty! Come and
4. The tomb is emp - ty, is emp - ty! Come and
5. The tomb is emp - ty, is emp - ty! Go and

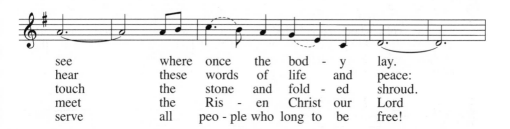

see where once the bod - y lay.
hear these words of life and peace:
touch the stone and fold - ed shroud.
meet the Ris - en Christ our Lord
serve all peo - ple who long to be free!

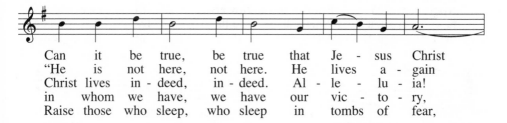

Can it be true, be true that Je - sus Christ
"He is not here, not here. He lives a - gain
Christ lives in - deed, in - deed. Al - le - lu - ia!
in whom we have, we have our vic - to - ry,
Raise those who sleep, who sleep in tombs of fear,

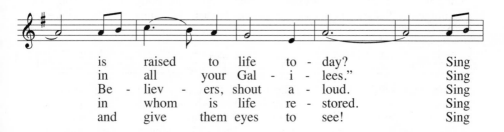

is raised to life to - day? Sing
in all your Gal - i - lees." Sing
Be - liev - ers, shout a - loud. Sing
in whom is life re - stored. Sing
and give them eyes to see! Sing

al - le - lu - ia! Sing al - le - lu - ia!

Text: Sts. 1-4, Sylvia G. Dunstan, 1955-1993, © 1991, GIA Publications, Inc.; St. 5, David Haas, b.1957, © 2003, GIA Publications, Inc.
Tune: David Haas, b.1957, © 2003, GIA Publications, Inc.

465 Christ Has Risen

1. Christ has ris - en while earth slum - bers, Christ has
2. Christ has ris - en for the peo - ple Whom he
3. Christ has ris - en to com - pan - ion For - mer
4. Christ has ris - en and for ev - er Lives to

ris - en where hope died, As he said and as he
died to love and save; Christ has ris - en for the
friends who fear the night, Sens - ing loss and lim - i -
chal - lenge and to change All whose lives are messed or

prom - ised, As we doubt - ed and de -
wom - en Bring - ing flowers to grace his
ta - tion Where their faith had once burned
man - gled, All who find re - lig - ion

nied. Let the moon em - brace the bless - ing; Let the
grave. Christ has ris - en for dis - ci - ples Hud - dled
bright. They be - moan what is no long - er, They ex -
strange. Christ is ris - en, Christ is pres - ent Mak - ing

sun sus - tain the cheer; Let the world con - firm the
in an up - stairs room. He whose word in - spired cre -
pect no hope - ful sign Till Christ ends their con - ver -
us what he has been— Ev - i - dence of trans - for -

ru - mor: Christ is ris - en, God is here!
a - tion Can't be si - lenced by the tomb.
sa - tion, Break - ing bread and shar - ing wine.
ma - tion In which God is known and seen.

Text: John L. Bell, b.1949
Tune: TRANSFORMATION, 8 7 8 7 D; John L. Bell, b.1949
© 1988, Iona Community, GIA Publications, Inc., agent

Lord, You Give the Great Commission 466

1. Lord, you give the great com - mis-sion: "Heal the
2. Lord, you call us to your serv - ice: "In my
3. Lord, you make the com - mon ho - ly: "This my
4. Lord, you show us love's true meas-ure: "Fa - ther,
5. Lord, you bless with words as - sur - ing: "I am

sick and preach the word." Lest the Church ne -
name bap - tize and teach." That the world may
bod - y, this my blood." Let us all, for
what they do, for - give." Yet we hoard as
with you to the end." Faith and hope and

glect its mis-sion, And the Gos - pel go un-heard,
trust your prom-ise, Life a - bun - dant meant for each,
earth's true glo - ry, Dai - ly lift life heav - en-ward,
pri - vate treas-ure All that you so free - ly give.
love re - stor-ing, May we serve as you in - tend,

Help us wit - ness to your pur-pose With re -
Give us all new fer - vor, draw us Clos - er
Ask - ing that the world a - round us Share your
May your care and mer - cy lead us To a
And, a - mid the cares that claim us, Hold in

newed in - teg - ri - ty;
in com - mun - i - ty;
chil - dren's lib - er - ty; With the Spir - it's gifts em -
just so - ci - e - ty;
mind e - ter - ni - ty;

power us For the work of min - is - try.

Text: Jeffery Rowthorn, b.1934, © 1978, Hope Publishing Co.
Tune: ABBOT'S LEIGH, 8 7 8 7 D; Cyril V. Taylor, 1907-1991, © 1942, 1970, Hope Publishing Co.

467 A Hymn of Glory Let Us Sing

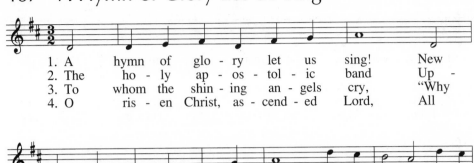

1. A hymn of glo - ry let us sing! New
2. The ho - ly ap - os - tol - ic band Up -
3. To whom the shin - ing an - gels cry, "Why
4. O ris - en Christ, as - cend - ed Lord, All

hymns through-out the world shall ring: Al - le - lu - ia! Al - leon the Mount of Ol - ives stand. Al - le - lu - ia! Al - le-
stand and gaze up - on the sky?" Al - le - lu - ia! Al - le-
praise to you let earth ac - cord: Al - le - lu - ia! Al - le-

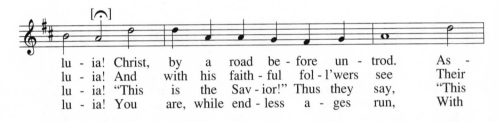

lu - ia! Christ, by a road be - fore un - trod. As -
lu - ia! And with his faith - ful fol - l'wers see Their
lu - ia! "This is the Sav - ior!" Thus they say, "This
lu - ia! You are, while end - less a - ges run, "With

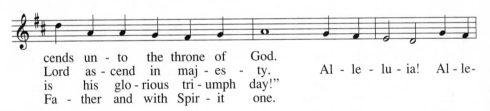

cends un - to the throne of God.
Lord as - cend in maj - es - ty. Al - le - lu - ia! Al - le-
is his glo - rious tri - umph day!"
Fa - ther and with Spir - it one.

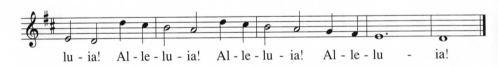

lu - ia! Al - le - lu - ia! Al - le - lu - ia! Al - le - lu - ia!

Text: *Hymnum canamus gloria*; Venerable Bede, 673-735; tr. *Lutheran Book of Worship*, © 1978
Tune: LASST UNS ERFREUEN, LM with alleluias; *Geistliche Kirchengasange*, Cologne, 1623; harm. by Ralph Vaughan Williams, 1872-1958,
© Oxford University Press

Hail the Day That Sees Him Rise 468

1. Hail the day that sees him rise, Al - le - lu - ia!
2. There for him high tri - umph waits; Al - le - lu - ia!
3. High - est heav'n its Lord re - ceives, Al - le - lu - ia!
4. See, he lifts his hands a - bove. Al - le - lu - ia!
5. Still for us he in - ter - cedes, Al - le - lu - ia!
6. There we shall with him re - main, Al - le - lu - ia!

To his throne a - bove the skies; Al - le - lu - ia!
Lift your heads, e - ter - nal gates; Al - le - lu - ia!
Yet he loves the earth he leaves: Al - le - lu - ia!
See, he shows the prints of love. Al - le - lu - ia!
His pre - vail - ing death he pleads, Al - le - lu - ia!
Part - ners of his end - less reign; Al - le - lu - ia!

Christ, a - while to mor - tals given, Al - le - lu - ia!
He has con - quered death and sin; Al - le - lu - ia!
Though re - turn - ing to his throne, Al - le - lu - ia!
Hark, his gra - cious lips be - stow, Al - le - lu - ia!
Near him - self pre - pares our place, Al - le - lu - ia!
There his face un - cloud - ed see, Al - le - lu - ia!

Re - as - cends his na - tive heav'n. Al - le - lu - ia!
Take the King of glo - ry in. Al - le - lu - ia!
Still he calls the world his own. Al - le - lu - ia!
Bless - ings on his church be - low. Al - le - lu - ia!
He the first fruits of our race. Al - le - lu - ia!
Live with him e - ter - nal - ly. Al - le - lu - ia!

Text: Charles Wesley, 1707-1788, alt.
Tune: LLANFAIR, 77 77 with alleluias; Robert Williams, 1781-1821

469 Go to the World!

1. Go to the world! Go in - to all the earth. Go
2. Go to the world! Go in - to ev - 'ry place.
3. Go to the world! Go strug-gle, bless and pray; the
4. Go to the world! Go as the ones I send, for

preach the cross where Christ re - news life's worth, bap -
Go live the Word of God's re - deem - ing grace.
nights of tears give way to joy - ous day, As
I am with you 'til the age shall end, When

tiz - ing as the sign of our re - birth.
Go seek God's pres - ence in each time and space.
ser - vant Church, you fol - low Christ's own way. Al -
all the hosts of glo - ry cry "A - men!"

le - lu - ia. Al - le - lu - ia.

Text: Sylvia G. Dunstan, 1955-1993, © 1991, GIA Publications, Inc.
Tune: SINE NOMINE, 10 10 10 with alleluias; Ralph Vaughan Williams, 1872-1958, © Oxford University Press

470 Sequence for Pentecost

1. Ho - ly Spir - it, Lord Di - vine, Come, from heights of
2. Come, O Fa - ther of the poor, Come, whose treas - ured

heav'n and shine, Come with bless - ed ra - diance bright!
gifts en - dure, Come, our heart's un - fail - ing light!

3. Of con - so - lers, wis - est, best, And our soul's most
4. In our la - bor rest most sweet, Pleas - ant cool - ness

wel - come guest, Sweet re - fresh - ment sweet re - pose.
in the heat, Con - so - la - tion in our woes.

5. Light most bless - ed, shine with grace In our heart's most
6. Left with - out your pres - ence here, Life it - self would

se - cret place, Fill your faith - ful through and through.
dis - ap - pear, Noth - ing thrives a - part from you!

7. Cleanse our soil - ed hearts of sin, Ar - id souls re -
8. Bend the stub - born heart and will, Melt the fro - zen,

fresh with - in, Wound - ed lives to health re - store.
warm the chill, Guide the way - ward home once more!

9. On the faith - ful who are true And pro -
10. Give us vir - tue's sure re - ward, Give us

fess their faith in you, In your sev'n - fold gift de - scend!
your sal - va - tion, Lord, Give us joys that nev - er end!

Text: Sequence for Pentecost, 13th. C.; tr. by Peter J. Scagnelli; b.1949, © 1983
Tune: Mode I; acc. by Adriaan Engels, 1906-2003, © Interkerkelijke Stichting voor het Kerklied Den Haag

471 Come Down, O Love Divine

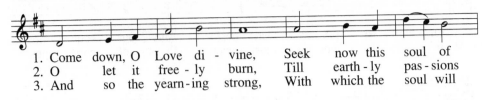

1. Come down, O Love di - vine, Seek now this soul of
2. O let it free - ly burn, Till earth - ly pas - sions
3. And so the yearn - ing strong, With which the soul will

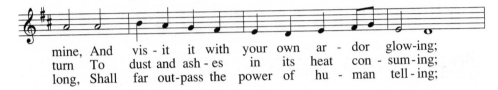

mine, And vis - it it with your own ar - dor glow-ing;
turn To dust and ash - es in its heat con - sum-ing;
long, Shall far out-pass the power of hu - man tell - ing;

O Com-fort - er, draw near, With - in my heart ap -
And let your glo - rious light Shine ev - er on my
For none can guess its grace, Till love cre - ates the

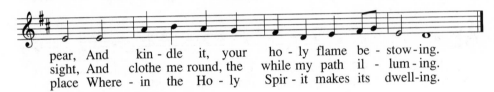

pear, And kin - dle it, your ho - ly flame be - stow-ing.
sight, And clothe me round, the while my path il - lum - ing.
place Where - in the Ho - ly Spir - it makes its dwell-ing.

Text: *Discendi, Amor Santo*; Bianco da Siena, d.c.1434; tr. by Richard F. Littledale, 1833-1890
Tune: DOWN AMPNEY, 66 11 D; Ralph Vaughan Williams, 1872-1958, © Oxford University Press

472 Come, Holy Ghost

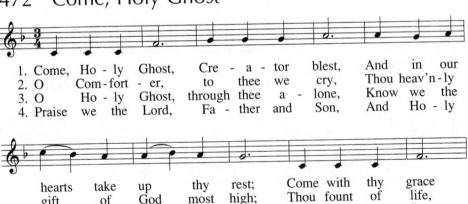

1. Come, Ho - ly Ghost, Cre - a - tor blest, And in our
2. O Com-fort - er, to thee we cry, Thou heav'n-ly
3. O Ho - ly Ghost, through thee a - lone, Know we the
4. Praise we the Lord, Fa - ther and Son, And Ho - ly

hearts take up thy rest; Come with thy grace
gift of God most high; Thou fount of life,
Fa - ther and the Son; Be this our firm
Spir - it with them one; And may the Son

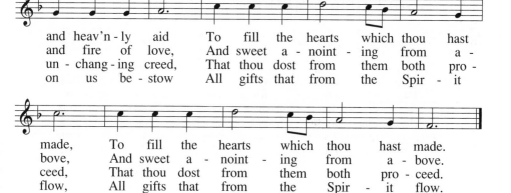

and heav'n-ly aid / To fill the hearts / which thou hast
and fire of love, / And sweet a-noint-ing / from a-
un-chang-ing creed, / That thou dost from / them both pro-
on us be-stow / All gifts that from / the Spir-it

made, To fill the hearts which thou hast made.
bove, And sweet a-noint-ing from a-bove.
ceed, That thou dost from them both pro-ceed.
flow, All gifts that from the Spir-it flow.

Text: *Veni, Creator Spiritus;* attr. to Rabanus Maurus, 776-856; tr. by Edward Caswall, 1814-1878, alt.
Tune: LAMBILLOTTE, LM with repeat; Louis Lambillotte, SJ, 1796-1855; harm. by Richard Proulx, b.1937, © 1986, GIA Publications, Inc.

Spirit Wind 473

Refrain

Spir-it Wind, Breath of God, breathe new life in-to the world.

Spir-it Wind, Breath of God, breathe new life in-to the world.

Verses

1. My soul cries out, "O bless the Lord!" O God, you
2. If you should take a-way our breath, what could we
3. All praise and thanks are yours, O God; may you re-

are the Ho-ly One; so man-y works your hands have
do but fall to dust? When you send forth the breath of
joice in all your works. May you find joy in us as

D.C.

made through-out the earth.
life we rise a-gain!
we re-joice in you!

Text: Psalm 104; Scott Soper, b.1961
Tune: Scott Soper, b.1961
© 1997, GIA Publications, Inc.

474 Veni Creator Spiritus

1. Ve - ni Cre - á - tor Spí - ri - tus,
2. Qui dí - ce - ris Pa - rá - cli - tus,
3. Tu se - pti - fór - mis mú - ne - re,
4. Ac - cén - de lu - men sén - si - bus,
5. Hó - stem re - pél - las lón - gi - us,
6. Per te sci - á - mus da Pa - trem,
7. De - o Pa - tri sit gló - ri - a,

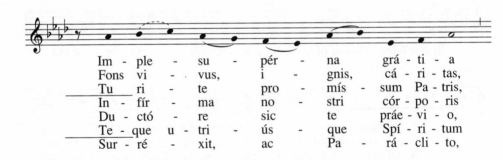

Men - tes tu - ó - rum ví - si - ta:
Al - tís - si - mi dó - num De - i,
Di - gi - tus pa - tér - nae déx - te - rae,
In - fun - de - a - mó - rem cór - di - bus,
Pa - cém - que do - nes pró - ti - nus:
No - scá - mus at - que Fí - li - um
Et Fí - li - o, qui a mór - tu - is

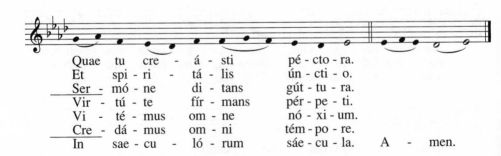

Im - ple - su - pér - na grá - ti - a
Fons vi - vus, i - gnis, cá - ri - tas,
Tu ri - te pro - mís - sum Pa - tris,
In - fír - ma no - stri cór - po - ris
Du - ctó - re sic te práe - vi - o,
Te - que u - tri - ús - que Spí - ri - tum
Sur - ré - xit, ac Pa - rá - cli - to,

Quae tu cre - á - sti pé - cto - ra.
Et spi - ri - tá - lis ún - cti - o.
Ser - mó - ne di - tans gút - tu - ra.
Vir - tú - te fír - mans pér - pe - ti.
Vi - té - mus om - ne nó - xi - um.
Cre - dá - mus om - ni tém - po - re.
In sae - cu - ló - rum sáe - cu - la. A - men.

Text: Attr. to Rabanus Maurus, 776-856
Tune: VENI CREATOR SPIRITUS, LM; Mode VIII; acc. by Richard Proulx, b.1937, © 1975, GIA Publications, Inc.

O Holy Spirit, by Whose Breath 475

1. O Ho - ly Spir - it, by whose breath
2. You are the seek - er's sure re - source,
3. In you God's en - er - gy is shown,
4. Flood our dull sens - es with your light;
5. From in - ner strife grant us re - lease;
6. Praise to the Fa - ther, Christ the Word,

Life ris - es vi - brant out of death:
Of burn - ing love the liv - ing source,
To us your var - ied gifts made known.
In mu - tual love our hearts u - nite.
Turn na - tions to the ways of peace.
And to the Spir - it, God the Lord;

Come to cre - ate, re - new, in - spire;
Pro - tec - tor in the midst of strife,
Teach us to speak; teach us to hear;
Your pow'r the whole cre - a - tion fills;
To full - er life your peo - ple bring
To whom all hon - or, glo - ry be

Come, kin - dle in our hearts your fire.
The giv - er and the Lord of life.
Yours is the tongue and yours the ear.
Con - firm our weak, un - cer - tain wills.
That as one bod - y we may sing:
Both now and for e - ter - ni - ty.

Text: *Veni, Creator Spiritus;* attr. to Rabanus Maurus, 776-865; tr. by John W. Grant, b.1919, © 1971
Tune: VENI CREATOR SPIRITUS, LM; Mode VIII; setting by Richard J. Wojcik, b.1923, © 1975, GIA Publications, Inc.

476 Send Us Your Spirit

Refrain

Come Lord Je-sus, send us your Spir-it, re-new the face of the earth. Come Lord Je-sus, send us your Spir-it, re-new the face of the earth.

Verses

1. Come to us, Spir-it of God, breathe in us
2. Fill us with the fire of your love, burn in us
3. Send us the wings of new birth, fill all the

now, we sing to-geth-er. Spir-it of
now, bring us to-geth-er. Come to us,
earth with the love you have taught us. Let all cre-

hope and of light, fill our lives,
dwell in us, change our lives, O Lord,
a - tion now be shak-en with love,

D.C.

come to us, Spir-it of God.
come to us, Spir-it of God.
come to us, Spir-it of God.

May be sung in canon.

Text: David Haas, b.1957
Tune: David Haas, b.1957; acc. by Jeanne Cotter, b.1964
© 1981, 1982, 1987, GIA Publications, Inc.

Send Down the Fire 477

Refrain

Send down the fire of your jus-tice,
Send down the rains of your love; Come,
send down the Spir-it, breathe life in your peo-ple, and
we shall be peo-ple of God.

Verses

1. Call us to be your com-pas-sion,
2. Call us to learn of your mer-cy,
3. Call us to an-swer op-pres-sion,
4. Call us to wit-ness your King-dom,

Teach us the song of your love; Give us
Teach us the way of your peace; Give us
Teach us the fire of your truth; Give us
Give us the pres-ence of Christ; May your

hearts that sing, Give us deeds that ring, Make us
hearts that feel, Give us hands that heal, Make us
right-eous souls, 'Til your jus-tice rolls, Make us
ho-ly light Keep us shin-ing bright, Ev-er

D.C.

ring with the song of your love.
walk in the way of your peace.
burn with the fire of your truth.
shine with the pres-ence of Christ.

Text: Marty Haugen, b.1950
Tune: Marty Haugen, b.1950
© 1989, GIA Publications, Inc.

478 Veni Sancte Spiritus

Ostinato Refrain

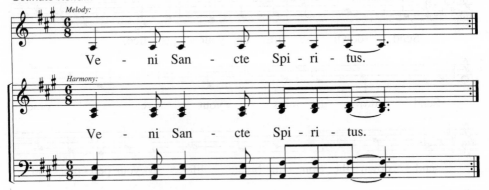

Ve - ni Sanc - te Spi - ri - tus.

Ve - ni Sanc - te Spi - ri - tus.

Text: *Come Holy Spirit;* Verses drawn from the Pentecost Sequence; Taizé Community, 1978
Tune: Jacques Berthier, 1923-1994
© 1979, Les Presses de Taizé, GIA Publications, Inc., agent

479 Holy Spirit, Come to Us

Ostinato Refrain

Ho-ly Spir-it, come to us, kin-dle in us the fire of your love.

Ho - ly Spir-it, come to us, ve - ni San-cte Spi - ri - tus.

Text: John 13:35, 15:12-13, 1 John 3:16, 4:10, 16
Tune: Jacques Berthier, 1923-1994
© 1998, Les Presses de Taizé. GIA Publications, Inc., agent

Spirit of God   480

Refrain

Spir - it of God, who dwells in me, O - pen my
eyes that I may see. Come fill my heart
and make me whole. Spir - it of God, I am yours.

Verses

1. This is the Spir-it of the liv-ing God,
2. Come, Ho-ly Spir-it, and set me free

Who hears your ev - 'ry sin-gle prayer.   O
To do the best I can.   O

this is the Spir-it of the liv - ing God,
come, Ho-ly Spir-it, and set me free

D.C.

Who is al - ways right there.
To be all that I am.

Text: James E. Moore, Jr., b.1951
Tune: James E. Moore, Jr., b.1951
© 2002, GIA Publications, Inc.

481 Spirit Blowing through Creation

Verses

1. Spir - it blow - ing through cre - a - tion,
2. As you moved up - on the wa - ters,
3. Love that sends the riv - ers danc - ing,
4. All the crea - tures you have fash - ioned,

Spir - it burn - ing in the skies,
As you ride up - on the wind,
Love that wa - ters all that lives,
All that live and breathe in you,

Let the hope of your sal - va - tion fill our eyes;
Move us all, your sons and daugh-ters deep with - in;
Love that heals and holds and rous - es and for - gives;
Find their hope in your com - pas - sion, strong and true;

God of splen - dor, God of glo - ry,
As you shaped the hills and moun - tains,
You are food for all your crea - tures,
You, O Spir - it of sal - va - tion,

You who light the stars a - bove,
Formed the land and filled the deep,
You are hun - ger in the soul,
You a - lone, be - neath, a - bove,

All the heav - ens tell the sto - ry of your love. *(To verse 2)*
Let your hand re - new and wak - en all who sleep. *(To refrain)*
In your hands the bro - ken - heart - ed are made whole. *(To verse 4)*
Come, re - new your whole cre - a - tion in your love. *(To refrain)*

Refrain

Spir-it re - new-ing the earth, re - new-ing the hearts of all peo-ple; Burn in the wea-ry souls, blow through the si-lent lips, come now a - wake us, Spir-it of God.

Text: Marty Haugen, b.1950
Tune: Marty Haugen, b.1950
© 1987, GIA Publications, Inc.

We Are One 482

We are one, we are one. We are one in the Spir - it, we are one. Hal-le-lu - jah, Hal-le-lu - jah, we are one in the Spir-it, we are one.

Text: Timothy Wright, ©
Tune: Congregational Praise Song, arr. Valeria A. Foster, © 2000, GIA Publications, Inc.

483　Holy, Holy, Holy! Lord God Almighty

1. Ho-ly, Ho-ly, Ho-ly! Lord God Al-might-y!
2. Ho-ly, Ho-ly, Ho-ly! all the saints a-dore thee,
3. Ho-ly, Ho-ly, Ho-ly! though the dark-ness hide thee,
4. Ho-ly, Ho-ly, Ho-ly! Lord God Al-might-y!

Ear-ly in the morn-ing our song shall rise to thee:
Cast-ing down their gold-en crowns a-round the glass-y sea;
Though the eye made blind by sin thy glo-ry may not see,
All thy works shall praise thy Name in earth, and sky, and sea;

Ho-ly, Ho-ly, Ho-ly! mer-ci-ful and might-y,
Cher-u-bim and ser-a-phim fall-ing down be-fore thee,
On-ly thou art ho-ly; there is none be-side thee,
Ho-ly, Ho-ly, Ho-ly! mer-ci-ful and might-y,

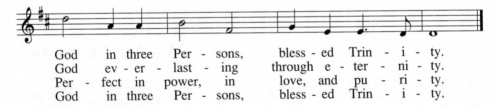

God in three Per-sons, bless-ed Trin-i-ty.
God ev-er-last-ing through e-ter-ni-ty.
Per-fect in power, in love, and pu-ri-ty.
God in three Per-sons, bless-ed Trin-i-ty.

Text: Reginald Heber, 1783-1826, alt.
Tune: NICAEA, 11 12 12 10; John Bacchus Dykes, 1823-1876

The Play of the Godhead   484

1. The play of the God-head, the Trin - i - ty's dance,
2. The warm mists of sum-mer, cool wa - ters that flow,
3. In God's gra-cious im - age of co - e - qual parts,

Em - brac - es the earth in a sa - cred ro - mance:
Turn crys - tal as ice when the win - try winds blow.
We gath - er as danc - ers, u - nit - ing our hearts.

With God the Cre - a - tor, and Christ the true Son,
The tap - root that nur - tures, the shoot grow - ing free,
Men, wom - en, and chil - dren, and all liv - ing things,

En - twined with the Spir - it, a web dai - ly spun
The life - giv - ing fruit, full and ripe on the tree:
We join in the round of bright na - ture that rings

In span - gles of mys - t'ry the great Three-in - One.
More mys - tic and won-drous, the great One - in - Three.
With rap - ture and rhy - thm: Cre - a - tion now sings!

Text: Mary Louise Bringle, b.1953
Tune: BEDFORD PARK, 11 11 11 11 11; Robert J. Batastini, b.1942
© 2002, 2003, GIA Publications, Inc.

485 O God, Almighty Father

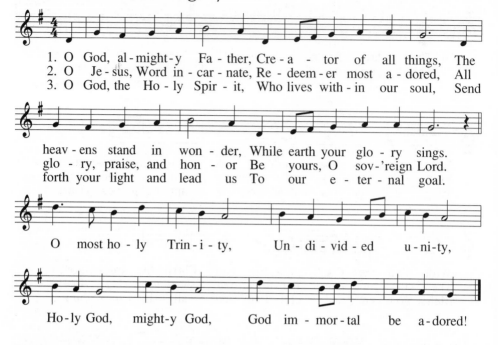

1. O God, al-might-y Fa-ther, Cre-a-tor of all things, The
2. O Je-sus, Word in-car-nate, Re-deem-er most a-dored, All
3. O God, the Ho-ly Spir-it, Who lives with-in our soul, Send

heav-ens stand in won-der, While earth your glo-ry sings.
glo-ry, praise, and hon-or Be yours, O sov-'reign Lord.
forth your light and lead us To our e-ter-nal goal.

O most ho-ly Trin-i-ty, Un-di-vid-ed u-ni-ty,

Ho-ly God, might-y God, God im-mor-tal be a-dored!

Text: *Gott Vater sei gepriesen*; anon; tr. by Irvin Udulutsch, OFM Cap., fl. 1959, alt. © 1959, The Liturgical Press
Tune: GOTT VATER SEI GEPRIESEN, 7 6 7 6 with refrain; *Limburg Gesangbuch*, 1838; harm. by Healey Willan, 1880-1968, © 1958,
Ralph Jusko Publications, Inc.

486 Come Now, Almighty King

1. Come now, al-might-y King, Help us your
2. Come now, In-car-nate Son, Your life in
3. Come, ho-ly Com-fort-er, Your sa-cred
4. To the great One in Three E-ter-nal

name to sing, Help us to praise.
us be-gun, Our prayer at-tend.
wit-ness bear In this glad hour.
prais-es be For ev-er-more!

Fa-ther all glo-ri-ous, Ev-er vic-to-ri-ous,
Come and your peo-ple bless And give your Word suc-cess;
Your grace to us im-part, Now rule in ev-'ry heart
Your sov-'reign maj-es-ty May we in glo-ry see

Come and reign o - ver us, An - cient of Days.
Strength-en your right - eous-ness, Sav - ior and Friend!
Nev - er from us de - part, Spir - it of Pow'r!
And to e - ter - ni - ty Love and a - dore!

Text: Anon. c.1757
Tune: ITALIAN HYMN, 66 4 666 4; Felice de Giardini, 1716-1796

Stand Up, Friends 487

Verses

1. Praise the God who chang - es plac-es, Leaves the loft - y seat,
2. Praise the Rab - bi, speak - ing, do - ing All that God in - tends,
3. Praise the Breath of Love, whose free-dom Spreads our wak-ing wings,
4. Praise, un - til we join the sing-ing Far be-yond our sight,

Wel-comes us with warm em-brac-es, Stoops to wash our feet.
Dy - ing, ris - ing, faith re - new-ing, Call - ing us his friends.
Lift - ing ev - 'ry blight and bur-den Till the spir - it sings;
With the End-ing and Be - gin-ning Danc - ing in the light.

Refrain

Stand up, friends! Hold your heads high!

Free-dom is our song! Al - le - lu - ia! Free-dom is our song!

1. 2. 3
Al - le - lu - ia! ia!

Text: Brian Wren, b.1936, © 1986, Hope Publishing Co.
Tune: David Haas, b.1957, © 1993, GIA Publications, Inc.

488　How Wonderful the Three-in-One

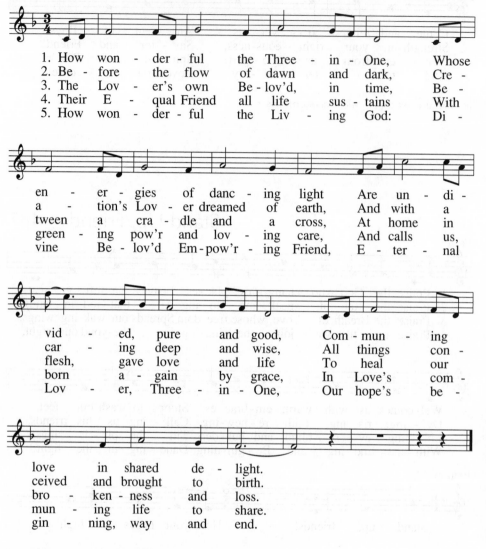

1. How won - der - ful the Three - in - One,　Whose
2. Be - fore the flow of dawn and dark,　Cre -
3. The Lov - er's own Be - lov'd, in time,　Be -
4. Their E - qual Friend all life sus - tains　With
5. How won - der - ful the Liv - ing God:　Di -

en - er - gies of danc - ing light　Are un - di -
a - tion's Lov - er dreamed of earth,　And with a
tween a cra - dle and a cross,　At home in
green - ing pow'r and lov - ing care,　And calls us,
vine Be - lov'd Em-pow'r - ing Friend,　E - ter - nal

vid - ed, pure and good,　Com - mun - ing
car - ing deep and wise,　All things con -
flesh, gave love and life　To heal our
born a - gain by grace,　In Love's com -
Lov - er, Three - in - One,　Our hope's be -

love in shared de - light.
ceived and brought to birth.
bro - ken - ness and loss.
mun - ing life to share.
gin - ning, way and end.

Text: Brian Wren, b.1936, © 1989, Hope Publishing Co.
Tune: PROSPECT, 8 8 8 8; *Southern Harmony*; arr. by Marty Haugen, b.1950, © 1991, GIA Publications, Inc.

Crown Him with Many Crowns 489

1. Crown him with man - y crowns, The Lamb up - on his
2. Crown him the Lord of life, Who tri - umphed o'er the
3. Crown him the Lord of love, Be - hold his hands and
4. Crown him the Lord of peace, Whose power a scep - ter
5. Crown him the Lord of years, The ris - en Lord sub -

throne; Hark! how the heav'n - ly an - them drowns All
grave, And rose vic - to - rious in the strife For
side, Rich wounds yet vis - i - ble a - bove In
sways From pole to pole, that wars may cease, Ab -
lime, Cre - a - tor of the roll - ing spheres, The

mu - sic but its own. A - wake, my soul, and sing Of
those he came to save. His glo - ries now we sing, Who
beau - ty glo - ri - fied. No an - gel in the sky Can
sorbed in prayer and praise. His reign shall know no end, And
Mas - ter of all time. All hail, Re - deem - er, hail! For

him who set us free, And hail him as your
died and rose on high, Who died, e - ter - nal
ful - ly bear that sight, But down - ward bends his
round his pierc - ed feet Fair flow'rs of Par - a -
you have died for me; Your praise and glo - ry

heav'n - ly King Through all e - ter - ni - ty.
life to bring, And lives that death may die.
burn - ing eye At mys - ter - ies so bright.
dise ex - tend Their fra - grance ev - er sweet.
shall not fail Through - out e - ter - ni - ty.

Text: Revelation 19:12; St. 1, 3-5, Matthew Bridges, 1800-1894; St. 2, Godfrey Thring, 1823-1903
Tune: DIADEMATA, SMD; George J. Elvey, 1816-1893

490 All Hail the Power of Jesus' Name

1. All hail the power of Je - sus' name! Let
2. Crown him, ye mar - tyrs of our God, Who
3. Ye cho - sen seed of Is - rael's race, A
4. O that, with yon - der sa - cred throng, We

an - gels pros - trate fall; Bring forth the roy - al
from his al - tar call; Ex - tol the stem of
rem - nant weak and small, Hail him who saved you
at his feet may fall, Join in the ev - er -

di - a - dem And crown him Lord of
Jes - se's rod, And crown him Lord of
by his grace, And crown him Lord of
last - ing song, And crown him Lord of

all; And crown him Lord of all; And
all; And crown him Lord of all; And
all; And crown him Lord of all; And
all; And crown him Lord of all; And

crown him Lord of all; Bring forth the roy - al
crown him Lord of all; Ex - tol the stem of
crown him Lord of all; Hail him who saved you
crown him Lord of all; Join in the ev - er -

di - a - dem And crown him Lord of all.
Jes - se's rod, And crown him Lord of all.
by his grace, And crown him Lord of all.
last - ing song, And crown him Lord of all.

Text: Edward Perronet, 1726-1792; alt. by John Rippon, 1751-1836, alt.
Tune: DIADEM, CM with repeats; from the *Primitive Baptist Hymn and Tune Book*, 1902; harm. by Richard Proulx, b.1937, © 1975,
GIA Publications, Inc.

Christ Is the King 491

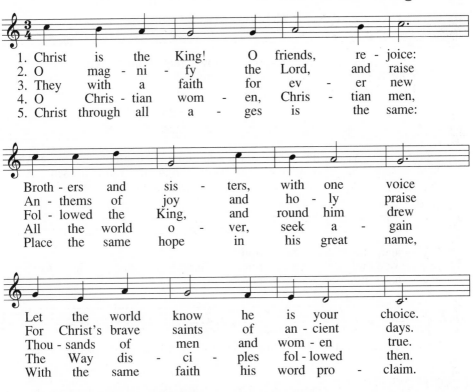

1. Christ is the King! O friends, re - joice:
2. O mag - ni - fy the Lord, and raise
3. They with a faith for ev - er new
4. O Chris - tian wom - en, Chris - tian men,
5. Christ through all a - ges is the same:

Broth - ers and sis - ters, with one voice
An - thems of joy and ho - ly praise
Fol - lowed the King, and round him drew
All the world o - ver, seek a - gain
Place the same hope in his great name,

Let the world know he is your choice.
For Christ's brave saints of an - cient days.
Thou - sands of men and wom - en true.
The Way dis - ci - ples fol - lowed then.
With the same faith his word pro - claim.

Al - le - lu - ia, al - le - lu - ia, al - le - lu - ia.

6. Let love's all reconciling might
Your scattered companies unite
In service to the Lord of light.
Alleluia, alleluia, alleluia.

7. So shall God's will on earth be done,
New lamps be lit, new tasks begun,
And the whole Church at last be one.
Alleluia, alleluia, alleluia.

Text: George K. A. Bell, 1883-1958, alt., © Oxford University Press
Tune: GELOBT SEI GOTT, 888 with alleluias; Melchior Vulpius, c.1560-1616

492 To Jesus Christ, Our Sovereign King

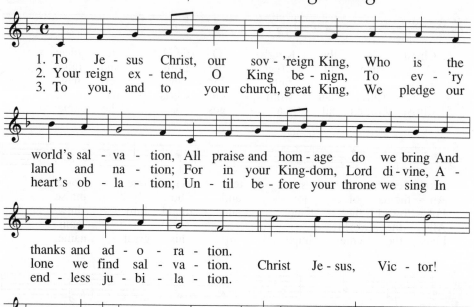

1. To Jesus Christ, our sov-'reign King, Who is the
2. Your reign ex-tend, O King be-nign, To ev-'ry
3. To you, and to your church, great King, We pledge our

world's sal-va-tion, All praise and hom-age do we bring And
land and na-tion; For in your King-dom, Lord di-vine, A-
heart's ob-la-tion; Un-til be-fore your throne we sing In

thanks and ad-o-ra-tion.
lone we find sal-va-tion. Christ Je-sus, Vic-tor!
end-less ju-bi-la-tion.

Christ Je-sus, Rul-er! Christ Je-sus, Lord and Re-deem-er!

Text: Martin B. Hellrigel, 1891-1981, alt., © 1941, Irene C. Mueller
Tune: ICH GLAUB AN GOTT, 8 7 8 7 with refrain; *Mainz Gesangbuch,* 1870; harm. by Richard Proulx, b.1937, © 1986, GIA Publications, Inc.

493 Rejoice, the Lord Is King!

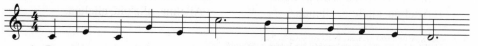

1. Re-joice, the Lord is King! Your Lord and King a-dore!
2. The Lord, our Sav-ior, reigns, The God of truth and love;
3. His king-dom can-not fail, He rules o'er earth and heav'n;
4. Re-joice in glo-rious hope! Our Lord the judge shall come

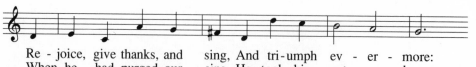

Re-joice, give thanks, and sing, And tri-umph ev-er-more:
When he had purged our sins, He took his seat a-bove:
The keys of death and hell Are to our Je-sus giv'n:
And take his ser-vants up To their e-ter-nal home:

Lift up your heart, lift up your voice! Re -
joice, a - gain I say, re - joice!

Text: Charles Wesley, 1707-1788
Tune: DARWALL'S 148TH, 6 6 6 6 88; John Darwall, 1731-1789; harm. from *The Hymnal 1940*

The King of Glory 494

The King of glo - ry comes, the na - tion re - joic - es.

Last time 𝄐

O - pen the gates be - fore him, lift up your voic - es.

1. Who is the king of glo - ry; how shall we call him?
2. In all of Gal - i - lee, in cit - y or vil - lage,
3. Sing then of Da - vid's Son, our Sav - ior and broth - er;
4. He gave his life for us, the pledge of sal - va - tion,
5. He con - quered sin and death; he tru - ly has ris - en.

D.C.

He is Em - man - u - el, the prom - ised of a - ges.
He goes a - mong his peo - ple cur - ing their ill - ness.
In all of Gal - i - lee was nev - er an - oth - er.
He took up - on him - self the sins of the na - tion.
And he will share with us his heav - en - ly vi - sion.

Text: Willard F. Jabusch, b. 1930, © 1966, 1982, Willard F. Jabusch. Administered by OCP Publications.
Tune: KING OF GLORY, 12 12 with refrain; Israeli; harm. by Richard Proulx, b.1937, © 1986, GIA Publications, Inc.

495 Canticle of the Sun

Refrain

The heav-ens are tell-ing the glo-ry of God,

and all cre-a-tion is shout-ing for joy. Come,

dance in the for-est, come, play in the field, and

sing, sing to the glo-ry of the Lord.

Verses

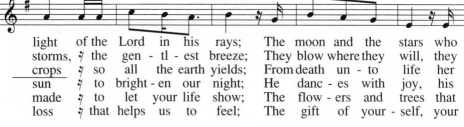

1. Praise for the sun, the bring-er of day, He car-ries the
2. Praise for the wind that blows through the trees, The seas' might-y
3. Praise for the rain that wa-ters our fields, And bless-es our
4. Praise for the fire who gives us his light, The warmth of the
5. Praise for the earth who makes life to grow, The crea-tures you
6. Praise for our death that makes our life real, The knowl-edge of

light of the Lord in his rays; The moon and the stars who
storms, ⁊ the gen-tl-est breeze; They blow where they will, they
crops ⁊ so all the earth yields; From death un-to life her
sun ⁊ to bright-en our night; He danc-es with joy, his
made ⁊ to let your life show; The flow-ers and trees that
loss ⁊ that helps us to feel; The gift of your-self, your

D.C.

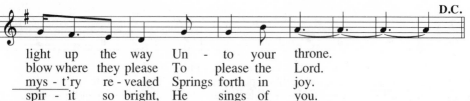

light up the way Un-to your throne.
blow where they please To please the Lord.
mys-t'ry re-vealed Springs forth in joy.
spir-it so bright, He sings of you.
help us to know The heart of love.
pres-ence re-vealed To lead us home.

Text: Marty Haugen, b.1950
Tune: Marty Haugen, b.1950
© 1980, GIA Publications, Inc.

How Great Thou Art 496

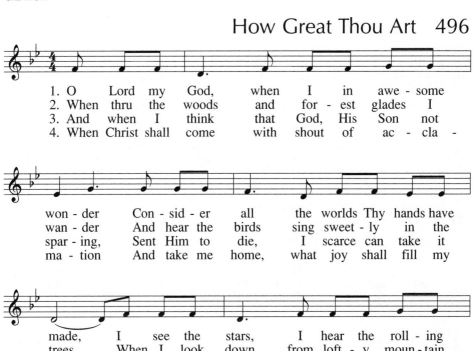

1. O Lord my God, when I in awe - some
2. When thru the woods and for - est glades I
3. And when I think that God, His Son not
4. When Christ shall come with shout of ac - cla -

won - der Con - sid - er all the worlds Thy hands have
wan - der And hear the birds sing sweet - ly in the
spar - ing, Sent Him to die, I scarce can take it
ma - tion And take me home, what joy shall fill my

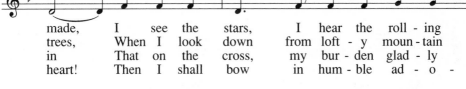

made, I see the stars, I hear the roll - ing
trees, When I look down from loft - y moun - tain
in That on the cross, my bur - den glad - ly
heart! Then I shall bow in hum - ble ad - o -

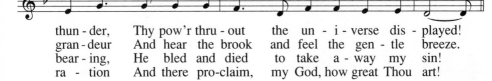

thun - der, Thy pow'r thru - out the un - i - verse dis - played!
gran - deur And hear the brook and feel the gen - tle breeze.
bear - ing, He bled and died to take a - way my sin!
ra - tion And there pro - claim, my God, how great Thou art!

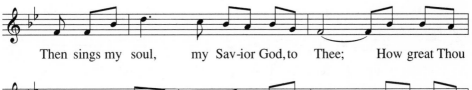

Then sings my soul, my Sav - ior God, to Thee; How great Thou

art, how great Thou art! Then sings my soul, my Sav - ior God, to

Thee; How great Thou art, How great Thou art!

Text: Stuart K. Hine, 1899-1989
Tune: O STORE GUD, 11 10 11 10 with refrain; Stuart K. Hine, 1899-1989
© 1953, 1981, Manna Music, Inc.

497 Sing Out, Earth and Skies

Verses

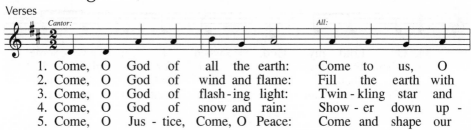

Cantor:

All:

1. Come, O God of all the earth: Come to us, O
2. Come, O God of wind and flame: Fill the earth with
3. Come, O God of flash-ing light: Twin-kling star and
4. Come, O God of snow and rain: Show-er down up -
5. Come, O Jus-tice, Come, O Peace: Come and shape our

Cantor:

Right-eous One; Come, and bring our love to birth:
right-eous-ness; Teach us all to sing your name:
burn-ing sun; God of day and God of night:
on the earth; Come, O God of joy and pain:
hearts a-new; Come and make op - pres-sion cease:

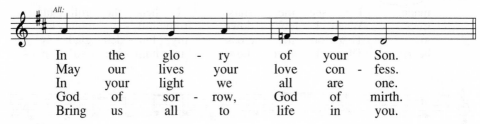

All:

In the glo - ry of your Son.
May our lives your love con - fess.
In your light we all are one.
God of sor - row, God of mirth.
Bring us all to life in you.

Refrain

Sing out, earth and skies! Sing of the God who loves you!

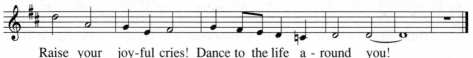

Raise your joy-ful cries! Dance to the life a - round you!

Text: Marty Haugen, b.1950
Tune: SING OUT, 7 7 7 7 with refrain; Marty Haugen, b.1950
© 1985, GIA Publications, Inc.

All You Works of God 498

Refrain

All you works of God, ev-'ry moun-tain, star and tree, bless the One who shapes your beau - ty, who has caused you all to be one great song of love and grace, ev - er an - cient, ev - er new. Raise your voic - es, all you works of God!

Verses

Solo: / *All:* / *Solo:*

1. Sun and moon: Stars of heav - en:
2. Winds of God: Cold and win - ter:
3. Night and day: Light and dark - ness:
4. All the earth: Bless your Mak - er!   Hills and moun-tains:
5. Wells and springs: Seas and riv - ers:
6. Fly - ing birds: Beasts and cat - tle:
7. All who live: Men and wom - en:

All: / *Solo:*

Chant your praise!

Show - ers and dew:
Snow - storms and ice:
Light - nings and clouds:
Green things that grow:
Whales in the deep:
Chil - dren at play:
Ser - vants of God:

All: **D.C.**

Raise up your joy - ful song.

Text: Marty Haugen, b.1950
Tune: Marty Haugen, b.1950
© 1989, GIA Publications, Inc.

499   Come to the Feast

Solo or S, A:

1. Oh,   ev - 'ry - one who   thirsts:
   and   ev - 'ry - one who   la - bors:
2. Oh,   ev - 'ry - one who   seeks:
   and   ev - 'ry - one who   mourns:
3. Let   all who seek their   God: Come to the wa-ters!
   the   ev - er - last - ing stream:
4. And   you who are en -   slaved:
   To   all who live in   fear:
5. And   all who are op -   pressed:
   and   you, the lost and   bro - ken:

Solo or S, A: 1. All: 2. All:

here   is   an   end   to   hun - ger:
all   you who have no mon - ey:
hear   me and share the rich - es:
now   is   an   end   to   sad - ness:
heed   now the One who calls you: Come to the feast! Come to the
drink   deep the Cup that saves you:
this   is   the feast of   free-dom:
join   in   the feast with cour - age:
this   is   the feast of   jus - tice:
this   is   the feast of   heal - ing:

Solo or S, A: All:

                                   1. the wa - ters of the   Jor - dan:
                                   2. the streams of joy and glad - ness:
feast! For this   is life: 3. the floods that o - ver-whelm you: For
                                   4. the wa - ters that have freed you:
                                   5. to   die and rise in   Je - sus:

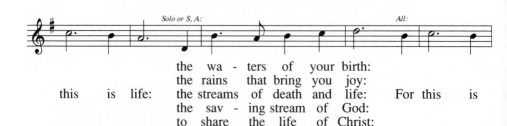

Solo or S, A: All:

                        the wa - ters of   your birth:
                        the rains   that bring you joy:
this   is   life: the streams of death and life: For this   is
                        the sav - ing stream of God:
                        to   share the life of Christ:

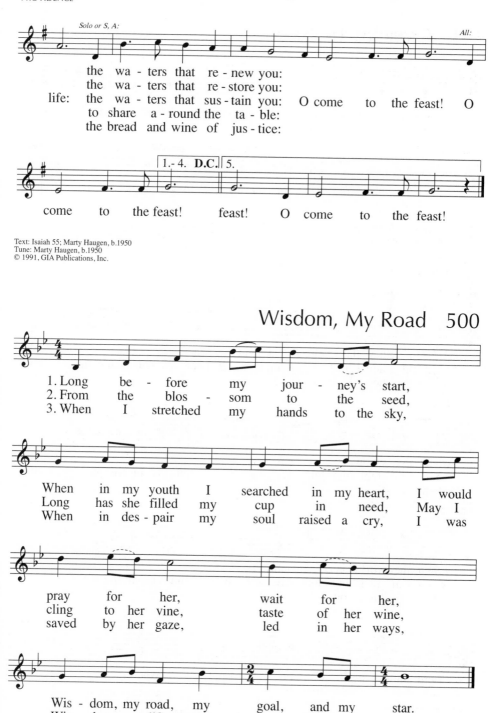

Solo or S, A:

the wa - ters that re - new you:
the wa - ters that re - store you:
life: the wa - ters that sus - tain you: O come to the feast! O
to share a - round the ta - ble:
the bread and wine of jus - tice:

1.- 4. D.C. ‖ 5.

come to the feast! feast! O come to the feast!

Text: Isaiah 55; Marty Haugen, b.1950
Tune: Marty Haugen, b.1950
© 1991, GIA Publications, Inc.

Wisdom, My Road 500

1. Long be - fore my jour - ney's start,
2. From the blos - som to the seed,
3. When I stretched my hands to the sky,

When in my youth I searched in my heart, I would
Long has she filled my cup in need, May I
When in des - pair my soul raised a cry, I was

pray for her, wait for her,
cling to her vine, taste of her wine,
saved by her gaze, led in her ways,

Wis - dom, my road, my goal, and my star.
Wis - dom, my life, my per - fect de - sign.
Wis - dom, my love, the light of my days.

Text: Based on Ecclesiasticus 51:13-22; Steven C. Warner, b.1954
Tune: Leslie Palmer Barnhart
© 1993, World Library Publications

501 Over My Head

Refrain

O - ver my head, I hear mu - sic in the air; o - ver my head,

I hear mu - sic in the air; o - ver my head, I hear

mu - sic in the air; there must be a God some - where.

Verses

Cantor: *Assembly:* *Cantor:*

1. Oh when the world is si - lent,
2. And when I'm feel - ing lone - ly, I hear mu - sic in the air;
3. Now when I think on Je - sus,

oh
and
now

Assembly: *Cantor:*

when the world is si - lent,
when I'm feel - ing lone - ly, I hear mu - sic in the air;
when I think on Je - sus,

oh
and
now

Assembly:

when the world is si - lent,
when I'm feel - ing lone - ly, I hear mu - sic in the air;
when I think on Je - sus,

All: **D.C.**

there must be a God some - where.

Text: African American Spiritual
Tune: African American Spiritual; arr. by John L. Bell, b.1949, © 1997, Iona Community, GIA Publications, Inc., agent

Come to the Water 502

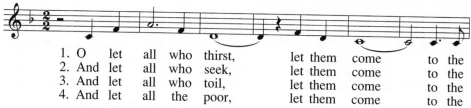

1. O let all who thirst, let them come to the
2. And let all who seek, let them come to the
3. And let all who toil, let them come to the
4. And let all the poor, let them come to the

wa - ter. And let all who have noth - ing,
wa - ter. And let all who have noth - ing,
wa - ter. And let all who are wea - ry,
wa - ter. Bring the ones who are lad - en,

let them come to the Lord: With - out mon - ey,
let them come to the Lord: With - out mon - ey,
let them come to the Lord: All who la - bor,
bring them all to the Lord: Bring the chil - dren

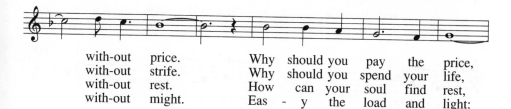

with-out price. Why should you pay the price,
with-out strife. Why should you spend your life,
with-out rest. How can your soul find rest,
with-out might. Eas - y the load and light:

ex - cept for the Lord?
ex - cept for the Lord?
ex - cept for the Lord?
𝄌 come to the Lord.

Text: Isaiah 55:1, 2, Matthew 11:28-30; John Foley, SJ, b.1939
Tune: John Foley, SJ, b.1939
© 1978, John B. Foley, SJ, and OCP Publications

503 Enséñame / Teach Us, Lord

Refrain

En - sé - ña - me, Se - ñor, el ca -
Oh, teach us, Lord, we pray, come and

mi - no y guí - a - me por la vi - da, Se - ñor,
guide us ⁊ in your way to a new life. Oh Lord,

Last time / *To verses* | *To repeat refrain*

en - sé - ña - me. En - sé - ña -
show us the way. Oh, teach us,

Verses 1, 2

1. En - sé - ña - me, Se - ñor, tu ver - dad
2. *Oh, show me how to live in your peace*

no i - llu - sión, la rea - li - dad. Oh, mués - tra - me con
in a world of loss and pain, and bring me to your

D.C.

tu a - mor que pue - do vi - vir.
light when all is done.

Verses 3, 4

3. Da - me, Se - ñor, tu fuer - za y va - lor cuan - do el mun -
4. *Oh, teach me how to pray with-out end. Spir - it, blow*

do te re - cha - za y dé - ja me a - cla - mar
⁊ *with-out, with - in, and whis-per to my heart*

tu glo - ria y po - der.
that life may be - gin.

Text: Donna Peña, b.1955
Tune: Donna Peña, b.1955; acc. by William Gokelman
© 2002, GIA Publications, Inc.

I Have Loved You   504

Refrain

I have loved you with an ev - er - last-ing love, I have

called you and you are mine; I have loved you with an

ev - er-last-ing love, I have called you and you are mine.

Verses

1. Seek the face of the Lord and long for
2. Seek the face of the Lord and long for
3. Seek the face of the Lord and long for

him: He will bring you his light and his peace.
him: He will bring you his joy and his hope.
him: He will bring you his care and his love.

Text: Jeremiah 31:3, Psalm 24:3; Michael Joncas, b.1951
Tune: Michael Joncas, b.1951
© 1979, OCP Publications

505 Rain Down

Refrain

Rain down, rain down, rain down your love on your peo - ple. Rain down, rain down, rain down your love, God of life.

Verses

1. Faith - ful and true is the word of our God.
2. We who re - vere and find hope in our God
3. God of cre - a - tion, we long for your truth;

All of God's works are so wor - thy of trust.
live in the kind - ness and joy of God's wing.
you are the wa - ter of life that we thirst.

God's mer - cy falls on the just and the right;
God will pro - tect us from dark - ness and death;
Grant that your love and your peace touch our hearts,

D.C.

full of God's love is the earth.
God will not leave us to starve.
all of our hope lies in you.

Text: Based on Psalm 33; Jaime Cortez, b.1963
Tune: Jaime Cortez, b.1963; acc. by Craig S. Kingsbury, b.1952
© 1991, 1992, Jaime Cortez. Published by OCP Publications.

You Are Our Center 506

Refrain

You are our cen-ter, you are our hope. This we know and be - lieve. You are our an-swer, you bring us home. You are all we need.

Verses

1. When pain - ful mem - 'ries haunt our minds, and
2. When dreams are shat - tered by name - less pow'rs, and
3. When our in - dif - ference feeds pov - er - ty, and
4. When faith is ques - tioned by doubt and fear, we

1. sor - row dark - ens our heart; when
2. hope seems far from our sight; when
3. greed leaves us want - ing more; when
4. wan - der lost and a - lone; when

1. chil - dren lie bro - ken from vio - lent ways, and
2. truth is shak - en by those we love, and
3. we have fall - en in sin and shame, and
4. death and bro - ken - ness tear our hearts, we

D.C.

1. hate and jeal - ous - y reign:
2. walls are built by fear:
3. dark - ness rules our days:
4. cry to you in our grief:

Text: Lori True, b.1961
Tune: Lori True, b.1961

507 Fresh As the Morning

Verses

1. God of the Bi - ble, God in the Gos - pel,
2. God in our strug - gles, God in our hun - ger,
3. Those with - out sta - tus, those who are noth - ing,
4. Not by your fin - ger, not by your an - ger
5. Hope we must car - ry, shin - ing and cer - tain

hope seen in Je - sus, hope yet to come,
suf - fer - ing with us, tak - ing our part,
you have made roy - al, gift - ed with rights,
will our world or - der change in a day,
through all our tur - moil, ter - ror and loss,

you are our cen - ter, day - light or dark - ness,
still you em - pow'r us, moth - er - ing Spir - it,
cho - sen as part - ners, mid - wives of jus - tice,
but by your peo - ple, fear - less and faith - ful,
bond - ing us glad - ly one to the oth - er,

free - dom or pris - on, you are our home.
feed - ing, sus - tain - ing, from your own heart.
birth - ing new sys - tems, light - ing new lights.
small pa - per lan - terns, light - ing the way.
till our world chang - es fac - ing the Cross.

Refrain

Fresh as the morn - ing, sure as the sun - rise,

God al - ways faith - ful, you do not change.

Fresh as the morn - ing, sure as the sun - rise,

God al - ways faith - ful, you do not change.

Text: Shirley Erena Murray, b.1931, © 1996, Hope Publishing Co.
Tune: Tony E. Alonso, b.1980, © 2001, GIA Publications, Inc.

You Are All We Have 508

Refrain

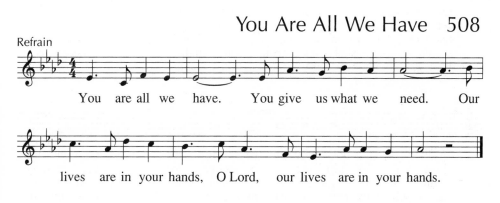

You are all we have. You give us what we need. Our

lives are in your hands, O Lord, our lives are in your hands.

Verses

1. Protect me, Lord; I come to you for safety.
   I say, "You are my God."
   All good things, Lord, all good things
   that I have come from you,
   the God of my salvation.

2. How wonderful are your gifts to me,
   how good they are!
   I praise the Lord who guides me
   and teaches me the way of truth and life.

3. You are near, the God I seek.
   Nothing can take me from your side.
   All my days I rest secure;
   you will show me the path that leads to life.

Text: Francis Patrick O'Brien, b.1958
Tune: Francis Patrick O'Brien, b.1958
© 1992, GIA Publications, Inc.

509 O God, You Search Me

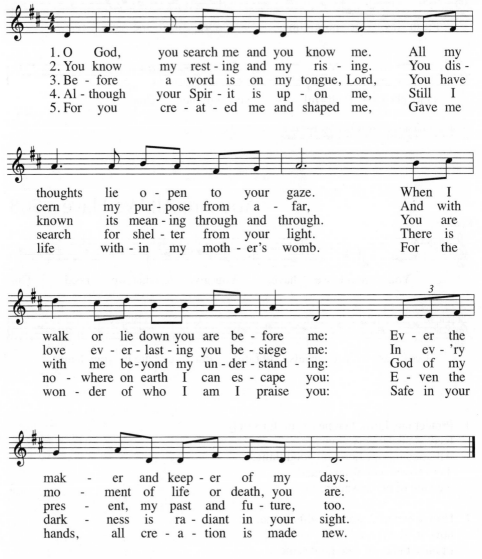

1. O God, you search me and you know me. All my
2. You know my rest-ing and my ris-ing. You dis-
3. Be-fore a word is on my tongue, Lord, You have
4. Al-though your Spir-it is up-on me, Still I
5. For you cre-at-ed me and shaped me, Gave me

thoughts lie o-pen to your gaze. When I
cern my pur-pose from a-far, And with
known its mean-ing through and through. You are
search for shel-ter from your light. There is
life with-in my moth-er's womb. For the

walk or lie down you are be-fore me: Ev-er the
love ev-er-last-ing you be-siege me: In ev-'ry
with me be-yond my un-der-stand-ing: God of my
no-where on earth I can es-cape you: E-ven the
won-der of who I am I praise you: Safe in your

mak - er and keep-er of my days.
mo - ment of life or death, you are.
pres - ent, my past and fu-ture, too.
dark - ness is ra-diant in your sight.
hands, all cre-a-tion is made new.

Text: Based on Psalm 139; Bernadette Farrell, b.1957
Tune: Bernadette Farrell, b.1957
© 1992, Bernadette Farrell. Published by OCP Publications.

Lord Jesus Christ / Jesus le Christ 510

Ostinato Refrain

Lord Je - sus Christ, your light shines with - in us.
Jé - sus le Christ, lu - mière in - té - rieu - re,

Let not my doubts nor my dark - ness speak to me.
ne lais - se pas mes té - nè - bres me par - ler.

Lord Je - sus Christ, your light shines with - in us.
Jé - sus le Christ, lu - mière in - té - rieu - re,

Let my heart al - ways wel - come your love.
don - ne - moi d'ac-cueil - lir ton a - mour.

Text: Psalm 139
Tune: Jacques Berthier, 1923-1994
© 1998, Les Presses de Taizé, GIA Publications, Inc., agent

511   Be Light for Our Eyes

Refrain

Come and be light for our eyes; be the air we
breathe, be the voice we speak! Come, be the song we
sing, be the path we seek!

Verses

1. Your life was giv - en; food for all peo - ple,
2. We hold your pres - ence, ris - en for ev - er!
3. Lead us to jus - tice, light in the dark - ness;

bod - y and blood, new life in our midst!
Your name now names us peo - ple of God!
sing - ing, pro - claim - ing Je - sus is Lord!

Death is no long - er, life is our fu - ture;
Filled with your vi - sion, peo - ple of mis - sion,
Teach us to speak, and help us to lis - ten

D.C.

Je - sus, Mes - si - ah, name of all names!
heal - ing, for - giv - ing; light for the world!
for when your truth and our dreams em - brace!

Text: David Haas, b.1957
Tune: David Haas, b.1957; keyboard arr. by David Haas, b.1957, and Marty Haugen, b.1950
© 1985, GIA Publications, Inc.

Christ, Be Our Light   512

1. Long - ing for light, we wait in dark - ness.
2. Long - ing for peace, our world is trou - bled.
3. Long - ing for food, man - y are hun - gry.
4. Long - ing for shel - ter, man - y are home - less.
5. Man - y the gifts, man - y the peo - ple,

Long - ing for truth, we turn to you.
Long - ing for hope, man - y de - spair.
Long - ing for wa - ter, man - y still thirst.
Long - ing for warmth, man - y are cold.
man - y the hearts that yearn to be - long.

Make us your own, your ho - ly peo - ple,
Your word a - lone has pow'r to save us.
Make us your bread, bro - ken for oth - ers,
Make us your build - ing, shel - ter - ing oth - ers,
Let us be ser - vants to one an - oth - er,

light for the world to see.
Make us your liv - ing voice.
shared un - til all are fed.
walls made of liv - ing stone.
mak - ing your king - dom come.

Christ, be our light! Shine in our hearts.

Shine through the dark - ness. Christ, be our light!

Shine in your church gath - ered to - day.

Text: Bernadette Farrell, b.1957
Tune: Bernadette Farrell, b.1957
© 1993, 2000, Bernadette Farrell. Published by OCP Publications.

513 I Want to Walk as a Child of the Light

1. I want to walk as a child of the light.
2. I want to see the bright-ness of God.
3. I'm look - ing for the com - ing of Christ.

I want to fol - low Je - sus.
I want to look at Je - sus.
I want to be with Je - sus.

God set the stars to give light to the world. The
Clear sun of right-eous-ness shine on my path, And
When we have run with pa - tience the race, We

star of my life is Je - sus.
show me the way to the Fa - ther.
shall know the joy of Je - sus.

In him there is no dark - ness at all. The

night and the day are both a - like. The

Lamb is the light of the cit - y of God.

Shine in my heart, Lord Je - sus.

Text: Ephesians 5:8-10, Revelation 21:23, John 12:46, 1 John 1:5, Hebrews 12:1; Kathleen Thomerson, b.1934, © 1970, 1975, Celebration
Tune: HOUSTON, 10 7 10 8 9 9 10 7; Kathleen Thomerson, b.1934, © 1970, 1975, Celebration; acc. by Robert J. Batastini, b.1942, © 1987, GIA
Publications, Inc.

This Little Light of Mine 514

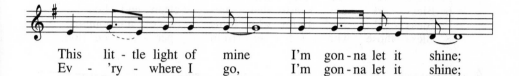

1. This lit - tle light of mine I'm gon - na let it shine,
2. Ev - 'ry - where I go, I'm gon - na let it shine,
3. Je - sus gave it to me, I'm gon - na let it shine,

This lit - tle light of mine I'm gon - na let it shine;
Ev - 'ry - where I go, I'm gon - na let it shine;
Je - sus gave it to me, I'm gon - na let it shine;

This lit - tle light of mine I'm gon - na let it shine,
Ev - 'ry - where I go, I'm gon - na let it shine,
Je - sus gave it to me, I'm gon - na let it shine,

Let it shine, let it shine, let it shine.
Let it shine, let it shine, let it shine.
Let it shine, let it shine, let it shine.

Text: African-American spiritual
Tune: African-American spiritual; harm. by Horace Clarence Boyer, b.1935, © 1992

515 We Are the Light of the World

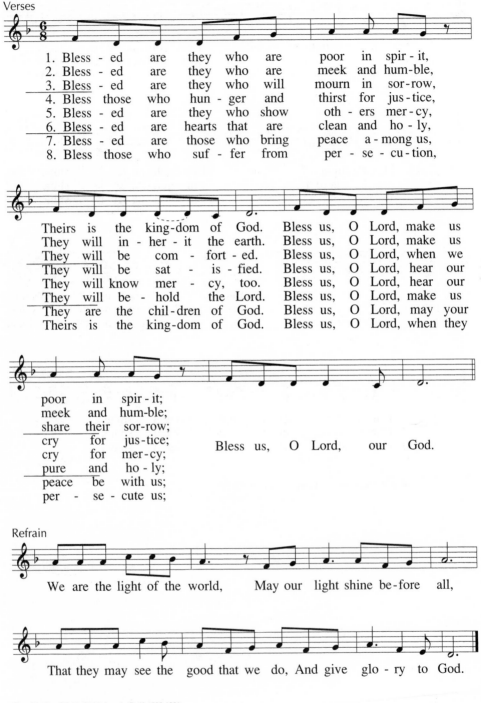

Verses

1. Bless - ed are they who are poor in spir - it,
2. Bless - ed are they who are meek and hum-ble,
3. Bless - ed are they who will mourn in sor-row,
4. Bless those who hun - ger and thirst for jus-tice,
5. Bless - ed are they who show oth - ers mer-cy,
6. Bless - ed are hearts that are clean and ho - ly,
7. Bless - ed are those who bring peace a - mong us,
8. Bless those who suf - fer from per - se - cu-tion,

Theirs is the king-dom of God. Bless us, O Lord, make us
They will in - her - it the earth. Bless us, O Lord, make us
They will be com - fort - ed. Bless us, O Lord, when we
They will be sat - is - fied. Bless us, O Lord, hear our
They will know mer - cy, too. Bless us, O Lord, hear our
They will be - hold the Lord. Bless us, O Lord, make us
They are the chil - dren of God. Bless us, O Lord, may your
Theirs is the king-dom of God. Bless us, O Lord, when they

poor in spir - it;
meek and hum-ble;
share their sor-row;
cry for jus-tice;
cry for mer-cy;
pure and ho - ly;
peace be with us;
per - se - cute us;

Bless us, O Lord, our God.

Refrain

We are the light of the world, May our light shine be-fore all,

That they may see the good that we do, And give glo - ry to God.

Text: Matthew 5:3-11, 14-16; Jean A. Greif, 1898-1981
Tune: Jean A. Greif, 1898-1981
© 1966, Vernacular Hymns Publishing Co.

We Are Marching   516

*Alternate text: dancing, singing, praying

Text: South African
Tune: South African
© 1984, Utryck, Walton Music Corporation, agent

517   Praise to You, O Christ, Our Savior

Refrain

Praise to you, O Christ, our Sav-ior, Word of the Fa-ther, call-ing us to life;

Son   of God who leads us to free-dom: glo-ry to you, Lord Je-sus Christ!

Verses

1. You   are the Word   who   calls us   out   of dark - ness;
2. You   are the one   whom   proph-ets hoped and longed   for;
3. You   are the Word   who   calls us   to   be   ser - vants;
4. You   are the Word   who   binds us   and   u - nites   us;

you   are   the Word   who   leads us   in - to light;
you   are   the one   who   speaks to   us   to - day;
you   are   the Word   whose   on - ly   law   is   love;
you   are   the Word   who   calls us   to   be   one;

you   are   the Word   who   brings   us   through the   des - ert:
you   are   the one   who   leads   us   to   our   fu - ture:
you   are   the Word - made - flesh   who   lives   a - mong   us:
you   are   the Word   who   teach - es   us   for - give - ness:

D.C.

glo - ry   to   you,   Lord   Je - sus   Christ!

Text: Bernadette Farrell, b.1957
Tune: Bernadette Farrell, b.1957
© 1986, Bernadette Farrell. Published by OCP Publications.

Tell It! Tell It Out with Gladness 518

1. Tell it! Tell it out with glad-ness— God's good news to
2. Lord, we thank thee for the treas-ure Hid with-in the
3. "Go and teach," thus spoke the Mas-ter, Ris - en vic - tor

ev - 'ry land, Sin for - giv - en, lives trans - fig - ured,
sa - cred page. We would be thy faith - ful her - alds
from the grave. Still he gives this great com - mis - sion

All in God's great lov - ing plan. In the Book is
To our deep - ly trou - bled age; We would pub - lish
To his faith - ful ones, and brave. Go and tell the

found the wit - ness To his might - y acts of yore:
thy sal - va - tion, Ev - er on thy side to stand,
gos - pel sto - ry Of what all through Christ can be.

Lis - ten, heed, o - bey, and serve him, Kneel be - fore him and a-dore.
Liv - ing, serv-ing, giv-ing, send-ing Life to quick-en ev - 'ry land.
Send it! Send it to the na - tions That God's love may set us free.

Text: Georgia Harkness, 1891-1974, © 1966, The Hymn Society. Administered by Hope Publishing Co.
Tune: HYMN TO JOY, 8 7 8 7 D; arr. from Ludwig van Beethoven, 1770-1827, by Edward Hodges, 1796-1867

519 Holy God, We Praise Thy Name

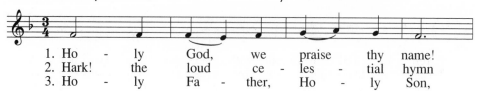

1. Ho - ly God, we praise thy name!
2. Hark! the loud ce - les - tial hymn
3. Ho - ly Fa - ther, Ho - ly Son,

Lord of all, we bow be - fore thee;
An - gel choirs a - bove are rais - ing;
Ho - ly Spir - it, Three we name thee,

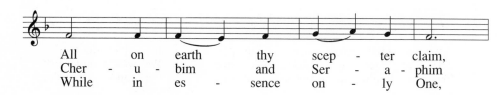

All on earth thy scep - ter claim,
Cher - u - bim and Ser - a - phim
While in es - sence on - ly One,

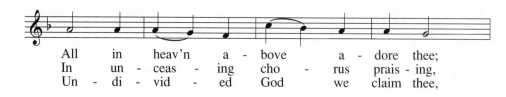

All in heav'n a - bove a - dore thee;
In un - ceas - ing cho - rus prais - ing,
Un - di - vid - ed God we claim thee,

In - fi - nite thy vast do - main,
Fill the heav'ns with sweet ac - cord:
And a - dor - ing bend the knee,

Repeat ad lib.

Ev - er - last - ing is thy reign.
Ho - ly, ho - ly, ho - ly Lord!
While we own the mys - ter - y.

Text: *Grosser Gott, wir loben dich;* ascr. to Ignaz Franz, 1719-1790; tr. by Clarence Walworth, 1820-1900
Tune: GROSSER GOTT, 7 8 7 8 77; *Katholisches Gesangbuch,* Vienna, c.1774

Joyful, Joyful, We Adore You 520

1. Joy - ful, joy - ful, we a - dore you, God of glo - ry,
2. All your works with joy sur - round you, Earth and heav'n re -
3. Al - ways giv - ing and for - giv - ing, Ev - er bless - ing,
4. Mor - tals join the might - y cho - rus, Which the morn - ing

Lord of love; Hearts un - fold like flowers be - fore you,
flect your rays, Stars and an - gels sing a - round you,
ev - er blest, Well - spring of the joy of liv - ing,
stars be - gan; God's own love is reign - ing o'er us,

Open - ing to the sun a - bove. Melt the clouds of
Cen - ter of un - bro - ken praise; Field and for - est,
O - cean depth of hap - py rest! Lov - ing Fa - ther,
Join - ing peo - ple hand in hand. Ev - er sing - ing,

sin and sad - ness; Drive the dark of doubt a - way;
vale and moun - tain, Flow - ery mead - ow, flash-ing sea,
Christ our broth - er, Let your light up - on us shine;
march we on - ward, Vic - tors in the midst of strife;

Giv - er of im - mor - tal glad-ness, Fill us with the light of day!
Chant-ing bird and flow - ing foun-tain, Prais-ing you e - ter - nal-ly!
Teach us how to love each oth - er, Lift us to the joy di-vine.
Joy - ful mu - sic leads us sun-ward In the tri - umph song of life.

Text: Henry van Dyke, 1852-1933, alt.
Tune: HYMN TO JOY, 8 7 8 7 D; arr. from Ludwig van Beethoven, 1770-1827, by Edward Hodges, 1796-1867

521 We Praise You

Verses

Cantor: *All:* We praise you,

1. For your sun that bright-ens the day:
2. For the glo - ry of all cre - a - tion:
3. For your love that greets the morn-ing: praise you,
4. For the treas - ure of joy and laugh-ter:
5. For your Word, your Ho - ly Wis - dom:

Lord! *Cantor:* *All:* We

For your moon that guides the night:
For all crea - tures great and small:
Lord! For your faith - ful - ness through night: We
For the mys - t'ry of sor - row and tears:
For the bread, the work of our hands:

praise you, Lord! *Cantor:*

For your source of light
For the seas, the hills
praise you, Lord! For your voice that sings
For the gift of love
For the wine, the cup

All: We praise you, Lord!

and breath:
and val - leys:
in all of us: praise you, Lord!
and heal - ing:
of bless - ing,

Cantor: *All:* We praise you,

For your song of death to life:
For the moun - tains strong and tall:
For your call to love and serve: We praise you,
For the awe - some pow'r of prayer:
For us all, your sa - cred pres - ence,

Lord!   All: Refrain

Lord!   We praise you,   Lord!   You

hear   our   cry!   We   praise   you,   Lord!

You are the an - swer!   We praise you,   Lord!

You   are   al - ways   near!   With

all   our   be-ing we   praise   you,   Lord!

Text: David Haas, b.1957
Tune: David Haas, b.1957
© 2002, GIA Publications, Inc.

Magnificat 522

Canon

Ma - gni - fi - cat,   ma - gni - fi - cat,   Ma - gni - fi - cat a - ni - ma

me - a   Do - mi - num.   Ma - gni - fi - cat,   ma - gni - fi - cat,

Ma - gni - fi - cat a - ni - ma   me - a!

Text: Luke 1:46, *My soul magnifies the Lord*; Taizé Community, 1978
Tune: Jacques Berthier, 1923-1994
© 1979, Les Presses de Taizé, GIA Publications, Inc., agent

523 All Creatures of Our God and King

1. All crea-tures of our God and King, Lift
2. O rush-ing wind and breez-es soft, O
3. O flow-ing wa-ters, pure and clear, Make
4. Dear moth-er earth, who day by day Un -
5. O ev-'ry one of ten-der heart, For -

up your voice and with us sing: Al-le-lu-ia! Al-le-
clouds that ride the winds a - loft: Al-le-lu-ia! Al-le-
mu - sic for your Lord to hear. Al-le-lu-ia! Al-le-
folds rich bless-ings on our way, Al-le-lu-ia! Al-le-
giv - ing oth-ers, take your part, Al-le-lu-ia! Al-le-

lu - ia! O burn-ing sun with gold-en beam And
lu - ia! O ris-ing morn, in praise re-joice, O
lu - ia! O fire so mas-ter-ful and bright, Pro -
lu - ia! The fruits and flow'rs that ver-dant grow, Let
lu - ia! All you who pain and sor-row bear, Praise

sil - ver moon with soft-er gleam:
lights of eve-ning, find a voice.
vid-ing us with warmth and light, Al-le-
them God's glo-ry al-so show.
God and cast on God your care.

lu - ia! Al-le-lu-ia! Al-le-lu-ia, al-le-

lu - ia, al-le-lu - ia!

6. And you, most kind and gentle death,
   Waiting to hush our final breath,
     Alleluia! Alleluia!
   You lead to heav'n the child of God,
   Where Christ our Lord the way has trod.
     Alleluia! Alleluia!
     Alleluia, alleluia, alleluia!

7. Let all things their Creator bless,
   And worship God in humbleness,
     Alleluia! Alleluia!
   Oh praise the Father, praise the Son,
   And praise the Spirit, Three in One!
     Alleluia! Alleluia!
     Alleluia, alleluia, alleluia!

Text: *Laudato si, mi Signor;* Francis of Assisi, 1182-1226; tr. by William H. Draper, 1855-1933, alt.
Tune: LASST UNS ERFREUEN, LM with alleluias; *Geistliche Kirchengesänge,* 1623; harm. by Ralph Vaughan Williams, 1872-1958, © Oxford
    University Press

All Glory Is Yours 524

Verses

1. How deep are your riches, your wisdom profound.
   Your knowledge surpasses all we dare imagine.
   You are God: all glory is yours!

2. God, how can we know you? Who knows your mind?
   What more can we do but serve you and love you?
   You are God: all glory is yours!

3. God, all things are from you, conceived and brought forth.
   Through you all things move, move and have being.
   Creation exults: all glory is yours!

Text: Romans 11:33-36; Bob Moore, b.1962
Tune: Bob Moore, b.1962
© 1999, GIA Publications, Inc.

525 You, Lord, Are Both Lamb and Shepherd

1. You, Lord, are both Lamb and Shep - herd.
2. Clothed in light up - on the moun - tain,
3. You, who walk each day be - side us,
4. Wor - thy is our earth - ly Je - sus!

You, Lord, are both prince and slave.
Stripped of might up - on the cross,
Sit in pow - er at God's side.
Wor - thy is our cos - mic Christ!

You, peace - mak - er and sword - bring - er
Shin - ing in e - ter - nal glo - ry,
You, who preach a way that's nar - row,
Wor - thy your de - feat and vic - t'ry.

Of the way you took and gave.
Beg - gar'd by a sol - dier's toss,
Have a love that reach - es wide.
Wor - thy still your peace and strife.

You, the ev - er - last - ing in - stant;
You, the ev - er - last - ing in - stant;
You, the ev - er - last - ing in - stant;
You, the ev - er - last - ing in - stant;

You, whom we both scorn and crave.
You, who are our gift and cost.
You, who are our pil - grim guide.
You, who are our death and life.

Text: *Christus Paradox*, Sylvia Dunstan, 1955-1993, © 1991, GIA Publications, Inc.
Tune: PICARDY, 8 7 8 7 8 7; French Carol; harm. by Richard Proulx, b.1937, © 1986, GIA Publications, Inc.

All the Ends of the Earth 526

Refrain

All the ends of the earth, all you crea-tures of the sea, lift up your eyes to the won-ders of the Lord. For the Lord of the earth, the Mas-ter of the sea, has come with jus-tice for the world.

Verse 1

1. Break in-to song at the deeds of the Lord, the won-ders he has done in ev-'ry age. *D.C.*

Verse 2

2. Heav-en and earth shall re-joice in his might; ev-'ry heart, ev-'ry na - tion call him Lord. *D.C.*

Verse 3

3. The Lord has made sal-va-tion known, faith-ful to the prom-is-es of old. Let the ends of the earth, let the sea and all it holds make mu-sic be-fore our King! *D.C.*

Text: Psalm 98; Bob Dufford, SJ, b.1943
Tune: Bob Dufford, SJ, b.1943; acc. by Bob Dufford and Chris Morash, alt.
© 1981, Robert J. Dufford, SJ, and OCP Publications

527 Canticle of the Turning

Verses

1. My soul cries out with a joy - ful shout that the God of my heart is great, And my spir - it sings of the won - drous things that you bring to the ones who wait. You fixed your sight on your ser - vant's plight, and my weak - ness you did not spurn, So from east to west shall my name be blest. Could the world be a - bout to turn?

2. Though I am small, my God, my all, you work great things in me, And your mer - cy will last from the depths of the past to the end of the age to be. Your ver - y name puts the proud to shame, and to those who would for you yearn, You will show your might, put the strong to flight, for the world is a - bout to turn.

3. From the halls of power to the for - tress tower, not a stone will be left on stone. Let the king be - ware for your jus - tice tears ev - 'ry ty - rant from his throne. The hun - gry poor shall weep no more, for the food they can nev - er earn; There are ta - bles spread, ev - 'ry mouth be fed, for the world is a - bout to turn.

4. Though the na - tions rage from age to age, we re - mem - ber who holds us fast: God's mer - cy must de - liv - er us from the con - quer - or's crush - ing grasp. This sav - ing word that our fore - bears heard is the prom - ise which holds us bound, 'Til the spear and rod can be crushed by God, who is turn - ing the world a - round.

Refrain

My heart shall sing of the day you bring. Let the
fires of your jus - tice burn. Wipe a - way all tears, for the
dawn draws near, and the world is a - bout to turn!

Text: Luke 1:46-58; Rory Cooney, b.1952
Tune: STAR OF THE COUNTY DOWN; Irish traditional; arr. by Rory Cooney, b.1952
© 1990, GIA Publications, Inc.

Laudate Dominum 528

Ostinato Refrain

Lau - da - te Do-mi-num, lau - da - te Do-mi-num om - nes
gen - tes, al - le - lu - ia. al - le - lu - ia.

Text: Psalm 117, *Praise the Lord, all you peoples;* Taizé Community, 1980
Tune: Jacques Berthier, 1923-1994
© 1980, Les Presses de Taizé, GIA Publications, Inc., agent

529 Halleluya! We Sing Your Praises

Refrain

Hal - le - lu - ya! We sing your prais-es, all our hearts are filled with glad - ness. Hal - le - lu - ya! We sing your prais-es, all our hearts are filled with glad - ness.

Verses

1. Christ the Lord to us said: I am
2. Now he sends us all out, strong in

wine,   I am   bread,   I   am   wine,   I   am
faith,   free of   doubt,   strong   in   faith,   free of

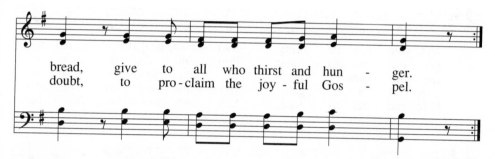

bread,   give   to   all   who   thirst   and   hun - ger.
doubt,   to   pro-claim   the   joy-ful   Gos - pel.

Text: South African
Tune: South African
© 1984, Utryck, Walton Music Corporation, agent

Let Us Sing to the Lord / Bénissez le Seigneur   530

Ostinato Refrain

(Cantor verse)

Let   us   sing   to   the   Lord!
Bé - nis - sez   le   Sei - gneur!

Let   us   sing   to   the   Lord!
Bé - nis - sez   le   Sei - gneur!

Let   us   sing   to   the   Lord!   Let   us   sing   to   the   Lord!
Bé - nis - sez   le   Sei - gneur!   Bé - nis - sez   le   Sei - gneur!

*Choose either part

Text: Daniel 3:57-75, Luke 1:46-47, 49, Psalm 5:1-2; Taizé Community
Tune: Jacques Berthier, 1923-1994
© 1998, Les Presses de Taizé, GIA Publications, Inc., agent

531 Praise, My Soul, the King of Heaven

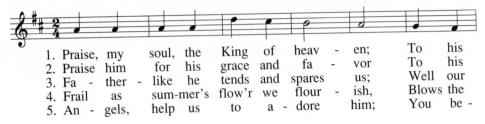

1. Praise, my soul, the King of heav - en; To his
2. Praise him for his grace and fa - vor To his
3. Fa - ther - like he tends and spares us; Well our
4. Frail as sum-mer's flow'r we flour - ish, Blows the
5. An - gels, help us to a - dore him; You be -

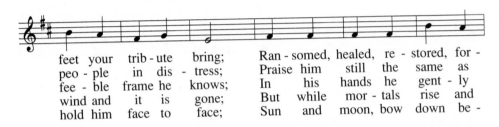

feet your trib - ute bring; Ran - somed, healed, re - stored, for -
peo - ple in dis - tress; Praise him still the same as
fee - ble frame he knows; In his hands he gent - ly
wind and it is gone; But while mor - tals rise and
hold him face to face; Sun and moon, bow down be -

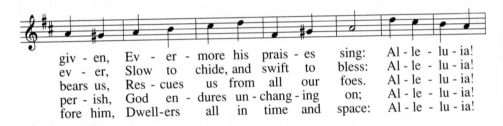

giv - en, Ev - er - more his prais - es sing: Al - le - lu - ia!
ev - er, Slow to chide, and swift to bless: Al - le - lu - ia!
bears us, Res - cues us from all our foes. Al - le - lu - ia!
per - ish, God en - dures un - chang - ing on; Al - le - lu - ia!
fore him, Dwell-ers all in time and space: Al - le - lu - ia!

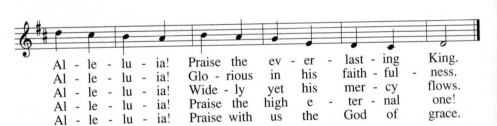

Al - le - lu - ia! Praise the ev - er - last - ing King.
Al - le - lu - ia! Glo - rious in his faith - ful - ness.
Al - le - lu - ia! Wide - ly yet his mer - cy flows.
Al - le - lu - ia! Praise the high e - ter - nal one!
Al - le - lu - ia! Praise with us the God of grace.

Text: Psalm 103; Henry F. Lyte, 1793-1847, alt.
Tune: LAUDA ANIMA, 8 7 8 7 8 7; John Goss, 1800-1880

Sing of the Lord's Goodness 532

1. Sing of the Lord's good - ness, Fa - ther of all wis - dom,
2. Pow - er he has wield - ed, hon - or is his gar - ment,
3. Cour - age in our dark - ness, com - fort in our sor - row,
4. Praise him with your sing - ing, praise him with the trum - pet,

come to him and bless his name. Mer - cy he has shown us,
ris - en from the snares of death. His word he has spo - ken,
Spir - it of our God most high; sol - ace for the wea - ry,
praise God with the lute and harp; praise him with the cym - bals,

his love is for - ev - er, faith - ful to the end of days.
one bread he has bro - ken, new life he now gives to all.
par - don for the sin - ner, splen - dor of the liv - ing God.
praise him with your danc - ing, praise God till the end of days.

Come, then, all you na - tions, sing of your Lord's good - ness,

mel - o - dies of praise and thanks to God.

Ring out the Lord's glo - ry, praise him with your mu - sic,

wor - ship him and bless his name.

Text: Ernest Sands, b.1949, © 1981, Ernest Sands
Tune: Ernest Sands, b.1949, © 1981, Ernest Sands; acc. by Paul Inwood, b.1947, © 1986, Paul Inwood
Published by OCP Publications.

533 Sing to God / Singt dem Herrn

Refrain

Sing to God with joy-ful hearts. Praise the Lord for
Singt dem Herrn ein neu-es Lied. Lob - singt ihm

ev - er - more, praise the Lord for ev - er - more.
al - le - zeit, lob - singt ihm al - le - zeit!

Verses *(Cantor)*

O

D.C.

Text: Psalm 96:2, 97:6, 98:1-8
Tune: Jacques Berthier, 1923-1994
© 1998, Les Presses de Taizé, GIA Publications, Inc., agent

534 Holy God

1. Ho - ly God, ho - ly and glo - ri - ous, Glo - ry most sub -
2. Ho - ly God, ho - ly and pow - er - ful, Pow - er with - out
3. Ho - ly God, ho - ly and beau - ti - ful, Beau - ty un - sur -
4. Ho - ly God, ho - ly and On - ly Wise, Wis - dom of great
5. Ho - ly God, ho - ly and Liv - ing One, Life that nev - er

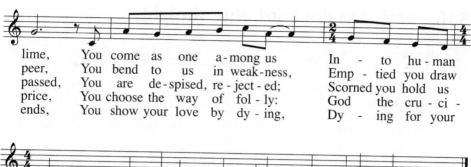

lime,	You come as one a-mong us	In - to hu - man
peer,	You bend to us in weak-ness,	Emp - tied you draw
passed,	You are de-spised, re - ject - ed;	Scorned you hold us
price,	You choose the way of fol - ly:	God the cru - ci -
ends,	You show your love by dy - ing,	Dy - ing for your

time,	And we be - hold your glo - ry.
near,	And we be - hold your pow - er.
fast,	And we be - hold your beau - ty.
fied,	Yet we be - hold your wis - dom.
friends,	And we be - hold you liv - ing.

Text: Susan R. Briehl, b.1952
Tune: MAGDALENA, 9 5 7 5 7; Marty Haugen, b.1950
© 2002, GIA Publications, Inc.

Jubilate, Servite / Raise a Song of Gladness 535

Canon—2 voices

Ju - bi - la - te De - o om - nis ter - ra.
Raise a song of glad-ness, peo-ples of the earth.

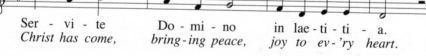

Ser - vi - te Do - mi - no in lae - ti - ti - a.
Christ has come, bring-ing peace, joy to ev - 'ry heart.

Al - le - lu - ia, al - le - lu - ia, in lae - ti - ti - a!
Al - le - lu - ia, al - le - lu - ia, joy to ev - 'ry heart!

Al - le - lu - ia, al - le - lu - ia, in lae - ti - ti - a!
Al - le - lu - ia, al - le - lu - ia, joy to ev - 'ry heart!

Text: Psalm 100, *Rejoice in God, all the earth, Serve the Lord with gladness*; Taizé Community, 1978
Tune: Jacques Berthier, 1923-1994
© 1979, Les Presses de Taizé, GIA Publications, Inc., agent

536 Praise to the Lord, the Almighty

1. Praise to the Lord, the Al - might - y, the king of cre - a - tion!
2. Praise to the Lord, a - bove all things so might - i - ly reign - ing;
3. Praise to the Lord, who shall pros - per our work and de - fend us;
4. Praise to the Lord— O let all that is in us a - dore him!

O my soul, praise him, for he is your health and sal - va - tion!
Keep - ing us safe at his side, and so gent - ly sus - tain - ing.
Sure - ly his good - ness and mer - cy shall dai - ly at - tend us.
All that has life and breath come now with prais - es be - fore him!

Come, all who hear: Broth - ers and sis - ters, draw near, Praise him in glad ad - o - ra - tion!
Have you not seen All you have need - ed has been Met by his gra - cious or - dain - ing?
Pon - der a - new What the Al - might - y can do, Who with his love will be - friend us.
Let the "A - men!" Sound from his peo - ple a - gain— Glad - ly with praise we a - dore him!

Text: *Lobe den Herren, den mächtigen König;* Joachim Neander, 1650-1680; tr. by Catherine Winkworth, 1827-1878, alt.
Tune: LOBE DEN HERREN, 14 14 47 8; *Stralsund Gesangbuch*, 1665; descant by C. S. Lang, 1891-1971, © 1953, Novello and Co. Ltd.

Glory and Praise to Our God 537

Refrain

Glo - ry and praise to our God, who a - lone gives
light to our days. Man - y are the
bless-ings he bears to those who trust in his ways.

Verses 1-3

1. We, the daugh - ters and sons of him who built the
2. In his wis - dom he strength - ens us, like gold that's
3. Ev - 'ry mo - ment of ev - 'ry day our God is

val - leys and plains, Praise the won-ders our God has
test - ed in fire. Though the pow - er of sin pre -
wait-ing to save, Al - ways read - y to seek the

D.C.

done in ev - 'ry heart that sings.
vails, our God is there to save.
lost, to an - swer those who pray.

Verse 4

4. God has wa - tered our bar - ren land and spent his
mer - ci - ful rain. Now the riv - ers of life run

D.C.

full for an - y - one to drink.

Text: Psalm 65, 66; Dan Schutte, b.1947
Tune: Dan Schutte, b.1947; acc. by Sr. Theophane Hytrek, OSF, 1915-1992, alt.
© 1976, Daniel L. Schutte and OCP Publications

538 You Are the Voice

Refrain

You are the voice of the liv - ing God,

call-ing us now to live in your love, to be

chil-dren of God once a - gain!

Verses

Cantor:

1. Praise for the light that shines through the night, from
2. Praise for the wa - ter that springs from the sea, the
3. Praise for the sing-ing and praise for the dance, with

dark - ness to light, from death to new life, and
seed that gives life to all who be - lieve, God's
new heart and voice, all raise the song of

praise to the morn-ing that brings forth the sun, to
love o - ver - flow-ing, our hearts know the joy to be
praise to cre - a - tion; all heav - en and earth, come

All:

o - pen our eyes to the Lord! To
daugh-ters and sons of the Lord! To be
sing of the glo - ry of God! Come

D.C.

o - pen our eyes to the Lord! For
daugh-ters and sons of the Lord! For
sing of the glo - ry of God! For

Text: David Haas, b.1957
Tune: David Haas, b.1957; acc. by Jeanne Cotter, b.1964
© 1983, 1987, GIA Publications, Inc.

When, in Our Music, God Is Glorified 539

1. When, in our mu - sic, God is glo - ri - fied,
2. How of - ten, mak - ing mu - sic, we have found
3. So has the Church, in lit - ur - gy and song,
4. And did not Je - sus sing a psalm that night
5. Let ev - 'ry in - stru-ment be tuned for praise!

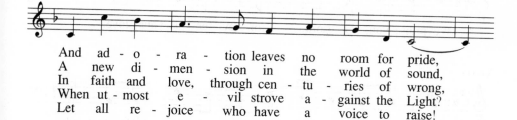

And ad - o - ra - tion leaves no room for pride,
A new di - men - sion in the world of sound,
In faith and love, through cen - tu - ries of wrong,
When ut - most e - vil strove a - gainst the Light?
Let all re - joice who have a voice to raise!

It is as though the whole cre - a - tion cried:
As wor - ship moved us to a more pro - found
Borne wit - ness to the truth in ev - 'ry tongue:
Then let us sing, for whom he won the fight:
And may God give us faith to sing al - ways:

Al - le - lu - ia!

Text: Mark 14:26; Fred Pratt Green, 1903-2000, © 1972, Hope Publishing Co.
Tune: ENGELBERG, 10 10 10 with alleluia; Charles V. Stanford, 1852-1924

540 We Praise You

Refrain

We praise you, O Lord,   for all your works are won-der-ful.

We praise you, O Lord,   for ev-er is your love.

Verses

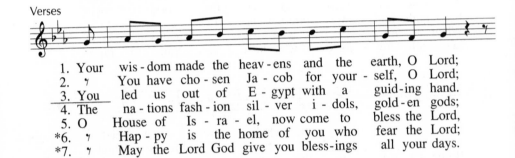

1. Your wis-dom made the heav-ens and the earth, O Lord;
2. ⸭ You have cho-sen Ja-cob for your-self, O Lord;
3. You led us out of E-gypt with a guid-ing hand.
4. The na-tions fash-ion sil-ver i-dols, gold-en gods;
5. O House of Is-ra-el, now come to bless the Lord,
*6. ⸭ Hap-py is the home of you who fear the Lord;
*7. ⸭ May the Lord God give you bless-ings all your days.

You formed the land then set the lights;
So ten-der-ly you spoke his name;
You raised your arm to set us free.
But none have hear-ing, speech or sight.
O House of Aar-on, bless God's name.
So fruit-ful shall your love be-come.
⸭ May you see God fill your land

And like your love the sun will rule the day,
Then called a ho-ly na-tion, Is-ra-el,
And like a ten-der vine you plant-ed us
Their mak-ers shall be like their emp-ty gods,
O bless the Lord, all you who hon-or God,
Your chil-dren flour-ish like the ol-ive plants,
Un-til your chil-dren bring their chil-dren home

*wedding verses

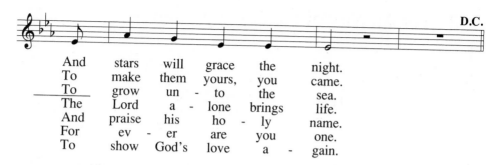

And stars will grace the night.
To make them yours, you came.
To grow un - to the sea.
The Lord a - lone brings life.
And praise his ho - ly name.
For ev - er are you one.
To show God's love a - gain.

Text: Mike Balhoff, b.1946
Tune: Darryl Ducote, b.1945, Gary Daigle, b.1957
© 1978, Damean Music. Distributed by GIA Publications, Inc.

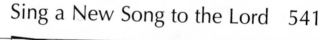

Sing a New Song to the Lord 541

1. Sing a new song to the Lord, He to whom won-ders be -
2. Now to the ends of the earth See his sal - va - tion is
3. Sing a new song and re-joice, Pub - lish his prais - es a -
4. Join with the hills and the sea Thun-ders of praise to pro -

long! Re - joice in his tri - umph and tell of his
shown; And still he re - mem-bers his mer - cy and
broad! Let voic - es in cho - rus, with trum - pet and
long! In judg - ment and jus - tice he comes to the

power, O sing to the Lord a new song!
truth, Un - chang - ing in love to his own.
horn, Re - sound for the joy of the Lord!
earth, O sing to the Lord a new song!

Text: Psalm 98; Timothy Dudley-Smith, b.1926, © 1973, Hope Publishing Co.
Tune: CANTATE DOMINO (ONSLOW SQUARE), Irregular; David G. Wilson, b.1940, © 1973, Jubilate Hymns, Ltd. (admin. by Hope Publishing Co.)

542 Let All Mortal Flesh Keep Silence

1. Let all mor - tal flesh keep si - lence,
2. King of kings, yet born of Mar - y,
3. Rank on rank the host of heav - en
4. At his feet the six - winged ser - aph,

And with fear and trem - bling stand;
As of old on earth he stood,
Spreads its van - guard on the way,
Cher - u - bim with sleep - less eye,

Pon - der noth - ing earth - ly mind - ed,
Lord of lords in hu - man ves - ture,
As the Light of Light de - scend - ing
Veil their fac - es to the Pres - ence,

For with bless - ing in his hand
In the Bod - y and the Blood
From the realms of end - less day,
As with cease - less voice they cry,

Christ our God to earth de - scend -
He will give to all the faith
That the pow'rs of hell may van -
"Al - le - lu - ia, al - le - lu -

ing, Our full hom - age to de - mand.
ful His own self for heav'n - ly food.
ish As the dark - ness clears a - way.
ia, Al - le - lu - ia, Lord, most high!"

Text: Liturgy of St. James, 5th C.; para. by Gerard Moultrie, 1829-1885
Tune: PICARDY, 8 7 8 7 8 7; French Carol; harm. by Richard Proulx, b.1937, © 1986, GIA Publications, Inc.

Lift Up Your Hearts   543

Refrain

Lift up your hearts to the Lord, praise God's gra-cious mer - cy! Sing out your joy to the Lord, whose love is en - dur - ing.

Verses

1. Shout with joy to the Lord, all the earth!
2. Let the earth wor - ship, sing - ing your praise.
3. God's right hand made a path through the night,
4. Lis - ten now, all you ser - vants of God,

Praise the name a - bove all names! Say to God, "How
Praise the glo - ry of your name! Come and see what
split the wa - ters of the sea. All cre - a - tion,
As I tell of these great works. Bless - ed be the

D.C.

won - drous your works, how glo - rious your name!"
God has re - vealed, bless God's ho - ly name!
lift up your voice: Our God set us free.
Lord of my life, whose love shall en - dure!

Text: Psalm 66; Roc O'Connor, SJ, b.1949
Tune: Roc O'Connor, SJ, b.1949; acc. by Robert J. Batastini, b.1942
© 1981, 1993, Robert F. O'Connor, SJ, and OCP Publications

544 Sing a New Song

Refrain

Sing a new song un-to the Lord; let your song be sung from moun-tains high. Sing a new song un-to the Lord, sing-ing al - le - lu - ia.

Verses

1. Yah - weh's peo - ple dance for joy. O come be - fore the Lord. And play for him on glad tam - bou - rines, and let your trum - pet sound.
2. Rise, O chil - dren, from your sleep; your Sav - ior now has come. He has turned your sor - row to joy, and filled your soul with song.
3. Glad my soul for I have seen the glo - ry of the Lord. The trum - pet sounds; the dead shall be raised. I know my Sav - ior lives.

Text: Psalm 98; Dan Schutte, b.1947
Tune: Dan Schutte, b.1947
© 1972, Daniel L. Schutte. Published by OCP Publications.

Now Thank We All Our God 545

1. Now thank we all our God With hearts and hands and
2. O may this gra-cious God Through all our life be
3. All praise and thanks to God The Fa - ther now be

voic - es, Who won - drous things has done, In
near us, With ev - er joy - ful hearts And
giv - en, The Son, and Spir - it blest, Who

whom his world re - joic - es; Who, from our moth-ers'
bless - ed peace to cheer us; Pre - serve us in his
reigns in high - est heav - en, E - ter - nal, Tri - une

arms, Hath blest us on our way With
grace, And guide us in dis - tress, And
God, Whom earth and heav'n a - dore; For

count-less gifts of love, And still is ours to - day.
free us from all sin, Till heav - en we pos - sess.
thus it was, is now, And shall be ev - er - more.

Text: *Nun danket alle Gott;* Martin Rinkart, 1586-1649; tr. by Catherine Winkworth, 1827-1878, alt.
Tune: NUN DANKET, 6 7 6 7 6 6 6 6; Johann Crüger, 1598-1662; harm. by A. Gregory Murray, OSB, 1905-1992

546 In the Lord I'll Be Ever Thankful

Ostinato Refrain

In the Lord I'll be ev - er thank - ful, in the Lord I will re - joice! Look to God, do not be a - fraid; lift up your voic - es, the Lord is near; lift up your voic - es, the Lord is near.

Text: Taizé Community
Tune: Jacques Berthier, 1923-1994
© 1986, 1991, Les Presses de Taizé, GIA Publications, Inc., agent

Father, We Thank Thee, Who Hast Planted 547

1. Fa - ther, we thank thee, who hast plant - ed
2. Watch o'er thy Church, O Lord, in mer - cy,

Thy ho - ly Name with - in our hearts.
Save it from e - vil, guard it still,

Knowl - edge and faith and life im - mor - tal
Per - fect it in thy love, u - nite it,

Je - sus, thy Son, to us im - parts.
Cleansed and con - formed un - to thy will.

Thou, Lord, didst make all for thy pleas - ure,
As grain, once scat - ter'd on the hill - sides,

Didst give us food for all our days,
Was in this bro - ken bread made one,

Giv - ing in Christ the Bread e - ter - nal;
So from all lands thy Church be gath - er'd

Thine is the power, be thine the praise.
In - to thy king - dom by thy Son.

Text: From the *Didache*, c.110; tr. by F. Bland Tucker, 1895-1984, alt., © 1940, The Church Pension Fund
Tune: RENDEZ À DIEU, 9 8 9 8 D; *Genevan Psalter*, 1551; attr. to Louis Bourgeois, c.1510-1561

548 For the Beauty of the Earth

1. For the beau - ty of the earth, For the glo - ry
2. For the beau - ty of each hour Of the day and
3. For the joy of ear and eye, For the heart and
4. For the joy of hu - man love, Broth - er, sis - ter,
5. For your church, that ev - er - more Lifts its ho - ly
6. For your - self, best Gift Di - vine! To this world so

of the skies, For the love which from our birth
of the night, Hill and vale, and tree and flow'r,
mind's de - light, For the mys - tic har - mo - ny
par - ent, child, Friends on earth, and friends a - bove;
hands a - bove, Of - f'ring up on ev - 'ry shore
free - ly giv'n; Word In - car - nate, God's de - sign,

O - ver and a - round us lies:
Sun and moon, and stars of light:
Link - ing sense to sound and sight: Lord of all, to
For all gen - tle thoughts and mild:
Its pure sac - ri - fice of love:
Peace on earth and joy in heav'n:

you we raise This our hymn of grate - ful praise.

Text: Folliot S. Pierpont, 1835-1917
Tune: DIX, 7 7 7 7 77; arr. from Conrad Kocher, 1786-1872, by William H. Monk, 1823-1889

549 We Gather Together

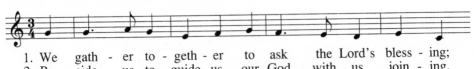

1. We gath - er to - geth - er to ask the Lord's bless - ing;
2. Be - side us to guide us, our God with us join - ing,
3. We all do ex - tol you our lead - er tri - um - phant,

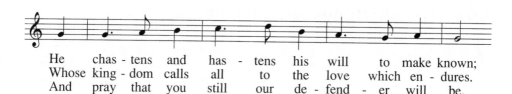

He chas - tens and has - tens his will to make known;
Whose king - dom calls all to the love which en - dures.
And pray that you still our de - fend - er will be.

The wick - ed op - press - ing now cease from dis - tress - ing:
So from the be - gin - ning the fight we were win - ning:
Let your con - gre - ga - tion es - cape trib - u - la - tion:

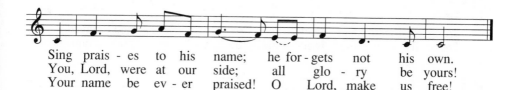

Sing prais - es to his name; he for - gets not his own.
You, Lord, were at our side; all glo - ry be yours!
Your name be ev - er praised! O Lord, make us free!

Text: *Wilt heden nu treden,* Netherlands folk hymn; tr. by Theodore Baker, 1851-1934, alt.
Tune: KREMSER, 12 11 12 11; *Neder-landtsch Gedenckclanck,* 1626; harm. by Edward Kremser, 1838-1914

Confitemini Domino / Come and Fill   550

Ostinato Refrain

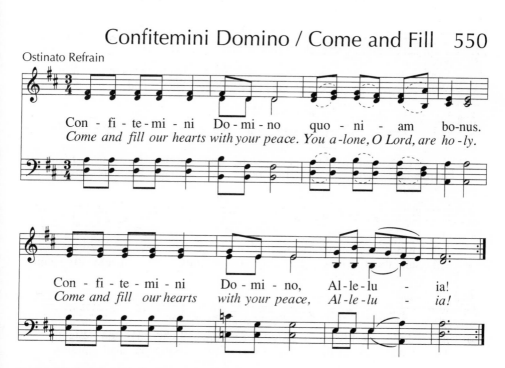

Con - fi - te - mi - ni Do - mi - no quo - ni - am bo-nus.
Come and fill our hearts with your peace. You a -lone, O Lord, are ho -ly.

Con - fi - te - mi - ni Do - mi - no, Al - le - lu - ia!
Come and fill our hearts with your peace, Al - le -lu - ia!

Text: Psalm 137, *Give thanks to the Lord for he is good;* Taizé Community, 1982
Tune: Jacques Berthier, 1923-1994
© 1982, 1991, Les Presses de Taizé, GIA Publications, Inc., agent

551 Let All Things Now Living

1. Let all things now liv - ing A song of thanks - giv - ing
2. His law he en - forc - es, The stars in their cours - es,

To God our Cre - a - tor tri - um - phant - ly raise;
The sun in its or - bit o - be - dient - ly shine,

Who fash-ioned and made us, Pro - tect - ed and stayed us,
The hills and the moun - tains, The riv - ers and foun - tains,

By guid - ing us on to the end of our days.
The depths of the o - cean pro - claim God di - vine.

God's ban - ners are o'er us, Pure light goes be - fore us,
We, too, should be voic - ing Our love and re - joic - ing

A pil - lar of fire shin - ing forth in the night:
With glad ad - o - ra - tion, a song let us raise:

Till shad - ows have van-ished And dark - ness is ban-ished,
Till all things now liv - ing U - nite in thanks - giv - ing,

As for - ward we trav - el from light in - to Light.
To God in the high - est, ho - san - na and praise.

Text: Katherine K. Davis, 1892-1980, © 1939, E.C. Schirmer Music Co.
Tune: ASH GROVE, 66 11 66 11 D; Welsh; harm. by Gerald H. Knight, 1908-1979, © The Royal School of Church Music

Come, Ye Thankful People, Come 552

1. Come, ye thank-ful peo-ple, come, Raise the song of har-vest-home: All is safe-ly gath-ered in, Ere the win-ter storms be-gin; God, our Mak-er, does pro-vide For our wants to be sup-plied; Come to God's own tem-ple, come, Raise the song of har-vest-home.

2. All the world is God's own field, Fruit un-to God's praise to yield; Wheat and tares to-geth-er sown, Un-to joy or sor-row grown; First the blade, and then the ear, Then the full corn shall ap-pear: Lord of har-vest, grant that we Whole-some grain and pure may be.

3. For the Lord our God shall come, And shall take the har-vest home; From the field shall in that day All of-fens-es purge a-way, Giv-ing an-gels charge at last In the fire the tares to cast, But the fruit-ful ears to store In God's gar-ner ev-er-more.

4. E-ven so, Lord, quick-ly come To your fi-nal har-vest home; Gath-er all your peo-ple in, Free from sor-row, free from sin; There, for ev-er pu-ri-fied, In your pres-ence to a-bide: Come, with all your an-gels, come, Raise the glo-rious har-vest-home.

Text: Henry Alford, 1810-1871, alt.
Tune: ST. GEORGE'S WINDSOR, 77 77 D; George J. Elvey, 1816-1893; harm. by Richard Proulx, b.1937, © 1986, GIA Publications, Inc.

553 We Give You Thanks

Verses

1. For the bread and wine we share here,
2. For the move-ment deep with-in us,
3. For the wa-ter bring-ing new life,

for the friends that we em-brace,
for the sto-ries that we bring,
for the fra-grance of re-lease,

for the peace we find in heal-ing,
for the signs of God's com-pas-sion,
for the fire that blaz-es for-ward,

for all who gath-er in this place,
for the jour-ney that we sing,
for the call to bring forth peace,

for the faith of those a-round us,
for the Word that holds our prom-ise,
for the blind-ness now en-light-ened,

for the dead and all those here,
for the gifts that we can claim,
for the bound that are now free,

for the hope we find in mem-'ry,
for the won-ders that sur-round us,
for the bright-ness of your new day,

for the love that draws us near:
for the song that sings our name:
for the king - dom we will be:

Refrain

We give you thanks, we give you thanks

for the grace to re - ceive, in you we be - lieve. We

give you thanks, we give you thanks. With

faith and hope and love, we give you thanks.

A Celtic Rune 554

Lord, hear our prayer.   Lord, hear our prayer.

Lord, in your mer - cy, Lord, hear our prayer.

555 Lead Me, Guide Me

Refrain

Lead me, guide me, a-long the way, For if you
lead me, I can-not stray. Lord, let me walk each
day with thee. Lead me, oh Lord, lead me.

Verses

1. I am weak and I need thy strength and pow'r to
2. Help me tread in the paths of right-eous-ness,
3. I am lost if you take your hand from me,

help me o-ver my weak-est hour. Help me through the
aid when Sa-tan and sin op-press. I am put-ting
blind with-out thy Light to see, Lord, just al-ways

D.C.

dark-ness thy face to see, Lead me, oh Lord, lead me.
all my trust in thee. Lead me, oh Lord, lead me.
let me thy ser-vant be. Lead me, oh Lord, lead me.

Text: Doris M. Akers, 1922-1995
Tune: Doris M. Akers, 1922-1995; harm. by Richard Smallwood
© 1953, Doris M. Akers, All rights administered by Unichappell Music, Inc.

O Lord, the Guardian of My Heart 556

Refrain

O Lord, the guard - ian of my heart, who rules the day and night, you guide me through my dark - est hours and lead me in - to light.

Verses

1. Teach me the way of your truth,
2. Take my weak - ness, O God.
3. Wipe a - way my fear,

help me to know your wis - dom. Keep me in your
Build my strength in faith. Save me in your
lift me from my sor - row. Wash a - way my

D.C.

pres - ence, Lord, show me how to love.
mer - cy, Lord, clothe me with your grace.
bro - ken - ness, heal my wound - ed soul.

Text: Carol E. Browning, b.1956
Tune: Carol E. Browning, b.1956
© 2000, GIA Publications, Inc.

557 Make Us Worthy

Refrain

Lord, make us wor-thy. Make us wor-thy to see your face.

Fill us with your word, O Lord, and heal us with your grace.

Verses

1. O - pen up your ten - der arms
2. Of - fer all your praise to God
3. You are strength when we are weak.
4. Fash - ion plough - shares from our swords.
5. Lord, you sent your heal - ing word

for your lost ones have come home.
who has blessed us with great love.
You are warmth when we are cold.
Rip the ha - tred from our minds.
to re - deem us from our sins.

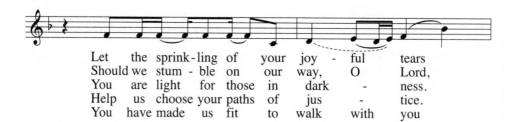

Let the sprink-ling of your joy - ful tears
Should we stum - ble on our way, O Lord,
You are light for those in dark - ness.
Help us choose your paths of jus - tice.
You have made us fit to walk with you

D.C.

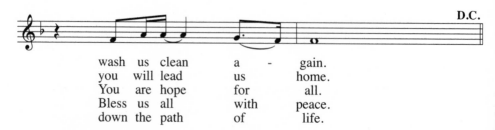

wash us clean a - gain.
you will lead us home.
You are hope for all.
Bless us all with peace.
down the path of life.

Text: Michael Mahler, b.1981
Tune: Michael Mahler, b.1981
© 2003, GIA Publications, Inc.

We Cannot Measure How You Heal   558

1. We can - not meas - ure how you heal Or
2. The pain that will not go a - way, The
3. So some have come who need your help And

an - swer ev - 'ry suf - f'rer's prayer, Yet
guilt that clings from things long past, The
some have come to make a - mends, As

we be - lieve your grace re - sponds Where faith and
fear of what the fu - ture holds, Are pres - ent
hands which shaped and saved the world Are pres - ent

doubt u - nite to care. Your hands, though blood - ied
as if meant to last. But pres - ent too is
in the touch of friends. Lord, let your Spir - it

on the cross, Sur - vive to hold and heal and
love which tends The hurt we nev - er hoped to
meet us here To mend the bod - y, mind, and

warn, To car - ry all through death to
find, The pri - vate ag - o - nies in -
soul, To dis - en - tan - gle peace from

life And cra - dle chil - dren yet un - born.
side, The mem - o - ries that haunt the mind.
pain, And make your bro - ken peo - ple whole.

Text: John L. Bell, b.1949
Tune: YE BANKS AND BRAES, 8 8 8 8 D; Scottish traditional; arr. by John L. Bell, b.1949
© 1989, Iona Community, GIA Publications, Inc., agent

559 Song over the Waters

Refrain

God, you have moved up-on the wa-ters, you have sung in the rush of wind and flame; and in your love, you have called us sons and daugh-ters, make us peo-ple of the wa-ter and your name.

Verses

1. Come fill our wait - ing hearts   with the
2. Give us a thirst for love, give us a
3. You are the breath of life, you are the
4. Come, o - pen ev - 'ry heart, come now and

spir - it of Je - sus, let us shine with your
hun - ger for jus - tice, make us one with the
hope of the hope - less, come and fill us with
wake us to won - der, make us ves - sels of

D.C.

light and peace.
mind of Christ.
light and peace.
light and peace.

Sprinkling Rite

Cantor: *All:*

(*Invocation*) Re - new us!

Cantor: *All:* D.C.

(*Invocation*) Re - new us!

Text: Marty Haugen, b.1950
Tune: Marty Haugen, b.1950
© 1987, GIA Publications, Inc.

Lord of All Hopefulness   560

1. Lord of all hope - ful - ness, Lord of all joy,
2. Lord of all ea - ger - ness, Lord of all faith,
3. Lord of all kind - li - ness, Lord of all grace,
4. Lord of all gen - tle - ness, Lord of all calm,

Whose trust, e - ver child - like, no cares can de - stroy,
Whose strong hands were skilled at the plane and the lathe,
Your hands swift to wel - come, your arms to em - brace,
Whose voice is con - tent - ment, whose pres - ence is balm,

Be there at our wak - ing, and give us, we pray,
Be there at our la - bors, and give us, we pray,
Be there at our hom - ing, and give us, we pray,
Be there at our sleep - ing, and give us, we pray,

Your bliss in our hearts, Lord, at the break of the day.
Your strength in our hearts, Lord, at the noon of the day.
Your love in our hearts, Lord, at the eve of the day.
Your peace in our hearts, Lord, at the end of the day.

Text: Jan Struther, 1901-1953, © Oxford University Press
Tune: SLANE, 10 11 11 12; Gaelic; harm. by Erik Routley, 1917-1982, © 1975, Hope Publishing Co.

561 Turn My Heart, O God

Refrain

Turn my heart, O God. Turn my heart, O
God. Take my pain and bro-ken-ness; shape my life for
you. Come and turn my heart, O God.

To verses | *To repeat refrain and last time*

Verses

turn my heart, O God.

Cantor:

1. From all that leads to death, to
2. From bit - ter - ness and hate, to
3. O let your Spir - it come and
4. O bring me home to you, Most

Assembly:

Come and turn my heart, O

seek the way of life: From
ten - der-ness and care: From
cleanse my in - most heart: Give
Ho - ly, Bless-ed One: And

God.   *Assembly:*
                                                         Come and

all that leads to sin,   to   ho - li - ness and grace:
self - ish - ness and greed, to   gen - 'rous car - ing love:
back to   me the joy   of walk - ing in your way:
let my spir - it rest   with - in your lov - ing heart:

turn   my heart, O   God.

                From all   de - spair and grief,   to
                From all   de - ceit and lies,   to
                O   fill   me with your grace   that
                For you a - lone can raise   my

Assembly: D.C.

Come and turn my heart, O   God.

                                                    D.C.

hope of life re - newed:
faith - ful - ness and truth:
I   might sing your praise:
wea - ry soul to   life:

Text: Marty Haugen, b.1950
Tune: Marty Haugen, b.1950
© 2002, GIA Publications, Inc.

562   I Lift My Soul to You

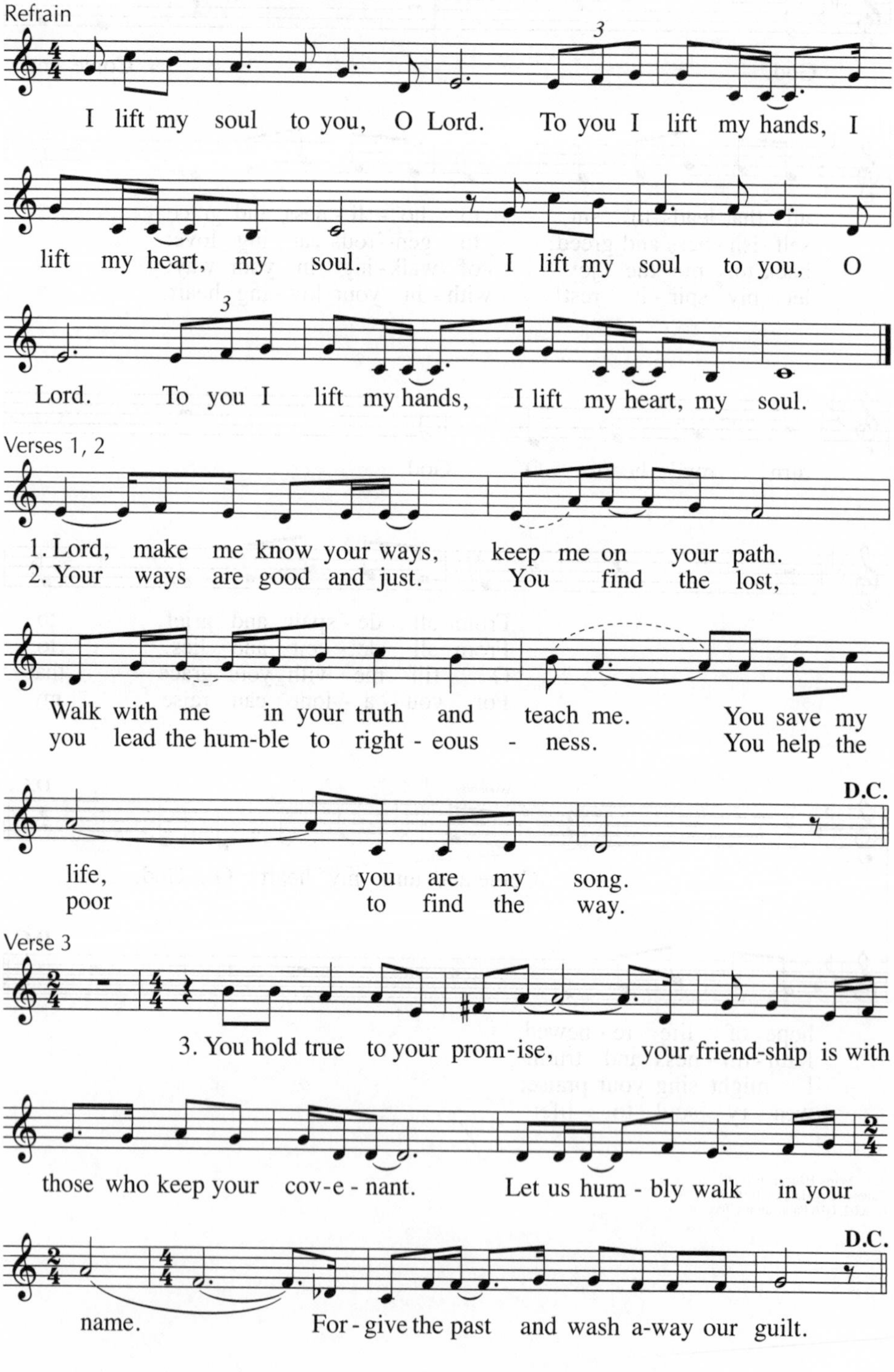

Refrain

I lift my soul to you, O Lord. To you I lift my hands, I

lift my heart, my soul. I lift my soul to you, O

Lord. To you I lift my hands, I lift my heart, my soul.

Verses 1, 2

1. Lord, make me know your ways, keep me on your path.
2. Your ways are good and just. You find the lost,

Walk with me in your truth and teach me. You save my
you lead the hum-ble to right - eous - ness. You help the

D.C.

life, you are my song.
poor to find the way.

Verse 3

3. You hold true to your prom-ise, your friend-ship is with

those who keep your cov-e - nant. Let us hum - bly walk in your

D.C.

name. For - give the past and wash a-way our guilt.

How Shall We Name God? 563

Verses

1. Source and Sov-'reign, Rock and Cloud, For - tress, Foun-tain,
2. Word and Wis - dom, Root and Vine, Shep - herd, Sav - ior,
3. Storm and Still - ness, Breath and Dove, Thun - der, Tem - pest,

Shel - ter, Light, Judge, De - fend - er, Mer - cy, Might,
Ser - vant, Lamb, Well and Wa - ter, Bread and Wine,
Whirl - wind, Fire, Com - fort, Coun-sel - or, Pres-ence,

1., 2. | *To refrain* | 3. | *To refrain*

Life whose life all life en - dowed:
Way who leads us to I AM:

En-er-gies that nev-er tire:

Refrain

May the church at prayer re - call That no sin-gle ho - ly

name But the truth be - hind them all Is the

To verses | D.C. | *Last time*

God whom we pro - claim. claim.

Text: Thomas H. Troeger, b.1945, © 1987, Oxford University Press
Tune: BIRINUS, 7 7 7 7 D; Paul Inwood, b.1947, © 2003, GIA Publications, Inc.

564 Healing River

1., 4. O heal - ing riv - er, send down your
2. This land is thirst - ing, this land is

wa - ters, Send down your wa - ters up - on this
parch - ing, No seed is grow - ing in the bar - ren

land. O heal - ing riv - er, send down your
ground. This land is thirst - ing, this land is

wa - ters, And wash the blood from off the
parch - ing, O heal - ing riv - er, send your wa - ters

1., 3.   *Last time*   *2.*

sand. down. 3. Let the seed of

free - dom, a - wake and flour - ish, Let the deep roots

nour - ish, let the tall stalks rise. Let the seed of

free - dom, a - wake and flour - ish, Proud leaves un -

D.C.

curl - ing a - gainst the skies.

The assembly echoes each phrase of the cantor at the interval of one half measure.

Text: Fran Minkoff
Tune: Fred Hellerman; arr. by Michael Joncas, b.1951
© 1964 (renewed), Appleseed Music, Inc.

Increase Our Faith 565

Refrain

Lord, in-crease our faith. With all our heart, may we

al-ways fol-low you. Teach us to pray al - ways.

Verses 1, 3

1. So I say to you: "ask, you will re-ceive;
3. If you, with all your sins, know how to give,

seek and you will find. Knock, it shall be
how much more will God give to all those who

D.C.

o - pened to you."
cry from their hearts!

Verse 2

2. Who-ev-er asks, they shall re-ceive; who - ev-er seeks shall

D.C.

find. Who-ev-er knocks, the door will be o - pened.

Text: Based on Luke 11:1-13, 17:5; David Haas, b.1957
Tune: David Haas, b.1957
© 1997, GIA Publications, Inc.

566 O Lord, Hear My Prayer

Ostinato Chorale

O Lord, hear my prayer, O Lord, hear my prayer:
*The Lord is my song, the Lord is my praise:

when I call an - swer me. O Lord, hear my prayer, O
all my hope comes from God. The Lord is my song, the

Lord, hear my prayer. Come and lis - ten to me. O
Lord is my praise: God, the well-spring of life. The

*Alternate text

Text: Psalm 102; Taizé Community, 1982
Tune: Jacques Berthier, 1923-1994
© 1982, Les Presses de Taizé, GIA Publications, Inc., agent

567 Down to the River to Pray

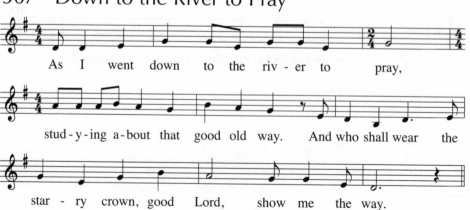

As I went down to the riv - er to pray,

stud - y - ing a - bout that good old way. And who shall wear the

star - ry crown, good Lord, show me the way.

Oh *broth-er let's go down, come on down, don't you

want to go down? Oh broth-er, let's go down,

down to the riv-er to pray.

*Sister, father, mother.

Text: American folk song
Tune: American folk song; arr. by Robert J. Batastini, b.1942, © 2003, GIA Publications, Inc.

Ubi Caritas 568

Refrain
Last time

U-bi cá-ri-tas et a-mor De-us i-bi est.

Verses

1. We feel your pres-ence here, your love and com-fort near.
*2a. And now we break this bread, our souls and bod-ies fed.
2b. And so we come to you, we need to be re-newed.
3. Bless us, your peo-ple, Lord, that we may serve the world.
4. So as we live each day, Lord, help us, that we may

As you wel-come us, fill our ev-'ry need,
Hear us as we pray, from this ta-ble, Lord,
Take our gifts, O Lord, use us for your good.
Wash a-way our sin, cleanse us from with-in.
keep our hearts and minds o-pen to your love that

D.C.

are we gra-cious hosts to those we meet?
let us be your pres-ence in the world.
Help us love each oth-er as we should.
Send us forth with strength to do your will.
char-i-ty and love in us a-bound.

*Verse 2a for Communion, verse 2b for other occasions.

Text: 1 Corinthians 13:2-8; *Where charity and love are found, God is there;* verses, Carol E. Browning, b.1956, © 1998, GIA Publications, Inc.
Tune: Carol E. Browning, b.1956, © 1998, GIA Publications, Inc.

569 Open My Eyes

Verses

1. O - pen my eyes, Lord. Help me to see your face.
2. O - pen my ears, Lord. Help me to hear your voice.
3. O - pen my heart, Lord. Help me to love like you.

O - pen my eyes, Lord. Help me to see. *(To verse 2)*
O - pen my ears, Lord. Help me to hear. *(To bridge)*
O - pen my heart, Lord. Help me to love.

Bridge

And the first shall be last, and our eyes are o - pened,

and we'll hear like nev-er be - fore. And we'll speak in new ways,

D.C.

and we'll see God's face in plac-es we've nev-er known.

Text: Based on Mark 8:22-25; Jesse Manibusan, b.1958
Tune: Jesse Manibusan, b.1958
© 1988, 1998, 1999, Jesse Manibusan. Published by OCP Publications.

570 O God, Why Are You Silent?

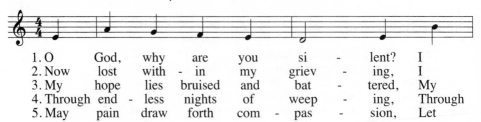

1. O God, why are you si - lent? I
2. Now lost with - in my griev - ing, I
3. My hope lies bruised and bat - tered, My
4. Through end - less nights of weep - ing, Through
5. May pain draw forth com - pas - sion, Let

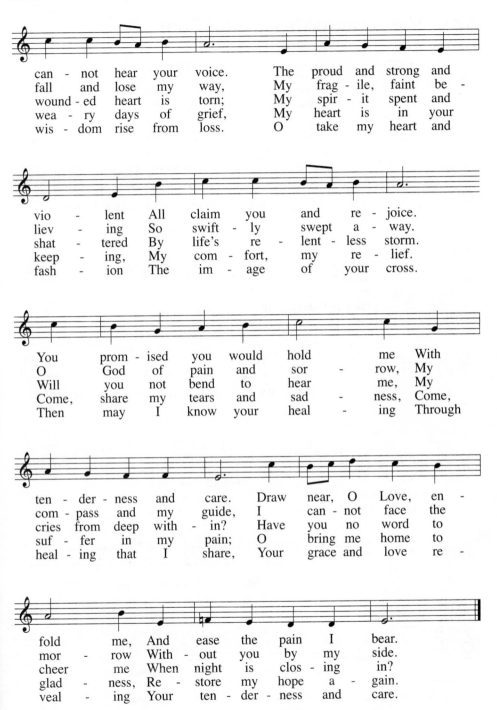

can - not hear your voice. The proud and strong and
fall and lose my way, My frag - ile, faint be -
wound - ed heart is torn; My spir - it spent and
wea - ry days of grief, My heart is in your
wis - dom rise from loss. O take my heart and

vio - lent All claim you and re - joice.
liev - ing So swift - ly swept a - way.
shat - tered By life's re - lent - less storm.
keep - ing, My com - fort, my re - lief.
fash - ion The im - age of your cross.

You prom - ised you would hold me With
O God of pain and sor - row, My
Will you not bend to hear me, My
Come, share my tears and sad - ness, Come,
Then may I know your heal - ing Through

ten - der - ness and care. Draw near, O Love, en -
com - pass and my guide, I can - not face the
cries from deep with - in? Have you no word to
suf - fer in my pain; O bring me home to
heal - ing that I share, Your grace and love re -

fold me, And ease the pain I bear.
mor - row With - out you by my side.
cheer me When night is clos - ing in?
glad - ness, Re - store my hope a - gain.
veal - ing Your ten - der - ness and care.

Text: Marty Haugen, b.1950, © 2003, GIA Publications, Inc.
Tune: PASSION CHORALE, 7 6 7 6 D; Hans Leo Hassler, 1564-1612; harm. by Marty Haugen, b.1950, © 2003, GIA Publications, Inc.

571 We Await with Wakeful Care

Verses

Cantor:

1. Sit - ting with a child in sick - ness,
2. Yearn - ing for a graced for - give - ness;
3. Thirst - ing for a day of jus - tice,

Assembly:

We a - wait with wake-ful care.

list - 'ning for a cry of pain,
sore, re - pent - ing; deep in need;
hun - g'ring, plead - ing, now we kneel;

We a - wait with wake - ful care.

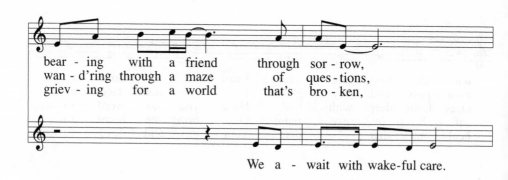

bear - ing with a friend through sor - row,
wan - d'ring through a maze of ques - tions,
griev - ing for a world that's bro - ken,

We a - wait with wake-ful care.

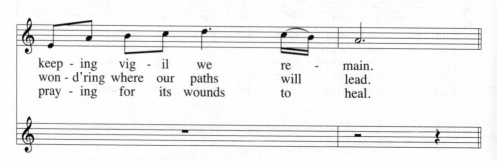

keep - ing vig - il we re - main.
won - d'ring where our paths will lead.
pray - ing for its wounds to heal.

Refrain

More than watch - ers for the morn - ing, we a -

wait with wake - ful care, hop - ing through the night of weep - ing our

God will lift us from de - spair.

Text: Mary Louise Bringle, b.1953, © 2002, GIA Publications, Inc.
Tune: Lori True, b.1961, © 2003, GIA Publications, Inc.

God Remembers 572

1. God re - mem - bers pain: Nail by nail, thorn by thorn,
2. God re - mem - bers joy: Touch of love, taste of food,
3. God re - mem - bers us: All we were, all we are,

Hun - ger, thirst, and mus - cles torn.   Time may dull our griefs   And
All our sens - es know is good.   Love and life flow by   And
Lives with - in our Lov - er's care.   Time may dull our minds   And

heal our less - er wounds, But in e - ter - nal Love Yes - ter - day is
pre - cious days are gone, But in e - ter - nal Love Ev - 'ry day is
death will take us all, But in e - ter - nal Love Ev - 'ry life is

now, And pain is in the heart of God.
now, And joy is in the heart of God.
now: Our life is hid with Christ in God.

Text: Colossians 3:3-4; Brian Wren, b.1936, © 1993, Hope Publishing Co.
Tune: GOD REMEMBERS, 5 6 7 5 6 6 5 8; Marty Haugen, b.1950, © 2003, GIA Publications, Inc.

573 By the Waters of Babylon

Refrain

By the wa-ters of Bab-y-lon, we shall cry,

we shall rest, and re-mem-ber Zi-on.

Verses

1. We long to play our harps
2. ⁷ May we not for - get
3. ⁷ Lord, we need your strength!

and raise a song to you.
be - lov-ed Je - ru - sa - lem!
⁷ Fill us with your spir - it!

But how can we sing our song in a
Lord, help us to sing our song in this
In - spire us to bring your song to this

D.C.

for-eign land?
for-eign land!
for-eign land!

Text: Psalm 137; Paul A. Tate, b.1968
Tune: Paul A. Tate, b.1968
© 1996, World Library Publications

God Weeps with Us Who Weep and Mourn 574

1. God weeps with us who weep and mourn, God's
tears flow down with ours, And God's own heart is
bruised and worn From all the heav-y hours Of
watch - ing while the soul's bright fire Burned
low - er day by day, And pulse and breath and
love's de - sire Dimmed down to ash and clay.

2. Through tears and sor - row, God, we share A
sense of your vast grief; The weight of bear - ing
ev - 'ry prayer For heal-ing and re - lief, The
bur - den of our ques - tions why, The
doubts that they en - gage, And as our friends and
*lov - ers die, Our hope - less - ness and rage.

3. And yet, be - cause, like us, you weep, We
trust you will re - ceive And in your ten - der
heart will keep The ones for whom we grieve, While
with your tears our hearts will taste The
deep, dear core of things From which both life and
death are graced By love's re - new - ing springs.

*Or "loved ones"

Text: Thomas H. Troeger, b.1945, © 1996, Oxford University Press
Tune: MOSHIER, CMD; Sally Ann Morris, b.1952, © 1998, GIA Publications, Inc.

575 Why Stand So Far Away

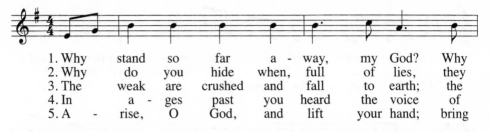

1. Why stand so far a-way, my God? Why
2. Why do you hide when, full of lies, they
3. The weak are crushed and fall to earth; the
4. In a - ges past you heard the voice of
5. A - rise, O God, and lift your hand; bring

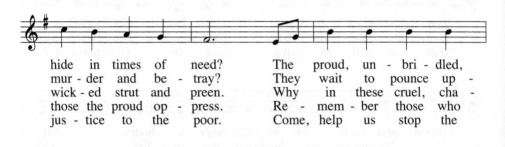

hide in times of need? The proud, un - bri - dled,
mur - der and be - tray? They wait to pounce up -
wick - ed strut and preen. Why in these cruel, cha -
those the proud op - press. Re - mem - ber those who
jus - tice to the poor. Come, help us stop the

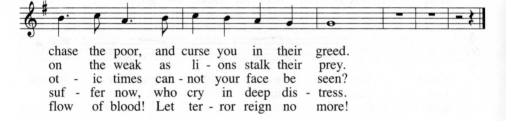

chase the poor, and curse you in their greed.
on the weak as li - ons stalk their prey.
ot - ic times can - not your face be seen?
suf - fer now, who cry in deep dis - tress.
flow of blood! Let ter - ror reign no more!

Text: Based on Psalm 10, Ruth Duck, b.1947, © 1992, GIA Publications, Inc.
Tune: Michael Mahler, b.1981, © 2003, GIA Publications, Inc.

576 Bless the Lord

Ostinato Refrain

Bless the Lord, my soul, and bless God's ho - ly name.

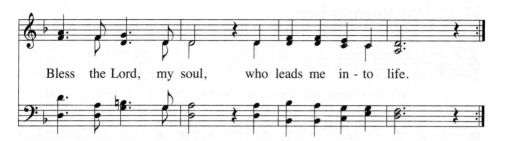

Bless the Lord, my soul, who leads me in - to life.

Text: Psalm 103
Tune: Jacques Berthier, 1923-1994
© 1998, Les Presses de Taizé, GIA Publications, Inc., agent

May God Bless and Keep You 577

Priest: May God bless and keep you, may God smile on you.
All: May God bless and keep us, may God smile on us.

May God show you kind - ness, fill you with peace.
May God show us kind - ness, fill us with peace.

And may God bless you, Fa - ther, Son, and Spir - it;
And may God bless us, Fa - ther, Son, and Spir - it;

may we al-ways love and serve, filled with God's peace.
may we al-ways love and serve, filled with God's peace.

Text: Numbers 6:24-26; David Haas, b.1957, © 1997, GIA Publications, Inc.
Tune: ADORO TE DEVOTE, Mode V; adapt. by David Haas, b.1957, © 1997, GIA Publications, Inc.

578 We Remember

Refrain

We re-mem-ber how you loved us to your death, and still we cel-e-brate, for you are with us here; and we be-lieve that we will see you when you come in your glo-ry, Lord. We re-mem-ber, we cel-e-brate, we be-lieve.

Verses

1. Here, a mil-lion wound-ed souls are yearn-ing just to touch you and be healed. Gath-er all your peo-ple, and hold them to your heart.
2. Now we re-cre-ate your love, we bring the bread and wine to share a meal. Sign of grace and mer-cy, the pres-ence of the Lord.
3. Christ, the Fa-ther's great "A-men" to all the hopes and dreams of ev-'ry heart, Peace be-yond all tell-ing, and free-dom from all fear.
4. See the face of Christ re-vealed in ev-'ry per-son stand-ing by your side, Gift to one an-oth-er, and tem-ples of your love.

D.C.

Text: Marty Haugen, b.1950
Tune: Marty Haugen, b.1950
© 1980, GIA Publications, Inc.

A Living Faith 579

1. Faith of our fa - thers, liv - ing still
2. Faith of our moth - ers, dar - ing faith,
3. Faith of our broth - ers, sis - ters too,
4. Faith born of God, O call us yet;

In spite of dun - geon, fire and sword;
Your work for Christ is love re - vealed,
Who still must bear op - pres - sion's might,
Bind us with all who fol - low you,

O how our hearts beat high with joy,
Spread-ing God's word from pole to pole,
Rais - ing on high, in pris - ons dark,
Shar - ing the strug - gle of your cross

When - e'er we hear that glo - rious word:
Mak - ing love known and free - dom real:
The cross of Christ still burn - ing bright:
Un - til the world is made a - new,

Faith of our fa - thers, ho - ly faith,
Faith of our moth - ers, ho - ly faith,
Faith for to - day, O liv - ing faith,
Faith born of God, O liv - ing faith,

We will be true to you till death.

Text: St. 1, Frederick W. Faber, 1814-1863, alt.; sts. 2-4, Joseph R. Alfred, © 1981, alt.
Tune: ST. CATHERINE, LM with refrain; Henry F. Hemy, 1818-1888; adapt. by James G. Walton, 1821-1905

580 Center of My Life

Refrain

O Lord, you are the cen-ter of my life:

I will al-ways praise you, I will al-ways serve you,

I will al-ways keep you in my sight.

Verses 1-3

1. Keep me safe, O God, I take ref-uge in you. I
2. I will bless the Lord who gives me coun-sel, who
3. And so my heart re-joic-es, my soul is glad;

say to the Lord, "You are my God. My
e - ven at night di-rects my heart. I
e - ven in safe-ty shall my bod-y rest. For

hap - pi - ness lies in you a - lone; my
keep the Lord ev - er in my sight: since
you will not leave my soul a-mong the dead, nor

D.C.

hap - pi - ness lies in you a - lone."
he is at my right hand, I shall stand firm.
let your be - lov - ed know de - cay.

Verse 4

4. You will show me the path of life, the

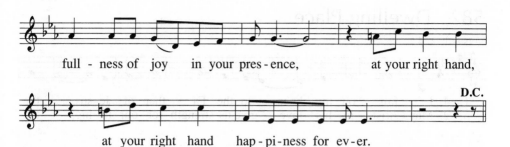

full - ness of joy   in your pres - ence,   at your right hand,

D.C.

at your right hand   hap - pi-ness for ev-er.

Text: Psalm 16; verses trans. © 1963, The Grail, GIA Publications, Inc., agent; refrain, Paul Inwood, b.1947, © 1985, Paul Inwood
Tune: Paul Inwood, b.1947, © 1985, Paul Inwood
Published by OCP Publications.

I Say "Yes," Lord / Digo "Sí," Señor 581

Verses

Cantor: All:

(Invocation)   I say "Yes," my Lord.   I say
                     Di - go "Sí," Se - ñor.   Di - go

Refrain

"Yes," my Lord.   I   say   "Yes," my Lord,   in
"Sí," Se - ñor.   Di - go   "Sí," Se -ñor,   en

all   the good times, through all   the   bad times,   I   say
tiem - pos ma - los,   en tiem - pos bue - nos,   Di - go

"Yes," my Lord,   to   ev - 'ry word you   speak.
"Sí," Se - ñor,   a   to - do lo   que ha - blas.

Text: Donna Peña, b.1955
Tune: Donna Peña, b.1955; arr. by Marty Haugen, b.1950
© 1989, GIA Publications, Inc.

582 Dwelling Place

Verses 1, 2, 4

1., 4. I fall on my knees to the Fa - ther of Je-sus, the
2. May Christ in his love give us strength for our liv-ing, the

Lord who has shown us the glo - ry of God. *(To verse 2)*
strength of the Spir - it the glo - ry of God.

% Refrain

May Christ find a dwell - ing place of faith in our hearts.

May our lives be root - ed in love,

root - ed in love.

Verse 3

3. May grace and peace be yours in God our

D.S.

Fa - ther, and in the Son.

Text: Ephesians 3:14-17; 1:2; John Foley, SJ, b.1939
Tune: John Foley, SJ, b.1939
© 1976, John B. Foley, SJ, and OCP Publications

We Walk by Faith 583

1., 5. We walk by faith, and not by sight: No
2. We may not touch his hands and side, Nor
3. Help then, O Lord, our un - be - lief, And
4. That when our life of faith is done In

gra - cious words we hear Of him who spoke as
fol - low where he trod; Yet in his prom - ise
may our faith a - bound; To call on you when
realms of clear - er light We may be - hold you

none e'er spoke, But we be - lieve him near.
we re - joice, And cry "My Lord and God!"
you are near, And seek where you are found:
as you are In full and end - less sight.

Text: Henry Alford, 1810-1871, alt.
Tune: SHANTI, CM; Marty Haugen, b.1950, © 1984, GIA Publications, Inc.

All Will Be Well 584

Ostinato Refrain

All will be well, and all will be well, all

To repeat

man - ner of things will be well.

Last time

well, will be well, will be well.

Text: *The Revelations of Divine Love,* Julian of Norwich; adapt. by Steven C. Warner, b.1954
Tune: Steven C. Warner, b.1954
© 1993, World Library Publications

585   Blest Be the Lord

Refrain

Blest be the Lord; blest be the Lord, the God of mer-cy, the God who saves. I shall not fear the dark of night, nor the ar-row that flies by day.

Verse 1

1. He will re-lease me from the nets of all my foes. He will pro-tect me from their wick-ed hands. Be-neath the shad-ow of his wings I will re-joice to find a dwell-ing place se-cure.

D.C.

Verse 2

2. I need not shrink be-fore the ter-rors of the night nor stand a-lone be-fore the light of day.

No harm shall come to me, no ar-row strike me down,

D.C.

no e - vil set - tle in my soul.

Verse 3

3. Al - though a thou - sand strong have fall - en at my side,

I'll not be shak - en with the Lord at hand.

His faith - ful love is all the ar - mor that I

D.C.

need to wage my bat - tle with the foe.

Text: Psalm 91; Dan Schutte, b.1947
Tune: Dan Schutte, b.1947; arr. by Sr. Theophane Hytrek, OSF, 1915-1992
© 1976, 1979, Daniel L. Schutte and OCP Publications

586 Amazing Grace

1. A - maz - ing grace! how sweet the sound, That
2. 'Twas grace that taught my heart to fear, And
3. The Lord has prom - ised good to me, His
4. Through man - y dan - gers, toils, and snares, I
5. When we've been there ten - thou - sand years, Bright

saved a wretch like me! I once was lost, but
grace my fears re - lieved; How pre - cious did that
word my hope se - cures; He will my shield and
have al - read - y come; 'Tis grace has brought me
shin - ing as the sun, We've no less days to

now am found, Was blind, but now I see.
grace ap - pear The hour I first be - lieved!
por - tion be As long as life en - dures.
safe thus far, And grace will lead me home.
sing God's praise Than when we'd first be - gun.

Text: St. 1-4, John Newton, 1725-1807; st. 5, attr. to John Rees, fl.1859
Tune: NEW BRITAIN, CM; *Virginia Harmony,* 1831; acc. by Diana Kodner, b.1957, © 1993, GIA Publications, Inc.

587 How Firm a Foundation

1. How firm a foun - da - tion, you saints of the
2. "Fear not, I am with you, O be not dis -
3. "When through the deep wa - ters I call you to
4. "The soul that on Je - sus still leans for re -

Lord, Is laid for your faith in this ex - cel - lent
mayed, For I am your God, and will still give you
go, The riv - ers of woe shall not you o - ver -
pose, I will not, I will not de - sert to its

Word!	What	more	can God	say	than to	you	has been
aid;	I'll	strength - en you,	help	you, and	cause	you to
flow;	For	I	will be	with	you, your	trou - bles to
foes;	That	soul,	though all	hell	should en - deav - or to

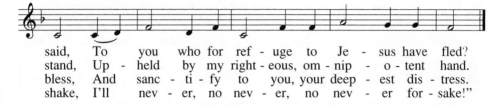

said,	To	you	who for	ref - uge	to	Je - sus have	fled?
stand,	Up - held	by my	right - eous, om - nip - o - tent	hand.
bless,	And	sanc - ti - fy	to	you, your deep - est	dis - tress.
shake,	I'll	nev - er,	no nev - er,	no nev - er	for - sake!"

Text: 2 Peter 1:4; "K" in Rippon's *A Selection of Hymns*, 1787
Tune: FOUNDATION, 11 11 11 11; Funk's *Compilation of Genuine Church Music*, 1832; harm. by Richard Proulx, b.1937,
  © 1975, GIA Publications, Inc.

O God, Our Help in Ages Past 588

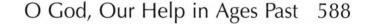
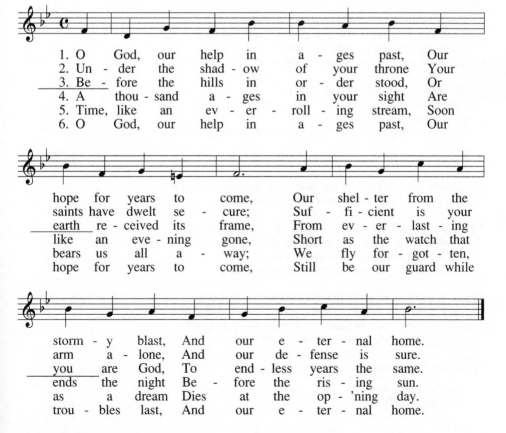

1. O	God,	our	help	in	a - ges	past,	Our
2. Un - der	the	shad - ow	of	your	throne	Your
3. Be - fore	the	hills	in	or - der	stood,	Or
4. A	thou - sand	a - ges	in	your	sight	Are
5. Time, like	an	ev - er - roll - ing	stream,	Soon
6. O	God,	our	help	in	a - ges	past,	Our

hope for	years	to	come,	Our	shel - ter	from	the
saints have	dwelt	se - cure;	Suf - fi - cient	is	your
earth	re - ceived	its	frame,	From	ev - er - last - ing
like	an	eve - ning	gone,	Short	as	the	watch	that
bears	us	all	a - way;	We	fly	for - got - ten,
hope for	years	to	come,	Still	be	our	guard	while

storm - y	blast,	And	our	e - ter - nal	home.
arm	a - lone,	And	our	de - fense	is	sure.
you	are	God,	To	end - less	years	the	same.
ends	the	night	Be - fore	the	ris - ing	sun.
as	a	dream	Dies	at	the	op - 'ning	day.
trou - bles	last,	And	our	e - ter - nal	home.

Text: Psalm (89)90; Isaac Watts, 1674-1748
Tune: ST. ANNE, CM; attr. to William Croft, 1678-1727; harm. composite from 18th C. versions

589 Psalm of Hope

Refrain

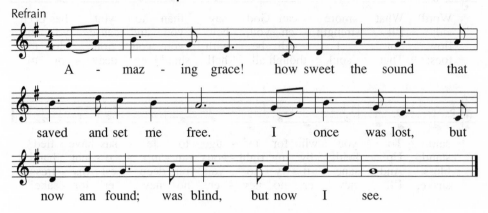

A - maz - ing grace! how sweet the sound that saved and set me free. I once was lost, but now am found; was blind, but now I see.

Verses

1. My God, my God, why have you abandoned me?
   Far from my prayers, far from my cries, all day and night I call.
   Yet, our ancestors put their trust in you.
   You rescued them, you saved them from all foes.

2. But here am I, the scorn of all my people.
   They say, "if God is now your friend, let God rescue you."
   From my mother's womb you are my God.
   You held me up, you placed me in your arms.

3. The evildoers circle in around me.
   I am enslaved in chains of death, I can count all my bones.
   O my strength, hasten to my aid.
   Come save my life, come quickly to my help.

4. I shall proclaim your name to the full assembly.
   Those who fear God, exult and praise;
   Glorify the Lord. All generations, all children of the earth:
   Proclaim for ever the wondrous deeds of God.

*1. You did not turn your face from all your people.
   You rescued them from chains of death, you raised them from despair.
   Ev'ry nation on earth from end to end
   Shall turn to you and bow before your throne.

*2. And so my soul shall live for you, O Lord of hope.
   My children shall bring forth your deeds and magnify your name.
   All my descendants shall know your ways, O Lord.
   May they proclaim the justice you have shown.

*Alternate Easter verses used with vs. 4 above.

Text: Refrain, John Newton, 1725-1807; Verses, Psalm 22, adapted by Felix Goebel-Komala, b.1961
Tune: PSALM OF HOPE, Irregular with refrain; Felix Goebel-Komala, b.1961
© 1994, GIA Publications, Inc.

You Are Near 590

Refrain

Yah-weh, I know you are near, stand-ing al - ways at my side. You guard me from the foe, and you lead me in ways ev - er - last-ing.

Verses

1. Lord, you have searched my heart, and you
2. Where can I run from your love? If I
3. You know my heart and its ways, you who
4. Mar - vel - ous to me are your works; how pro -

know when I sit and when I stand. Your
climb to the heav - ens you are there; if I
formed me be - fore I was born in the
found are your thoughts, my Lord. E - ven

hand is up - on me pro - tect - ing me from death,
fly to the sun - rise or sail be - yond the sea,
se - cret of dark - ness be - fore I saw the sun,
if I could count them, they num - ber as the stars,

D.C.

keep - ing me from harm.
still I'd find you there.
in my moth - er's womb.
you would still be there.

Text: Psalm 139; Dan Schutte, b.1947
Tune: Dan Schutte, b.1947; acc. by Sr. Theophane Hytrek, OSF, 1915-1992
© 1971, Daniel L. Schutte. Published by OCP Publications.

591 Only in God

Refrain

On - ly in God will my soul be at rest. From him comes my

hope, my sal - va - tion. He a - lone is my rock of

safe - ty, my strength, my glo - ry, my God.

Verses

1. Trust in him at all times, O peo - ple, and pour out
2. Man - y times have I heard him tell of his long last -

your hearts. God him - self is a ref - uge for
ing love. You your-self, Lord, re - ward all who

D.C.

us and a strong - hold for our fear.
la - bor for love of your name.

Text: Psalm 62:1, 2, 8, 11, 12; John Foley, SJ, b.1939
Tune: John Foley, SJ, b.1939
© 1976, John B. Foley, SJ and OCP Publications

The Lord Is My Light 592

Verses 1, 3

1. The Lord is my light   and   my sal - va - tion, the Lord   is my
3. ⁏ Wait on the Lord   and   be of good   cour-age, O wait   on the

light   and   my sal - va - tion, the Lord   is my light   and
Lord   and   be of good   cour - age, ⁏ wait   on the Lord   and

my sal - va - tion;   whom   shall   I   fear?
be of good   cour - age.   He   shall strength-en   thine   heart.

℆ Refrain

Whom   shall   I   fear,   whom   shall I   fear?   The Lord   is the

strength   of   my   life;   whom   shall I   fear?

Verse 2

2. In   the   time   of   trou-ble   he shall hide   me, O   in   the time of

trou-ble,   he shall   hide   me,   in the   time   of   trou-ble,

D.S.

he   shall   hide   me;   whom   shall   I   fear?

Text: Lillian Bouknight
Tune: Lillian Bouknight; arr. by Paul Gainer
© 1980, Savgos Music, Inc.

593 On Eagle's Wings

Verse 3

3. You need not fear the ter - ror of the night, nor the ar - row that flies by day; though thou - sands fall a - bout you, near you it shall not come.

D.S.

Verse 4

4. For to his an - gels he's giv - en a com - mand to guard you in all of your ways; up - on their hands they will bear you up, lest you dash your foot a - gainst a stone.

D.S.

Coda

And hold you, hold you in the palm of his hand.

Text: Psalm 91; Michael Joncas, b.1951
Tune: Michael Joncas, b.1951
© 1979, OCP Publications

594 A Mighty Fortress Is Our God

1. A might-y for-tress is our God, A sword and shield vic-to-rious, Who breaks the cruel op-pres-sor's rod And wins sal-va-tion glo-rious. The old sa-tan-ic foe Has sworn to work us woe! With craft and dread-ful might He arms him-self to fight. On earth he has no e-qual.

2. No strength of ours can match his might! We would be lost, re-ject-ed. But now a cham-pion comes to fight, Whom God a-lone e-lect-ed. You ask who this may be? The Lord of hosts is he! Christ Je-sus, might-y Lord, God's on-ly Son, a-dored. He holds the field vic-to-rious.

3. Though hordes of dev-ils fill the land All threat-n'ing to de-vour us, We trem-ble not, un-moved we stand; They can-not o-ver-pow'r us. Let this world's ty-rant rage; In bat-tle we'll en-gage! His might is doomed to fail; One lit-tle word sub-dues him. God's judge-ment must pre-vail!

4. God's Word for-ev-er shall a-bide, No thanks to foes, who fear it; For God, our Lord, fights by our side With weap-ons of the Spir-it. Were they to take our house, Goods, hon-or, child, or spouse, Though life be wrenched a-way, They can-not win the day. The King-dom's ours for-ev-er!

Text: Psalm (45) 46; *Ein' feste Burg ins unser Gott;* Martin Luther, 1483-1546; tr. © 1978, *Lutheran Book of Worship*
Tune: EIN' FESTE BURG, 8 7 8 7 66 66 7; Martin Luther, 1483-1546; harm. by J.S. Bach, 1685-1750

Though the Mountains May Fall 595

Refrain

Though the moun - tains may fall and the hills turn to dust,

yet the love of the Lord will stand

as a shel - ter for all who will call on his name.

Sing the praise and the glo - ry of God.

Verses

1. Could the Lord ev - er leave you? Could the
2. Should you turn and for - sake him, he will
3. Go to him when you're wea - ry; he will
4. As he swore to your fa - thers, when the

Lord for - get his love? Though a moth - er for -
gent - ly call your name. Should you wan - der a -
give you ea - gle's wings. You will run, nev-er
flood de - stroyed the land; He will nev - er for -

D.C.

sake her child, he will not a - ban - don you.
way from him, he will al - ways take you back.
tire, for your God will be your strength.
sake you; he will swear to you a - gain.

Text: Isaiah 54:6-10, 49:15, 40:31-32; Dan Schutte, b.1947
Tune: Dan Schutte, b.1947; acc. by Michael Pope, SJ
© 1975, Daniel L. Schutte and OCP Publications

596 Be Not Afraid

Verse 1

1. You shall cross the bar-ren des - ert, but you shall not die of thirst. You shall wan - der far in safe-ty though you do not know the way. You shall speak your words in for-eign lands and all will un - der - stand. You shall see the face of God and live.

Refrain

Be not a - fraid. I go be - fore you al - ways. Come, fol-low me, and I will give you rest.

Verse 2

2. If you pass through rag - ing wa-ters in the sea, you shall not drown. If you walk a-mid the burn-ing flames, you shall not be harmed. If you stand be - fore the

pow'r of hell and death is at your side,

know that I am with you through it all.

D.S.

Verse 3

3. Bless-ed are your poor, for the king-dom shall be

theirs. Blest are you that weep and mourn, for

one day you shall laugh. And if wick-ed tongues in -

sult and hate you all be-cause of me,

D.S.

bless-ed, bless-ed are you!

597 All That We Have

Refrain

All that we have and all that we of-fer Comes from a
heart both fright-ened and free. Take what we bring now and
give what we need, All done in his name.

Verses

1. Some would re - ly on their pow - er,
2. Some - times the road may be lone - some,
3. Some - times when trou - bles are man - y,

Oth - ers put trust in their gold.
Of - ten we may lose our way;
Life can seem emp - ty, it's true,

Some have on - ly their Sav - ior,
Take cour - age and al - ways re - mem - ber
But look at the life of the Mas - ter,

D.C.

Whose faith - ful - ness nev - er grows old.
Love is - n't just for a day.
Who lov - ing - ly suf - fered for you.

Text: Gary Ault, b.1944
Tune: Gary Ault b.1944; acc. by Gary Daigle, b.1957, alt.
© 1969, 1979, Damean Music. Distributed by GIA Publications, Inc.

How Can I Keep from Singing   598

1. My life flows on in end-less song A -
2. Through all the tu - mult and the strife, I
3. What, though my joys and com-fort die, The
4. The peace of Christ makes fresh my heart, A

bove earth's lam - en - ta - tion. I hear the real though
hear that mu - sic ring - ing; It sounds and ech - oes
Lord, my sav - ior liv - eth. What though the dark - ness
foun - tain ev - er spring-ing. All things are mine since

far - off hymn That hails a new cre - a - tion.
in my soul; How can I keep from sing-ing?
gath - er 'round? Songs in the night it giv - eth.
I am his; How can I keep from sing-ing?

No storm can shake my in-most calm, While to that rock I'm

cling - ing. Since Christ is Lord of heav-en and earth,

How can I keep from sing-ing?

Text: Robert Lowry, 1826-1899
Tune: HOW CAN I KEEP FROM SINGING, 8 7 8 7 with refrain; Robert Lowry, 1826-1899; harm. by Robert J. Batastini, b.1942, © 1988, GIA
   Publications, Inc.

599 The Lord Is Near

Refrain*

O the Lord is near to all who call on him; he is
**May the an - gels lead you in - to par - a - dise; may the

close to all who seek his face, slow to an - ger and full of com-
mar - tyrs come to wel - come you, and take you to the ho - ly

pas - sion and a - bound - ing in mer - ci - ful love.
cit - y, the new and e - ter - nal Je - ru - sa - lem.

Verse 1

1. The Lord is my light and my sal - va - tion, there is

noth - ing at all I fear; the Lord is the

D.C.

ref - uge of my life; of whom should I be a - fraid?

Verse 2

2. One thing I ask of the Lord; there is

on - ly one thing I seek: to dwell in the

D.C.

house of the Lord all the days of my life.

Verse 3

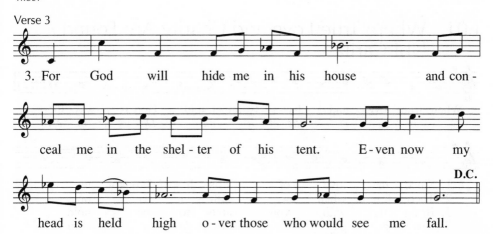

3. For God will hide me in his house and con -

ceal me in the shel - ter of his tent. E - ven now my

D.C.

head is held high o - ver those who would see me fall.

The refrain may be sung in a two-voice canon at a distance of one measure, or a three-voice canon at a distance of one-half measure.

**Alternate refrain for funerals*

Text: Psalm 27; Michael Joncas, b.1951
Tune: Michael Joncas, b.1951
© 1979, OCP Publications

Seek Ye First 600

Canon

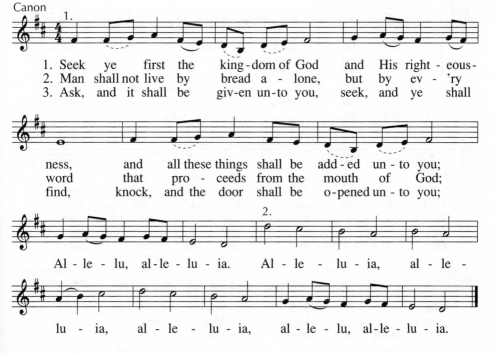

1. Seek ye first the king - dom of God and His right - eous-
2. Man shall not live by bread a - lone, but by ev - 'ry
3. Ask, and it shall be giv-en un-to you, seek, and ye shall

ness, and all these things shall be add - ed un - to you;
word that pro - ceeds from the mouth of God;
find, knock, and the door shall be o-pened un - to you;

Al - le - lu, al-le - lu - ia. Al - le - lu - ia, al - le -

lu - ia, al - le - lu - ia, al - le - lu, al-le - lu - ia.

Text: Matthew 6:33, 7:7; adapt. by Karen Lafferty, b.1948
Tune: SEEK YE FIRST, Irregular; Karen Lafferty, b.1948
© 1972, Maranatha! Music and CCCM Music

601 Where True Love and Charity Are Found / Ubi Caritas

Where true love and char-i-ty are found, God is al-ways there.
U - bi cá - ri - tas et a - mor De-us i - bi est.

1. Since the love of Christ has brought us
2. There-fore when we gath - er as one
3. Bring us with your saints to be - hold
1. *Con - gre - gá - vit nos in u - num*
2. *Si - mul er - go cum in u - num*
3. *Si - mul quo - que cum be - á - tis*

all to - geth - er, Let us all re -
in Christ Je - sus, Let our love en -
your great beau - ty, There to see you,
Chri - sti a - mor. Ex - sul - té - mus
con - gre - gá - mur: Ne nos men - te
vi - de - á - mus. Glo - ri - án - ter

joice and be glad, now and al - ways.
fold each race, creed, ev - 'ry per - son.
Christ our God, throned in great glo - ry;
et in ip - so iu - cun - dé - mur.
di - vi - dá - mur, ca - ve - á - mus.
vul - tum tu - um, Chri - ste De - us:

Let ev - 'ry one love the Lord God,
Let en - vy, di - vi - sion and strife
There to pos - sess heav - en's peace and joy,
Ti - me - á - mus et a - mé - mus
Ces - sent iúr - gi - a ma - líg - na,
Gáu - di - um, quod est im - mén - sum

the liv - ing God; And with sin - cere
cease a - mong us; May Christ our Lord
your truth and love, For end - less a -
De - um vi - vum. Et ex cor - de
ces - sent li - tes. Et in mé - di -
at - que pro - bum. Sáe - cu - la per

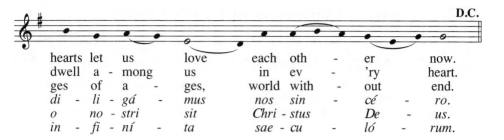

hearts	let	us	love	each	oth - er	now.
dwell	a - mong	us	in	ev - 'ry	heart.
ges	of	a - ges,	world	with - out	end.
di - li - gá - mus	*nos*	*sin - cé - ro.*
o	*no - stri*	*sit*	*Chri - stus*	*De - us.*
in - fi - ní - ta	*sae - cu - ló - rum.*

Text: Latin, 9th C.; tr. by Richard Proulx, b.1937, © 1975, 1986, GIA Publications, Inc.
Tune: UBI CARITAS, 12 12 12 12 with refrain; Mode VI; acc. by Richard Proulx, b.1937, © 1986, GIA Publications, Inc.

Lord of All Nations, Grant Me Grace 602

1. Lord	of	all	na - tions,	grant	me	grace
2. Break	down	the	wall	that	would	di - vide
3. For - give	me,	Lord,	where	I	have	erred
4. Give	me	your	cour - age,	Lord,	to	speak
5. With	your	own	love	may	I	be	filled

To	love	all	peo - ple,	ev - 'ry	race
Your	chil - dren,	Lord,	on	ev - 'ry	side.
By	love - less	act	and	thought - less	word.
When - ev - er	strong	op - press	the	weak.
And	by	your	Ho - ly	Spir - it	willed,

To	see	each	mor - tal	as	I	ought,
My	neigh - bor's	good	let	me	pur - sue,
Make	me	to	see	the	wrong	I	do
Should	I	my - self	as	vic - tim	live,
That	all	whose	lives	are	touched	by	mine,

My	kin - dred,	whom	your	love	has	bought.
Let	Chris - tian	love	bind	warm	and	true.
Will	cru - ci - fy	my	Lord	a - new.
Re - mem - b'ring	you,	may	I	for - give.
May	know	your	heal - ing	touch	di - vine.

Text: Philippians 2:1-18; Olive W. Spannus, b.1916, © 1969, Concordia Publishing House
Tune: VENI CREATOR SPIRITUS, LM; Mode VIII; setting by Richard J. Wojcik, b.1923, © 1975, GIA Publications, Inc.

603 There's a Wideness in God's Mercy

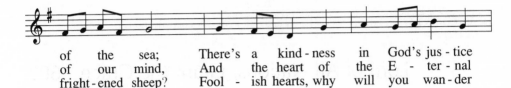

1. There's a wide-ness in God's mer-cy Like the wide-ness
2. For the love of God is broad-er Than the meas-ures
3. Trou-bled souls, why will you scat-ter Like a crowd of

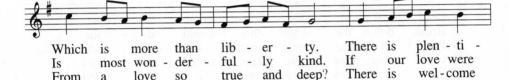

of the sea; There's a kind-ness in God's jus-tice
of our mind, And the heart of the E-ter-nal
fright-ened sheep? Fool-ish hearts, why will you wan-der

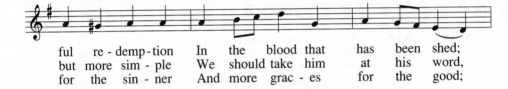

Which is more than lib-er-ty. There is plen-ti-
Is most won-der-ful-ly kind. If our love were
From a love so true and deep? There is wel-come

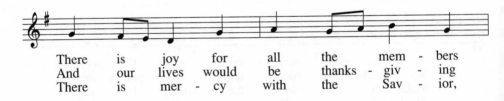

ful re-demp-tion In the blood that has been shed;
but more sim-ple We should take him at his word,
for the sin-ner And more grac-es for the good;

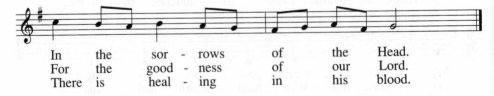

There is joy for all the mem-bers
And our lives would be thanks-giv-ing
There is mer-cy with the Sav-ior,

In the sor-rows of the Head.
For the good-ness of our Lord.
There is heal-ing in his blood.

Text: Frederick W. Faber, 1814-1863, alt.
Tune: IN BABILONE, 8 7 8 7 D; *Oude en Nieuwe Hollanste Boerenlities*, c.1710

The Call Is Clear and Simple 604

1. The call is clear and sim - ple: "Love God and hu - man -
kind," But love de - mands much wis - dom And clar - i - ty of mind. "Be wi - ly as a ser - pent, Though gen - tle as a dove," For man - y are the dan - gers Up - on the path of love.

2. God, help us sort our mo - tives, That lov - ing may be whole. High aims or base am - bi - tion? Com - pas - sion or con - trol? Then help us clear our sched - ules Of ev - 'ry fran - tic task That leads a - way from do - ing The one thing that you ask.

3. God, teach us strength and wis - dom When false love takes the lead. Too well we learn sub - mis - sion And si - lence our own need. When oth - ers would mis - use us Or lure us t'ward the wrong, God, tem - per love with cour - age To keep our bound - 'ries strong.

4. O wise and ho - ly Lov - er, Teach us as sea - sons turn To know our - selves and oth - ers— Deep, hon - est love to learn. So may we nur - ture liv - ing In all we say and do, In strong and gen - tle giv - ing To hu - man - kind and you.

Text: Ruth Duck, b.1947, © 1992, GIA Publications, Inc.
Tune: PASSION CHORALE, 7 6 7 6 D; Hans Leo Hassler, 1564-1612; harm. by J. S. Bach, 1685-1750

605 Neither Death nor Life

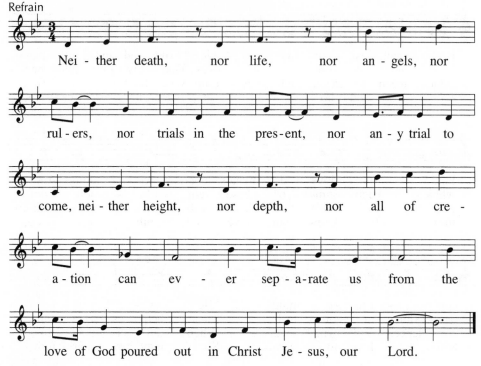

Refrain

Nei - ther death, nor life, nor an - gels, nor rul - ers, nor trials in the pres - ent, nor an - y trial to come, nei - ther height, nor depth, nor all of cre - a - tion can ev - er sep - a-rate us from the love of God poured out in Christ Je - sus, our Lord.

Verses

1. Dwell in the One who raised Christ from the dead;
   Though your body shall die, in Christ you shall rise
   through the Spirit who brings you to life.

2. All who are led by the Spirit shall live as children of God,
   and heirs with Christ Jesus,
   God's adopted and chosen and loved.

3. All of the suffering we now must endure
   is nothing to the glory so soon to be revealed
   when creation itself is set free.

4. All of creation awaits the new birth,
   the fullness of redemption, through labor pains of love,
   and so we wait in patience and hope.

5. All things work for good for the ones who love God,
   and if God is for us, then who can be against us?
   God's justified cannot be condemned.

6. Who can separate us from the love of Christ?
   Will hardship or distress, persecution or famine,
   or nakedness or peril or sword?

Text: Romans 8:11-19, 22-25, 28-35, 38; Marty Haugen, b.1950
Tune: Marty Haugen, b.1950
© 2001, GIA Publications, Inc.

Koinonia 606

How can I say that I love the Lord whom I've nev-er, ev - er seen be-fore; and for-get to say that I love the one whom I walk be-side each and ev-'ry day? How can I look up - on your face and ig - nore God's love? You I must em - brace! You're my broth-er; you're my sis-ter; and I love you with the love of my Lord.

1.

2. Love of my Lord!

Koinonia, *derived from the original* κοινωνια, *is a Greek word meaning* fellowship.

Text: V. Michael McKay
Tune: V. Michael McKay
© Schaff Music Publishing

607 No Greater Love

Refrain

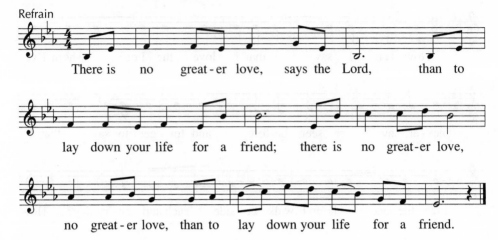

There is no great-er love, says the Lord, than to lay down your life for a friend; there is no great-er love, no great-er love, than to lay down your life for a friend.

Verses

1. As the Father has loved me, so I have loved you.
   Live on in my love.
   You will live in my love if you keep my commands,
   even as I have kept my Father's.

2. All this I tell you that my joy may be yours
   and your joy may be complete.
   Love one another as I have loved you:
   This is my command.

3. You are my friends if you keep my commands;
   no longer slaves but friends to me.
   All I heard from my Father,
   I have made known to you: Now I call you friends.

4. It was not you who chose me, it was I who chose you,
   chose you to go forth and bear fruit.
   Your fruit must endure, so you will receive
   all you ask the Father in my name.

Text: John 15:9-17; Michael Joncas, b.1951
Tune: Michael Joncas, b.1951
© 1988, GIA Publications, Inc.

God Is Love   608

Refrain

God is love,   and   all   who live in   love,   live in God.

Verse 1

1. God   is   light,   in   God   there is   no   dark - ness.   Come

D.C.

live   in   the   love   of   the   Lord.

Verse 2

2. Come   to   the   Lord,   re - ceive   the   light,   and

D.C.

live   in   the   love   of   the   Lord.

Verse 3

3. We   are   called   to be God's   own   chil - dren,   to

D.C.

live   in   the   love   of   the   Lord.

Verse 4

4. All   of you are   one,   u – nit - ed   in   Je - sus,   to

D.C.

live   in   the   love   of   the   Lord.

Text: 1 John 1:5, 3:2, 4:15, Psalm 33:6, Galatians 3:28; David Haas, b.1957
Tune: David Haas, b.1957
© 1987, GIA Publications, Inc.

609 Faith, Hope and Love

Refrain

Faith, hope and love, let these en - dure a -
mong you; and the great-est of these is love, the
great - est of these is love.

Verse 1

1. If I speak with the voice of an - gels but
do not love, I am like a nois - y gong, a clang - ing
cym - bal. I am noth - ing, I am noth - ing with - out love.

D.C.

Verse 2

2. If I see all that's held in mys - ter - y, feed and
clothe the poor, if my faith should call me on to move a
moun - tain, still I'm noth-ing, I am noth-ing with-out love.

D.C.

Verse 3

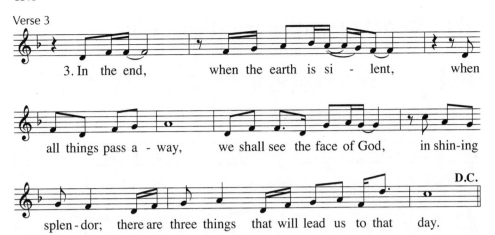

3. In the end, when the earth is si - lent, when all things pass a - way, we shall see the face of God, in shin-ing splen - dor; there are three things that will lead us to that day.

Text: Francis Patrick O'Brien, b.1958
Tune: Francis Patrick O'Brien, b.1958
© 2001, GIA Publications, Inc.

Where Charity and Love Prevail   610

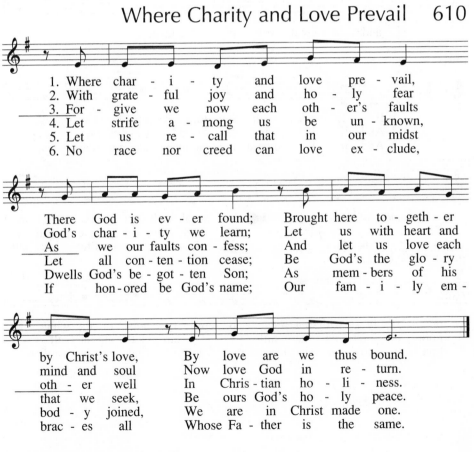

1. Where char - i - ty and love pre - vail,
2. With grate - ful joy and ho - ly fear
3. For - give we now each oth - er's faults
4. Let strife a - mong us be un - known,
5. Let us re - call that in our midst
6. No race nor creed can love ex - clude,

There God is ev - er found; Brought here to - geth - er
God's char - i - ty we learn; Let us with heart and
As we our faults con - fess; And let us love each
Let all con - ten - tion cease; Be God's the glo - ry
Dwells God's be - got - ten Son; As mem - bers of his
If hon - ored be God's name; Our fam - i - ly em -

by Christ's love, By love are we thus bound.
mind and soul Now love God in re - turn.
oth - er well In Chris - tian ho - li - ness.
that we seek, Be ours God's ho - ly peace.
bod - y joined, We are in Christ made one.
brac - es all Whose Fa - ther is the same.

Text: *Ubi caritas;* trans. by Omer Westendorf, 1916-1998
Tune: CHRISTIAN LOVE, CM; Paul Benoit, OSB, 1893-1979
© 1960, 1961, World Library Publications

611 Set Your Heart on the Higher Gifts

Refrain

Set your heart on the high-er gifts, on the things that come from your Mak - er in heav - en. These three gifts are all that re-main: faith, hope and love, and the great - est is love.

Verses

1. If I speak with the tongues of the liv - ing,
2. And if I un - der - stand ev - 'ry mys - t'ry,
3. And if I should re - nounce all my rich - es,

and of an - gels, but speak with-out love, I am
hav - ing wis - dom, but think with-out love, had I
feed the hun - gry, give o - ver my life; with-out

D.C.

on - ly brass with-out song, an emp - ty noise on the wind.
faith to scat - ter the hills, I am noth-ing at all.
love my prof - it is loss, my car - ing finds no re - ward.

Text: 1 Corinthians 12:31–13:13; Steven C. Warner, b.1954
Tune: Steven C. Warner, b.1954
© 1992, 1994, World Library Publications

Not for Tongues of Heaven's Angels 612

1. Not for tongues of heav - en's an - gels,
2. Love is hum - ble, love is gen - tle,
3. Nev - er jeal - ous, nev - er self - ish,
4. Soon will fade the word of wis - dom,

Not for wis - dom to dis - cern,
Love is ten - der, true, and kind;
Love will not re - joice in wrong;
Faith and hope be one day past:

Not for faith that mas - ters moun - tains,
Love is gra - cious, ev - er pa - tient,
Nev - er boast - ful nor re - sent - ful,
When we see our Sav - ior clear - ly,

For this bet - ter gift we yearn:
Gen - er - ous of heart and mind—
Love be - lieves and suf - fers long—
Love it is a - lone will last

May love be ours, Lord; may love be ours.

May love be ours, O Lord.

Text: Timothy Dudley-Smith, b.1926, © 1985, Hope Publishing Co.
Tune: COMFORT, 8 7 8 7 with refrain; Michael Joncas, b.1951, © 1988, GIA Publications, Inc.

613 Love Divine, All Loves Excelling

1. Love di - vine, all loves ex - cel - ling,
2. Come, al - might - y to de - liv - er,
3. Fin - ish then your new cre - a - tion,

Joy of heav'n to earth come down!
Let us all your life re - ceive;
Pure and spot - less, gra - cious Lord,

Fix in us your hum - ble dwell - ing,
Sud - den - ly re - turn and nev - er,
Let us see your great sal - va - tion

All your faith - ful mer - cies crown.
Nev - er more your tem - ples leave.
Per - fect - ly in you re - stored.

Je - sus, source of all com - pas - sion,
Lord, we would be al - ways bless - ing,
Changed from glo - ry in - to glo - ry,

Love un - bound - ed, love all pure;
Serve you as your hosts a - bove,
Till in heav'n we take our place,

Vis - it us with your sal - va - tion,
Pray, and praise you with - out ceas - ing,
Till we sing be - fore the al - might - y

Let your love in us en - dure.
Glo - ry in your pre - cious love.
Lost in won - der, love and praise.

Text: Charles Wesley, 1707-1788, alt.
Tune: HYFRYDOL, 8 7 8 7 D; Rowland H. Prichard, 1811-1887

What Wondrous Love Is This 614

1. What won-drous love is this, O my soul, O my soul?
2. To God and to the Lamb I will sing, I will sing;
3. And when from death I'm free, I'll sing on, I'll sing on;

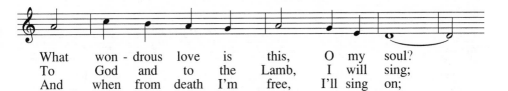

What won-drous love is this, O my soul?
To God and to the Lamb, I will sing;
And when from death I'm free, I'll sing on;

What won-drous love is this that caused the Lord of bliss
To God and to the Lamb who is the great I Am,
And when from death I'm free, I'll sing and joy-ful be,

To bear the dread-ful curse for my soul, for my soul;
While mil-lions join the theme, I will sing, I will sing;
And through e-ter-ni-ty I'll sing on, I'll sing on!

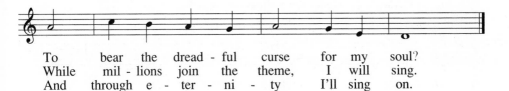

To bear the dread-ful curse for my soul?
While mil-lions join the theme, I will sing.
And through e-ter-ni-ty I'll sing on.

Text: Alexander Means, 1801-1853
Tune: WONDROUS LOVE, 12 9 12 12 9; *Southern Harmony*, 1835; harm. from *Cantate Domino*, 1980, © 1980, World Council of Churches

615 My Song Will Be for You Forever

1. My song will be for you forever,
2. You have clothed me in your prom - ise,
3. I am here to be your ser - vant,
4. With your voice, you sing with - in me,
5. I will pledge my love for - ev - er,

you, the mu - sic in my heart, For your love is
you, my love, my light, my friend. You, the way and
you a - noint me with your love. You will hold me
you, the one who knows me well. You, my joy, my
I will call your name out loud. I will reach my

all a - round me, and your good - ness al - ways here.
path be - fore me, you will lead and guide me home.
in my long - ing, all my hope in your em - brace.
life and bless - ing, when you call, you know my name.
hand out to you, and I know you'll reach for me.

My song will be for you for - ev - er,

You, the mu - sic in my heart.

Text: David Haas, b.1957
Tune: David Haas, b.1957

Eye Has Not Seen 616

Refrain

Eye has not seen, ear has not heard what God has read-y for

those who love him; Spir-it of love, come, give us the mind of

Je - sus, teach us the wis-dom of God.

Verses 1-3

1. When pain and sor - row weigh us down, be near to us, O
2. Our lives are but a sin - gle breath, we flow-er and we
3. To those who see with eyes of faith, the Lord is ev - er

Lord, for - give the weak - ness of our faith, and
fade, yet all our days are in your hands, so
near, re - flect - ed in the fac - es of

D.C.

bear us up with - in your peace-ful word.
we re - turn in love what love has made.
all the poor and low - ly of the world.

Verse 4

4. We sing a mys-t'ry from the past in halls where saints have

trod, yet ev - er new the mu - sic rings to

D.C.

Je - sus, Liv - ing Song of God.

Text: 1 Corinthians 2:9-10; Marty Haugen, b.1950
Tune: Marty Haugen, b.1950
© 1982, GIA Publications, Inc.

617 There Is a Balm in Gilead

Refrain

There is a balm in Gil - e - ad To make the wound - ed whole, There is a balm in Gil - e - ad To heal the sin - sick soul.

Verses

1. Some - times I feel dis - cour - aged And think my work's in vain, But then the Ho - ly Spir - it Re - vives my soul a - gain.
2. If you can - not preach like Pe - ter, If you can - not pray like Paul, You can tell the love of Je - sus, And say, "He died for all!"
3. Don't ev - er feel dis - cour - aged, For Je - sus is your friend; And if you lack for knowl - edge He'll ne'er re - fuse to lend.

D.C.

Text: Jeremiah 8:22, African-American spiritual
Tune: BALM IN GILEAD, Irregular; African-American spiritual; acc. by Marty Haugen, b.1950, © 2003, GIA Publications, Inc.

Only You, O God 618

Refrain

On - ly you, O God, and you a-lone, the bro - ken heart con - sole, On - ly you, O God, and you a-lone, the wound - ed world make whole.

Verses

1. O God, our rock and ha - ven, Our strong - hold, safe and sure, Though earth be torn and shak - en, In you we stand se - cure.
2. You guard us, faith - ful fa - ther, With - in your shel - t'ring palm; You nurse us, lov - ing moth - er, With milk and heal - ing balm.
3. We pray do not a - ban - don The ones you call your own; Our com - fort and com - pan - ion, We trust in you a - lone.

D.C.

Text: Susan R. Briehl, b.1952, © 2003, GIA Publications, Inc.
Tune: BALM IN GILEAD, 7 6 7 6 with refrain; African-American spiritual; acc. by Marty Haugen, b.1950, © 2003, GIA Publications, Inc.

619 The Clouds' Veil

Refrain

E-ven though the rain hides the stars, e-ven though the
mist swirls the hills, e-ven when the dark clouds
veil the sky, God is by my side. E-ven when the
sun shall fall in sleep, e-ven when at dawn the sky shall
weep, e-ven in the night when storms shall rise,
God is by my side. God is by my side.

Verses

1. Bright the stars at night that
2. Deep the feast of life where
3. Blest are they who sing the

mir - ror heav-en's way to you. Bright the stars in
saints shall gath - er in deep peace. Deep in heav - en's
fel - low-ship of saints in light. Blest is heav - en's

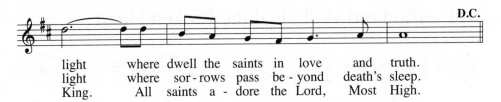

D.C.

light   where dwell the saints in love   and   truth.
light   where sor-rows pass be-yond   death's sleep.
King.   All   saints a - dore the Lord,   Most High.

Text: Liam Lawton, b.1959
Tune: Liam Lawton, b.1959; arr. by John McCann, b.1961
© 1997, GIA Publications, Inc.

Our God Is Rich in Love   620

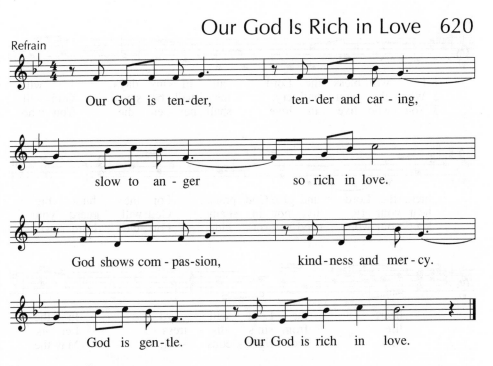

Refrain

Our God is ten-der,   ten-der and car-ing,

slow to an-ger   so rich in love.

God shows com-pas-sion,   kind-ness and mer-cy.

God is gen-tle.   Our God is rich in love.

Verses

1. Our God is merciful. God's gentle kindness knows no end.
   And though our sins be great or small, God's love is our reward.

2. Our God is tender as a parent to a child.
   God remembers how we were made, remembers that we are dust.

3. God's love is eternal for those who live the law;
   for those who live the covenant; for those who keep the faith.

Text: Psalm 103: Bob Moore, b.1962
Tune: Bob Moore, b.1962
© 1993, GIA Publications, Inc.

621 The Lord Will Heal the Broken Heart

Refrain

The Lord will heal the bro-ken heart. God will seek the lost and find them.

Verses

1. I will bless the Lord all of my days, I will
2. When the poor shall cry, they shall be saved. God will
3. You who live in love shall nev-er die. You who

bless the Lord and give God praise, For the hum - ble
hear your cry, live not in shame. God will guard your
keep your word need nev-er hide. For the Lord will

heart the Lord will guard. In the
life from sin's dis - tress. Let us
seek the right-eous soul. May the

D.C.

Fa - ther's care may you rest from harm.
fear the Lord, may God's name be blessed.
peace of God be your life and hope.

Text: Psalm 34; Liam Lawton, b.1959
Tune: Liam Lawton, b.1959; arr. John McCann, b.1961
© 2000, GIA Publications, Inc.

I Heard the Voice of Jesus Say 622

1. I heard the voice of Je - sus say, "Come
2. I heard the voice of Je - sus say, "Be -
3. I heard the voice of Je - sus say, "I

un - to me and rest; Lay down, O wea - ry
hold, I free - ly give The liv - ing wa - ter;
am this dark world's light; Look un - to me, your

one, lay down Your head up - on my breast." I
thirst - y one, Stoop down, and drink, and live." I
morn shall rise, And all your day be bright." I

came to Je - sus as I was, So
came to Je - sus, and I drank Of
looked to Je - sus, and I found In

wea - ry, worn, and sad; I found in him a
that life - giv - ing stream; My thirst was quenched, my
him my star, my sun; And in that light of

rest - ing place, And he has made me glad.
soul re - vived, And now I live in him.
life I'll walk Till trav - 'ling days are done.

Text: Horatius Bonar, 1808-1889
Tune: KINGSFOLD, CMD; English; harm. by Ralph Vaughan Williams, 1872-1958, © Oxford University Press

623 With You by My Side

Verses

Cantor:

1. When I'm feel - ing all a - lone, and I'm
2. When I feel all sick in - side, with
3. And as I go through my life, I will

far a - way from home, God, I need you to hear me.
no safe place to hide, God, I need you to lis - ten.
keep you in my sight to walk with me and be my strength.

When my friends all turn a - way, then I ache to hear you say
When it seems I can't go on, then I long to hear the song
God, I know your plan for me: to help all those in need.

that you are with me through it all.
re - mind - ing me you are my friend.
To you a - lone I give my life!

Refrain

All:

You are the light, you're the song that I'm sing - ing;

whom should I fear when you are with me? For

you are my God, and with you there is noth - ing I can't

do, with you by my side.

Text: David Haas, b.1957.
Tune: David Haas, b.1957; choral arr. by David Haas and Kate Cuddy, b.1953
© 1998, GIA Publications, Inc.

Shepherd of My Heart 624

Verses

1. My shep-herd is the Lord, for noth-ing shall I want;
2. If I should walk one day in - to the vale of dark-ness,
3. You a-noint my head with oil; my cup is o - ver-flow-ing;

green are the pas - tures where I'm led to re - pose.
no e - vil shall I fear with God at my side.
good - ness and kind-ness crown the days of my life.

Near wa - ters still and deep God will re - fresh my soul.
There with your crook and staff you give me strength and com-fort;
With - in the Lord's own house I dwell in peace for ev - er;

I am led on-ward in ways true to the Name.
you spread a ban-quet in the sight of my foes.
with - in the house of God my soul is at rest.

Refrain

Guide me, O shep-herd of my heart; lead me home-ward through the

dark, in - to ev-er-last-ing day. Show me the way of truth and

light; keep me al-ways in your sight. May my life nev-er

part from the shep-herd of my heart.

Text: Psalm 23; Francis Patrick O'Brien, b.1958
Tune: Francis Patrick O'Brien, b.1958
© 1992, GIA Publications, Inc.

625 You Are All I Want

Refrain

You are all I want, you are all I need, you a - lone are my de -

light. You shep-herd me with love, you lead me through the

dark - ness of night. In you my heart shall rest.

Verse 1

1. O Lord, you are my God, my shep-herd and my life. There's

noth-ing I shall want. As I lie in fields of green, near

D.C.

cool and gen-tle streams, my heart is calm, my spir-it re-freshed.

Verses 2, 3

2. With your staff, strong and true, you guide my life for you.
3. You have spread a lav - ish feast, for all my foes to see. You

Faith - ful is your name. You are al - ways near, you
give me all I need. You a - noint my head with oil, you

D.C.

com - fort all my fears. In the face of death, I shall not hide.
soothe and heal my soul. My heart is full. I sing for joy.

Verse 4

4. Your good-ness shall pur-sue me, your kind-ness o-ver-whelms me. You shel-ter all my days. In your house I will dwell, and live with you for-ev-er. In your arms of love, I am home.

D.C.

Text: Psalm 23; Lori True, b.1961
Tune: Lori True, b.1961; acc. by David Haas, b.1957
© 2003, GIA Publications, Inc.

Nada Te Turbe / Nothing Can Trouble 626

Ostinato Refrain

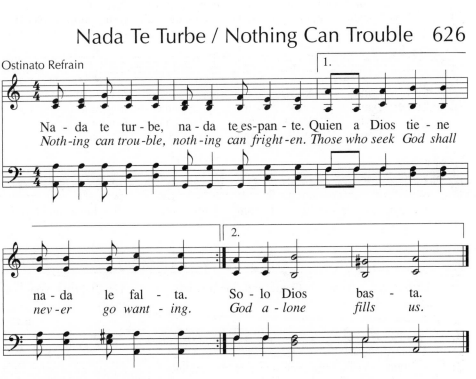

Na - da te tur - be, na - da te_es-pan - te. Quien a Dios tie - ne
Noth -ing can trou-ble, noth -ing can fright-en. Those who seek God shall

na - da le fal - ta. So - lo Dios bas - ta.
nev-er go want - ing. God a - lone fills us.

Text: St. Teresa of Jesus; Taizé Community, 1986, 1991
Tune: Jacques Berthier, 1923-1994
© 1986, 1991, Les Presses de Taizé, GIA Publications, Inc., agent

627 You Are Mine

Verses

1. I will come to you in the si - lence,
2. I am hope for all who are hope - less,
3. I am strength for all the de - spair - ing,
4. am the Word that leads all to free - dom, I

I will lift you from all your fear. In the
I am eyes for all who long to see.
heal - ing for the ones who dwell in shame.
am the peace the world can - not give.

You will hear my voice, I claim you as my choice, be
shad - ows of the night, I will be your light,
All the blind will see, the lame will all run free, and
I will call your name, em - brac - ing all your pain, stand

still and know I am here. *(To verse 2)*
come and rest in me. *(To refrain)*
all will know my name. *(To refrain)*
up, now walk, and live! *(To refrain)*

Refrain

Do not be a - fraid, I am with you. I have called you

each by name. Come and fol - low me, I will bring you

D.C.

home; I love you and you are mine.

4. I

Text: David Haas, b.1957
Tune: David Haas, b.1957
© 1991, GIA Publications, Inc.

With a Shepherd's Care 628

Refrain

With a shep-herd's care, God leads us. With a fa-ther's strength, God guides us. With a moth-er's love, God nur-tures us, and cra-dles us in gen - tle arms.

Verses

1. When we are lost, and can - not find the way, God
2. When we are weak, and cares press all a - round, God
3. When we are scared, and feel so all a - lone, God

cares for us and keeps us safe. For
strength - ens us to face each day. For
loves us and is by our side. For

God is our light and our faith - ful guide, and
God is our rock and our sav - ing help, and
God is our hope and our con - stant friend, and

D.C.

leads us with a shep - herd's care.
guides us with a fa - ther's strength.
nur - tures with a moth - er's love.

Text: James J. Chepponis, b.1956
Tune: James J. Chepponis, b.1956
© 1992, GIA Publications, Inc.

629 Live in the Light

Refrain

Let your love be a light for our days, and a fire to keep us warm in the night. Let your love be a guide on our way. May we learn to al - ways live in the light.

Verses 1, 2

1. When I'm a - lone or when I lose my way.
2. When I'm a - fraid of do - ing what is right,

Yours is the hand I can hold on
when there is no one who will help

to.
me.

When I was fall - en you
When I am sti - fled by

lift - ed me up. I was weak Lord, and you
fear and re - gret, your com - pas - sion and strength

D.C.

pulled me through!
set me free!

Verse 3

3. God of all cre - a - tion,

God be-yond all time and all space,

God, look down with mer - cy and

D.C.

keep me al - ways in your em - brace.

Text: Michael Mahler, b.1981
Tune: Michael Mahler, b.1981
© 2000, GIA Publications, Inc.

630 Come to Me, O Weary Traveler

1. Come to me, O wea - ry trav - 'ler; Come to me with
2. Do not fear, my yoke is eas - y; Do not fear, my
3. Take my yoke and leave your trou - bles; Take my yoke and
4. Rest in me, O wea - ry trav - 'ler; Rest in me and

your dis - tress; Come to me, you heav - y bur-dened;
bur - den's light; Do not fear the path be - fore you;
come with me. Take my yoke, I am be - side you;
do not fear. Rest in me, my heart is gen - tle;

Come to me and find your rest.
Do not run from me in fright.
Take and learn hu - mil - i - ty.
Rest and cast a - way your care.

Text: Matthew 11:28-30; Sylvia G. Dunstan, 1955-1993, © 1991, GIA Publications, Inc.
Tune: DUNSTAN, 8 7 8 7; Bob Moore, b.1962, © 1993, GIA Publications, Inc.

631 The King of Love My Shepherd Is

1. The King of love my shep - herd is, Whose good-ness
2. Where streams of liv - ing wa - ter flow My ran-somed
3. Con - fused and fool - ish oft I strayed, But yet in
4. In death's dark vale I fear no ill With you, dear
5. You spread a ta - ble in my sight; Your sav - ing
6. And so through all the length of days Your good-ness

fails me nev - er; I noth - ing lack if
soul he's lead - ing, And where the ver - dant
love he sought me; And on his shoul - der
Lord, be - side me, Your rod and staff my
grace be - stow - ing; And O what trans - port
fails me nev - er; Good Shep - herd, may I

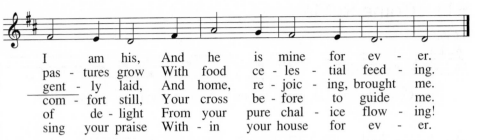

I am his, And he is mine for ev - er.
pas - tures grow With food ce - les - tial feed - ing.
gent - ly laid, And home, re - joic - ing, brought me.
com - fort still, Your cross be - fore to guide me.
of de - light From your pure chal - ice flow - ing!
sing your praise With - in your house for ev - er.

Text: Psalm 23; Henry W. Baker, 1821-1877, alt.
Tune: ST. COLUMBA, 8 7 8 7; Gaelic; harm. by A. Gregory Murray, OSB, 1905-1992, © Downside Abbey

Jesus, Lead the Way   632

1. Je - sus, lead the way Through our life's long day,
2. Je - sus be our light, In the midst of night,
3. When in deep - est grief, Strength - en our be - lief.
4. Je - sus, still lead on 'Til our rest be won:

When at times the way is cheer - less,
Let not faith - less fear o'er - take us,
When temp - ta - tions come al - lur - ing,
If you lead us through rough plac - es,

Help us fol - low, calm and fear - less;
Let not faith and hope for - sake us;
Make us pa - tient and en - dur - ing;
Grant us your re - deem - ing grac - es.

Guide us by your hand To the prom - ised land.
May we feel you near As we wor - ship here.
Lord we seek your grace In this ho - ly place.
When our course is o'er, O - pen heav - en's door.

Text: *Jesu, geh voran*; Nicholas L. von Zinzendorf, 1700-1760; tr. by Jane Borthwick, 1813-1897, alt.
Tune: ROCHELLE, 55 88 55; Adam Drese, 1620-1701; harm. alt.

633 Come to Me

Text: Matthew 11:28-30; Michael Joncas, b.1951
Tune: Michael Joncas, b.1951
© 1989, GIA Publications, Inc.

Shelter Me, O God 634

Refrain

Shel-ter me, O God; hide me in the shad-ow of your wings. You a-lone are my hope.

Verses

1. When my foes sur-round me, set me high a-bove their
2. As a moth - er gath - ers her young be-neath her
3. Though I walk in dark-ness, through the nee - dle's eye of

D.C.

reach. Hear me when I call your name.
care, gath - er me in - to your arms.
death, you will nev - er leave my side.

Text: Psalm 16:1, 61:5, Luke 13:34; Bob Hurd, b.1950, © 1984, Bob Hurd
Tune: Bob Hurd, b.1950, © 1984, Bob Hurd; harm. by Craig S. Kingsbury, b.1952, © 1984, OCP Publications
Published by OCP Publications.

We Will Walk with God 635

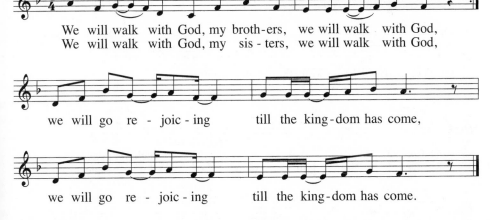

We will walk with God, my broth-ers, we will walk with God,
We will walk with God, my sis - ters, we will walk with God,

we will go re - joic - ing till the king-dom has come,

we will go re - joic - ing till the king-dom has come.

Text: Swaziland traditional, trans. by John L. Bell, b.1949, © 2002, The Iona Community, GIA Publications, Inc., agent
Tune: Swaziland traditional

636   Blest Are They

Verses 1-3

1. Blest are they, the poor in spir - it,
2. Blest are they, the low - ly ones,
3. Blest are they who show mer - cy,

theirs is the king - dom of God.
they shall in - her - it the earth.
mer - cy shall be theirs.

Blest are they, full of sor - row,
Blest are they who hun - ger and thirst,
Blest are they, the pure of heart,

they shall be con - soled.
they shall have their fill.
they shall see God!

Refrain

Re - joice and be glad! Bless-ed are you,

ho - ly are you! Re - joice and be glad!

Yours is the king-dom of God!

Verses 4, 5

4. Blest are they who seek peace;
5. Blest are you who suf - fer hate,

they are the chil - dren of God.
all be - cause of me. Re -

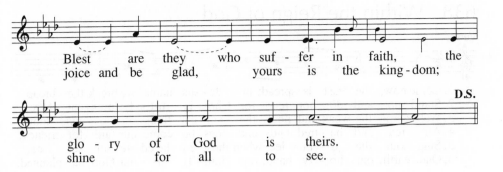

Blest are they who suf - fer in faith, the
joice and be glad, yours is the king - dom;

D.S.

glo - ry of God is theirs.
shine for all to see.

Text: Matthew 5:3-12; David Haas, b.1957
Tune: David Haas, b.1957; vocal arr. by David Haas and Michael Joncas, b.1951
© 1985, GIA Publications, Inc.

The Kingdom of God   637

Ostinato Refrain

The king - dom of God is jus - tice and peace and

joy in the Ho - ly Spir - it. Come, Lord, and

Last time

o - pen in us the gates of your king - dom.

Last time

Text: Community of Taizé
Tune: Community of Taizé
© 2001, Les Presses de Taizé, GIA Publications, Inc., agent

638 Within the Reign of God

Verses

1. Come now, the feast is spread; in Je-sus' name we break the bread.
2. Stand up and do not fear, for Christ is tru-ly pres-ent here.
3. Wel-come the weak and poor, the sin-ner finds an o-pen door,
4. All fear and ha-tred ends and foes be-come our faith-ful friends,
5. Sing out the ju-bi-lee when those en-slaved are all set free,
6. One earth, one ho-ly band, one fam-'ly as our God has planned,

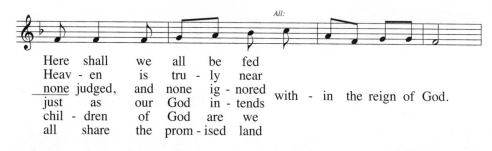

Here shall we all be fed
Heav-en is tru-ly near
none judged, and none ig-nored
just as our God in-tends   with-in the reign of God.
chil-dren of God are we
all share the prom-ised land

Come take this ho-ly food; re-ceive the bod-y and the blood.
Now at the wed-ding feast, the great-est here shall be the least.
Here shall the wea-ry rest, the stran-ger be a wel-come guest.
All you who seek God's face are wel-come in this ho-ly place.
No more can we for-get the ones who bear life's crush-ing debt.
Come now, the feast is spread, in Je-sus' name we break the bread;

Grace is a might-y flood
All bonds shall be re-leased
So shall we all be blest   with-in the reign of God.
join in the feast of grace
God's jus-tice guides us yet
here shall we all be fed

Refrain

Bless-ed are they who will feast in the reign of God.

Bless-ed are they who will share the bread of life.

Bless-ed are they who are least in the reign of God;

they shall re-joice at the feast of life.

Text Marty Haugen, b.1950
Tune: Marty Haugen, b.1950
© 1999, GIA Publications, Inc.

The Kingdom of God 639

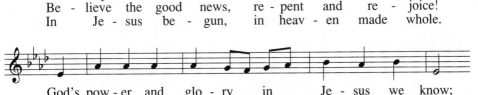

1. The king-dom of God is jus-tice and joy;
2. The king-dom of God is mer-cy and grace;
3. The king-dom of God is chal-lenge and choice:
4. God's king-dom is come, the gift and the goal;

For Je-sus re-stores what sin would de-stroy.
The cap-tives are freed, the sin-ners find place,
Be-lieve the good news, re-pent and re-joice!
In Je-sus be-gun, in heav-en made whole.

God's pow-er and glo-ry in Je-sus we know;
The out-cast are wel-comed God's ban-quet to share;
God's love for us sin-ners brought Christ to his cross:
The heirs of the king-dom shall an-swer his call;

And here and here-af-ter the king-dom shall grow.
And hope is a-wak-ened in place of de-spair.
Our cri-sis of judge-ment for gain or for loss.
And all things cry "Glo-ry!" to God all in all.

Text: Bryn A. Rees, 1911-1983, © Mrs. Olwen Scott
Tune: LAUDATE DOMINUM, 10 10 11 11; Charles H. H. Parry, 1848-1918

640 Bring Forth the Kingdom

Verses

Cantor:

1. You are salt for the earth, O peo - ple:
2. You are a light on the hill, O peo - ple:
3. You are a seed of the Word, O peo - ple:
4. We are a blest and a pil - grim peo - ple:

All: ... *Cantor:*

Salt for the King-dom of God! Share the fla - vor of
Light for the Cit - y of God! Shine so ho - ly and
Bring forth the King-dom of God! Seeds of mer - cy and
Bound for the King-dom of God! Love our jour-ney and

All:

life, O peo - ple: Life in the King-dom of God!
bright, O peo - ple: Shine for the King-dom of God!
seeds of jus - tice, Grow in the King-dom of God!
love our home-land: Love is the King-dom of God!

Refrain

Bring forth the King-dom of mer - cy, Bring forth the

King-dom of peace; Bring forth the King-dom of jus - tice,

Bring forth the Cit - y of God!

Text: Marty Haugen, b.1950
Tune: Marty Haugen, b.1950
© 1986, GIA Publications, Inc.

641 The Reign of God

1. The reign of God, like farm - er's field, Bears
2. Like mus - tard tree, the reign of God From
3. Though hid - den now, the reign of God May,
4. The reign of God is come in Christ; The

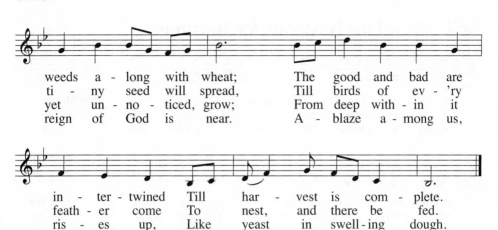

weeds a - long with wheat; The good and bad are
ti - ny seed will spread, Till birds of ev - 'ry
yet un - no - ticed, grow; From deep with - in it
reign of God is near. A - blaze a - mong us,

in - ter - twined Till har - vest is com - plete.
feath - er come To nest, and there be fed.
ris - es up, Like yeast in swell - ing dough.
kind - ling hearts, The reign of God is here!

Text: Delores Dufner, OSB, b.1939, © 2003, GIA Publications, Inc.
Tune: MCKEE, CM; African American; adapt. by Harry T. Burleigh, 1866-1949

Christ Is Made the Sure Foundation 642

1. Christ is made the sure foun - da - tion, Christ the head and
2. To this tem - ple where we call you, Come, O Lord of
3. Grant, we pray, to all your peo - ple, All the grace they

cor - ner-stone; Cho - sen of the Lord, and pre - cious,
hosts, to - day; With your wont - ed lov - ing kind - ness
ask to gain; What they gain from you for ev - er

Bind - ing all the Church in one; Ho - ly Zi - on's
Hear your ser - vants as they pray, And your full - est
With the bless - ed to re - tain, And here - af - ter

help for ev - er, And her con - fi - dence a - lone.
ben - e - dic - tion Shed in all its bright ar - ray.
in your glo - ry Ev - er - more with you to reign.

Text: *Angularis fundamentum;* 11th C.; tr. by John M. Neale, 1818-1866, alt.
Tune: ST. THOMAS, 8 7 8 7 8 7; John Wade, 1711-1786

643 As a Fire Is Meant for Burning

1. As a fire is meant for burning
   With a bright and warm-ing flame,
   So the church is meant for mis - sion,
   Giv - ing glo - ry to God's name.
   Not to preach our creeds or cus - toms,
   But to build a bridge of care,
   We join hands a - cross the na - tions,
   Find-ing neigh - bors ev - 'ry - where.

2. We are learn - ers; we are teach - ers;
   We are pil - grims on the way.
   We are seek - ers; we are giv - ers;
   We are ves - sels made of clay.
   By our gen - tle, lov - ing ac - tions,
   We would show that Christ is light.
   In a hum - ble, lis - t'ning Spir - it,
   We would live to God's de - light.

3. As a green bud in the spring - time
   Is a sign of life re - newed,
   So may we be signs of one - ness
   'Mid earth's peo - ples, man - y hued.
   As a rain - bow lights the heav - ens
   When a storm is past and gone,
   May our lives re - flect the ra - diance
   Of God's new and glor - ious dawn.

Text: Ruth Duck, b.1947, © 1992, GIA Publications, Inc.
Tune: BEACH SPRING, 8 7 8 7 D; *The Sacred Harp*, 1844; harm. by Marty Haugen, b.1950, © 1985, GIA Publications, Inc.

Sing a New Church 644

1. Sum-moned by the God who made us Rich in
2. Ra - diant ris - en from the wa - ter; Robed in
3. Trust the good - ness of cre - a - tion; Trust the
4. Bring the hopes of ev - 'ry na - tion; Bring the
5. Draw to - geth - er at one ta - ble All the

our di - ver - si - ty, Gath-ered in the name of
ho - li - ness and light, Male and fe - male in God's
Spir - it strong with - in. Dare to dream the vi - sion
art of ev - 'ry race. Weave a song of peace and
hu - man fam - i - ly; Shape a cir - cle ev - er

Je - sus, Rich - er still in u - ni - ty:
im - age, Male and fe - male, God's de - light:
prom - ised Sprung from seed of what has been.
jus - tice: Let it sound through time and space.
wid - er And a peo - ple ev - er free.

Let us bring the gifts that dif - fer And, in

splen - did, var-ied ways, Sing a new church in - to

be - ing, One in faith and love and praise.

Text: Delores Dufner, OSB, b.1939, © 1991, Sisters of St. Benedict. Published by OCP Publications.
Tune: NETTLETON, 8 7 8 7 D, from *Wyeth's Repository of Sacred Music, Pt. II*, 1813

645 Somos el Cuerpo de Cristo / We Are the Body of Christ

Refrain

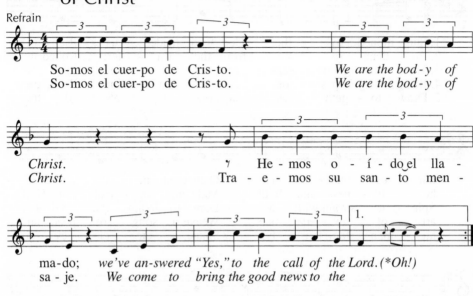

So-mos el cuer-po de Cris-to.   We are the bod-y of
So-mos el cuer-po de Cris-to.   We are the bod-y of

Christ.   He - mos o - í - do el lla -
Christ.   Tra - e - mos su san - to men -

ma-do; we've an-swered "Yes," to the call of the Lord. (*Oh!)
sa - je. We come to bring the good news to the

2.   To verses   Final ending

world.   world. (*Oh!)
             3. Que

Verses

Cantor: All:

1. Dios vie-ne al mun-do a tra - vés de no - so-tros.
   mun-do a cum-plir la mi - sión de la I-gle-sia,
2. Ca - da per - so - na es par-te del rei - no;   Som-os el cuer-po de
   To - das las ra - zas que ha-bi-tan la tie-rra,
3. nues-tras ac - cio - nes re - fle-jen jus - ti - cia;
   Va - mos al mun-do a cui - dar su re - ba-ño.

Cantor:

God is re-vealed when we love one an-oth - er.
Bring-ing the light of God's mer - cy to oth - ers,
Put - ting a stop to all dis-crim - i - na - tion,
Cris-to.   All are in - vit - ed to feast in the ban-quet.
Stop-ping a - buse and re - liev-ing the hun - gry,
Serv - ing each oth - er we build up the king-dom;

*Sing after Verse 2 (optional)

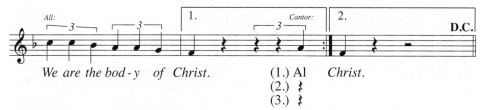

We are the bod-y of Christ.

(1.) Al   Christ.
(2.)
(3.)

O Christ the Great Foundation   646

1. O   Christ the great foun - da - tion On   which your peo - ple stand
2. Bap - tized in   one con - fes - sion, One   church in   all the earth,
3. Where ty - rants' hold is   tight - ened, Where strong de - vour the weak,
4. This   is   the mo - ment glo - rious When   he   who once was dead

To preach your true sal - va - tion In   ev - 'ry   age and   land:
We   bear our Lord's im - pres - sion, The   sign of sec - ond   birth:
Where in - no - cents are fright - ened The   right - eous fear to   speak,
Shall lead his church vic - to - rious, Their cham - pion and their   head.

Pour out your Ho - ly Spir - it To make us strong and pure,
One   ho - ly   peo - ple gath - ered In love be - yond our own,
There let your church a - wak - ing At - tack the pow'rs of   sin
The Lord of   all   cre - a - tion His heav'n - ly king - dom brings

To keep the faith un - bro - ken As   long as worlds en - dure.
By grace we were in - vit - ed, By   grace we make you known.
And, all their ram - parts break - ing, With you the vic - tory win.
The fi - nal con - sum - ma - tion, The glo - ry of all things.

647 Where Your Treasure Is

Refrain

Where your treas-ure is, there your heart shall be. All that
you pos-sess will nev - er set you free. Seek the
things that last; come and learn from me. Where your

Fourth time to Vs. 4 | To verses 1-3 | Last time

treas-ure is, your heart shall be. be.

Verses 1-3

1. What do you gain from all your wor - ry,
2. Look at the ra - vens high a - bove you.
3. Be - hold the lil - ies in their splen - dor.

What you should eat or what to wear?
They do not work their whole life through,
In grace and beau - ty are they dressed,

There is no peace in stress or hur - ry. Do you not
And yet God feeds them and pro - tects them. So how much
And yet so soon their bloom is fad - ed. So how much

D.C.

know that you are held with - in God's care?
more will God pro - tect and care for you?
more will those who look to God be blessed?

Verse 4

(be.) 4. Do not fear, lit-tle flock, for God de-lights to

give you the bless-ed reign of God.

Give your pos-ses-sions to the need-y; gain a

D.C.

treas - ure that will not fade.

Text: Luke 12:22-34; Marty Haugen, b.1950
Tune: Marty Haugen, b.1950
© 2000, GIA Publications, Inc.

Jesus, Your Spirit in Us 648

Ostinato Refrain

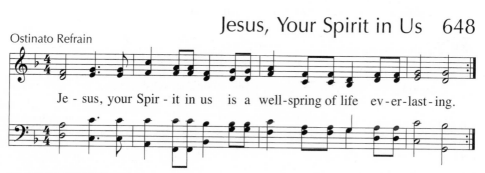

Je - sus, your Spir - it in us is a well-spring of life ev-er-last-ing.

Text: Psalm 63:1-4, 7-8; Taizé Community
Tune: Taizé Community
© 2003, Les Presses de Taizé, GIA Publications, Inc., agent

649 Your Wonderful Love

Verse 1

Cantor:

1. From dark-ness to light, from sad-ness to joy,

lead us, lead us O God. The

way may be cloud-y, the storms give us

fright, but to - geth-er we con-quer the night.

Refrain All:

We will walk through the dark-ness, ev-er close by your

side. We will car - ry each oth - er, your com - pas-sion our

guide. We will share in the sto - ry of bod - y and

Last time to Coda

blood. We will live in your won-der - ful love.

4

To verses 2, 3

Verse 2

Cantor:

2. Called as com-pan-ions, called to be free, sis-ters and broth-ers as one. Shar-ing the bur-den, light-'ning the load as we bring forth the day of your Son.

D.S.

Verse 3

Cantor:

3. One day we'll rise and, healed of our pain, we'll walk, walk in the sun. No more con - fu-sion, we'll be whole a-gain, We will fol-low 'til king - dom comes.

D.S.

Coda

love. We will live in your won-der-ful love.

Text: Francis Patrick O'Brien, b.1958
Tune: Francis Patrick O'Brien, b.1958

650 Pues Si Vivimos / When We Are Living

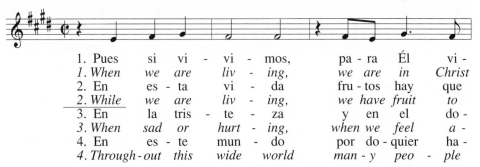

1. Pues si vi - vi - mos, pa - ra Él vi -
1. When we are liv - ing, we are in Christ
2. En es - ta vi - da fru - tos hay que
2. While we are liv - ing, we have fruit to
3. En la tris - te - za y en el do -
3. When sad or hurt - ing, when we feel a -
4. En es - te mun - do por do - quier ha -
4. Through - out this wide world man - y peo - ple

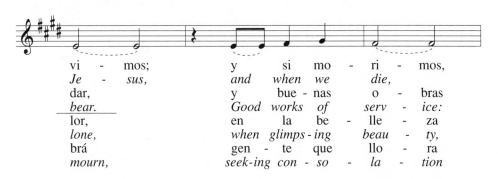

vi - mos; y si mo - ri - mos,
Je - sus, and when we die,
dar, y bue - nas o - bras
bear. Good works of serv - ice:
lor, en la be - lle - za
lone, when glimps - ing beau - ty,
brá gen - te que llo - ra
mourn, seek - ing con - so - la - tion

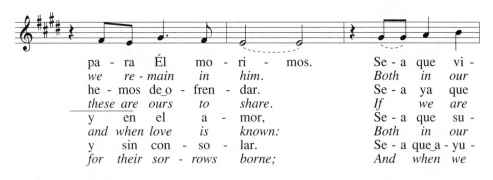

pa - ra Él mo - ri - mos. Se - a que vi -
we re - main in him. Both in our
he - mos de_o - fren - dar. Se - a ya que
these are ours to share. If we are
y en el a - mor, Se - a que su -
and when love is known: Both in our
y sin con - so - lar. Se - a que a - yu -
for their sor - rows borne; And when we

va - mos o que mu - ra - mos,
liv - ing, and in our dy - ing,
de - mos o que re - ci - ba - mos,
giv - ing or are re - ceiv - ing,
fra - mos o que go - ce - mos,
suf - f'ring and our re - joic - ing,
de - mos o que a - li - men - te - mos,
help them or when we feed them,

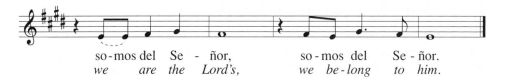

so-mos del Se - ñor,   so-mos del Se - ñor.
we   are   the   Lord's,   we be-long   to him.

Text: Verse 1, Romans 14:8; traditional Spanish; vss. 2-4, Robert Escamilla, © 1983, Abingdon Press; tr. by Ronald F. Krisman, b.1946, © 2004, Abingdon Press
Tune: Traditional Spanish; arr. by Ronald F. Krisman, b.1946, © 2004, GIA Publications, Inc.

Bambelela / Never Give Up   651

Bam - be-le - la,   bam - be-le - la,   O
Nev - er give up,   nev - er give up,   no

bam - be-le - la,   bam - be-le - la,
nev - er give up,   nev - er give up,

bam - ba, bam - ba, bam - ba, bam - ba, bam - ba,   O
nev - er, nev - er, nev - er, nev - er, nev - er,   no

Last time

bam - ba,   bam - be-le - la.
nev - er,   nev - er give up.   *Last time*

Text: Traditional South African
Tune: Traditional South African; tr. by Mairi Munro and Martine Stemerick; adapt. by Mairi Munro and Philip Jakob
© 2002, JL Zwane Memorial Congregation

652 We Will Serve the Lord

Verses

1. Wealth can be an i - dol built of gleam - ing gold,
2. Pleas - ure is a si - ren, prom - is - ing the flesh
3. Pow - er is a hun - ger, burn - ing in the breast, to
4. Fath - er of all mer - cy, Giv - er of all life,

bring-ing dreams of par - a - dise, fu - tures bought and sold.
brief re - lief from emp - ti - ness, a hid - ing place from death.
walk a - mong the might - y and tram - ple on the rest.
here we speak our cov - e - nant a - bove the nois - y strife.

Some will choose to gath - er it, all that they can hoard, but
Some will choose to chase it un - til it leaves them bored, but
Some will choose to gain it by lie or guile or sword, but
Hear us shout in glo - ry a - bove the pa - gan horde:

as for me and my house, we will serve the Lord! *To verse 2*
as for me and my house, we will serve the Lord! *To refrain*
as for me and my house, we will serve the Lord! *To refrain*
as for me and my house, we will serve the Lord! *To refrain*

Refrain

As for me and my house, we will serve the Lord,

we will serve the Lord, we will serve the Lord!

Text: Rory Cooney, b.1952
Tune: Rory Cooney, b.1952
© 1986, North American Liturgy Resources. Published by OCP Publications.

On a Journey Together 653

Verses

1. Walking on cobblestones,
   tearing my feet to the bones,
   tryin' to make it on my own,
   wondering where I'm going and how I'm gonna get there,
   sure can't do it all alone.

2. All of the mistakes I made,
   taking many wrong turns,
   are really lessons that I learned.
   So every time I start to stumble
   I remain humble to God's love and his word.

3. Traveling on this road to Jesus,
   knowing that vision is the key
   to understand where we've been and where we are and want to be,
   now it starts with you and me.

Text: John Angotti
Tune: John Angotti
© 1998, 1999, World Library Publications

654 All That Is Hidden

1. If you would fol-low me, fol-low where life will lead:
2. If you would hon-or me, hon-or the least of these:
3. If you would speak of me, live all your life in me:
4. If you would rise with me, rise through your des-ti-ny:

do not look for me a-mong the dead, for I am
you will not find me dressed in fin-er-y. My Word cries
my ways are not the ways that you would choose; my thoughts are
do not re-fuse the death which brings you life, for as the

hid-den in pain, ris-en in love;
out to be heard; breaks through the world:
far be-yond yours, as heav-en from earth:
grain in the earth must die for re-birth,

there is no har-vest with-out sow-ing of grain.
my Word is on your lips and lives in your heart.
if you be-lieve in me my voice will be heard.
so I have plant-ed your life deep with-in mine.

All that is hid-den will be made clear. All that is

dark now will be re-vealed. What you have heard in the dark

pro-claim in the light; what you hear in whis-pers

pro-claim from the house - tops.

Text: Refrain based on Luke 12:2-3; Bernadette Farrell, b.1957
Tune: Bernadette Farrell, b.1957; arr. by Paul Inwood, b.1947
© 1986, 1988, Bernadette Farrell. Published by OCP Publications.

Take This Moment 655

1. Take this mo - ment, sign, and space; Take my
2. Take the time to call my name, Take the
3. Take the tired - ness of my days, Take my
4. Take the lit - tle child in me, Scared of
5. Take my tal - ents, take my skills, Take what's

friends a - round; Here a - mong us
time to mend Who I am and
past re - gret, Let - ting your for -
grow - ing old; Help him/her here to
yet to be; Let my life be

make the place Where your love is found.
what I've been, All I've failed to tend.
give - ness touch All I can't for - get.
find his/her worth Made in Christ's own mold.
yours, and yet, Let it still be me.

Text: John L. Bell, b.1949
Tune: TAKE THIS MOMENT, 7 5 7 5; John L. Bell, b.1949
© 1989, Iona Community, GIA Publications, agent

656 Whatsoever You Do

Refrain

What - so - ev - er you do to the least of my peo - ple, that you do un - to me.

Verses

1. When I was hun - gry, you gave me to eat;
2. When I was home - less, you o - pened your door;
3. When I was wea - ry, you helped me find rest;
4. When I was lit - tle, you taught me to read;
5. When in a pris - on, you came to my cell;
6. In a strange coun - try, you made me at home;
7. Hurt in a bat - tle, you bound up my wounds;
8. When I was Black, or La - ti - no, or white;
9. When I was a - ged, you both - ered to smile;
10. You saw me cov - ered with spit - tle and blood;
11. When I was laughed at, you stood by my side;

When I was thirst - y, you gave me to drink.
When I was na - ked, you gave me your coat.
When I was anx - ious, you calmed all my fears.
When I was lone - ly, you gave me your love.
When on a sick - bed, you cared for my needs.
Seek - ing em - ploy - ment, you found me a job.
Search - ing for kind - ness, you held out your hand.
Mocked and in - sult - ed, you car - ried my cross.
When I was rest - less, you lis - tened and cared.
You knew my fea - tures, though grim - y with sweat.
When I was hap - py, you shared in my joy.

D.C.

Now en - ter in - to the home of my Fa - ther.

Text: Matthew 5:3-12; Willard F. Jabusch, b.1930
Tune: WHATSOEVER YOU DO, 10 10 11 with refrain; Willard F. Jabusch, b.1930; harm. by Robert J. Batastini, b.1942
© 1966, 1982, Willard F. Jabusch. Administered by OCP Publications.

'Tis the Gift to Be Simple   657

'Tis the gift to be sim-ple, 'tis the gift to be free, 'tis the

gift to come down where we ought to be, and

when we find our-selves in the place just right, 'twill

be in the val - ley of love and de - light.

When true sim - plic - i - ty is gained to bow and to bend we

shan't be a-shamed, to turn, turn, will be our de-light till by

turn - ing, turn - ing we come round right.

Text: Shaker Song, 18th. C.
Tune: SIMPLE GIFTS; acc. Margaret W. Mealy, b.1922, © 1984

658 Keep in Mind

Refrain

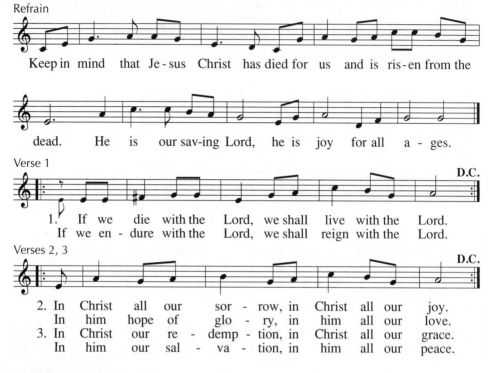

Keep in mind that Je-sus Christ has died for us and is ris-en from the dead. He is our sav-ing Lord, he is joy for all a-ges.

Verse 1

D.C.

1. If we die with the Lord, we shall live with the Lord.
   If we en-dure with the Lord, we shall reign with the Lord.

Verses 2, 3

D.C.

2. In Christ all our sor-row, in Christ all our joy.
   In him hope of glo-ry, in him all our love.
3. In Christ our re-demp-tion, in Christ all our grace.
   In him our sal-va-tion, in him all our peace.

Text: 2 Timothy 2:8-12; Lucien Deiss, CSSp, b.1921
Tune: Lucien Deiss, CSSp, b.1921
© 1965, World Library Publications, Inc.

659 Jesus in the Morning

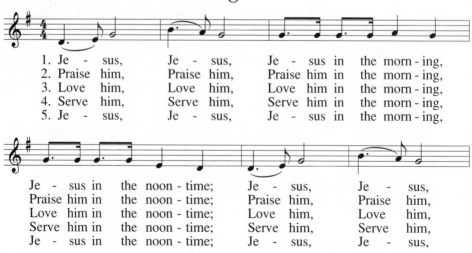

1. Je - sus, Je - sus, Je - sus in the morn-ing,
2. Praise him, Praise him, Praise him in the morn-ing,
3. Love him, Love him, Love him in the morn-ing,
4. Serve him, Serve him, Serve him in the morn-ing,
5. Je - sus, Je - sus, Je - sus in the morn-ing,

Je - sus in the noon - time; Je - sus, Je - sus,
Praise him in the noon - time; Praise him, Praise him,
Love him in the noon - time; Love him, Love him,
Serve him in the noon - time; Serve him, Serve him,
Je - sus in the noon - time; Je - sus, Je - sus,

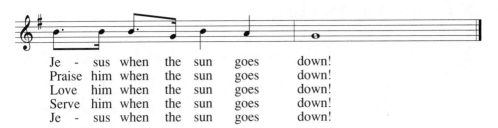

Je - sus when the sun goes down!
Praise him when the sun goes down!
Love him when the sun goes down!
Serve him when the sun goes down!
Je - sus when the sun goes down!

Text: African-American folk song
Tune: African-American folk song

Deliver Us, O Lord of Truth 660

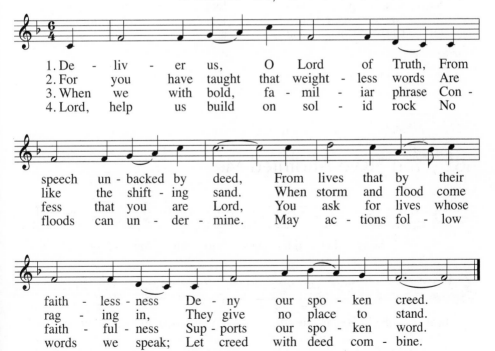

1. De - liv - er us, O Lord of Truth, From
2. For you have taught that weight - less words Are
3. When we with bold, fa - mil - iar phrase Con -
4. Lord, help us build on sol - id rock No

speech un - backed by deed, From lives that by their
like the shift - ing sand. When storm and flood come
fess that you are Lord, You ask for lives whose
floods can un - der - mine. May ac - tions fol - low

faith - less - ness De - ny our spo - ken creed.
rag - ing in, They give no place to stand.
faith - ful - ness Sup - ports our spo - ken word.
words we speak; Let creed with deed com - bine.

Text: Herman G. Stuempfle, Jr., b.1923, © 1997, GIA Publications, Inc.
Tune: LAND OF REST, CM; American; harm. by Annabel M. Buchanan, 1888-1983, © 1938, J. Fisher and Bro.

661 The Servant Song

1., 6. Will you let me be your ser-vant, Let me be as
2. We are pil-grims on a jour-ney, We are trav-'lers
3. I will hold the Christ-light for you In the night-time
4. I will weep when you are weep-ing; When you laugh I'll
5. When we sing to God in heav-en We shall find such

Christ to you; Pray that I may have the grace to
on the road; We are here to help each oth-er
of your fear; I will hold my hand out to you,
laugh with you. I will share your joy and sor-row
har-mo-ny, Born of all we've known to-geth-er

Let you be my ser - vant, too.
Walk the mile and bear the load.
Speak the peace you long to hear.
'Til we've seen this jour - ney through.
Of Christ's love and ag - o - ny.

Text: Richard Gillard, b.1953
Tune: Richard Gillard, b.1953; harm. by Betty Pulkingham, b.1929
© 1977, Scripture in Song

662 You Have Anointed Me

Verse 1

1. To bring glad tid - ings to the low - ly, to

heal the bro-ken heart, You have a - noint - ed

me. To pro - claim lib-er-ty to cap - tives, re -

lease to pris - on - ers, You have a - noint - ed me.

Refrain

Your Spir - it, O God, is up - on me,

You have a - noint - ed me.

Verse 2

2. To an-nounce a year of fa - vor, to

com - fort those who mourn, You have a - noint - ed

me. To give to them the oil of glad - ness, and

D.S.

share a man-tle of joy, You have a - noint - ed me.

Text: Mike Balhoff, b.1946, Gary Daigle, b.1957, Darryl Ducote, b.1945
Tune: Mike Balhoff, b.1946, Gary Daigle, b.1957, Darryl Ducote, b.1945; acc. by Gary Daigle
© 1981, Damean Music. Distributed by GIA Publications, Inc.

663   City of God

Verses 1, 2

1.   A-wake from your slum-ber!   A - rise from your
2. We are sons of the morn-ing;   we are daugh-ters of

sleep!   A   new   day   is   dawn - ing
day.   The   One   who has   loved   us

for   all those who weep.   The peo - ple   in
has bright-ened our way.   The Lord   of all

dark - ness   have seen a great light.   The Lord of our
kind - ness   has called us to   be   a light for his

long-ing   has con-quered the   night.
peo - ple   to set their hearts   free.

℅ Refrain

Let us   build the cit-y   of God.   May our tears   be

turned in - to danc - ing!   For the Lord, our light and our

love,   has   turned   the night in - to   day!

Text: Dan Schutte, b.1947
Tune: Dan Schutte, b.1947; acc. by Robert J. Batastini, b.1942
© 1981, Daniel L. Schutte and OCP Publications

664 Go Make a Difference

Refrain

Go make a dif - f'rence. We can make a dif - f'rence.

Go make a dif - f'rence in the world.

Go make a dif - f'rence. We can make a dif - f'rence.

To verses | *To repeat refrain* |

Go make a dif - f'rence in the world.

Verses 1, 2

1. We are the salt of the earth, called to let the peo - ple
2. We are the hands of Christ reach-ing out to those in

see the love of God in you and me.
need, the face of God for all to see.

We are the light of the world, not to be hid - den but be
We are the spir - it of hope; we are the voice of

D.C.

seen. Go make a dif - f'rence in the world.
peace. Go make a dif - f'rence in the world.

Verse 3

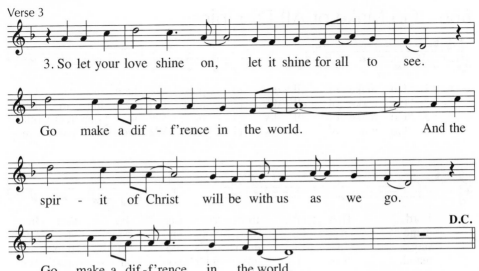

3. So let your love shine on, let it shine for all to see.
Go make a dif - f'rence in the world. And the
spir - it of Christ will be with us as we go.
D.C.
Go make a dif -f'rence in the world.

Text: Matthew 5:13-16; Steve Angrisano, b.1965, and Tom Tomaszek, b.1950
Tune: Steve Angrisano, b.1965, and Tom Tomaszek, b.1950; acc. by Rick Modlin, b.1966
© 1997, 1998, Steve Agrisano and Thomas N. Tomaszek. Published by OCP Publications.

The Church of Christ 665

1. The Church of Christ in ev - 'ry age Be - set by
2. A - cross the world, a - cross the street, The vic - tims
3. Then let the ser - vant Church a - rise, A car - ing
4. For he a - lone, whose blood was shed, Can cure the
5. We have no mis - sion but to serve In full o -

change but Spir - it led, Must claim and test its
of in - jus - tice cry For shel - ter and for
Church that longs to be A part - ner in Christ's
fe - ver in our blood, And teach us how to
be - dience to our Lord: To care for all, with -

her - i - tage And keep on ris - ing from the dead.
bread to eat, And nev - er live un - til they die.
sac - ri - fice, And clothed in Christ's hu - man - i - ty.
share our bread And feed the starv - ing mul - ti - tude.
out re - serve, And spread his lib - er - at - ing Word.

Text: Fred Pratt Green, 1903-2000, © 1971, Hope Publishing Co.
Tune: O WALY, WALY, LM; arr. by John L. Bell, b.1949, © 1989, The Iona Community, GIA Publications, Inc., agent

666 Go Make of All Disciples

1. "Go make of all dis - ci - ples:" We hear the call, O
2. "Go make of all dis - ci - ples:" Bap-tiz - ing in the
3. "Go make of all dis - ci - ples:" We at your feet would
4. "Go make of all dis - ci - ples:" We wel-come your com -

Lord, That comes from you, our Fa - ther, In
name Of Fa - ther, Son, and Spir - it— From
stay Un - til each life's vo - ca - tion Ac -
mand; "Lo, I am with you al - ways:" We

your e - ter - nal Word. In - spire our ways of
age to age the same. We call each new dis -
cents your ho - ly way. We cul - ti - vate the
take your guid - ing hand. The task looms large be -

learn - ing Through earn - est, fer - vent prayer, And
ci - ple To fol - low you, O Lord, Re -
na - ture God plants in ev - 'ry heart, Re -
fore us— We fol - low with - out fear. In

let our dai - ly liv - ing Re - veal you ev - 'ry-where.
deem - ing soul and bod - y By wa - ter and the Word.
veal - ing in our wit - ness The Mas - ter Teach-er's art.
heav'n and earth your pow - er Shall bring God's king - dom here.

Text: Matthew 28:19-20; Leon M. Adkins, 1896-1986, alt., © 1964, Abingdon Press
Tune: ELLACOMBE, 7 6 7 6 D; *Gesangbuch der Herzogl*, Wirtemberg, 1784

One Lord 667

Refrain

One Lord, one faith, one call to serve each oth - er. One heart, one mind, one com - mon ground; we stand all as one.

To verses | *Last time*

Verses

1. Give us new hands, o - pen and free,
2. Give us new eyes, lov - ing and wise,
3. Give us new hearts, hum - ble yet strong,
4. Breathe out your Spir - it up - on the land.

to serve with grace and dig - ni - ty. May we be wor-
to seek the good we all have in - side. May we be wor-
to love like you our whole life long. May we be wor-
In hope and peace we'll firm - ly stand, to live lives wor-

D.C.

thy of our call.
thy of our call.
thy of our call. We have but
thy of our call.

Text: Ephesians 4:1-24; Lori True, b.1961
Tune: Lori True, b.1961
© 2003, GIA Publications, Inc.

668 Lord, Whose Love in Humble Service

1. Lord, whose love in hum - ble serv - ice
2. Still your chil - dren wan - der home - less;
3. As we wor - ship, grant us vi - sion,
4. Called from wor - ship in - to serv - ice

Bore the weight of hu - man need, Who did on the
Still the hun - gry cry for bread; Still the cap - tives
Till your love's re - veal - ing light, Till the height and
Forth in your great name we go, To the child, the

Cross for - sak - en, Show us mer - cy's per - fect deed;
long for free - dom; Still in grief we mourn our dead.
depth and great - ness Dawns up - on our hu - man sight:
youth, the a - ged, Love in liv - ing deeds to show;

We, your ser - vants, bring the wor - ship
As, O Lord, your deep com - pas - sion
Mak - ing known the needs and bur - dens
Hope and health, good - will and com - fort,

Not of voice a - lone, but heart: Con - se - crat - ing
Healed the sick and freed the soul, Use the love your
Your com - pas - sion bids us bear, Stir - ring us to
Coun - sel, aid, and peace we give That your chil - dren,

to your pur - pose Ev - 'ry gift which you im - part.
Spir - it kin - dles Still to save and make us whole.
faith - ful serv - ice, Your a - bun - dant life to share.
Lord, in free - dom, May your mer - cy know and live.

Text: Albert F. Bayly, 1901-1984, © Oxford University Press
Tune: IN BABILONE, 8 7 8 7 D; *Oude en Nieuwe Hollanste Boerenlities*, c.1710

God Has Chosen Me   669

Verses

1. God has cho - sen me, God has cho - sen me to
2. God has cho - sen me, God has cho - sen me to
3. God is call - ing me, God is call - ing me in

bring good news to the poor. God has cho - sen me,
set a - light a new fire. God has cho - sen me,
all whose cry is un - heard. God is call - ing me,

God has cho - sen me to bring new sight to those
God has cho - sen me to bring to birth a new
God is call - ing me to raise up the voice with no

search - ing for light: God has cho - sen me, cho - sen me:
king - dom on earth: God has cho - sen me, cho - sen me:
pow - er or choice: God is call - ing me, call - ing me:

Refrain

And to tell the world that God's king - dom is near, to re -

move op - pres - sion and break down fear, yes, God's time is near,

God's time is near, God's time is near, God's time is near.

Text: Bernadette Farrell, b.1957
Tune: Bernadette Farrell, b.1957
© 1990, Bernadette Farrell. Published by OCP Publications.

670 How Can We Be Silent

Verses

1. How can we be si-lent when we know our God is near, bring-ing
2. How can we be si-lent when our God has con-quered death, stretch-ing
3. How can we be si-lent as we turn our eyes a - way and ig-
4. How can we be si-lent, not give praise with all our hearts, for Christ
5. How can we be si-lent when our souls are filled with awe at the

light to those in dark-ness, to the worth-less, end-less worth?
out his arms to suf-fer so that we might have new life?
nore the poor and bro-ken who lie bleed-ing in the street?
Je - sus is our Sav-ior and com-pas-sion is our king?
beau - ty of cre - a - tion and the mer-cy of our Lord?

How can we be si-lent when we are the voice of Christ, speak-ing
How can we be si-lent when we know that Je - sus rose, and will
How can we be si-lent when we're called to heal and serve in the
How can we be si-lent when God gave us life to be vi-brant
How can we be si-lent when we yearn to sing new songs? In our

jus - tice to the na-tions, breath-ing love to all the earth?
come a - gain in glo - ry, end - ing suf - fer - ing and strife?
im - age of Lord Je - sus, who has stooped to wash our feet?
in - stru-ments of wor-ship, made to laugh and dance and sing?
hearts a fire is burn-ing and it will not be ig - nored!

Refrain*

1. None can stop the Spir - it burn-ing now in - side us.

3. We will shape the fu - ture. We will not be si - lent!

*May be sung as a canon.

Text: Michael Mahler, b.1981
Tune: Michael Mahler, b.1981
© 2003, GIA Publications, Inc.

Here I Am, Lord 671

Text: Isaiah 6; Dan Schutte, b.1947
Tune: Dan Schutte, b.1947; arr. by Michael Pope, SJ, and John Weissrock
© 1981, OCP Publications

672 Good News

Verses

1. When Je - sus worked here on earth he
2. The eld - ers of the syn - a - gogue were
3. The way he lived was proof of it: he
4. So pass it on to - day, good friend: the

preached in his home - town, I - sa - iah's hopes
shocked by Mar - y's son, That he was des -
qui - et - ed our strife. The cross it - self he
mes - sage is the same. De - liv - 'rance Christ a -

now ful - filled, those claims of great re - nown.
tined to be the Christ for ev - 'ry - one.
would not flee e'en though it cost his life.
lone can give, for this to earth he came.

Refrain

To bring good news to the need - y, to make the

blind to see, the bro - ken hearts healed a - gain, to

1.
set the cap - tive free.

2.
cap - tive free.

Text: Howard S. Olson, b.1922
Tune: Almaz Belihu; Yemissrach Dimts Literature Program, Ethiopia
© 1993, Howard S. Olson

Stand Firm 673

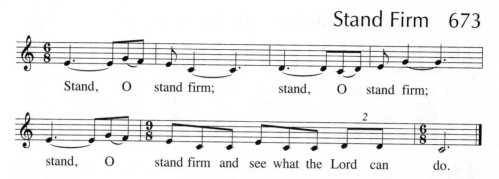

Stand, O stand firm; stand, O stand firm;

stand, O stand firm and see what the Lord can do.

Text: Cameroon traditional
Tune: Cameroon traditional; arr. by John L. Bell, b.1949, © 1998, The Iona Community, GIA Publications, Inc., agent

Thuma Mina / Send Me, Jesus 674

1. Thu - ma mi - na, Thu - ma mi - na,
2. Send me, Je - sus, send me, Je - sus,
3. Lead me, Je - sus, lead me, Je - sus,
4. Fill me, Je - sus, fill me, Je - sus,

Thu - ma mi - na So - man - dla.
send me, Je - sus, send me, Lord.
lead me, Je - sus, lead me, Lord.
fill me, Je - sus, fill me, Lord.

Text: South African
Tune: THUMA MINA, South African
© 1984, Utryck, Walton Music Corp., agent

675 You Are Called to Tell the Story

1. You are called to tell the sto - ry, Pass - ing
2. You are called to teach the rhy - thm Of the
3. You are called to set the ta - ble, Bless - ing
4. May the One whose love is broad - er Than the

words of life a - long, Then to
dance that nev - er ends, Then to
bread as Je - sus blessed, Then to
meas - ure of all space Give us

blend your voice with oth - ers As you
move with - in the cir - cle, Hand in
come with thirst and hun - ger, Need - ing
words to sing the sto - ry, Move a -

sing the sa - cred song. Christ be known in all our
hand with stran - gers, friends. Christ be known in all our
care like all the rest. Christ be known in all our
mong us in this place. Christ be known in all our

sing - ing, Fill - ing all with songs of love.
danc - ing, Touch - ing all with hands of love.
shar - ing, Feed - ing all with signs of love.
liv - ing, Fill - ing all with gifts of love.

Text: Ruth Duck, b.1947, © 1992, GIA Publications, Inc.
Tune: ROSEMARY, 8 7 8 7 8 7; Marty Haugen, b.1950, © 2002, GIA Publications, Inc.

I Am for You 676

1. There is a moun-tain, there is a sea.
2. There was a wom-an small as a star,
3. There was a man who walked in the storm,
4. We are a-noint - ed, ser - vants of God;
5. There is a world that waits in the womb;

There is a wind with - in all breath-ing,
Full of the pa - tient dreams of her na - tion,
Caught in be - tween the waves and the light - ning,
We have been born a - gain of Spir - it.
There is a hope un - born God is bear - ing,

There is an arm to break ev - 'ry chain,
Wel - com - ing in an an - gel of God,
Shar - ing his bread with those cast a - side,
We are the word God speaks to the world,
Though the powers of death prowl the night,

There is a fire in all things liv - ing.
Wel - com - ing in God's bold in - vi - ta - tion.
Heal - ing by touch the lost and the dy - ing.
Free - dom and light to all who will hear it.
There is a day our God is pre - par - ing.

There is a voice that speaks from the flame:
"Let it be done," she sang, "un - to me.
Send - ing us forth, he says to his friends:
So let us be the word of the Lord:
Sing 'round the fire to wak - en the dawn:

"I am for you, I am for you, I am for you is my name."
I am for you, I am for you, I am for you: let it be."
"I am for you, I am for you, I am for you to the end."
I am for you, I am for you, I am for you ev - er - more.
I am for you, I am for you, I am for you: We are one.

677 Come and Follow Me

Verses

1. Come, be my light, be my voice to the na-
2. Go, take your gift to the poor and the lone-

tions. Be my hands, be my heart for the world.
ly. As you love, so will I live in you.

Would you go where I go? Where I lead,
Will you feed, feed my lambs? Share your hope

will you fol-low? Would you leave ev-'ry-thing
with the hope-less? Bring new sight to the blind

for my sake? By the pow-er of the Spir-
in my name? With a tow-el and a ba-

it, ev-'ry-one with ears to hear it will em-
sin, t'ward the king-dom we will has-ten, through the

brace the call to love with-in their heart.
nar-row gate that leads to Cal-va-ry.

𝄋 Refrain

If an-y-one would come and fol-low me, my dis-

Text: Tom Franzak, b.1954
Tune: Tom Franzak, b.1954; acc. by Gerard Chiusano, b.1953

678 Lord, When You Came / Pescador de Hombres

Verses

1. Lord, when you came to the sea - shore
2. Lord, you knew what my boat car - ried:
3. Lord, have you need of my la - bor,
4. Lord, send me where you would have me,

1. Tú has ve - ni - do_a la_o - ri - lla,
2. Tú sa - bes bien lo que ten - go,
3. Tú ne - ce - si - tas mis ma - nos,
4. Tú pes - ca - dor de_o - tros, ma - res,

You weren't seek - ing the wise or the wealth - y,
Nei - ther mon - ey nor weap - ons for fight - ing,
Hands for serv - ice, a heart made for lov - ing,
To a vil - lage, or heart of the cit - y;

no_has bus - ca - do ni_a sa - bios, ni_a ri - cos,
en mi bar - ca no_hay o - ro ni_es - pa - das,
mi can - san - cio que_a o - tros des - can - se,
an - sia_e - ter - na, al - mas que es - pe - ran.

But on - ly ask - ing that I might fol - low.
But nets for fish - ing, my dai - ly la - bor.
My arms for lift - ing the poor and bro - ken?
I will re - mem - ber that you are with me.

tan só - lo quie - res que yo te si - ga.
tan só - lo re - des y mi tra - ba - jo.
a - mor que quie - ra se - guir a - man - do.
A - mi - go bue - no, que_a - sí me lla - mas.

Refrain

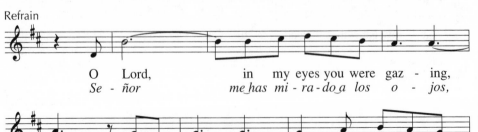

O Lord, in my eyes you were gaz - ing,
Se - ñor me_has mi - ra - do_a los o - jos,

Kind - ly smil - ing, my name you were
son - ri - en - do has di - cho mi

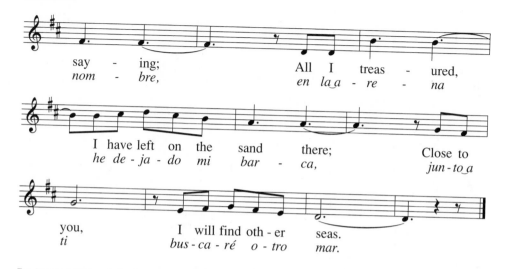

say - ing;
nom - bre,

All I treas - ured,
en la_a - re - na

I have left on the sand there;
he de - ja - do mi bar - ca,

Close to
jun - to_a

you,
ti

I will find oth - er seas.
bus - ca - ré o - tro mar.

Text: *Pescador de Hombres*, Cesáreo Gabaráin, © 1979, published by OCP Publications; trans. by Willard Francis Jabusch, b.1930, © 1982, administered by OCP Publications
Tune: Cesáreo Gabaráin, © 1979, published by OCP Publications; acc. by Diana Kodner, b.1957

You Walk along Our Shoreline 679

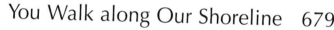

1. You walk a - long our shore - line Where land meets un - known sea.
2. You call us, Christ, to gath - er The peo - ple of the earth.
3. We cast our net, O Je - sus; We cry the king - dom's name;

We hear your voice of pow - er, "Now come and fol - low me.
We can - not fish for on - ly Those lives we think have worth.
We work for love and jus - tice; We learn to hope through pain.

And if you still will fol - low Through storm and wave and shoal,
We spread your net of gos - pel A - cross the wa - ter's face,
You call us, Lord, to gath - er God's daugh - ters and God's sons,

Then I will make you fish - ers But of the hu - man soul."
Our boat a com - mon shel - ter For all found by your grace.
To let your judg - ment heal us So that all may be one.

Text: Sylvia Dunston, 1955-1993, © 1991, GIA Publications, Inc.
Tune: AURELIA, 7 6 7 6 D; Samuel Sebastian Wesley, 1810-1876

680 The Love of the Lord

1. All that I count - ed as gain
2. Rich - es and hon - ors will fade,
3. Sil - ver and gold have I none,
4. Faith is the wealth I pos - sess

now I con - sid - er as loss,
earth - ly de - light dis - ap - pear,
no land to count as my home, yet
Find - ing its source in my God:

emp - ty and worth - less to me in the
fade like the grass of the field in the
wealth be - yond meas - ure I own in the
faith in the prom - ise of Christ is my

1., 3.
light of the love of the Lord.
light of the love of the Lord.
light of the love of the Lord.
life and my love of the Lord.

2., 4.
Lord.
Lord.

What more could bring us hope than to know the pow'r of his

life? What more could bring us peace than to

share in his suf-f'ring and death? What more could be our

fi - nal wish than to live in the love of the Lord?

Text: Philippians 3:7-11; Michael Joncas, b.1951
Tune: Michael Joncas, b.1951
© 1988, GIA Publications, Inc.

Anthem 681

Refrain

We are called, we are cho-sen. We are Christ for one an-oth-er. We are

prom-ised to to-mor-row, while we are for him to-day. We are

sign, we are won-der. We are sow-er, we are seed. We are

har-vest, we are hun-ger. We are ques-tion, we are creed.

Verses

1. Then where can we stand jus-ti-fied? In what can we be-
2. Then how are we to stand at all, this world of bend-ed
3. Then shall we not stand emp-ty at the al-tar of our

lieve? In no one else but Christ who suf-fered, noth-ing
knee? In noth-ing more than bar-ren shad-ows. No one
dreams: When Christ prom-ised us our-selves. Who mark

more than Christ who rose. Who was jus-tice for the poor.
else but Christ could save us. Who was jus-tice for the poor.
time a-gainst to-mor-row. Who are jus-tice for the poor.

Who was rage a-gainst the night. Who was
Who was rage a-gainst the night. Who was
Who are rage a-gainst the night. Who are

D.C.

hope for peace-ful peo-ple. Who was light.
hope for peace-ful peo-ple. Who was light.
hope for peace-ful peo-ple. Who are light.

Text: Tom Conry, b.1951
Tune: Tom Conry, b.1951; acc. by Robert J. Batastini, b.1942
© 1978, OCP Publications

682 Blest Are We / Bendecidos, Somos Santos

Refrain

Blest are we, ho-ly chil-dren of light are we!

¡Ben - de-ci-dos, so-mos san - tos hi-jos de la luz!

Blest are we, cho - sen peo-ple of God.

Ben - de - ci - dos, y e - le-gi - dos por Dios.

Blest are we, God has plans for you and me.

Ben - de - ci - dos, Dios nos quie-re ser cual Je - sús.

Blest are we! We are the chil-dren of God!

¡Ben - de-ci - dos, so-mos los hi - jos de Dios!

*Last time, repeat final 4 bars.

Verses

1. For our world, each sis - ter and broth - er: We are called,
2. For the poor, the meek and the low - ly: We are called,
3. For all those who yearn for free - dom: We are called,

1. Por el mun-do, por to - dos sus pue-blos: ¡So-mos lla-ma-dos
2. Por los po-bres, los man - sos y hu-mil - des: ¡So-mos lla-ma-dos
3. Por los que su-fren y quie-ren ser li - bra-dos: ¡So-mos lla-ma-dos

called to serve! We are here to love one an-oth - er:
called to serve! For the weak, the sick and the hun - gry:
called to serve! For the world, to be God's king - dom:

pa - ra ser - vir! Que nos a-me-mos los u - nos a los o - tros;
pa - ra ser - vir! Por los en-fer-mos, ham-brien - tos, y dé-bi-les:
pa - ra ser - vir! Ven-ga a no-so-tros el Rei-no de los Cie-los:

We are called, called to serve!
We are called, called to serve!
We are called, called to serve!

D.C.

¡So-mos lla-ma - dos pa - ra ser - vir!
¡So-mos lla-ma - dos pa - ra ser - vir!
¡So-mos lla-ma - dos pa - ra ser - vir!

D.C.

Text: David Haas, b.1957, Spanish tr. by Ronald F. Krisman, b.1946
Tune: David Haas, b.1957
© 2003, GIA Publications, Inc.

683 I Will Choose Christ

Refrain

I will choose Christ,   I will choose love,   I choose

to   serve.   I give my heart,   I give my life,

To verses | *Final ending*

I give my all   to you.   I give my all   to you.

Verse 1

1. How man-y times   must he   call   my   name   and show to

me   that he is God?   And as a ser - vant   he

D.C.

calls to   me,   "You   must serve   too."

Verse 2

2. Christ, my teach - er   and   heal - er,   teach my

heart   and heal my   soul.   And as I walk   this

D.C.

road with you,   teach me   to   love.

Verse 3

3. As I look up - on your cross, so too must I die with you. And with the death of my own de - sires, I'll rise with you.

Text: Tom Booth, b.1961
Tune: Tom Booth, b.1961; acc. by Ed Bolduc
© 1997, Tom Booth. Published by OCP Publications.

Guide My Feet   684

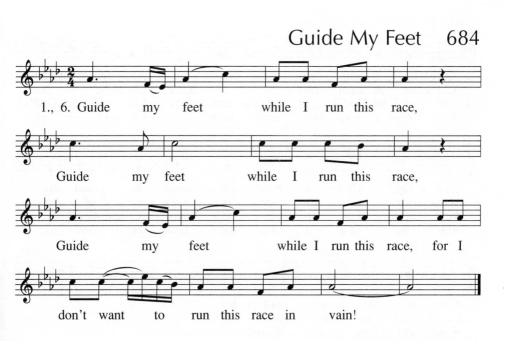

1., 6. Guide my feet while I run this race,

Guide my feet while I run this race,

Guide my feet while I run this race, for I

don't want to run this race in vain!

2. Hold my hand… 3. Stand by me... 4. I'm your child... 5. Search my heart...

Text: African-American spiritual
Tune: African-American spiritual; harm. by Diana Kodner, b. 1957, © 1994, GIA Publications, Inc.

685 Song of St. Patrick

Refrain

May the Spir - it of Christ be our hope through the day, be our
guard through the night, our com - pan - ion on the way.

Verse 1

1. Christ be ev-er be - fore us, Christ be ev-er be -
hind us, Christ be ev-er with - in.

D.C.

Verses 2-5

2. Christ up - on our left hand watch - ing, At our right hand
3. Christ be in each ho - ly si - lence, Christ be in our
4. Let us be God's light in the dark - ness, Let us be God's
5. God Cre - a - tor, bless and keep us, Christ, be ev - er

guid - ing, Christ a - bove, be - neath us guard - ing,
speak - ing, Christ in ev - 'ry work we of - fer,
kind - ness; Let us be God's jus - tice and mer - cy,
near us; Spir - it be the light be - fore us,

D.C.

Near to us a - bid - ing.
Ev - er in our seek - ing.
Hands and feet of Christ.
Gen - tle be our path - way.

Text: Based on *St. Patrick's Breastplate*; Marty Haugen, b.1950
Tune: Marty Haugen, b.1950
© 1986, GIA Publications, Inc.

Come and Journey with a Savior   686

1. Come and jour - ney with a Sav - ior Who has
2. Come and jour - ney jour-ney in - ward, Come and
3. Come and jour - ney, jour-ney out - ward, Tell - ing
4. Come and jour - ney, jour-ney out - ward, Where that
5. Come and jour - ney, jour-ney up - ward, Sing his
6. Come and jour - ney, jour-ney on - ward, All our

called us from our birth, Who has washed us in the
seek him deep with - in, Where he meets us in our
oth - ers of his name, Tell - ing oth - ers of his
cross calls us to care, Where in - jus - tice and where
prais - es, of - fer prayer. In the storm and in the
gifts we now shall bring, To the build - ing of a

wa - ters, And who loved us on the earth.
liv - ing, In our striv - ing and our sin.
glo - ry, Of his cross and of the shame.
hun - ger And the poor call us to share.
still - ness, Find his pres - ence ev - 'ry - where.
cit - y That is ho - ly, Christ its king.

Come and jour - ney, come and jour - ney With a Sav-ior who has

come. We are all God's sons and daugh - ters. In the

Spir-it we are one. In the Spir-it we are one.

Text: Herbert O'Driscoll, b.1928, ©
Tune: COME AND JOURNEY, 8 7 8 7 with refrain; Marty Haugen, b.1950, © 1998, GIA Publications, Inc.

687 The Summons

1. Will you come and fol - low me If I but call your name? Will you go where you don't know And nev - er be the same? Will you let my love be shown, Will you let my name be known, Will you let my life be grown In you and you in me?

2. Will you leave your - self be - hind If I but call your name? Will you care for cruel and kind And nev - er be the same? Will you risk the hos - tile stare Should your life at - tract or scare? Will you let me an - swer prayer In you and you in me?

3. Will you let the blind - ed see If I but call your name? Will you set the pris - 'ners free And nev - er be the same? Will you kiss the lep - er clean, And do such as this un - seen, And ad - mit to what I mean In you and you in me?

4. Will you love the 'you' you hide If I but call your name? Will you quell the fear in - side And nev - er be the same? Will you use the faith you've found To re - shape the world a - round, Through my sight and touch and sound In you and you in me?

5. Lord, your sum - mons ech - oes true When you but call my name. Let me turn and fol - low you And nev - er be the same. In your com - pa - ny I'll go Where your love and foot - steps show. Thus I'll move and live and grow In you and you in me.

Text: John L. Bell, b.1949, © 1987, Iona Community, GIA Publications, Inc., agent
Tune: KELVINGROVE, 7 6 7 6 777 6; Scottish traditional; arr. by John L. Bell, b.1949, © 1987, Iona Community, GIA Publications, Inc., agent

Take Up Your Cross 688

Refrain

If you lose your life for my sake, you will find it; if you want to save your life, let it go. Take up your cross, de-ny your-self: Come, fol-low me, fol-low me.

Verse 1

1. How will you prof-it by gain-ing the world, while you for-feit all of your life? What will you give in re-turn? What will you give in re-turn?

Verse 2

2. Be-fore I re-turn in glo-ry, I will give you the gift of my love: you will nev-er taste death, you will nev-er taste death.

Text: Matthew 16:24-28; David Haas, b.1957
Tune: David Haas, b.1957
© 2001, GIA Publications, Inc.

689 I Danced in the Morning

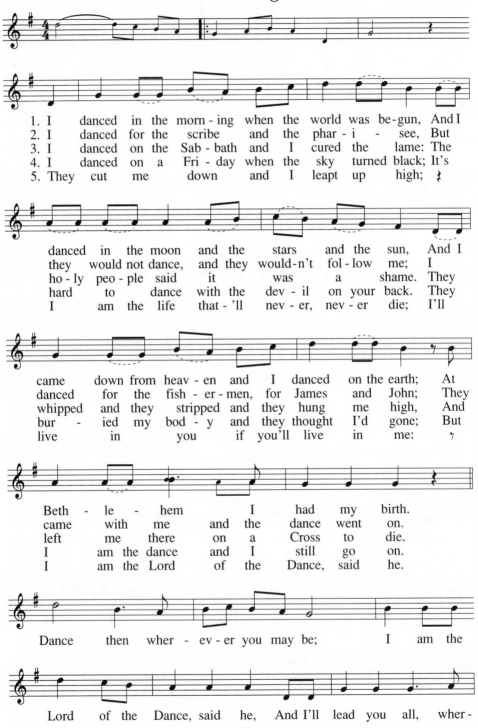

1. I danced in the morn-ing when the world was be-gun, And I
2. I danced for the scribe and the phar-i - see, But
3. I danced on the Sab-bath and I cured the lame: The
4. I danced on a Fri-day when the sky turned black; It's
5. They cut me down and I leapt up high; ⁏

danced in the moon and the stars and the sun, And I
they would not dance, and they would-n't fol-low me; I
ho - ly peo - ple said it was a shame. They
hard to dance with the dev - il on your back. They
I am the life that-'ll nev-er, nev-er die; I'll

came down from heav-en and I danced on the earth; At
danced for the fish-er-men, for James and John; They
whipped and they stripped and they hung me high, And
bur - ied my bod-y and they thought I'd gone; But
live in you if you'll live in me: ⁊

Beth - le - hem I had my birth.
came with me and the dance went on.
left me there on a Cross to die.
I am the dance and I still go on.
I am the Lord of the Dance, said he.

Dance then wher - ev - er you may be; I am the

Lord of the Dance, said he, And I'll lead you all, wher-

ev - er you may be, And I'll lead you all in the Dance, said he.

Text: Sydney Carter, b.1915, © 1963, Stainer & Bell, Ltd., London, England. (admin. by Hope Publishing Co.)
Tune: LORD OF THE DANCE, Irregular; adapted from a traditional Shaker melody by Sydney Carter, b.1915, © 1963, Stainer & Bell, Ltd., London, England. (admin. by Hope Publishing Co.)

Take Up Your Cross   690

1. Take up your cross,   the Sav-ior said,   If you would
2. Take up your cross,   let not its weight   Fill your weak
3. Take up your cross,   heed not the shame,   And let your
4. Take up your cross,   then, in his strength,   And calm - ly
5. Take up your cross,   and fol-low Christ,   Nor think till

my   dis - ci - ple   be;   Take up   your cross   with will - ing
spir - it   with a - larm;   His strength shall bear   your spir - it
fool - ish heart be   still;   The Lord for   you   ac - cept-ed
ev - 'ry dan-ger brave: It   guides you   to   a bet-ter
death   to   lay it   down;   For   on - ly   those   who bear the

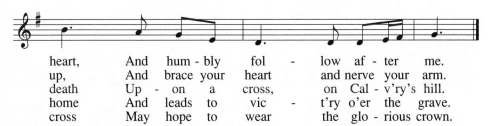

heart,   And   hum - bly   fol   -   low af - ter   me.
up,   And   brace your   heart   and nerve your   arm.
death   Up - on   a   cross,   on Cal - v'ry's hill.
home   And   leads   to   vic   -   t'ry o'er the   grave.
cross   May   hope   to   wear   the glo - rious crown.

Text: Charles W. Everest, 1814-1877, alt.
Tune: O WALY WALY, LM; English; harm. by Martin West, b.1929, © 1983, Hope Publishing Co.

691 Give the Lord Your Heart

Verses

1. If you want to see the king-dom God has
2. You can store your wealth in barns or banks or
3. If you spend your life - time sow - ing seeds of
   Si tú quie - res un te - so - ro en el

planned for you, you must give all your pos - ses -
prop - er - ty, but you'll leave this world with - out
world - ly gain you will har - vest on - ly hard-
Rei - no, a los po - bres da - les to -

sions to the poor. For a per-son rich in goods,
one sin - gle cent. In the mid-dle of the night,
ship and dis-tress. You will nev-er learn the joys
do y lo ten-drás. Pa - ra los ri - cos, ¡qué di-fí -

it seems im - pos - si - ble. The de -
our God may call for you and you
of sim - ple ser - vi-tude, and your
cil es es - te di - cho! Su de -

sire for wealth is too strong to ig - nore.
won't re - call what all your life has meant.
hun - gry heart will nev - er find true rest.
se - o de ri - que - zas do-mi - na - rá.

Refrain

Un-less you love the Lord, un - less you thank
Si - no a-mas al Se - ñor, si-no das gra-cias al

the Lord, un-less you give the Lord your heart.
Se - ñor, *si - no* *le* *das* *tu co - ra - zón.*

Un - less you love the Lord,
Si - no a - mas *al* *Se - ñor,*

un - less you thank the Lord,
si - no *das gra - cias* *al* *Se - ñor,*

un - less you give the Lord your heart.
si - no *le* *das* *tu co - ra - zón.*

Text: Based on Luke 12:16-21, Matthew 19:21-23; Michael Mahler, b.1981
Tune: Michael Mahler, b.1981
© 2003, GIA Publications, Inc.

Take, O Take Me As I Am 692

Ostinato Refrain

Take, O take me as I am; sum - mon out what I shall

be; set your seal up-on my heart and live in me.

Text: John L. Bell, b.1949
Tune: John L. Bell, b.1949
© 1995, The Iona Community, GIA Publications, Inc., agent

693 Two Fishermen

1. Two fish-er-men, who lived a-long The Sea of Gal-i-
2. And as he walked a-long the shore 'Twas James and John he'd
3. O Si-mon Pe-ter, An-drew, James And John be-lov-ed
4. And you, good Chris-tians, one and all Who'd fol-low Je-sus'

lee, Stood by the shore to cast their nets In -
find, And these two sons of Zeb - e-dee Would
one, You heard Christ's call to speak good news Re -
way, Come leave be-hind what keeps you bound To

to an age - less sea. Now Je - sus watched them
leave their boats be - hind. Their work and all they
vealed to God's own Son. Su - san - na, Mar - y,
trap - pings of our day, And lis - ten as he

from a - far Then called them each by name; It
held so dear They left be - side their nets. Their
Mag - da - lene Who trav - eled with your Lord, You
calls your name To come and fol - low near, For

changed their lives, these sim - ple men; They'd nev - er be the same.
names they'd heard as Je - sus called; They came with-out re - gret.
min - is - tered to him with joy For he is God a-dored.
still he speaks in var - ied ways To those his call will hear.

Leave all things you have And come and fol - low

me, And come and fol - low me.

Text: Suzanne Toolan, SM, b.1927, © 1986, GIA Publications, Inc.
Tune: LEAVE ALL THINGS, CMD with refrain; Suzanne Toolan, SM, b.1927, © 1970, GIA Publications, Inc.

We Have Been Told 694

Text: David Haas, b.1957
Tune: David Haas, b.1957; vocal arr. by David Haas and Marty Haugen, b.1950
© 1983, GIA Publications, Inc.

695   Here Am I, Lord

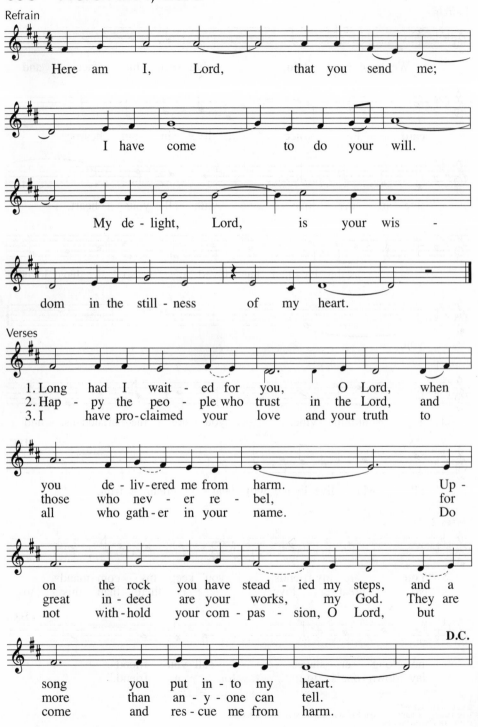

Refrain

Here am I, Lord, that you send me;
I have come to do your will.
My de-light, Lord, is your wis-dom
in the still-ness of my heart.

Verses

1. Long had I wait-ed for you, O Lord, when
2. Hap-py the peo-ple who trust in the Lord, and
3. I have pro-claimed your love and your truth to

1. you de-liv-ered me from harm. Up-
2. those who nev-er re-bel, for
3. all who gath-er in your name. Do

1. on the rock you have stead-ied my steps, and a
2. great in-deed are your works, my God. They are
3. not with-hold your com-pas-sion, O Lord, but

D.C.

1. song you put in-to my heart.
2. more than an-y-one can tell.
3. come and res-cue me from harm.

Text: Psalm 40, Timothy Valentine, S.J., b.1959
Tune: Timothy Valentine, S.J., b.1959
© 1998, GIA Publications, Inc.

Now We Remain 696

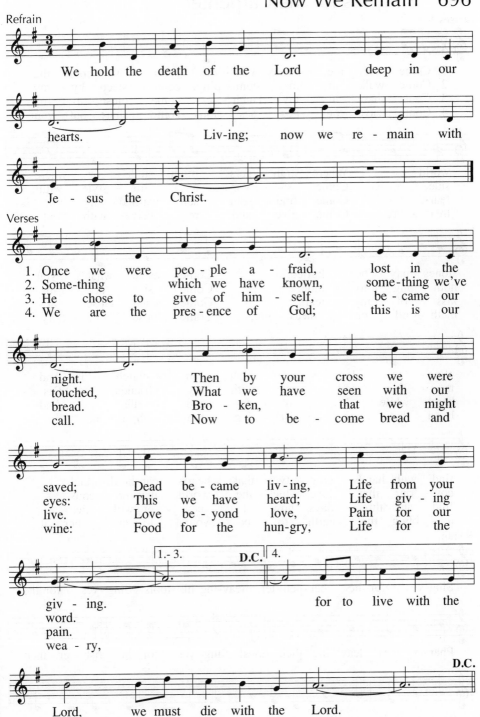

Refrain

We hold the death of the Lord deep in our hearts. Liv-ing; now we re-main with Je - sus the Christ.

Verses

1. Once we were peo - ple a - fraid, lost in the night. Then by your cross we were saved; Dead be - came liv-ing, Life from your giv - ing.

2. Some-thing which we have known, some-thing we've touched, What we have seen with our eyes: This we have heard; Life giv - ing word.

3. He chose to give of him - self, be - came our bread. Bro - ken, that we might live. Love be - yond love, Pain for our pain.

4. We are the pres - ence of God; this is our call. Now to be - come bread and wine: Food for the hun-gry, Life for the wea - ry, for to live with the Lord, we must die with the Lord.

1.- 3. | D.C.   4.   D.C.

Text: Corinthians, 1 John, 2 Timothy; David Haas, b.1957
Tune: David Haas, b.1957
© 1983, GIA Publications, Inc.

697 Sing Yes for the Carpenter

Verses

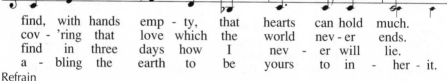

1. Come with me, come wan-der, come wel-come the
2. Come walk in my com-p'ny, come sleep by my
3. Come share in my laugh-ter, come close to my
4. Come leave your pos-ses-sions, come share out your

world Where stran-gers might smile or where
side, Come sa-vor a life-style with
fears, Come find your-self washed with the
treas-ure. Come give and re-ceive with-out

stones may be hurled; Come leave what you
noth-ing to hide; Come sit at my
kiss of my tears; Come stand close at
meth-od or meas-ure; Come loose ev-'ry

cling to, lay down what you clutch And
ta-ble and eat with my friends, Dis-
hand while I suf-fer and die And
bond that's re-sist-ing the Spir-it, En-

find, with hands emp-ty, that hearts can hold much.
cov-'ring that love which the world nev-er ends.
find in three days how I nev-er will lie.
a-bling the earth to be yours to in-her-it.

Refrain

Sing yes for the car-pen-ter leav-ing his tools! Sing yes for the

Phar-i-sees leav-ing their rules! Sing yes for the fish-er-men

leav-ing their nets! Sing yes for the peo-ple who leave their re-grets!

Text: John L. Bell, b.1949
Tune: SING HEY, Irregular; John L. Bell, b.1949
© 1987, The Iona Community, GIA Publications, Inc., agent

Embrace My Way and Cross 698

Refrain

Will you come and fol-low in my steps to serve the poor and lost? Can you leave all things with-out re-gret, em-brace my way and cross?

Verses

1. In a wel-come place is my a-bode, In all hearts both young and old. There I en-ter in and will be known As com-pas-sion, gent-ly shown.
2. In the serv-ing line I will be found, On the streets of an-y town. For I have no bounds of time and space, But am found in ev-'ry face.
3. Wheth-er lone-ly rich or gra-cious poor, You will find me at your door. I will call you from your wan-d'ring ways In-to Gos-pel liv-ing days.

D.C.

Text: Rob Glover, b.1950
Tune: ROCKY POINT, 9 7 9 7 with refrain; Rob Glover, b.1950
© 1997, GIA Publications, Inc.

699 Unless a Grain of Wheat

Refrain

Un - less a grain of wheat shall fall up -

on the ground and die, it re - mains but a

sin - gle grain with no life.

Verses

1. If we have died with him then we shall
2. If an - y - one serves me then they must
3. Make your home in me as I make
4. If you re - main in me and my word
5. Those who love me are loved by my
6. Peace I leave with you, my peace I

live with him; if we hold firm, we shall
fol - low me; where - ev - er I am, my
mine in you; those who re - main in me
lives in you, then you will be my dis -
Fa - ther; we shall be with them and
give to you; peace which the world can - not

D.C.

reign with him.
ser - vants will be.
bear much fruit.
ci - ples.
dwell in them.
give is my gift.

Text: John 12:24; Bernadette Farrell, b.1957
Tune: Bernadette Farrell, b.1957
© 1983, Bernadette Farrell. Published by OCP Publications.

You Are Strong, You Are Holy 700

Verses

1. Lord, you lead through sea and des - ert, You
2. Lord, you lead to cool - ing wa - ters, You
3. So we fol - low where you lead us, Where you

lead to prom - ised lands. We are your own ho - ly
lead to green - ing fields. Lord, you lead to deep - 'ning
walk a - long the shore, Where you suf - fer in the

peo - ple, In your cov - e - nant we stand!
val - leys Where your com - fort is re - vealed!
gar - den, When you rise to die no more!

Refrain

You are strong, you are ho - ly, you are mer - cy and

peace. You are love, you are jus - tice. Your

grace and fa - vor nev - er cease!

Text: Sylvia Dunstan, 1955-1993, © 1991, GIA Publications, Inc.
Tune: JUSTICE, 8 6 8 7 with refrain; Paul A. Tate, b.1968, © 2003, GIA Publications, Inc.

701 Only This I Want

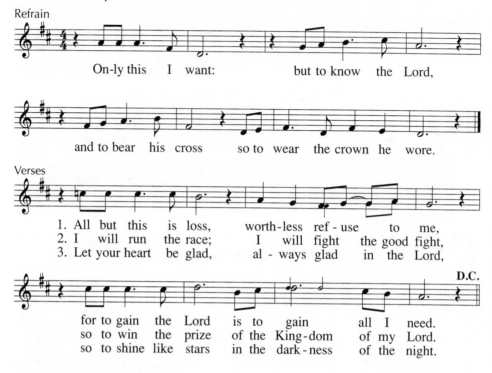

Refrain

On-ly this I want: but to know the Lord, and to bear his cross so to wear the crown he wore.

Verses

1. All but this is loss, worth-less ref-use to me,
2. I will run the race; I will fight the good fight,
3. Let your heart be glad, al-ways glad in the Lord,

for to gain the Lord is to gain all I need.
so to win the prize of the King-dom of my Lord.
so to shine like stars in the dark-ness of the night.

Text: Philippians 3:7-16; 2:15, 18; Dan Schutte, b.1947
Tune: Dan Schutte, b.1947; arr. by Michael Pope, SJ
© 1981, Daniel L. Schutte and OCP Publications

702 Voices That Challenge

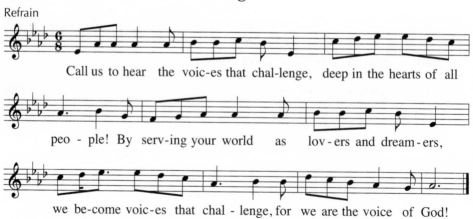

Refrain

Call us to hear the voic-es that chal-lenge, deep in the hearts of all peo-ple! By serv-ing your world as lov-ers and dream-ers, we be-come voic-es that chal-lenge, for we are the voice of God!

Verses 1, 2

1. Voic-es that chal-lenge: the chil - dren who long to be
the low - ly and bro - ken de -
the old and the fear - ful who
2. Voic-es that chal-lenge: the lives and the cries of the
the young ones who dream of a
the sick and the dy - ing who

| 1., 2., 4., 5. | 3., 6. | D.C. |

heard and re - spec - ted!
stroyed by op - pres - sion!
hope for a new day!
poor and the si - lenced!
world free of ha - tred!
cry for com - pas - sion!

Verse 3

3. Voic-es that chal-lenge: the ones who seek peace by their
the wom - en who suf - fer the
the peo - ple with AIDS and those
the proph - ets and he - roes who
the heal - ers who teach us for -
the vic - tims of vio - lent a -
the Christ who gave his

| 1.- 6. | 7. | D.C. |

wit - ness and cour - age!
pain of in - jus - tice!
plagued with ad - dic - tion!
call us to ques - tion!
give - ness and mer - cy!
buse and a - gres - sion!
life that we might live!

Text: David Haas, b.1957
Tune: David Haas, b.1957
© 1990, GIA Publications, Inc.

703 Abundant Life

1. We can-not own the sun-lit sky, The
2. When bod-ies shiv-er in the night And
3. God calls hu-man-i-ty to join As

moon, the wild-flow'rs grow-ing, For we are
wea - ry, wait for morn-ing, When chil-dren
part - ners in cre - at-ing A fu - ture

part of all that is With - in life's
have no bread but tears, And war - horns
free from want or fear, Life's good - ness

riv - er flow - ing. With o - pen
sound their warn - ing, God calls hu -
cel - e - brat-ing, That new world

hands re-ceive and share The gifts of God's cre -
man-i-ty to wake, To join in com-mon
beck-ons from a - far, In - vites our shared en -

a - tion, That all may have a-bun-dant
la - bor, That all may have a-bun-dant
deav-or, That all may have a-bun-dant

life In ev - 'ry earth-ly na-tion.
life In one-ness with their neigh-bor.
life And peace en-dure for - ev-er.

Text: Ruth Duck, b.1947, © 1992, GIA Publications, Inc.
Tune: LA GRANGE, 8 7 8 7 D; Marty Haugen, b.1950, © 1994, GIA Publications, Inc.

God, Whose Purpose Is to Kindle 704

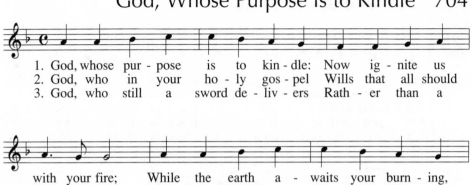

1. God, whose pur - pose is to kin - dle: Now ig - nite us
2. God, who in your ho - ly gos - pel Wills that all should
3. God, who still a sword de - liv - ers Rath - er than a

with your fire; While the earth a - waits your burn - ing,
tru - ly live, Make us sense our share of fail - ure,
plac - id peace, With your sharp - ened word dis - turb us,

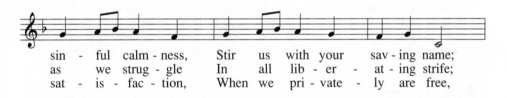

With your pas - sion us in - spire. O - ver - come our
Our tran - quil - li - ty for - give. Teach us cour - age
From com - pla - cen - cy re - lease! Save us now from

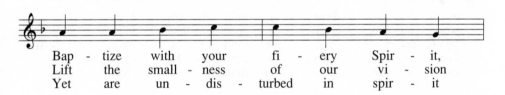

sin - ful calm - ness, Stir us with your sav - ing name;
as we strug - gle In all lib - er - at - ing strife;
sat - is - fac - tion, When we pri - vate - ly are free,

Bap - tize with your fi - ery Spir - it,
Lift the small - ness of our vi - sion
Yet are un - dis - turbed in spir - it

Crown our lives with tongues of flame.
By your own a - bun - dant life.
By our neigh - bor's mis - er - y.

Text: Luke 12:49; David E. Trueblood, 1900-1994, © 1967, David Elton Trueblood
Tune: HYMN TO JOY, 8 7 8 7 D; arr. from Ludwig van Beethoven, 1770-1827, by Edward Hodges, 1796-1867

705 A Place at the Table

Verses

1. For ev - 'ry - one born, a place at the ta - ble, for
2. For wom - an and man, a place at the ta - ble, re -
3. For young and for old, a place at the ta - ble, a
4. For just and un - just, a place at the ta - ble, a -
5. For ev - 'ry - one born, a place at the ta - ble, to

ev - 'ry - one born, clean wa - ter and bread, a
vis - ing the roles, de - cid - ing the share, with
voice to be heard, a part in the song, the
bus - er, a - bused, with need to for - give, in
live with - out fear, and sim - ply to be, to

shel - ter, a space, a safe place for grow - ing, for
wis - dom and grace, di - vid - ing the pow - er, for
hands of a child in hands that are wrin - kled, for
an - ger, in hurt, a mind - set of mer - cy, for
work, to speak out, to wit - ness and wor - ship, for

ev - 'ry - one born, a star o - ver - head.
wom - an and man, a sys - tem that's fair.
young and for old, the right to be - long. And
just and un - just, a new way to live.
ev - 'ry - one born, the right to be free.

Refrain

God will de - light when we are cre - a - tors of

jus - tice and joy, yes, God will de - light

when we are cre - a - tors of jus - tice,

jus - tice and joy!

Text: Shirley Erena Murray, b.1931, © 1998, Hope Publishing Co.
Tune: Lori True, b.1961, © 2001, GIA Publications, Inc.

We Come with Joy 706

1. We come with joy in Je - sus Christ, Who
2. A lit - tle bread is all we have, So
3. Like rip - ples in a pool, our gifts, How -

knows our hu - man need, Who, moved with pit - y
mea - ger our sup - ply— A lit - tle time, a
ev - er small they are, Will reach and heal a

for the world, Would ev - 'ry hun - ger feed,
lit - tle love Can hard - ly sat - is - fy.
need - y world, Will com - fort near and far.

Who blessed the fish and bar - ley loaves Till
But let us bring the best we have De -
For Christ will bless our bit of bread, The

food was mul - ti - plied, Whose boun - ty o - ver -
spite our pov - er - ty, Put all our gifts in
loaves our hands pro - vide, Till emp - ty bas - kets

flowed their want Till all were sat - is - fied.
Je - sus' hands, Im - per - fect though they be.
o - ver - flow And all are sat - is - fied.

Text: Delores Dufner, OSB, b.1939, © 1994, GIA Publications, Inc.
Tune: FOREST GREEN, CMD; English; harm. by Ralph Vaughan Williams, 1872-1958, alt., © Oxford University Press

707 Freedom Is Coming

O yes, I know.

Text: South African
Tune: South African
© 1984, Utryck, Walton Music Corp., agent

If You Believe and I Believe 708

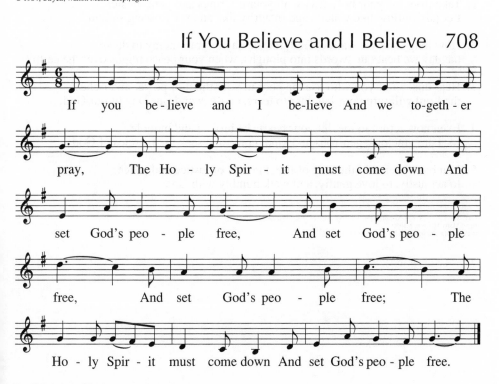

If you be-lieve and I be-lieve And we to-geth-er pray, The Ho-ly Spir-it must come down And set God's peo-ple free, And set God's peo-ple free, And set God's peo-ple free; The Ho-ly Spir-it must come down And set God's peo-ple free.

Text: Zimbabwean traditional
Tune: Zimbabwean traditional; adapt. of English traditional; as taught by Tarasai; arr. by John L. Bell, b.1949, © 1991, Iona Community,
  GIA Publications, Inc., agent

709 Let Justice Roll Like a River

Refrain

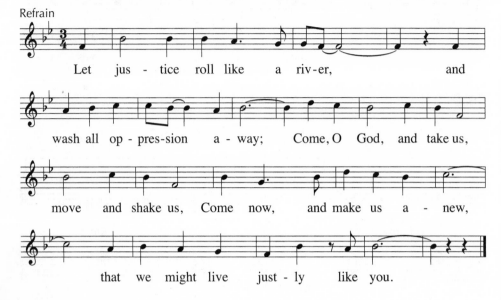

Let jus - tice roll like a riv-er, and

wash all op - pres-sion a - way; Come, O God, and take us,

move and shake us, Come now, and make us a - new,

that we might live just - ly like you.

Verses

1. Take from me your holy feasts, all your off'rings and your music;
   Let justice flow like waters, and integrity like an ever-flowing stream.

2. How long shall we wait, O God, for the day of your mercy to dawn,
   the day we beat our swords into ploughs, when your peace reigns over the earth?

3. Hear this, all of you who use the poor in your thirst of power and riches:
   the Lord will turn your laughter to tears, on the wondrous Day of our God.

4. Even now return to me, let your hearts be broken and humble,
   for I am gracious, gen'rous and kind; come and seek the mercies of God.

5. You have been told the way of life, the way of justice and peace;
   to act justly, to love gently, and walk humbly with God.

Text: Amos 5:21-24, 8:4, Micah 4:3-4, 6:8, Joel 2:12-14; Marty Haugen, b.1950
Tune: Marty Haugen, b.1950
© 1991, GIA Publications, Inc.

We Are Called   710

1. Come!   Live in   the light!   Shine with the
2. Come!   O-pen   your heart!   Show your
3. Sing!   Sing   a new song!   Sing   of that

joy and   the   love of   the   Lord! We   are   called
mer-cy   to   all those in   fear! We   are   called
great day   when   all will   be   one! God will   reign,

to   be   light   for   the   king - dom,   to
to   be   hope   for   the   hope - less   so all
and   we'll   walk   with   each   oth - er   as

live   in   the   free - dom   of the   cit - y   of   God!
ha - tred   and   blind - ness   will   be   no   more!
sis - ters   and   broth - ers   u - nit - ed   in   love!

We are called   to act   with jus-tice,   we are   called to

love ten - der - ly,   we are called   to serve one   an-oth-er;

to   walk   hum - bly with   God!

Text: Micah 6:8; David Haas, b.1957
Tune: David Haas, b.1957
© 1988, GIA Publications, Inc.

711 We Shall Overcome

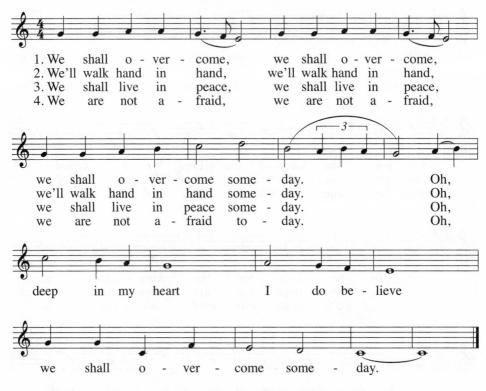

1. We shall o - ver - come, we shall o - ver - come,
2. We'll walk hand in hand, we'll walk hand in hand,
3. We shall live in peace, we shall live in peace,
4. We are not a - fraid, we are not a - fraid,

we shall o - ver - come some - day. Oh,
we'll walk hand in hand some - day. Oh,
we shall live in peace some - day. Oh,
we are not a - fraid to - day. Oh,

deep in my heart I do be - lieve

we shall o - ver - come some - day.

5. We shall stand together...   8. We shall be like him...
6. The truth will make us free...   9. The whole wide world around...
7. The Lord will see us through...

Text: adapt. by Zilphia Horton, Frank Hamilton, Guy Carawan, and Pete Seeger, © 1960, 1963, Ludlow Music
Tune: adapt. by Zilphia Horton, Frank Hamilton, Guy Carawan, and Pete Seeger, © 1960, 1963, Ludlow Music; harm. by J. Jefferson Cleveland, b.1937,
    © 1981, by Abingdon Press

712 For the Healing of the Nations

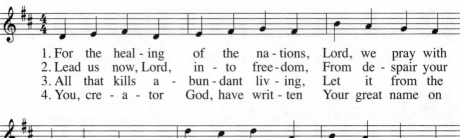

1. For the heal - ing of the na - tions, Lord, we pray with
2. Lead us now, Lord, in - to free - dom, From de - spair your
3. All that kills a - bun - dant liv - ing, Let it from the
4. You, cre - a - tor God, have writ - ten Your great name on

one ac - cord; For a just and e - qual shar - ing
world re - lease; That re-deemed from war and ha - tred,
earth be banned; Pride of stat - us, race or school - ing,
hu - man - kind; For our grow - ing in your like - ness

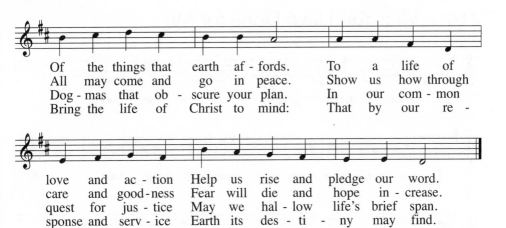

Of the things that earth af - fords. To a life of
All may come and go in peace. Show us how through
Dog - mas that ob - scure your plan. In our com - mon
Bring the life of Christ to mind: That by our re -

love and ac - tion Help us rise and pledge our word.
care and good - ness Fear will die and hope in - crease.
quest for jus - tice May we hal - low life's brief span.
sponse and serv - ice Earth its des - ti - ny may find.

Text: Fred Kaan, b.1929, alt., © 1968, Hope Publishing Co.
Tune: ST. THOMAS, 8 7 8 7 8 7; John Wade, 1711-1786

Here Am I 713

1. Here am I, Where un - der - neath the bridg - es
2. Here am I, With peo - ple in the line - up,
3. Here am I, Where two or three are gath - ered,

Of our win - ter cit - ies Home - less peo - ple sleep.
Anx - ious for a hand - out, Ach - ing for a job.
Read - y to be al - tered, Shar - ing wine and bread.

Here am I, Where in de - cay - ing hous - es Lit - tle
Here am I, When pen - sion - ers and strik - ers Sing and
Here am I, Where those who hear the preach - ing Change their

chil - dren shiv - er, Cry - ing at the cold. Where are you?
march to - geth - er, Want - ing some - thing new. Where are you?
way of liv - ing, Find the way to life. Where are you?

Text: Brian Wren, b.1936
Tune: STANISLAUS, 3 7 6 5 D 3; Daniel Charles Damon, b.1955
© Words 1983, music 1995, Hope Publishing Co.

714 What You Have Done for Me

Verse 1

1. I am the hun-gry, I am the poor,
I am the stran-ger out-side your door. So
when you feed the hun-gry, when you clothe the poor
I will no long-er be just a stran-ger at your door.

𝄋 Refrain

What you have done for the least of my chil-dren
you have done for me. What you have giv-en, with
noth-ing left to give, you have giv-en me.

To verses

4   *Last time*   3

me.

Verse 2

2. Come all you bless-ed, come and re-joice. In-

her - it the king-dom pre - pared for you. For

you are my chil-dren, called to serve as keep-ers of the

D.S.

vi - sion and speak-ers of the word.

Verse 3

3. I will look to you when life on earth has end - ed.

Those who give will re-ceive, those who seek will find; so

D.S.

seek my face in ev-'ry face and see the eyes of God!

Text: Based on Matthew 25:24-41; Tony E. Alonso, b.1980
Tune: Tony E. Alonso, b.1980
© 2001, GIA Publications, Inc.

715 On Holy Ground

Text: Donna Peña, b.1955
Tune: Donna Peña, b.1955; acc. by Diana Kodner, b.1957
© 1992, 1994, GIA Publications, Inc.

The Harvest of Justice 716

Refrain: May we find rich - ness in the har - vest of jus -
1. Gath - er with pa - tience for those who have noth -
2. For to have mer - cy on those for - got -
3. For to have lit - tle is to be in a - bun -

tice which Christ Je - sus has rip-ened for
ing. Leave them your rich - es, and you will re -
ten, this is my true law, this is my com -
dance. To give what re - mains, to give all we

us. Bread for the jour - ney,
ceive. Make room for the poor ones,
mand: Clothe the na - ked,
have, is to walk with the poor ones,

bread for the hun - gry, all for the
make way for the stran - ger; for I am the
be home for the or - phan, be hope for the
and be - come the stran - ger, one with the

glo - ry and praise of God.
Lord, the Lord your God.
wid - ow, and wel - come the lost.
Lord, the Lord our God.

Text: Philippians 1:11, Leviticus 19:9, 23:22, Deuteronomy 24:19; David Haas, b.1957
Tune: David Haas, b.1957
© 1985, GIA Publications, Inc.

717 O God of Every Nation

1. O God of ev - 'ry na - tion, Of
2. From search for wealth and pow - er And
3. Lord, strength - en all who la - bor That
4. Keep bright in us the vi - sion Of

ev - 'ry race and land, Re - deem your whole cre -
scorn of truth and right, From trust in bombs that
we may find re - lease From fear of rat - tling
days when wars shall cease, When ha - tred and di -

a - tion With your al - might - y hand; Where
show - er De - struc - tion through the night, From
sa - ber, From dread of war's in - crease; When
vi - sion Give way to love and peace, Till

hate and fear di - vide us And
pride of race and sta - tion And
hope and cour - age fal - ter, Your
dawns the morn - ing glo - rious When

bit - ter threats are hurled, In love and mer - cy
blind - ness to your way, De - liv - er ev - 'ry
still small voice be heard; With faith that none can
Christ a - lone shall reign And he shall rule vic -

guide us And heal our strife - torn world.
na - tion, E - ter - nal God, we pray.
al - ter, Up - hold us by your word.
to - rious O'er all the world's do - main.

Text: William W. Reid, b.1923, alt., © 1958, 1986, The Hymn Society (Administered by Hope Publishing Co.)
Tune: PASSION CHORALE, 7 6 7 6 D; Hans Leo Hassler, 1564-1612; harm. by J. S. Bach, 1685-1750

World Peace Prayer 718

Refrain

Lead us from death to life, from false-hood to truth, from de-
spair to hope, from fear to trust. Lead us from
hate to love, from war to peace; let peace fill our
hearts, let peace fill our world, let peace fill our u – ni-verse.

Verses

1. Still all the an-gry cries, still all the an-gry guns,
2. So man-y lone-ly hearts, so man-y bro-ken lives,
3. Let jus-tice ev-er roll, let mer-cy fill the earth,

   still now your peo-ple die, earth's sons and daugh-ters.
   long-ing for love to break in – to their dark-ness.
   let us be – gin to grow in – to your peo-ple.

   Let jus-tice roll, let mer – cy pour down,
   Come, teach us love, come, teach us peace,
   We can be love, we can bring peace,

   D.C.

   come and teach us your way of com - pas-sion.
   come and teach us your way of com - pas-sion.
   we can still be your way of com - pas-sion.

Text: Refrain, Upanishads, Satish Kumar; verses, Marty Haugen, b.1950, © 1985, GIA Publications, Inc.
Tune: Marty Haugen, b.1950, © 1985, GIA Publications, Inc.

719 The Peace of God

Refrain

Let your gen-tle-ness be known, so all may know the Lord is near. Do not wor-ry, do not wor-ry; reach out to God in prayer. Stay with all that you have learned, and all that you have heard and seen, and the peace of God, the peace of God will be with you.

Verse 1

1. What-ev-er is true, what-ev-er is just, all that is pure and pleas-ing and all that is wor-thy of praise: think on these things.

D.C.

Verse 2

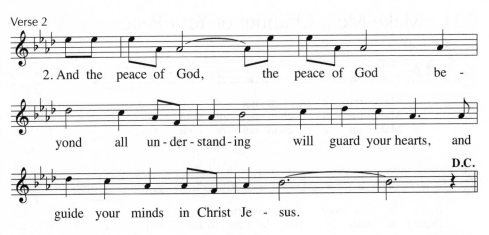

2. And the peace of God, the peace of God be-
yond all un-der-stand-ing will guard your hearts, and
guide your minds in Christ Je - sus.

D.C.

Text: Based on Philippians 4:5-9, David Haas, b.1957
Tune: David Haas, b.1957

Prayer of Peace 720

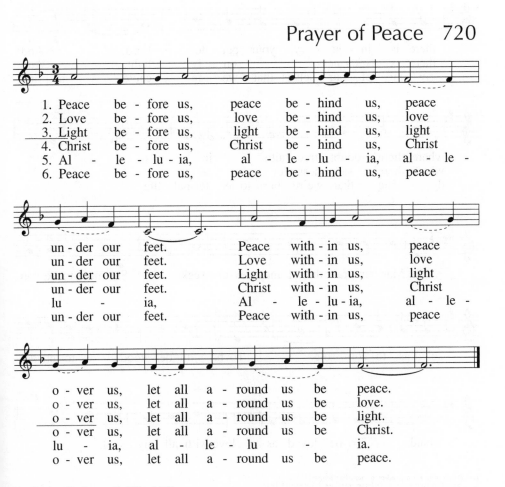

1. Peace be - fore us, peace be - hind us, peace
2. Love be - fore us, love be - hind us, love
3. Light be - fore us, light be - hind us, light
4. Christ be - fore us, Christ be - hind us, Christ
5. Al - le - lu - ia, al - le - lu - ia, al - le -
6. Peace be - fore us, peace be - hind us, peace

un - der our feet. Peace with - in us, peace
un - der our feet. Love with - in us, love
un - der our feet. Light with - in us, light
un - der our feet. Christ with - in us, Christ
lu - ia, Al - le - lu - ia, al - le -
un - der our feet. Peace with - in us, peace

o - ver us, let all a - round us be peace.
o - ver us, let all a - round us be love.
o - ver us, let all a - round us be light.
o - ver us, let all a - round us be Christ.
lu - ia, al - le - lu - ia.
o - ver us, let all a - round us be peace.

Text: Based on a Navajo prayer; David Haas, b.1957
Tune: David Haas, b.1957

721 Make Me a Channel of Your Peace

Verses 1, 2, 4

1. Make me a chan-nel of your peace. Where
2. Make me a chan-nel of your peace. Where
4. Make me a chan-nel of your peace. It

there is ha-tred, let me bring your love. Where
there's de-spair in life, let me bring hope. Where
is in par-don-ing that we are par-doned, in

there is in-ju-ry, your par-don, Lord, And
there is dark-ness, on-ly light, And
giv-ing of our-selves that we re-ceive, and in

1.
where there's doubt, true faith in you.

2., 4.
where there's sad-ness, ev-er joy.
dy-ing that we're born to e-ter-nal life.

Verse 3

3. Oh, Mas-ter, grant that I may nev-er seek So much to be con-

soled as to con-sole. To be un-der-stood as to under-

D.C.

stand. To be loved as to love with all my soul.

Text: *Prayer of St. Francis;* adapt. by Sebastian Temple, 1928-1997
Tune: Sebastian Temple, 1928-1997; acc. by Robert J. Batastini, b.1942
© 1967, OCP Publications
Dedicated to Mrs. Frances Tracy

Give Us Your Peace 722

Refrain

Je - sus, give us your peace. Bring us to - geth-er. Let all the fight - ing cease.

Shat - ter all our hearts of stone. Give us a heart

Repeat each time

To verses
Last time

for love a - lone. Oh woh

Verses

1. Some days the road I walk is lone - ly,
2. Some days the walk - ing makes me wea - ry
3. Some days the strength I need is fail - ing,

and it's so hard to find a friend.
and my soul yearns to be re - lieved.
and then, O Lord, I turn to you.

E - ven then I know, some-where in my soul,
You, my Lord, are strong. You pull me a - long.
I need nev - er fear, you are al - ways near.

D.S.

your love is far too great to com-pre-hend. Oh woh
Your love is far too great to be be - lieved. Oh woh
What-ev - er hap-pens, you will pull me through. Oh woh

Text: Michael Mahler, b.1981
Tune: Michael Mahler, b.1981
© 2001, GIA Publications, Inc.

723 Let There Be Peace on Earth

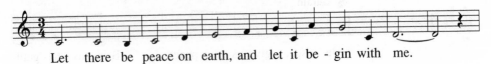

Let there be peace on earth, and let it be - gin with me.

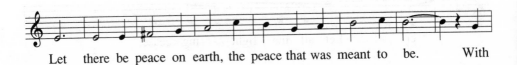

Let there be peace on earth, the peace that was meant to be. With

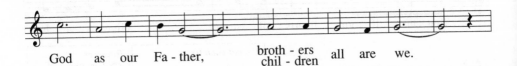

God as our Fa - ther, broth - ers / chil - dren all are we.

Let me / us walk with my broth-er / each oth - er in per-fect har-mo - ny.

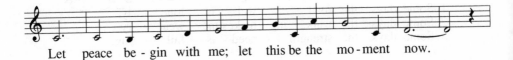

Let peace be - gin with me; let this be the mo - ment now.

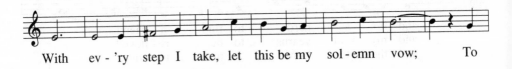

With ev - 'ry step I take, let this be my sol - emn vow; To

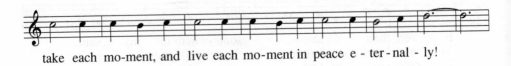

take each mo-ment, and live each mo-ment in peace e - ter-nal - ly!

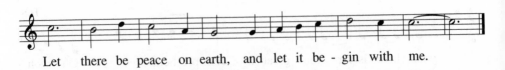

Let there be peace on earth, and let it be - gin with me.

Text: Sy Miller, 1908-1941, Jill Jackson, b.1913, © 1955, 1983, Jan-Lee Music
Tune: Sy Miller, 1908-1941, Jill Jackson, b.1913, © 1955, 1983, Jan-Lee Music; acc. by Diana Kodner, b.1957, © 1993, GIA Publications, Inc.
Used with permission

Dona Nobis Pacem 724

Canon

1. Do - na no - bis pa - cem, pa - cem.
Do - na no - bis pa - cem.

2. Do - na no - bis pa - cem.
Do - na no - bis pa - cem.

3. Do - na no - bis pa - cem.
Do - na no - bis pa - cem.

Text: *Grant us peace;* Unknown
Tune: Traditional; acc. by Diana Kodner, b.1957, © 1994, GIA Publications, Inc.

725 Peace Is Flowing Like a River

1. Peace is flow - ing like a riv - er,
2. Joy is flow - ing like a riv - er,
3. Faith is flow - ing like a riv - er,
4. Hope is flow - ing like a riv - er,
5. Love is flow - ing like a riv - er,

Flow - ing out through you and me; Flow - ing out in - to the

des - ert, Set - ting all the cap - tives free.

Text: Unknown
Tune: Unknown; acc. by Diana Kodner, b.1957, © 1993, GIA Publications, Inc.

726 In Christ There Is No East or West

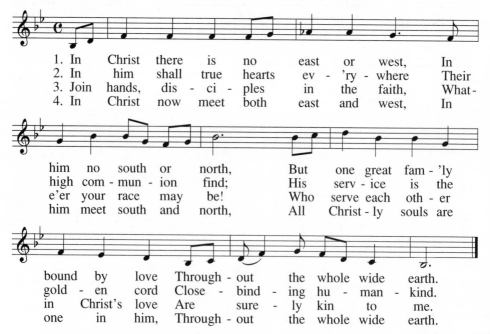

1. In Christ there is no east or west, In
2. In him shall true hearts ev - 'ry - where Their
3. Join hands, dis - ci - ples in the faith, What-
4. In Christ now meet both east and west, In

him no south or north, But one great fam - 'ly
high com - mun - ion find; His serv - ice is the
e'er your race may be! Who serve each oth - er
him meet south and north, All Christ - ly souls are

bound by love Through - out the whole wide earth.
gold - en cord Close - bind - ing hu - man - kind.
in Christ's love Are sure - ly kin to me.
one in him, Through - out the whole wide earth.

Text: Galatians 3:23; John Oxenham, 1852-1941
Tune: MC KEE, CM; African-American; adapt. by Harry T. Burleigh, 1866-1949

We Are Many Parts 727

Text: 1 Corinthians 12, 13; Marty Haugen, b.1950
Tune: Marty Haugen, b.1950
© 1980, 1986, GIA Publications, Inc.

728 They'll Know We Are Christians

1. We are one in the Spir - it, we are
2. We will walk with each oth - er, we will
3. We will work with each oth - er, we will
4. All praise to the Fa - ther, from

one in the Lord, We are one in the
walk hand in hand, We will walk with each
work side by side, We will work with each
whom all things come, And all praise to Christ

Spir - it, we are one in the Lord, And we
oth - er, we will walk hand in hand, And to -
oth - er, we will work side by side, And we'll
Je - sus, his on - ly Son, And all

pray that all u - ni - ty may one day be re -
geth - er we'll spread the news that God is in our
guard hu - man's dig - ni - ty and save hu - man's
praise to the Spir - it, who makes us

stored:
land:
pride: And they'll know we are Chris - tians by our
one:

love, by our love, Yes, they'll know we are

Chris - tians by our love.

Text: Peter Scholtes, b.1938
Tune: ST. BRENDAN'S, 7 6 7 6 8 6 with refrain; Peter Scholtes, b.1938
© 1966, F.E.L. Publications, assigned to The Lorenz Corp., 1991

Diverse in Culture, Nation, Race 729

1. Di - verse in cul - ture, na - tion, race, We come to - geth - er by your grace. God, let us be a meet - ing ground Where hope and heal - ing love are found.
2. God, let us be a bridge of care Con - nect - ing peo - ple ev - 'ry - where. Help us con - front all fear and hate And lust for pow'r that sep - a - rate.
3. When cha - sms wid - en, storms a - rise, O Ho - ly Spir - it, make us wise. Let our re - solve, like steel, be strong To stand with those who suf - fer wrong.
4. God, let us be a ta - ble spread With gifts of love and bro - ken bread, Where all find wel - come, grace at - tends, And en - e - mies a - rise as friends.

May be sung as a two- or four-voice canon.

Text: Ruth Duck, b.1947, © 1992, GIA Publications, Inc.
Tune: TALLIS' CANON, LM; Thomas Tallis, c.1510-1583

Jesus Christ, Yesterday, Today and for Ever 730

Ostinato Refrain

Je - sus Christ, Je - sus Christ,
Je - su - cris - to a - yer, Je - su - cris - to hoy,

yes - ter - day, to - day and for ev - er.
siem - pre se - rá el Se - ñor.

Text: Suzanne Toolan, SM, b.1927; Spanish tr. by Ronald F. Krisman, b.1946
Tune: Suzanne Toolan, SM, b.1927
© 1988, 2004, GIA Publications, Inc.

731 Jesus Is the Resurrection

Refrain

Je-sus is the res-ur-rec-tion and the life.

To repeat and last time | *To verses*

All who be-lieve will live.

Verse 1

1. We come to this house, we gath-er in his name. We know that our Sav - ior lives.

[1.] [2.] D.C.

Verse 2

2. Just as Laz - a - rus rose and Mar - tha be - lieved, the glo - ry of the Lord shall be re - vealed.

[1.] [2.] D.C.

Text: Derek Campbell, b.1963
Tune: Derek Campbell, b.1963
© 2002, GIA Publications, Inc.

732 Christ Has Promised to Be Present

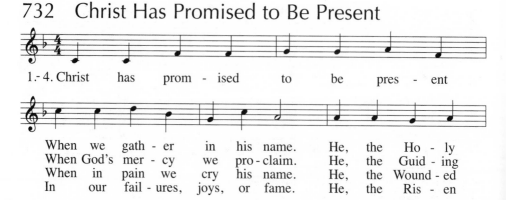

1.-4. Christ has prom-ised to be pres-ent

When we gath-er in his name. He, the Ho - ly
When God's mer - cy we pro-claim. He, the Guid-ing
When in pain we cry his name. He, the Wound-ed
In our fail-ures, joys, or fame. He, the Ris-en

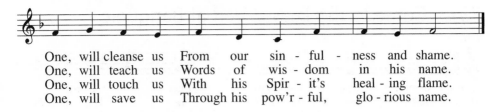

One, will cleanse us From our sin - ful - ness and shame.
One, will teach us Words of wis - dom in his name.
One, will touch us With his Spir - it's heal - ing flame.
One, will save us Through his pow'r - ful, glo - rious name.

Text: Rae E. Whitney, © 1994, Selah Publishing Co., Inc.
Tune: STUTTGART, 8 7 8 7; *Psalmodia Sacra*, 1715; adapt. and harm. by William Henry Havergal, 1793-1870, alt.

Alleluia! Give the Glory 733

Refrain

Al - le - lu - ia! Al - le - lu - ia! Al - le -

1.
lu - ia! Give the glo - ry and the

hon - or to the Lord!

2.
glo - ry and the hon - or to the Lord!

Verses

1. Where two or three are gath - ered in my
2. I am the vine and you are the

name, there I am in the
branch - es. A - bide in

D.C.
midst of them; there I'll be.
me and bear much fruit.

Text: Matthew 18:20, John 15:5; adapt. by Ken Canedo, b.1953, and Bob Hurd, b.1950
Tune: Ken Canedo, b.1953; choral arr. by Craig S. Kingsbury, b.1952; acc. by Dominic MacAller, b.1959
© 1991, Ken Canedo and Bob Hurd. Published by OCP Publications.

734 Come to the Feast / Ven al Banquete

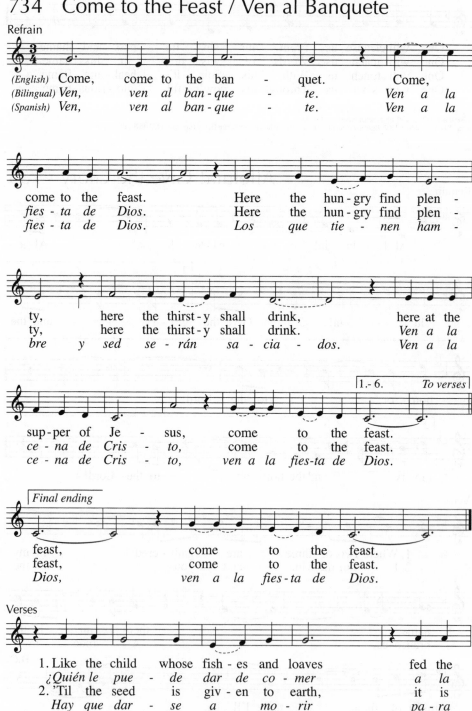

Refrain

(English) Come, come to the ban - quet. Come,
(Bilingual) Ven, ven al ban-que - te. Ven a la
(Spanish) Ven, ven al ban-que - te. Ven a la

come to the feast. Here the hun - gry find plen -
fies - ta de Dios. Here the hun - gry find plen -
fies - ta de Dios. Los que tie - nen ham -

ty, here the thirst-y shall drink, here at the
ty, here the thirst-y shall drink. Ven a la
bre y sed se - rán sa - cia - dos. Ven a la

1.- 6.   To verses

sup-per of Je - sus, come to the feast.
ce - na de Cris - to, come to the feast.
ce - na de Cris - to, ven a la fies-ta de Dios.

Final ending

feast, come to the feast.
feast, come to the feast.
Dios, ven a la fies-ta de Dios.

Verses

1. Like the child whose fish - es and loaves fed the
   ¿Quién le pue - de dar de co - mer a la
2. 'Til the seed is giv - en to earth, it is
   Hay que dar - se a mo - rir pa - ra
3. In the stran - ger by our side, in the
   Los des - am - pa - ra - dos ven - drán a par -

mul	-	ti	-	tude,				in	the	Lord	the
mul	-	*ti*	-	*tud?*				*Con*	*Je*	*- sús,*	*al*
just	one	grain;						but	once	sown	its
co	-	*se*	-	*char,*				*las*	*se*	*- mi -*	*llas*
least	and	last,						in	the	thirst	for
tir	*el*	*pan*						*y*	*ve*	*- rán*	*su*

lit	-	tle	we	have,		bro	-	ken	and	shared,	be	-
com	-	*par*	*- tir*	*lo*		*po*	-	*co*	*que*	*hay,*	*re*	*- ci -*
death	brings	new	birth,	the		har	-	vest	is	rich;	what's	
de	*li*	*- ber*	*- tad*	*y*		*re*	*- su*	*- rrec*	*- ción,*	*la*	*pro*	-
jus	-	tice	we	share,		Christ		is	here	in	the	
dig	-	*ni*	*- dad*	*de*		*nue*	*-vo en*	*Je*	*- sús,*	*Sal*	*- va*	-

D.C.

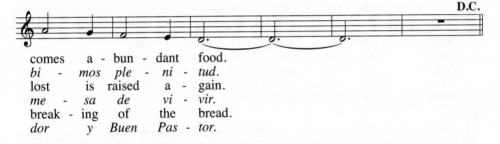

comes	a	- bun	- dant	food.
bi	-	*mos*	*ple*	*- ni - tud.*
lost	is	raised	a	- gain.
me	-	*sa*	*de*	*vi - vir.*
break	- ing	of	the	bread.
dor	*y*	*Buen*	*Pas*	*- tor.*

Text: Bob Hurd, b.1950, Pia Moriarty, b.1948, Jaime Cortez, b.1963
Tune: Bob Hurd, b.1950; acc. by Dominic MacAller, b.1959, alt.
© 1994, 1995, Bob Hurd and Pia Moriarty. Published by OCP Publications.

735 Gather 'Round This Table

Verses

Cantor:

1. Come, gath - er 'round this ta - ble, all you from far and near,
2. O come and join the ban - quet, ho - ly and hap - py feast,
3. And here we taste sal - va - tion, break now the bless-ed bread;
4. The cup of God's own glad-ness, sweet and a - bun-dant wine,
5. And here we share the sto - ries an - cient and ev - er new,

gath - er 'round this ta - ble, for all are wel - come
God has spread a ban - quet where the great - est shall be
joined with all cre - a - tion, ev - 'ry hun - ger shall be
saved from sin and sad - ness, let your spir - its bright - ly
cross and crown and glo - ry, our death and life a -

All:

here, yes all are wel - come here.
least, the great - est shall be least.
fed, all hun - gers shall be fed.
shine, all spir - its bright - ly shine.
new, our death and life a - new.

Refrain

Bless - ed are they who will feast in the Reign of God.

Bless-ed are they who will share the bread of life.

Bless-ed are they who are least in the Reign of God;

they shall re - joice at the feast of life.

Text: Marty Haugen, b.1950
Tune: Marty Haugen, b.1950
© 1999, 2001, GIA Publications, Inc.

What Is This Place 736

1. What is this place where we are meet - ing?
2. Words from a - far, stars that are fall - ing,
3. And we ac - cept bread at his ta - ble,

On - ly a house, the earth its floor, Walls and a roof
Sparks that are sown in us like seed. Names for our God,
Bro - ken and shared, a liv - ing sign. Here in this world,

shel - ter - ing peo - ple, Win - dows for light, an o - pen door.
dreams, signs and won - ders Sent from the past are all we need.
dy - ing and liv - ing, We are each oth - er's bread and wine.

Yet it be - comes a bod - y that lives When
We in this place re - mem - ber and speak A -
This is the place where we can re - ceive What

we are gath - ered here, And know our God is near.
gain what we have heard: God's free re - deem - ing word.
we need to in - crease: Our jus - tice and God's peace.

Text: *Zomaar een dak boven wat hoofen;* Huub Oosterhuis, b.1933; trans. by David Smith, b.1933, © 1967, Gooi en Sticht, bv., Baarn,
  The Netherlands. Exclusive English language agent: OCP Publications
Tune: KOMT NU MET ZANG, 9 8 9 8 9 66; Valerius' *Neder-landtsche gedenck-klanck;* acc. by Robert J. Batastini, b.1942, © 1987,
  GIA Publications, Inc.

737   God Is Here! As We His People

1. God is here! As we his peo-ple Meet to of-fer praise and prayer, May we find in ful-ler meas-ure What it is in Christ we share: Here, as in the world a-round us, All our var-ied skills and arts Wait the com-ing of his Spir-it In-to o-pen minds and hearts.

2. Here are sym-bols to re-mind us Of our life-long need of grace; Here are ta-ble, font and pul-pit, Here the cross has cen-tral place: Here in hon-es-ty of preach-ing, Here in si-lence as in speech, Here in new-ness and re-new-al God the Spir-it comes to each.

3. Here our chil-dren find a wel-come In the Shep-herd's flock and fold; Here, as bread and wine are tak-en, Christ sus-tains us as of old: Here the ser-vants of the Ser-vant Seek in wor-ship to ex-plore What it means in dai-ly liv-ing To be-lieve and to a-dore.

4. Lord of all, of church and king-dom, In an age of change and doubt, Keep us faith-ful to the gos-pel, Help us work your pur-pose out: Here, in this day's ded-i-ca-tion, All we have to give, re-ceive; We who can-not live with-out you, We a-dore you! We be-lieve!

Text: Fred Pratt Green, 1903-2000, © 1979, Hope Publishing Co.
Tune: ABBOT'S LEIGH, 8 7 8 7 D; Cyril V. Taylor, 1907-1991, © 1942, 1970, Hope Publishing Co.

As We Gather at Your Table   738

1. As we gath - er at your Ta - ble,
2. Turn our wor - ship in - to wit - ness
3. Gra - cious Spir - it, help us sum - mon

As we lis - ten to your Word,
In the sac - ra - ment of life;
Oth - er guests to share that feast

Help us know, O God, your pres - ence:
Send us forth to love and serve you,
Where tri - um - phant Love will wel - come

Let our hearts and minds be stirred. Nour - ish us with
Bring - ing peace where there is strife. Give us, Christ, your
Those who had been last and least. There no more will

sa - cred sto - ry Till we claim it as our own;
great com - pas - sion To for - give as you for - gave;
en - vy blind us Nor will pride our peace de - stroy,

Teach us through this ho - ly ban - quet
May we still be - hold your im - age
As we join with saints and an - gels

How to make Love's vic - t'ry known.
In the world you died to save.
To re - peat the sound - ing joy.

Text: Carl P. Daw, Jr., b.1944, © 1989, Hope Publishing Co.
Tune: HOLY MANNA, 8 7 8 7 D; William Moore, fl.1830; acc. by Kelly Dobbs Mickus, b.1966, © 2003, GIA Publications, Inc.

739   Come, Let Us Sing with Joy to the Lord

Refrain

Come, let us sing with joy to the Lord! Shout to the rock of our

sal - va - tion! Come, let us greet him with a song of praise, for

great is our God, the King of all kings! Come, let us sing with joy

To verses | *Last time*

to the Lord! Come, let us sing with joy

to the Lord! Come, let us sing with joy to the Lord!

Come, let us sing with joy to the Lord!

Verses

Cantor: *All:*

1. Let us bow down and wor - ship the Lord:
2. Great is the Lord and wor - thy of praise:
3. All that has life and breath shall re - joice:
4. Heav-en and earth re - joice in his name:

Come, let us sing with joy

Cantor:

For this is our God, whose peo - ple we are:
to the Lord! Sing to the Lord and bless his name:
The great and the small, all crea - tures of God:
He gov-erns the world with jus - tice and truth:

Come, let us sing with joy to the Lord!

D.C.

Come, let us sing with joy to the Lord!

Text: Psalms 95 and 96; Paul A. Tate, b.1968
Tune: Paul A. Tate, b.1968
© 2001, World Library Publications

Come to Us 740

1. Come to me, come to us, you who are bur - dened.
2. Come to me, come to us, pil - grim or stran - ger,
3. Come to me, come to us, bro - ken or build - ing,

Come to the word, and come to the meal.
look - ing for change, or chal - lenge, or light.
Come with your chil - dren, your choic - es, your chains.

Come with-out ques - tion or pres - sure or price:
We are the peo - ple whose call - ing is care,
All are in - vit - ed to friend-ship or rest, to

Come, be em - braced by the bod - y of Christ.
bear - ers of mer - cy, nour - ished in prayer.
share in our strug - gle, our call and our quest.

Text: Rory Cooney, b.1952
Tune: Rory Cooney, b.1952
© 1986, North American Liturgy Resources. Published by OCP Publications.

741 All Are Welcome

1. Let us build a house where love can dwell And
2. Let us build a house where proph - ets speak, And
3. Let us build a house where love is found In
4. Let us build a house where hands will reach Be -
5. Let us build a house where all are named, Their

all can safe - ly live, A place where saints and
words are strong and true, Where all God's chil - dren
wa - ter, wine and wheat: A ban - quet hall on
yond the wood and stone To heal and strength-en,
songs and vi - sions heard And loved and treas - ured,

chil - dren tell How hearts learn to for -
dare to seek To dream God's reign a -
ho - ly ground, Where peace and jus - tice
serve and teach, And live the Word they've
taught and claimed As words with - in the

give. Built of hopes and dreams and vi - sions,
new. Here the cross shall stand as wit - ness
meet. Here the love of God, through Je - sus,
known. Here the out - cast and the stran - ger
Word. Built of tears and cries and laugh - ter,

Rock of faith and vault of grace; Here the
And as sym - bol of God's grace; Here as
Is re - vealed in time and space; As we
Bear the im - age of God's face; Let us
Prayers of faith and songs of grace, Let this

love of Christ shall end di - vi - sions:
one we claim the faith of Je - sus:
share in Christ the feast that frees us: All are wel - come,
bring an end to fear and dan - ger:
house pro-claim from floor to raft - er:

all are wel-come, all are wel-come in this place.

Text: Marty Haugen, b. 1950
Tune: TWO OAKS, 9 6 8 6 8 7 10 with refrain; Marty Haugen, b. 1950
© 1994, GIA Publications, Inc.

Gather Your People 742

Refrain

Gath-er your peo-ple, O Lord. Gath-er your peo-ple, O

Lord. One bread, one bod-y, one spir-it of

love. Gath-er your peo-ple, O Lord.

Verses

1. Draw us forth to the ta - ble of life:
2. We are parts of the bod - y of Christ,
3. No more harm on the moun - tain of God;
4. Wash us, Lord, in the wa - ters of life;

broth - ers and sis - ters, each of us called to
need - ing each oth - er, each of the gifts the
swords in - to plow-shares. Free us, O Lord, from
wa - ters of mer - cy, wa - ters of hope that

D.C.

walk in your light.
Spir - it pro - vides.
hard - ness of heart.
flow from your side.

Text: 1 Corinthians 12, Isaiah 2:3-4, 11:9; Bob Hurd, b.1950
Tune: Bob Hurd, b.1950; choral arr. by Craig S. Kingsbury, b.1952; acc. by Dominic MacAller, b.1959
© 1991, Bob Hurd. Published by OCP Publications.

743 Gather Us In

1. Here in this place new light is stream - ing,
2. We are the young— our lives are a mys - t'ry,
3. Here we will take the wine and the wa - ter,
4. Not in the dark of build - ings con - fin - ing,

Now is the dark - ness van - ished a - way,
We are the old— who yearn for your face,
Here we will take the bread of new birth,
Not in some heav - en, light - years a - way, But

See in this space our fears and our dream-ings,
We have been sung through - out all of his - t'ry,
Here you shall call your sons and your daugh-ters,
here in this place the new light is shin - ing,

Brought here to you in the light of this day.
Called to be light to the whole hu - man race.
Call us a - new to be salt for the earth.
Now is the King - dom, now is the day.

Gath - er us in— the lost and for - sak - en,
Gath - er us in— the rich and the haugh - ty,
Give us to drink the wine of com - pas - sion,
Gath - er us in and hold us for ev - er,

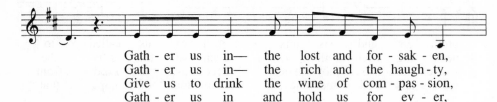

Gath - er us in— the blind and the lame;
Gath - er us in— the proud and the strong;
Give us to eat the bread that is you;
Gath - er us in and make us your own;

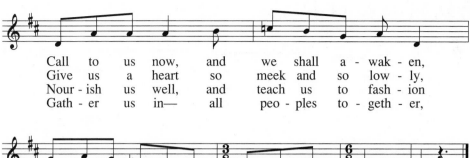

Call to us now, and we shall a - wak - en,
Give us a heart so meek and so low - ly,
Nour - ish us well, and teach us to fash - ion
Gath - er us in— all peo - ples to - geth - er,

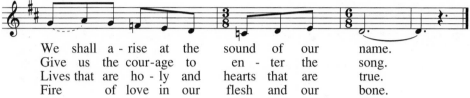

We shall a - rise at the sound of our name.
Give us the cour-age to en - ter the song.
Lives that are ho - ly and hearts that are true.
Fire of love in our flesh and our bone.

Text: Marty Haugen, b.1950
Tune: GATHER US IN, Irregular; Marty Haugen, b.1950
© 1982, GIA Publications, Inc.

Come All You People 744

Come all you peo - ple, come and praise your Mak - er,

Come all you peo - ple, come and praise your Mak - er,

Come all you peo - ple, come and praise your Mak - er,

Come now and wor - ship the Lord.

Text: Alexander Gondo
Tune: Alexander Gondo; arr. by John L. Bell, b.1949, © 1994, The Iona Community, GIA Publications, Inc., agent

745 Gathered as One

Verses

1. Man - y fac - es, the young and the old,
2. Man - y pil - grims, shar - ing at feast,
3. Man - y voic - es, raised up in song,

gath-ered as one in our God! Through-out his - t'ry the
                                All   are wel-come the
                                In   one fam - 'ly where

sto - ry's re - told,   gath-ered as one in our   God!   Like
great-est and least,
all   can be - long,

those come be - fore us,   we   lis - ten and learn.   We re -

mem - ber   the prom-ise   and a - wait your re - turn.   So with-

out hes - i - ta - tion   a   new gen - er - a - tion pro-

Refrain
All:

claims the sal-va - tion of   God!   Gath-ered as one   in

Je - sus your Son,   lift-ing our voic-es in   praise,   we

know and be - lieve   and   long to re - ceive   the

bread that is strength for our days, gath-ered as

one! one!

Text: Deanna Light and Paul A. Tate, b.1968
Tune: Deanna Light and Paul A. Tate, b.1968
© 1997, World Library Publications

All People That on Earth Do Dwell   746

1. All peo - ple that on earth do dwell, Sing
2. Know that the Lord is God in - deed; With -
3. O en - ter then his gates with praise; Ap -
4. For why? the Lord our God is good: His
5. To Fa - ther, Son, and Ho - ly Ghost, The
* Praise God, from whom all bless - ings flow; Praise

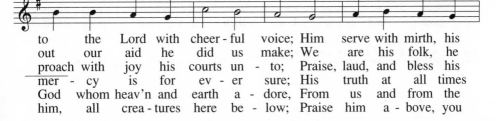

to the Lord with cheer - ful voice; Him serve with mirth, his
out our aid he did us make; We are his folk, he
proach with joy his courts un - to; Praise, laud, and bless his
mer - cy is for ev - er sure; His truth at all times
God whom heav'n and earth a - dore, From us and from the
him, all crea - tures here be - low; Praise him a - bove, you

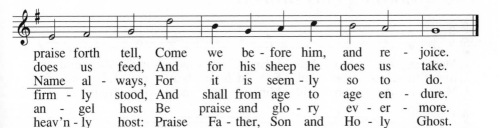

praise forth tell, Come we be - fore him, and re - joice.
does us feed, And for his sheep he does us take.
Name al - ways, For it is seem - ly so to do.
firm - ly stood, And shall from age to age en - dure.
an - gel host Be praise and glo - ry ev - er - more.
heav'n - ly host: Praise Fa - ther, Son and Ho - ly Ghost.

*May be sung alone or as an alternate to stanza 5.

Text: Psalm (99)100; William Kethe, d. c.1593; Doxology, Thomas Ken, 1637-1711
Tune: OLD HUNDREDTH, LM; Louis Bourgeois, c.1510-1561

747 Come, Host of Heaven's High Dwelling Place

1. Come, Host of Heav'n's high dwell - ing place, Come, earth's dis - put - ed guest; Find where we meet a wel - come home, Stay here and take your rest.
2. Sur - round these walls with faith and love That through the nights and days, When hu - man tongues from speak - ing cease, These stones may ech - o praise.
3. Bless and in - spire those gath - ered here With pa - tience, hope, and peace, And all the joys that know the depth In which all sor - rows cease.
4. Here may the los - er find his worth, The stran - ger find a friend; Here may the hope - less find their faith And aim - less find an end.
5. Build, from the hu - man fab - ric, signs Of how your king - dom thrives, Of how the Ho - ly Spir - it chang - es life By chang - ing lives.
6. So, to the Lord whose care en - folds The world held in his hands, Be glo - ry, hon - or, pow'r and praise For which this com - p'ny stands.

Text: John L. Bell, b.1949, © 1989, Iona Community, GIA Publications, Inc., agent
Tune: ST. COLUMBA, 8 6 8 6; Irish traditional; arr. by John L. Bell, b.1949, © 1989, Iona Community, GIA Publications, Inc., agent

748 Morning Has Broken

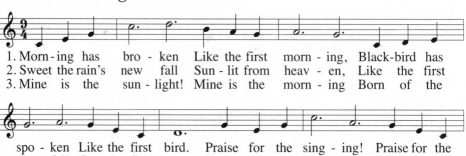

1. Morn - ing has bro - ken Like the first morn - ing, Black-bird has spo - ken Like the first bird. Praise for the sing - ing! Praise for the
2. Sweet the rain's new fall Sun - lit from heav - en, Like the first dew - fall On the first grass. Praise for the sweet - ness Of the wet
3. Mine is the sun - light! Mine is the morn - ing Born of the one light E - den saw play! Praise with e - la - tion, Praise ev - 'ry

morn - ing! Praise for them, spring - ing Fresh from the Word!
gar - den, Sprung in com - plete - ness Where his feet pass.
morn - ing, God's re - cre - a - tion Of the new day!

Text: Eleanor Farjeon, 1881-1965, *The Children's Bells,* © David Higham Assoc. Ltd.
Tune: BUNESSAN, 5 5 5 4 D; Gaelic; acc. by Robert J. Batastini, b.1942, © 1999, GIA Publications, Inc.

This Day God Gives Me 749

1. This day God gives me Strength of high heav - en,
2. This day God sends me Strength as my guard - ian,
3. God's way is my way, God's shield is 'round me,
4. Ris - ing I thank you, Might - y and strong One,

Sun and moon shin - ing, Flame in my hearth,
Might to up - hold me, Wis - dom as guide.
God's host de - fends me, Sav - ing from ill.
King of cre - a - tion, Giv - er of rest,

Flash - ing of light - ning, Wind in its swift - ness,
Your eyes are watch - ful, Your ears are lis - t'ning,
An - gels of heav - en, Drive from me al - ways
Firm - ly con - fess - ing God in three Per - sons,

Depths of the o - cean, Firm - ness of earth.
Your lips are speak - ing, Friend at my side.
All that would harm me, Stand by me still.
One - ness of God - head, Trin - i - ty blest.

Text: Ascribed to St. Patrick; James Quinn, SJ, b.1919, © 1969. Used by permission of Selah Publishing Co., Inc.
Tune: ANDREA, 5 5 5 4 D; David Haas, b.1957, © 1993, GIA Publications, Inc.

750 God of Day and God of Darkness

1. God of day and God of dark - ness, Now we
2. Still the na - tions curse the dark - ness, Still the
3. Show us Christ in one an - oth - er, Make us
4. You shall be the path that guides us, You the
5. Praise to you in day and dark - ness, You our

stand be - fore the night; As the shad - ows stretch and
rich op - press the poor; Still the earth is bruised and
ser - vants strong and true; Give us all your love of
light that in us burns; Shin - ing deep with - in all
source and you our end; Praise to you who love and

deep - en, Come and make our dark - ness bright. All cre -
bro - ken By the ones who still want more. Come and
jus - tice So we do what you would do. Let us
peo - ple, Yours the love that we must learn, For our
nur-ture us As a fa - ther, moth - er, friend. Grant us

a - tion still is groan - ing For the dawn - ing of your
wake us from our sleep - ing, So our hearts can - not ig -
call all peo - ple ho - ly, Let us pledge our lives a -
hearts shall wan - der rest - less 'Til they safe to you re -
all a peace-ful rest - ing, Let each mind and bod - y

might, When the Sun of peace and jus - tice
nore All your peo - ple lost and bro - ken,
new, Make us one with all the low - ly,
turn, Find - ing you in one an - oth - er,
mend, So we rise re - freshed to - mor - row,

Fills the earth with ra - diant light.
All your chil - dren at our door.
Let us all be one in you.
We shall all your face dis - cern.
Hearts re - newed to King - dom tend.

Text: Marty Haugen, b.1950, © 1985, 1994, GIA Publications, Inc.
Tune: BEACH SPRING, 8 7 8 7 D; *The Sacred Harp*, 1844; harm. by Marty Haugen, b.1950, © 1985, GIA Publications, Inc.

Day Is Done 751

1. Day is done, but love un - fail - ing Dwells ev - er
2. Dark de-scends, but light un - end - ing Shines through our
3. Eyes will close, but you un - sleep-ing Watch by our

here; Shad - ows fall, but hope, pre - vail - ing,
night; You are with us, ev - er lend - ing
side; Death may come, in love's safe keep - ing

Calms ev - 'ry fear. God, our Mak - er, none for - sak - ing,
New strength to sight: One in love, your truth con - fess - ing,
Still we a - bide. God of love, all e - vil quell-ing,

Take our hearts, of Love's own mak - ing, Watch our sleep-ing,
One in hope of heav - en's bless-ing, May we see, in
Sin for - giv - ing, fear dis - pel - ling, Stay with us, our

guard our wak - ing, Be al - ways near.
love's pos - sess - ing, Love's end - less light!
hearts in - dwell - ing, This e - ven - tide.

Text: James Quinn, SJ, b.1919, © 1969, Used by permission of Selah Publishing Co., Inc.
Tune: AR HYD Y NOS, 8 4 8 4 888 4; Welsh

752 At Evening

1. Now it is eve - ning: Lights of the cit - y
2. Now it is eve - ning: Lit - tle ones sleep - ing
3. Now it is eve - ning: Food on the ta - ble
4. Now it is eve - ning: Here in our meet - ing

Bid us re - mem - ber Christ is our Light.
Bid us re - mem - ber Christ is our Peace.
Bids us re - mem - ber Christ is our Life.
May we re - mem - ber Christ is our Friend.

Man - y are lone - ly, Who will be neigh - bor?
Some are ne - glect - ed, Who will be neigh - bor?
Man - y are hun - gry, Who will be neigh - bor?
Some may be stran - gers, Who will be neigh - bor?

Where there is car - ing Christ is our Light.
Where there is car - ing Christ is our Peace.
Where there is shar - ing Christ is our Life.
Where there's a wel - come Christ is our Friend.

Text: Fred Pratt Green, 1903-2000, © 1974, Hope Publishing Co.
Tune: EVENING HYMN, 5 5 5 4 D; David Haas, b.1957, © 1985, GIA Publications, Inc.

Watch, O Lord 753

Refrain

Watch, O Lord, with all those a - wake this night,

Watch, O Lord, with all those who weep; Give your

an - gels and saints charge o - ver all who sleep.

Verses

Cantor: *All:*   *Cantor:*

1. Tend your ail - ing ones: Rest your
2. Soothe your suf-f'ring ones: in your love, Lord;   Heal af -
3. Hold your griev-ing ones: Raise your
4. Guard your lit - tle ones: Guide your

All: *Cantor:*

wea - ry ones: Bless your
flict - ed ones: in your love, Lord;   Shield your
fal - len ones: Mend your
search - ing ones: Grant us

All: **D.C.**

dy - ing ones:
joy-ous ones: in your love, O Lord of all.
bro-ken ones:
all your peace:

Text: St. Augustine; adapt. Marty Haugen, b.1950
Tune: Marty Haugen, b.1950
© 2003, GIA Publications, Inc.

754 Praise and Thanksgiving

1. Praise and thanks - giv - ing, Fa - ther, we of - fer, For all things
2. Lord, bless the la - bor We bring to serve you, That with our
3. Fa - ther, pro - vid - ing Food for your chil - dren, Your wis - dom
4. Then will your bless - ing Reach ev - 'ry peo - ple, Free - ly con -

liv - ing You have made good. Har - vest of sown fields, Fruits of the
neigh-bor We may be fed. Sow - ing or till - ing, We would work
guid - ing Teach-es us share One with an - oth - er, So that re -
fess - ing Your gra-cious hand. Where you are reign - ing No one will

or - chard, Hay from the mown fields, Blos - som and wood.
with you, Har - vest - ing, mill - ing, For dai - ly bread.
joic - ing With us, all oth - ers May know your care.
hun - ger, Your love sus - tain - ing, Fruit - ful the land.

Text: Albert F. Bayly, 1901-1984, © 1988, Oxford University Press
Tune: BUNESSAN, 5 5 5 4 D; Gaelic; harm. Robert J. Batastini, b.1942, © 1999, GIA Publications, Inc.

755 The Trumpet in the Morning

Verses

1. O the wea - ry world is trudg - ing t'ward the
2. Ev - 'ry pris - on wall will crum - ble, ev - 'ry
3. Then the rich will grasp at shad - ows for the
4. Let the bank - er and the pres - i - dent be -
5. Let the proph - ets speak in par - a - bles, let
6. Come and join the great thanks - giv - ing, take your

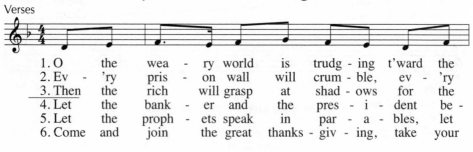

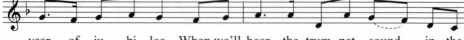

year of ju - bi - lee, When we'll hear the trum-pet sound in the
chain will fall a - way When we hear the trum-pet sound in the
land is God's a - lone, When we hear the trum-pet sound in the
ware the trum-pet's call, And beat swords of greed and com-merce in - to
sto - ry - tell - ers spin Tales of faith - ful-ness and res - cue 'til the
neigh-bor by the hand And be - come the voice of free - dom that will

morn - ing. Far and wide we hear the
morn - ing. And the debts that stole our
morn - ing. Ev - 'ry im - mi - grant be
e - qual shares for all. Let the teach - ers speak in
ban - quet shall be - gin; How God wove the world with
thun - der through the land. Let the earth re - pose in

clar - i - on an - nounce that all are free When we
dream - ing we will no more have to pay When we
wel - come, all the home - less find a home, When we
wis - dom, let the mu - sic - mak - ers play, Let the
won - der, how God led us through the sea, Why we
sab - bath while her chil - dren's hearts re - new, And give

hear the trum - pet sound in the morn - ing.
hear the trum - pet sound in the morn - ing.
hear the trum - pet sound in the morn - ing.
weav - ers weave the tent where we shall gath - er on that day.
keep a day of rest and call a year of ju - bi - lee!
back to God in jus - tice what God's boun - ty gave to you.

Refrain

Low - ly eyes shall be lift - ed, while the ty - rants taste their fear,

For that sound is both a gos - pel and a warn - ing. When we

rise as a peo - ple who pro - claim that God is near, Who will

dare to sound the trum - pet in the morn - ing?

Text: Leviticus 25, Deuteronomy 15, Joel 2; Rory Cooney, b.1952, © 1998, GIA Publications, Inc.
Tune: MORNING TRUMPET, 15 11 15 11 with refrain; B.F. White, 1800-1879, from *Southern Harmony*; arr. by Rory Cooney, b.1952, © 1998, GIA Publications, Inc.

756 On That Day

Refrain

On that day, on that hal - le - lu - ja day, on that

day, on that hal - le - lu - ja day there'll be

sing - in', there'll be shout -in', and joy flows like a foun-

Last time to coda

tain on that day.

Verses

1. We'll see the ho - ly cit - y there; the
2. Twelve gates to the king-dom we shall see; all
3. No need of the sun or moon to shine; the

new Je - ru - sa - lem. No more
na - tions will walk as one. Lift - ing our
glo - ry of God is there. Dark - ness to

sor - row, no more cry - in'.
voic - es, claim - ing our choic - es.
light, God's face in our sight.

D.C.

No more death, no more pain.
Glo - ry and hon - or shall be:
Joy from God's love we will share:

Coda

day,   on that   day.

Text: Kate Cuddy, b.1953
Tune: Kate Cuddy, b.1953
© 1997, GIA Publications, Inc.

O Holy City, Seen of John   757

1. O   Ho - ly   Cit - y,   seen   of   John,   Where
2. O   shame   to   us   who   rest   con - tent   While
3. Give   us,   O   God,   the   strength   to   build   The
4. Al - read - y   in   the   mind   of   God   That

Christ, the Lamb, does   reign,   With - in   those four - square
lust   and greed   for   gain   In   street   and   shop   and
Cit - y   that   has   stood   Too   long   a   dream, whose
Cit - y   ris - es   fair: Lo,   how   its   splen - dor

walls   shall come No   night,   nor   need, nor   pain,   And
ten - e - ment Wring   gold   from   hu - man   pain,   And
laws   are   love, Whose ways,   the   com - mon   good,   And
chal - leng - es   The   souls   that   great - ly   dare: Yea,

where the tears are wiped from eyes That   shall   not   weep a - gain.
bit - ter lips in blind de - spair Cry, "Christ has died in   vain."
where the shin-ing sun be - comes God's grace for   hu - man good.
bids   us seize the whole of   life   And   build   its   glo - ry   there.

Text: Revelation 21; W. Russell Bowie, 1882-1969, © Harper and Row
Tune: MORNING SONG, 8 6 8 6 8 6; *Kentucky Harmony,* 1816; harm. by C. Winfred Douglas, 1867-1944, © 1940, The Church Pension Fund

758 Soon and Very Soon

1. Soon and ver - y soon we are goin' to see the King,
2. No more cry - in' there we are goin' to see the King,
3. No more dy - in' there we are goin' to see the King,
4. Soon and ver - y soon we are goin' to see the King,

Soon and ver - y soon we are goin' to see the King,
No more cry - in' there we are goin' to see the King,
No more dy - in' there we are goin' to see the King,
Soon and ver - y soon we are goin' to see the King,

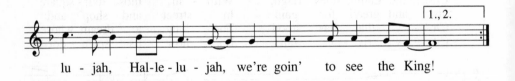

Soon and ver - y soon we are goin' to see the King,
No more cry - in' there we are goin' to see the King, Hal - le -
No more dy - in' there we are goin' to see the King, Hal - le -
Soon and ver - y soon we are goin' to see the King,

1., 2.

lu - jah, Hal - le - lu - jah, we're goin' to see the King!

3., 4.

Hal - le - lu - jah, Hal - le - lu -

jah, Hal - le - lu - jah, Hal - le - lu - jah.

Text: Andraé Crouch, b.1945
Tune: Andraé Crouch, b.1945
© 1976, Bud John Songs, Inc./Crouch Music/ASCAP

Mine Eyes Have Seen the Glory 759

1. Mine eyes have seen the glo - ry of the
2. I have seen him in the watch - fires of a
3. He has sound - ed forth the trum - pet that shall
4. In the beau - ty of the lil - ies Christ was

com - ing of the Lord; He is tram - pling out the
hun - dred cir - cling camps; They have build - ed him an
nev - er call re - treat; He is sift - ing out all
born a - cross the sea, With a glo - ry in his

vin - tage where the grapes of wrath are stored; He hath
al - tar in the eve - ning dews and damps; I can
hu - man hearts be - fore his judg - ment seat; O be
bos - om that trans - fig - ures you and me; As he

loosed the fate - ful light - ning of his ter - ri - ble swift
read the right - eous sen - tence by the dim and flar - ing
swift, my soul, to an - swer him; be ju - bi - lant, my
died to make us ho - ly, let us die that all be

sword; His truth is march-ing on.
lamps; His day is march-ing on.
feet! Our God is march-ing on.   Glo - ry! Glo-ry! Hal - le -
free! While God is march-ing on.

lu - jah! Glo - ry! Glo - ry! Hal - le - lu - jah! Glo - ry!

Glo - ry! Hal - le - lu - jah! His truth is march-ing on.

Text: Julia W. Howe, 1819-1910
Tune: BATTLE HYMN OF THE REPUBLIC, 15 15 15 6 with refrain; attr. to William Steffe, d.1911

760 Take Me Home

Refrain

Take me home, to your dwell-ing place, in your sweet em-brace, read-y to hold me in your arms. Take me home, to your lov-ing eyes, with you a-lone I'll rise, sing-ing for-ev-er, in your arms, take me home.

Verses

1. O my God, you've led me through it all, through all the hurt and my shame. O my God, I have trav-eled far to meet you, to see your face and call up-on your name!

2. With you all pain is left be-hind, no sor-row or death, on that day. O my God, how I've longed to know your love, come wipe my tears, and take my fear a-way!

3. O my God, the road is long and hard, o-pen your heart, come to me. God, with you, my sor-row turns to danc-ing, reach out your hand and set my spir-it free!

D.C.

Text: David Haas, b.1957
Tune: David Haas, b.1957
© 2001, GIA Publications, Inc.

Shall We Gather at the River   761

1. Shall we gath - er at the riv - er, Where bright
2. On the mar - gin of the riv - er, Wash - ing
3. Ere we reach the shin - ing riv - er, Lay we
4. Soon we'll reach the shin - ing riv - er, Soon our

an - gel feet have trod; With its crys - tal tide for
up its sil - ver spray, We will walk and wor - ship
ev - 'ry bur - den down; Grace our spir - its will de-
pil - grim-age will cease, Soon our hap - py hearts will

ev - er Flow-ing by the throne of God?
ev - er, All the hap - py gold - en day.
liv - er, And pro - vide a robe and crown.
quiv - er With the mel - o - dy of peace.

Yes, we'll gath - er at the riv - er, The beau - ti - ful, the

beau - ti - ful riv - er; Gath - er with the saints at the

riv - er That flows by the throne of God.

Text: Robert Lowry, 1826-1899
Tune: Robert Lowry, 1826-1899

762 We Shall Rise Again

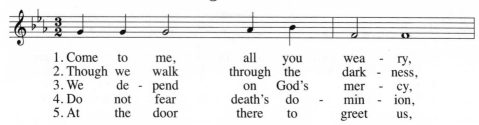

1. Come to me, all you wea - ry,
2. Though we walk through the dark - ness,
3. We de - pend on God's mer - cy,
4. Do not fear death's do - min - ion,
5. At the door there to greet us,

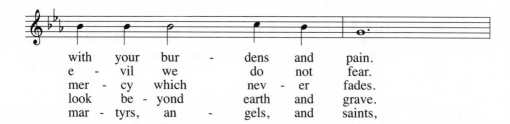

with your bur - dens and pain.
e - vil we do not fear.
mer - cy which nev - er fades.
look be - yond earth and grave.
mar - tyrs, an - gels, and saints,

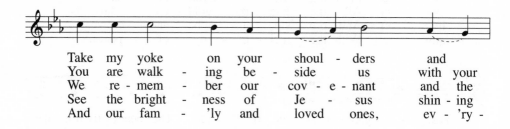

Take my yoke on your shoul - ders and
You are walk - ing be - side us with your
We re - mem - ber our cov - e - nant and the
See the bright - ness of Je - sus shin - ing
And our fam - 'ly and loved ones, ev - 'ry -

learn from me: I am gen - tle and
rod and your staff. On - ly good - ness and
prom - ise Je - sus made: If we die with Christ
out to light our way. Lov - ing Fa - ther and
one freed from their chains. We shall feel their ac -

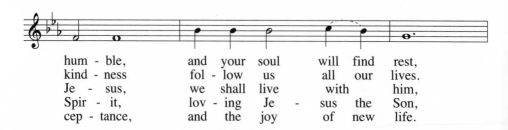

hum - ble, and your soul will find rest,
kind - ness fol - low us all our lives.
Je - sus, we shall live with him,
Spir - it, lov - ing Je - sus the Son,
cep - tance, and the joy of new life.

For my yoke is eas - y and my
We shall dwell in the Lord's house for so
And if we are faith - ful, we shall
All God's peo - ple to - geth - er, we shall
We shall join in the gath - er - ing, re - u -

bur - den is light.
man - y years to come!
reign with him!
live on as one!
nit - ed in God's love!

We shall rise a-gain on the last day with the

faith - ful, rich and poor. Com-ing to the house of Lord

Je - sus, we will find an o - pen door there, we will

find an o - pen door.

Text: Matthew 11:29-30, Psalm 23, John 11, 2 Timothy 2; Jeremy Young, b.1948
Tune: RESURRECTION; Irregular with refrain; Jeremy Young, b.1948
© 1987, GIA Publications, Inc.

763   I Will Be the Vine

Refrain

I will be the vine and you will be the branch-es. All you who live in me will nev-er, nev-er die. I will be the sign, I will of-fer man-y chanc-es; so live, oh live in me and you shall have new life.

Verses 1, 2

1. Re - main in me, as I re-main in you. You may ask what you will, ask what you will, and you shall re - ceive.
2. As the Fa - ther loved me, so have I loved you. Re - main in my love, re - main in my love, and I will give you life.

Verse 3

3. If you are my friends, you will live my com - mands. There is no great-er love, no great-er

D.C.

love than to lay down your life for your friends.

Text: Liam Lawton, b.1959
Tune: Liam Lawton, b.1959; arr. by John McCann, b.1961
© 1998, GIA Publications, Inc.

Jerusalem, My Happy Home   764

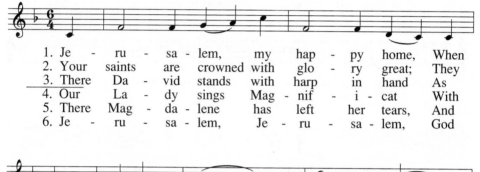

1. Je - ru - sa - lem, my hap - py home, When
2. Your saints are crowned with glo - ry great; They
3. There Da - vid stands with harp in hand As
4. Our La - dy sings Mag - nif - i - cat With
5. There Mag - da - lene has left her tears, And
6. Je - ru - sa - lem, Je - ru - sa - lem, God

shall I with you be? When shall my sor - rows
see God face to face; They tri - umph still, they
mas - ter of the choir: Ten thou - sand times that
tune sur - pass - ing sweet; And all the vir - gins
cheer - ful - ly does sing With bless - ed saints, whose
grant that I may see Your end - less joy, and

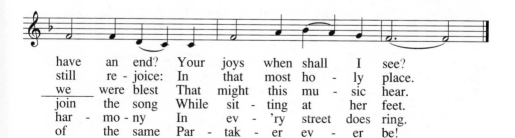

have an end? Your joys when shall I see?
still re - joice: In that most ho - ly place.
we were blest That might this mu - sic hear.
join the song While sit - ting at her feet.
har - mo - ny In ev - 'ry street does ring.
of the same Par - tak - er ev - er be!

Text: Joseph Bromehead, 1747-1826, alt.
Tune: LAND OF REST, CM; American; harm. by Richard Proulx, b.1937, © 1975, GIA Publications, Inc.

765 Do Not Let Your Hearts Be Troubled

Refrain

Do not let your hearts be trou - bled, have

faith in God and faith in me. I will go forth to pre -

pare a place for you, then I'll come back to take you

with me, that where I am, you may al - so be.

Verse 1

1. In God's house there are man - y plac - es for you a -

lone to dwell in safe - ty. You know the way to

D.C.

where I'll lead you, if you are lost, I will show the way.

Verses 2, 3

2. I am the way, the truth and the life,
3. The words I speak are not on - ly of my - self,

on - ly through me can you know what I know. If you knew
it is your God who lives with - in me. If you be -

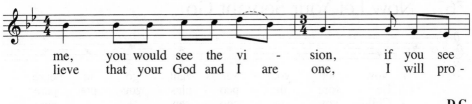

me,   you would see the vi - sion,   if you see
lieve   that your God and I   are   one,   I will pro -

me,   you see your God.
vide   when   you call my   name.

Text: John 14:1-3, 6-7, 10-14; David Haas, b.1957
Tune: David Haas, b.1957
© 1995, GIA Publications, Inc.

Steal Away to Jesus   766

Refrain

Steal a-way,   steal a-way,   steal a-way to Je-sus!

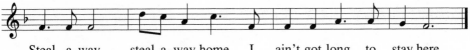

Steal a-way,   steal a-way home, I ain't got long to stay here.

Verses

1. My   Lord, he calls me,   He calls me   by   the thun-der; The
2. Green trees are bend-ing,   Poor sin-ners stand a trem-bling; The
3. My   Lord, he calls me,   He calls me   by   the light-ning; The

trum-pet sounds with-in   my soul; I ain't got long to stay here.

Text: African-American spiritual
Tune: African-American spiritual

767 Now Let Your Servant Go

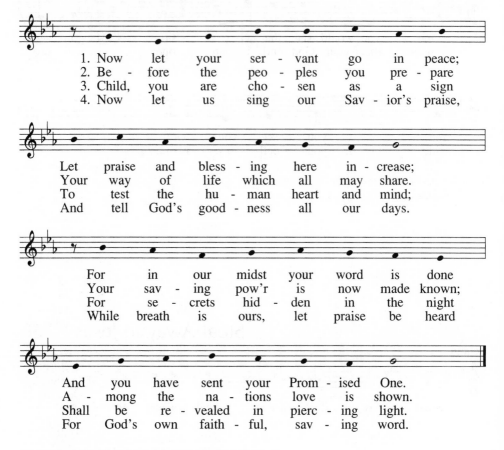

1. Now let your ser - vant go in peace;
2. Be - fore the peo - ples you pre - pare
3. Child, you are cho - sen as a sign
4. Now let us sing our Sav - ior's praise,

Let praise and bless - ing here in - crease;
Your way of life which all may share.
To test the hu - man heart and mind;
And tell God's good - ness all our days.

For in our midst your word is done
Your sav - ing pow'r is now made known;
For se - crets hid - den in the night
While breath is ours, let praise be heard

And you have sent your Prom - ised One.
A - mong the na - tions love is shown.
Shall be re - vealed in pierc - ing light.
For God's own faith - ful, sav - ing word.

Text: *Nunc dimittis*, Luke 2:29-35; Ruth Duck, b.1947, © 1992, GIA Publications, Inc.
Tune: CONDITOR ALME SIDERUM, LM; Mode IV; acc. by Gerard Farrell, OSB, b.1919, © 1986, GIA Publications, Inc.

No Wind at the Window 768

1. No wind at the win-dow, No knock on the door; No light from the lamp-stand, No foot on the floor; No dream born of tired-ness, No ghost raised by fear: Just an an - gel and a wom-an And a voice in her ear.

2. "O Mar-y, O Mar-y, Don't hide from my face. Be glad that you're fa - vored And filled with God's grace. The time for re - deem - ing The world has be - gun; And you are re - quest-ed To moth - er God's son.

3. "This child must be born that The king-dom might come: Sal - va - tion for man - y, De - struc - tion for some; Both end and be - gin - ning, Both mes - sage and sign; Both vic - tor and vic - tim, Both yours and di - vine."

4. No pay - ment was prom-ised, No prom - is - es made; No wed - ding was dat - ed, No blue - print dis - played. Yet Mar - y, con - sent - ing To what none could guess, Re - plied with con - vic - tion, "Tell God I say yes."

Text: John L. Bell, b.1949
Tune: COLUMCILLE, Irregular; Gaelic, arr. by John L. Bell, b.1949
© 1992, Iona Community, GIA Publications, Inc., agent

769 Praise We the Lord This Day

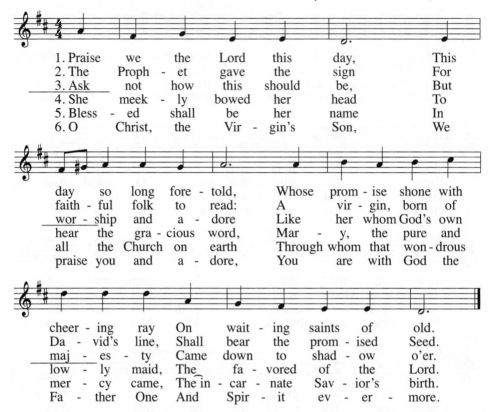

1. Praise we the Lord this day, This day so long fore-told, Whose prom-ise shone with cheer-ing ray On wait-ing saints of old.
2. The Proph-et gave the sign For faith-ful folk to read: A vir-gin, born of Da-vid's line, Shall bear the prom-ised Seed.
3. Ask not how this should be, But wor-ship and a-dore Like her whom God's own maj-es-ty Came down to shad-ow o'er.
4. She meek-ly bowed her head To hear the gra-cious word, Mar-y, the pure and low-ly maid, The fa-vored of the Lord.
5. Bless-ed shall be her name In all the Church on earth Through whom that won-drous mer-cy came, The in-car-nate Sav-ior's birth.
6. O Christ, the Vir-gin's Son, We praise you and a-dore, You are with God the Fa-ther One And Spir-it ev-er-more.

Text: Matthew 1:23; *Hymns for the Festivals and Saints' Days*, 1846
Tune: SWABIA, SM; Johann M. Speiss, 1715-1772; adapt. by William H. Havergal, 1793-1870

770 Transform Us

1. Trans-form us as you, trans-fig-ured, Stood a-part on Ta-bor's height. Lead us up our sa-cred moun-tains,
2. Trans-form us as you, trans-fig-ured, Once spoke with those ho-ly ones. We, sur-round-ed by the wit-ness
3. Trans-form us as you, trans-fig-ured, Would not stay with-in a shrine. Keep us from our great temp-ta-tion—

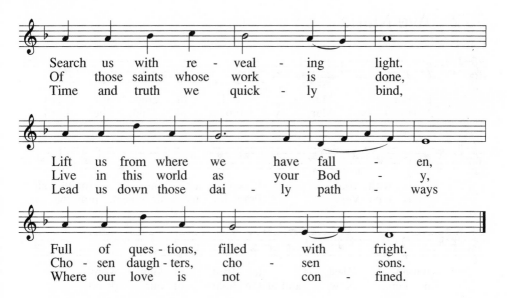

Search us with re - veal - ing light.
Of those saints whose work is done,
Time and truth we quick - ly bind,

Lift us from where we have fall - en,
Live in this world as your Bod - y,
Lead us down those dai - ly path - ways

Full of ques - tions, filled with fright.
Cho - sen daugh - ters, cho - sen sons.
Where our love is not con - fined.

Text: Sylvia Dunstan, 1955-1993, © 1993, GIA Publications, Inc.
Tune: PICARDY, 8 7 8 7 8 7; French Carol; harm. by Richard Proulx, b.1937, © 1986, GIA Publications, Inc.

'Tis Good, Lord, to Be Here   771

1. 'Tis good, Lord, to be here! Your
2. 'Tis good, Lord, to be here, Your
3. Ful - fill - er of the past! Prom -
4. Be - fore we taste of death, We
5. 'Tis good, Lord, to be here! Yet

glo - ry fills the night; Your face and gar - ments,
beau - ty to be - hold, Where Mo - ses and E -
ise of things to be! We hail your bod - y
see your king - dom come; We long to hold the
we may not re - main; But since you bid us

like the sun, Shine with un - bor - rowed light.
li - jah stand, Your mes - sen - gers of old.
glo - ri - fied, And our re - demp - tion see.
vi - sion bright, And make this hill our home.
leave the mount, Come with us to the plain.

Text: Luke 9:32-33; Joseph A. Robinson, 1858-1933, alt., © Esme. D. E. Bird
Tune: SWABIA, SM; Johann M. Speiss, 1715-1772; adapt. by William H. Havergal, 1793-1870

772 Ave Maria

Verses

1. Hail Mar - y full of grace, the Lord
2. Ho - ly Mar - y moth-er of God, the Lord

is with you. Bless-ed are you a - mong all
is with you. Pray for us sin - ners, pray for us

wom-en, Blest is the fruit of your womb.
sin - ners, Now and at the hour of our death.

Refrain

Je - sus, formed in your faith, A - ve Ma - ri - a al - le -

lu - ia. Je - sus, born in your love,

A - ve Ma - ri - a al - le - lu - ia.

Text: Hail Mary; additional text by Dan Kantor, b.1960
Tune: Dan Kantor, b.1960; arr. by Rob Glover, b.1950
© 1993, GIA Publications, Inc.

773 Magnificat

Refrain

All that I am sings of the God who brings new life to birth in

me. My spir-it soars on the wings of my Lord.

Verses

1. My soul gives glory to the Lord, rejoicing in my saving God,
   Who looks upon me in my state, and all the world will call me blest;
   For God works marvels in my sight, and holy, holy is God's name!

2. God's mercy is from age to age, on those who follow in fear;
   Whose arm is power and strength, and scatters all the proud of heart;
   Who casts the mighty from their thrones and raises up the lowly ones!

3. God fills the starving with good things, the rich are left with empty hands;
   Protecting all the faithful ones, rememb'ring Israel with mercy,
   The promise known to those before and to their children for ever!

Text: Luke 1:46-55; David Haas, b.1957
Tune: David Haas, b.1957
© 1990, GIA Publications, Inc.

Ave Maria 774

A - ve Ma - rí - a, grá - ti - a ple - na,

Dó - mi - nus te - cum, be - ne - di - cta tu in mu - li - é -

ri - bus, et be - ne - dí - ctus fru - ctus ven - tris tu - i, Je - sus.

San - cta Ma - rí - a, Ma - ter De - i, o - ra pro no - bis pec - ca -

tó - ri - bus, nunc et in ho - ra mor - tis no - strae. A - men.

Text: *Hail, Mary, full of grace,* Luke 1:29; Latin, 13th C.
Tune: AVE MARIA, Irregular; Mode I; acc. by Robert LeBlanc, b.1948, © 1986, GIA Publications, Inc.

775 O Sanctissima / O Most Virtuous

1. O   san - ctís - si - ma,   O   pi - ís - si - ma,
2. Tu   so - lá - ti - um   Et   re - fú - gi - um,
3. Ec - ce   dé - bi - les,   Per - quam   flé - bi - les,
4. Vir - go   ré - spi - ce,   Ma - ter,   ád - spi - ce,

1. O   most   vir - tu - ous   And   most   pi - ous,
2. Our   pro - tec - tion and   Con - so - la - tion,
3. See   us   pow - er - less   In   our   hope - less-ness:
4. Maid - en,   look   on us,   Moth - er,   care   for us.

Dul - cis   vir - go   Ma - rí - a!
Vir - go   ma - ter   Ma - rí - a!
Sal - va   nos,   Ma - rí - a!
Au - di   nos,   Ma - rí - a!

Dear - est   maid - en,   sweet   Mar - y,
Vir - gin   moth - er,   good   Mar - y,
Aid   us,   save   us,   Mar - y!
Hear   our   pleas,   O   Mar - y!

Ma - ter a - má - ta,   In - te - me - rá - ta,
Quid - quid op - tá - mus,   Per   te spe - rá - mus,
Tol - le lan - guó - res,   Sa - na do - ló - res,
Tu   me - di - cí - nam,   Por - tas di - ví - nam;

Moth - er af - fec - tion-ate,   Vir - gin in - vi - o - late,
What - e'er our souls de - sire,   May you help us to ac - quire.
Wipe a - way the tears we shed,   Heal us of our grief and dread.
Balm and our sur - e - ty,   Gate - way to di - vin - i - ty,

O - ra,   o - ra pro   no - bis.
O - ra,   o - ra pro   no - bis.
O - ra,   o - ra pro   no - bis.
O - ra,   o - ra pro   no - bis.

In - ter - cede and pray for   us,   O   Mar - y!
In - ter - cede and pray for   us,   O   Mar - y!
In - ter - cede and pray for   us,   O   Mar - y!
In - ter - cede and pray for   us,   O   Mar - y!

Text: St. 1, *Stimmen der Völker in Liedern*, 1807; st. 2, *Arundel Hymnal*, 1902; tr. Neil Borgstrom, b.1953, © 1994, GIA Publications, Inc.
Tune: O DU FRÖLICHE, 55 7 55 7; Tattersall's *Improved Psalmody*, 1794

Sing We of the Blessed Mother 776

1. Sing we of the bless-ed Moth-er Who re-ceived the
2. Sing we, too, of Mar-y's sor-rows, Of the sword that
3. Sing a-gain the joys of Mar-y When she saw the
4. Sing the great-est joy of Mar-y When on earth her

an-gel's word, And o-be-dient to the sum-mons
pierced her through, When be-neath the cross of Je-sus
ris-en Lord, And in prayer with Christ's a-pos-tles,
work was done, And the Lord of all cre-a-tion

Bore in love the in-fant Lord; Sing we of the
She his weight of suf-f'ring knew, Looked up-on her
Wait-ed on his prom-ised word: From on high the
Brought her to his heav'n-ly home: Vir-gin Moth-er,

joys of Mar-y At whose breast that child was fed
Son and Sav-ior Reign-ing from the aw-ful tree,
blaz-ing glo-ry Of the Spir-it's pres-ence came,
Mar-y bless-ed, Raised on high and crowned with grace,

Who is Son of God e-ter-nal
Saw the price of our re-demp-tion
Heav'n-ly breath of God's own be-ing,
May your Son, the world's re-deem-er,

And the ev-er-last-ing Bread.
Paid to set the sin-ner free.
To-kened in the wind and flame.
Grant us all to see his face.

Text: George B. Timms, 1910-1997, © 1975, Oxford University Press
Tune: OMNE DIE, 8 7 8 7 D; *Trier Gesängbuch,* 1695

777 I Sing a Maid

1. I sing a maid of ten - der years To
2. She watched him grow to man - hood's strength To
3. And if the song had end - ed then, Our

whom an an - gel came, And knelt, as to a
meet his des - ti - ny. And when the dan - ger
eyes would fill with tears, But ah! the song had

might - y queen, And bowed bright wings of
of his truth Brought him to Cal - va -
just be - gun To ech - o down the

flame: A na - tion's hope in her re - ply, This
ry, She stood by him all pow - er - less To
years! Now lift your voic - es, hearts and souls, To

maid of match - less grace; For God's own son be -
ease his dy - ing pain, 'Til in the dark - est
sing with one ac - cord To hon - or Mar - y,

came her child, And she his rest - ing place.
hour of all, She held her son a - gain.
Moth - er of The Christ, the Ris - en Lord!

Text: M. D. Ridge, b.1938, © 1987, GIA Publications, Inc.
Tune: THE FLIGHT OF THE EARLS, CMD; traditional Celtic melody; harm. by Michael Joncas, b.1951, © 1987, GIA Publications, Inc.

Sing of Mary, Meek and Lowly   778

1. Sing of Mar - y meek and low - ly, Vir - gin - moth - er
2. Sing of Je - sus, son of Mar - y, In the home at
3. *Sing of Jo - seph, strong and gen - tle, No - bly born of
4. Glo - ry be to God the Fa - ther; Glo - ry be to

pure and mild, Sing of God's own Son most ho - ly,
Naz - a - reth. Toil and la - bor can - not wea - ry
Da - vid's house; Just and up - right man of la - bor,
God the Son; Glo - ry be to God the Spir - it;

Who be - came her lit - tle child. Fair - est child of
Love en - dur - ing un - to death. Con - stant was the
Whom God chose as Mar - y's spouse; Cho - sen, too, as
Glo - ry to the Three in One. From the heart of

fair - est moth - er, God the Lord who came to earth,
love he gave her, Though he went forth from her side,
Je - sus' guard-ian, Guid - ing him since in - fan - cy.
bless - ed Mar - y, From all saints the song as - cends,

Word made flesh, our ver - y broth - er,
Forth to preach, and heal, and suf - fer,
Ho - ly Child of ho - ly par - ents,
And the church the strain re - ech - oes

Takes our na - ture by his birth.
Till on Cal - va - ry he died.
Ho - ly is their fam - i - ly.
Un - to earth's re - mot - est ends.

*For the Feast of the Holy Family, otherwise may be omitted.

Text: Vss. 1, 2, 4, Roland F. Palmer, 1891-1985, © Estate of Roland Palmer; vs. 3, Omer Westendorf, 1916-1998, © 1984, World Library Publications
Tune: PLEADING SAVIOR, 8 7 8 7 D; Christian Lyre, 1830; harm. by Richard Proulx, b.1937, © 1986, GIA Publications, Inc.

779 Hail Mary: Gentle Woman

Hail Mar-y, full of grace, the
Lord is with you. Bless-ed are you a-mong
wom-en, and blest is the fruit of your womb, Je - sus.
Ho-ly Mar - y, Moth-er of God,
pray for us sin - ners now and at the hour of
death. A - men.

Refrain

Gen - tle wom-an, qui-et light, morn-ing
star, so strong and bright, gen-tle
Moth - er, peace-ful dove, teach us
wis - dom; teach us love.

Verse 1

1. You were cho - sen by the Fa - ther;

you were cho - sen for the Son.

You were cho - sen from all wom - en

and for wom - an, shin - ing one.

Verse 2

2. Bless - ed are you a - mong wom - en,

blest in turn all wom - en, too.

Bless-ed they with peace - ful spir - its.

Bless-ed they with gen - tle hearts.

Text: *Hail Mary,* alt.; Carey Landry, b.1944
Tune: Carey Landry, b.1944; arr. by Martha Lesinski, alt.
© 1975, 1978, Carey Landry and North American Liturgy Resources. Published by OCP Publications.

780 Salve, Regína / Hail, Queen of Heaven

Sal - ve, Re - gí - na, ma - ter mi - se - ri - cór - di - ae:
Hail, Queen of Heav - en, hail, our Moth - er com-pas-sion-ate,

Vi - ta, dul - cé - do et spes no - stra sal - ve.
True life and com - fort and our hope, we greet you!

Ad te cla - má - mus, éx - su - les fí - li - i He - vae.
To you we ex - iles, chil-dren of Eve, raise our voic - es.

Ad te sus - pi - rá-mus, ge - mén - tes et flen - tes
We send up sighs to you, as mourn-ing and weep-ing,

in hac la - cri - má - rum val - le. E - ia er - go,
we pass through this vale of sor - row. Then turn to us,

ad - vo - cá - ta no - stra, il - los tu - os mi - se - ri -
O most gra-cious Wom - an, those eyes of yours, so full of

cór - des ó - cu - los ad nos con - vér - te. Et Je - sum,
love and ten - der-ness, so full of pit - y. And grant us

be - ne - dí - ctum fru - ctum ven - tris tu - i, no - bis post
af - ter these, our days of lone - ly ex - ile, the sight of

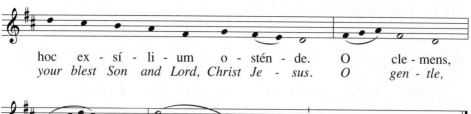

hoc ex - sí - li - um o - stén - de. O cle - mens,
your blest Son and Lord, Christ Je - sus. *O* *gen - tle,*

O pi - a, O dul - cis Vir - go Ma - rí - a.
O *lov - ing,* *O* *ho - ly, sweet Vir - gin Mar - y.*

Text: Latin, c.1080, tr. by John C. Selner, SS, 1904-1992, © 1954, GIA Publications, Inc.
Tune: SALVE REGINA, Irregular; Mode V; acc. by Gerard Farrell, OSB, b.1919, © 1986, GIA Publications, Inc.

O Mary of Promise 781

1., 5. O Mar - y of prom - ise, and daugh - ter so fair,
2. O Mar - y of wan - d'rings, and Moth - er of God,
3. In si - lence of won - der, in break - ing of light,
4. O Mar - y of a - ges, O Mar - y of love,

Give a moth - er's sweet bless - ing on this road that we share.
May we walk on the path that the faith - ful have trod.
May we rise to God's will as a bird takes to flight.
May we soar to your wis - dom on the wings of a dove.

May all of our jour - neys be blessed by your grace,
May the cross of your Son keep us true to the way,
May the voice of our Mak - er be com - pass and guide.
May all of your chil - dren a - bide in your gaze,

As when you said "Yes" to the an - gel's em - brace.
As pil - grims and ser - vants an - nounc - ing the day.
Till safe in God's king - dom we soon shall a - bide.
Till la - bors are done and ful - filled are our days.

Text: Steven C. Warner, b.1954, © 1993, 2001, World Library Publications
Tune: SIOBHAN NI LAOGHAIRE, 11 12 11 11; Gaelic folk hymn; arr. by Steven C. Warner, b.1954, © 1993, 2001, World Library Publications

782 My Soul Proclaims

Refrain

My soul pro-claims the great-ness of God, re-joic-ing in God, my Sav-ior, the Ho-ly One has raised me up, I live in God's love and fa-vor.

Verses

Cantor: ... *All:*

1. The Might-y One works great things in me:
2. The arm of God is jus-tice and might:
3. God top-ples ev-'ry ty-rant and crown:
4. With won-drous things, God's ban-quet is spread:

My

soul re-joic-es in God.

Cantor:

All faith-ful ser-vants God's
God puts the proud and the
The low-ly raised and the
The rich go hun-gry, the

All:

mer-cy shall see:
schem-ing to flight: My soul re-joic-es,
might-y brought down:
hun-gry are fed:

D.C.

sings and re-joic-es, glad-ly re-joic-es in God.

Text: *Magnificat*, Luke 1:46-55; Marty Haugen, b.1950
Tune: Marty Haugen, b.1950
© 2001, GIA Publications, Inc.

Immaculate Mary 783

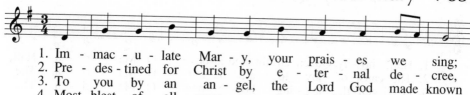

1. Im - mac - u - late Mar - y, your prais - es we sing;
2. Pre - des - tined for Christ by e - ter - nal de - cree,
3. To you by an an - gel, the Lord God made known
4. Most blest of all wom - en, you heard and be - lieved,
5. The an - gels re - joiced when you brought forth God's Son;

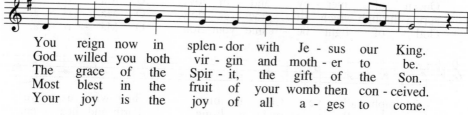

You reign now in splen - dor with Je - sus our King.
God willed you both vir - gin and moth - er to be.
The grace of the Spir - it, the gift of the Son.
Most blest in the fruit of your womb then con - ceived.
Your joy is the joy of all a - ges to come.

A - ve, A - ve, A - ve, Ma - ri - a.

A - ve, A - ve, Ma - ri - a.

6. Your child is the Savior, all hope lies in him:
   He gives us new life and redeems us from sin.

7. In glory for ever now close to your Son,
   All ages will praise you for all God has done.

Text: St. 1, Jeremiah Cummings, 1814-1866, alt.; St. 2-7, Brian Foley, b.1919, © 1971, Faber Music Ltd.
Tune: LOURDES HYMN, 11 11 with refrain; *Grenoble*, 1882

784 Hail, Holy Queen Enthroned Above

1. Hail, ho - ly Queen en - throned a - bove, O Ma - ri - a. Hail,
2. The cause of joy to all be - low, O Ma - ri - a. The
3. O gen - tle, lov - ing, ho - ly one, O Ma - ri - a. The

Queen of mer - cy and of love, O Ma - ri - a.
spring through which all grac - es flow, O Ma - ri - a.
God of light be - came your Son, O Ma - ri - a.

Tri - umph, all ye Cher - u - bim, Sing with us, ye
An - gels, all your prais - es bring, Earth and heav - en,
Tri - umph, all ye Cher - u - bim, Sing with us, ye

Ser - a - phim, Heav'n and earth re - sound the hymn:
with us sing, All cre - a - tion ech - o - ing:
Ser - a - phim, Heav'n and earth re - sound the hymn:

Sal - ve, Sal - ve, Sal - ve, Re - gi - na.

Text: *Salve, Regina, mater misericordia;* c.1080; tr. *Roman Hymnal,* 1884; st. 2-3 adapt. by M. Owen Lee, CSB, b.1930
Tune: SALVE REGINA COELITUM, 8 4 8 4 777 4 5; *Choralmelodien zum Heiligen Gesänge,* 1808; harm. by Healey Willan, 1880-1968, © Willis
Music Co.

785 Lift High the Cross

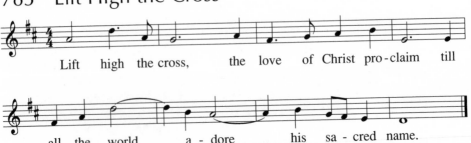

Lift high the cross, the love of Christ pro - claim till

all the world a - dore his sa - cred name.

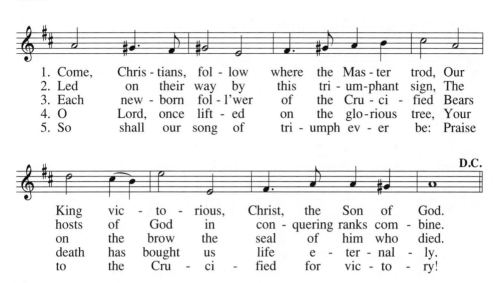

1. Come, Chris-tians, fol-low where the Mas-ter trod, Our
2. Led on their way by this tri-um-phant sign, The
3. Each new-born fol-l'wer of the Cru-ci-fied Bears
4. O Lord, once lift-ed on the glo-rious tree, Your
5. So shall our song of tri-umph ev-er be: Praise

D.C.

King vic-to-rious, Christ, the Son of God.
hosts of God in con-quering ranks com-bine.
on the brow the seal of him who died.
death has bought us life e-ter-nal-ly.
to the Cru-ci-fied for vic-to-ry!

Text: 1 Corinthians 1:18; George W. Kitchin, 1827-1912, and Michael R. Newbolt, 1874-1956, alt.
Tune: CRUCIFER, 10 10 with refrain; Sydney H. Nicholson, 1875-1947
© 1974, Hope Publishing Co.

For All the Saints Who've Shown Your Love   786

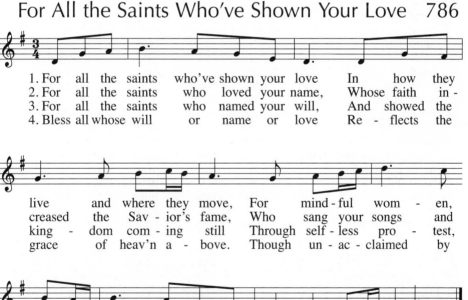

1. For all the saints who've shown your love In how they
2. For all the saints who loved your name, Whose faith in-
3. For all the saints who named your will, And showed the
4. Bless all whose will or name or love Re-flects the

live and where they move, For mind-ful wom-en,
creased the Sav-ior's fame, Who sang your songs and
king-dom com-ing still Through self-less pro-test,
grace of heav'n a-bove. Though un-ac-claimed by

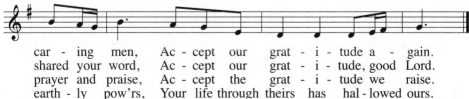

car-ing men, Ac-cept our grat-i-tude a-gain.
shared your word, Ac-cept our grat-i-tude, good Lord.
prayer and praise, Ac-cept the grat-i-tude we raise.
earth-ly pow'rs, Your life through theirs has hal-lowed ours.

Text: John L. Bell, b.1949, © 1996, The Iona Community, GIA Publications, Inc., agent
Tune: O WALY, WALY, LM; arr. by John L. Bell, b.1949, © 1989, The Iona Community, GIA Publications, Inc., agent

787 Litany of the Saints

Cantor: / *Assembly:*

Lord, have mer - cy. Lord, have mer - cy.
Christ, have mer - cy. Christ, have mer - cy.

Cantor: / *Assembly:*

Lord, have mer - cy. Lord, have mer - cy.

Cantor: / *Assembly:*

Holy Mary, Mother of	God,	pray	for	us.
Saint	Mich - ael,	pray	for	us.
Holy angels of	God,	pray	for	us.
Saint John the	Bap - tist,	pray	for	us.
Saint	Jo - seph,	pray	for	us.
Saint Peter and Saint	Paul,	pray	for	us.
Saint	An - drew,	pray	for	us.
Saint	John,	pray	for	us.
Saint Mary	Mag - dalene,	pray	for	us.
Saint	Ste - phen,	pray	for	us.
Saint Ig -	na - tius,	pray	for	us.
Saint	Law - rence,	pray	for	us.
Saint Perpetua and Saint Fe - lic -	ity,	pray	for	us.
Saint	Ag - nes,	pray	for	us.
Saint	Gre - gory,	pray	for	us.
Saint Au -	gus - tine,	pray	for	us.
Saint Atha -	na - sius,	pray	for	us.
Saint	Ba - sil,	pray	for	us.
Saint	Mar - tin,	pray	for	us.
Saint	Ben - edict,	pray	for	us.
Saint Francis and Saint	Dom - inic,	pray	for	us.
Saint Francis	Xa - vier,	pray	for	us.
Saint John Vi -	an - ney,	pray	for	us.
Saint	Cath - erine,	pray	for	us.
Saint Te -	re - sa,	pray	for	us.
All holy men and	wom - en,	pray	for	us.

Cantor: / *Assembly:*

Lord, be mer - ci - ful,	Lord, save your peo - ple.
From all e - vil,	Lord, save your peo - ple.
From ev - 'ry sin,	Lord, save your peo - ple.
From ev - er - last - ing death,	Lord, save your peo - ple.

Cantor: / *Assembly:*

By your com - ing as man,	Lord, save your peo - ple.
By your death and ris - ing to new life,	Lord, save your peo - ple.
By your gift of the Ho - ly Spir - it,	Lord, save your peo - ple.

Text: *Litany of the Saints, Roman Missal*
Music: *Litany of the Saints, Roman Missal*

Litany of the Saints 788

Repeat each invocation immediately after the priest or cantor:

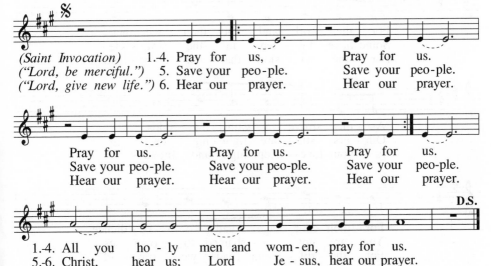

Text: *Litany of the Saints,* © 1972, ICEL
Tune: John D. Becker, b.1953, © 1987. Published by OCP Publications.

789 For the Faithful Who Have Answered

Verses

1. For the faith-ful who have an-swered
2. Man-y eyes have glimpsed the prom-ise.
3. For this cloud of faith-ful wit-ness,

When they heard your call to serve,
Man-y hearts have yearned to see.
For the com-mon life we share,

For the man-y ways you led them
Man-y ears have heard you call-ing
For the work of peace and jus-tice,

Test-ing will and stretch-ing nerve,
Us to great-er lib-er-ty.
For the gos-pel that we bear,

For their work and for their wit-ness
Some have fal-len in the strug-gle.
For the vi-sion that our home-land

As they strove a-gainst the odds,
Oth-ers still are fight-ing on.
Is your love— deep, high and broad—

For their cour-age and o-be-dience
You are not a-shamed to own us.
For the dif-f'rent roads we trav-el

We give thanks and praise, O God.
We give thanks and praise, O God.
We give thanks and praise, O God.

Refrain

We give you thanks, we give you thanks

for the gos-pel we bear, the faith we share. We

give you thanks, we give you thanks. With

faith and hope and love, we give you thanks.

Text: Sylvia Dunstan, 1955-1993, © 1991, GIA Publications, Inc.
Tune: WE GIVE YOU THANKS, 8 7 8 7 D with refrain; David Haas, b.1957, © 1998, GIA Publications, Inc.

790 Ye Watchers and Ye Holy Ones

1. Ye watch - ers and ye ho - ly ones,
2. O high - er than the cher - u - bim,
3. Re - spond, ye souls in end - less rest,
4. O friends, in glad - ness let us sing,

Bright ser - aphs, cher - u - bim, and thrones,
More glo - rious than the ser - a - phim,
Ye pa - tri - archs and proph - ets blest,
Su - per - nal an - thems ech - o - ing,

Raise the glad strain,
Lead their prais - es,
Al - le - lu - ia, Al - le - lu - ia!
Al - le - lu - ia,

Cry out, do - min - ions, prince - doms, powers,
O bear - er of the e - ter - nal Word,
Ye ho - ly Twelve, ye mar - tyrs strong,
To God the Fa - ther, God the Son,

Vir - tues, arch - an - gels, an - gels' choirs,
Most gra - cious, mag - ni - fy the Lord,
All saints tri - um - phant, raise in song,
And God the Spir - it, Three in One,

Al - le - lu - ia, Al - le - lu - ia, Al - le - lu - ia,

Al - le - lu - ia, Al - le - lu - ia!

Text: Athelstan A. Riley, 1858-1945, © Oxford University Press
Tune: LASST UNS ERFREUEN, LM with alleluias; *Geistliche Kirchengasänge*, Cologne, 1623; harm. by Ralph Vaughan Williams, 1872-1958,
© Oxford University Press

For All the Saints 791

1. For all the saints who from their la - bors rest, All
2. You were their rock, their for - tress and their might;
3. O may your sol - diers, faith - ful, true and bold,
4. O blest com - mun - ion, fam - i - ly di - vine!
5. And when the strife is fierce, the war - fare long,
6. The gold - en eve - ning bright - ens in the west;

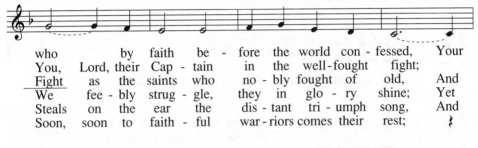

who by faith be - fore the world con - fessed, Your
You, Lord, their Cap - tain in the well - fought fight;
Fight as the saints who no - bly fought of old, And
We fee - bly strug - gle, they in glo - ry shine; Yet
Steals on the ear the dis - tant tri - umph song, And
Soon, soon to faith - ful war - riors comes their rest;

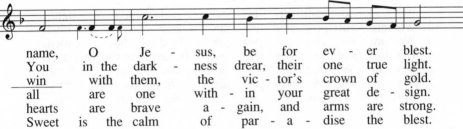

name, O Je - sus, be for ev - er blest.
You in the dark - ness drear, their one true light.
win with them, the vic - tor's crown of gold.
all are one with - in your great de - sign.
hearts are brave a - gain, and arms are strong.
Sweet is the calm of par - a - dise the blest.

Al - le - lu - ia! Al - le - lu - ia!

7. But then there breaks a yet more glorious day:
The saints triumphant rise in bright array;
The King of glory passes on his way.
Alleluia! Alleluia!

8. From earth's wide bounds, from ocean's farthest coast,
Through gates of pearl streams in the countless host,
Singing to Father, Son, and Holy Ghost:
Alleluia! Alleluia!

Text: William W. How, 1823-1897
Tune: SINE NOMINE, 10 10 10 with alleluias; Ralph Vaughan Williams, 1872-1958, © Oxford University Press

792　For the Life of the World

Refrain

For the life of the world, we will stand to - geth - er, we will serve the Lord. For the life of the world, we will cry for jus - tice, and ev - 'ry heart will sing that Je - sus Christ is Lord!

Verses

1. We walk to - geth - er to be chil - dren of light,
2. We are em - pow - ered by the love of Christ,
3. We are the cho - sen peo - ple God has called,
4. The lost and bro - ken will be healed from their shame,
1. Nos da la fuer - za y el a - mor de Dios.
2. Hoy lu - cha - re - mos por jus - ti - cia, Se - ñor.
3. Glo - ri - fi - que - mos al Se - ñor Je - sús.

our God calls each of us by name!
whose life has con - quered sin and death!
the life we live is not our own!
the poor will see the face of God!
Su vi - da qui - ta nues - tro mal.
Te ser - vi - re - mos y sin fin.
Can - tan - do le - van - té - mo - nos,

Christ moves with - in us, we are God's work of art!
There is no oth - er name but Je - sus the Lord!
If we will die with Christ, then we will be free!
Sent by the Spir - it, we are called to serve!
No que - da na - die me - nos el Se - ñor.
Ten - dre - mos paz sin ham - bre ni do - lor.
Por - que él vie - ne ¡a - le - gré - mo - nos!

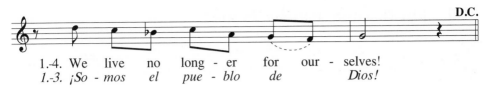

D.C.

1.-4. We live no long - er for our - selves!
1.-3. ¡So - mos el pue - blo de Dios!

Text: David Haas, b.1957; Spanish verses by Jeffrey Judge
Tune: David Haas, b.1957; acc. by Jeanne Cotter, b.1964
© 1993, GIA Publications, Inc.

Wade in the Water 793

Refrain

Wade in the wa - ter, wade in the wa - ter, chil - dren,

wade in the wa - ter, God's a gon-na trou - ble the wa - ter.

Verses

Cantor:

1. See that host all dressed in white,
2. See that band all dressed in red,
3. Look o - ver yon - der, what do I see?
4. If you don't be - lieve I've been re - deemed,

All:

God's a gon - na trou - ble the wa - ter;

Cantor:

The lead - er looks like the Is - ra - el - ite,
Looks like the band that Mo - ses led,
The Ho - ly Ghost a com - in' on me,
Just fol - low me down to Jor - dan's stream,

All:

D.C.

God's a gon - na trou - ble the wa - ter.

Text: African-American spiritual
Tune: African-American spiritual; harm. by Diana Kodner, b.1957, © 1994, GIA Publications, Inc.

794 Who Calls You by Name

Refrain

Cantor: Bless-ed be God! O Bless-ed be God! *All:* Bless-ed be God! O

Cantor: Bless-ed be God! Who calls you by name! *All:* Who calls you by name!

Cantor: Ho-ly and cho - sen one! *All:* Ho-ly and cho - sen one!

Verses

1. Come, and re - turn to the Lord!
2. Seek to be chil - dren of light!
3. Sing now with all your heart!

Live by the Word of God, who
Live in the love of God, who
Praise and glo - ry be to our God, who

D.C.

calls you by name! Who calls you by name!
calls you by name! Who calls you by name!
calls you by name! Who calls you by name!

Text: David Haas, b.1957
Tune: David Haas, b.1957
© 1988, GIA Publications, Inc.

795 Christ Will Be Your Strength

Christ will be your strength! Learn to know and fol-low him!

Text: David Haas, b.1957
Tune: David Haas, b.1957
© 1988, GIA Publications, Inc.

There Is One Lord 796

Ostinato Refrain

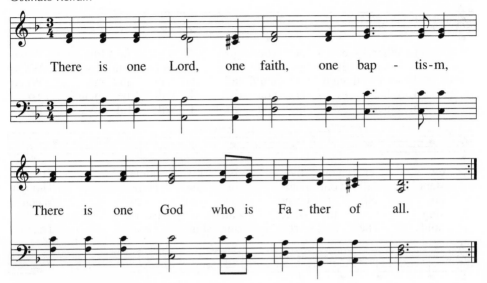

There is one Lord, one faith, one bap - tis-m,

There is one God who is Fa - ther of all.

Text: Ephesians 4; Taizé Community, 1984
Tune: Jacques Berthier, 1923-1994
© 1984, Les Presses de Taizé, GIA Publications, Inc., agent

Baptized in Water 797

1. Bap - tized in wa - ter, Sealed by the Spir - it, Cleansed by the
2. Bap - tized in wa - ter, Sealed by the Spir - it, Dead in the
3. Bap - tized in wa - ter, Sealed by the Spir - it, Marked with the

blood of Christ our King: Heirs of sal - va - tion, Trust - ing his
tomb with Christ our King: One with his ris - ing, Freed and for-
sign of Christ our King: Born of one Fa - ther, We are his

prom - ise, Faith - ful - ly now God's praise we sing.
giv - en, Thank-ful - ly now God's praise we sing.
chil - dren, Joy - ful - ly now God's praise we sing.

Text: Michael Saward, b.1932, © 1982, Jubilate Hymns, Ltd. (admin. by Hope Publishing Co.)
Tune: BUNESSAN, 5 5 8 D; Gaelic melody; acc. by Marty Haugen, b.1950, © 1987, GIA Publications, Inc.

798 Covenant Hymn

1. Wher - ev - er you go, I will fol - low, Wher-
2. What - ev - er you dream, I am with you, When
3. And though you should fall, you will find me, When
4. Wher - ev - er you die, I will be there To
5. Wher - ev - er you go, I will fol - low, Be -

ev - er you live is my home. Though
stars call your name in the night. Though
no oth - er friend can you claim, When
sing you to sleep with a psalm, To
hold! The ho - ri - zon shines clear. The

days be of bless - ing or sor - row, Though
shad - ows and mist cloud the fu - ture, To -
foes beat you down or be - tray you And
soothe you with tales of our jour - ney, Your
pos - si - ble gleams like a cit - y: To -

house be of can - vas or stone, Though
geth - er we bear there a light. Like
oth - ers de - sert you in shame. When
fears and your doubts I will calm. We'll
geth - er we've noth - ing to fear. So

E - den be lost to the past, Though
A - bram and Sar - ah we stand, With
home and dreams aren't e - nough, And
live when jour - neys are done For -
speak with words bold and true The

moun - tains be - fore us be vast, Wher -
on - ly a prom - ise in hand. But
you run a - way from my love, I'll
ev - er in mem - 'ry as one. And
mes - sage my heart speaks to you. You

ev - er you go, I am with you, I
lead where you dream: I will fol - low. To
raise you from where you have fall - en. ↗
we will be bur - ied to - geth - er, And
won't be a - lone, I have prom - ised. Wher -

nev - er will leave you a - lone.
dream with you is my de - light.
Faith - ful to you is my name.
wak - en to greet a new dawn.
ev - er you go, I am here.

Text: Ruth 1:16; Rory Cooney, b.1952
Tune: Gary Daigle, b.1957
© 1993, GIA Publications, Inc.

I Come with Joy 799

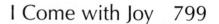
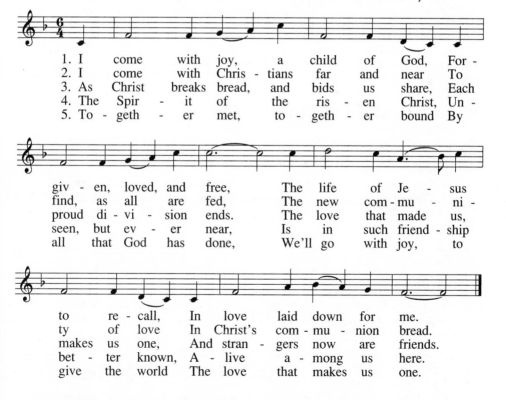

1. I come with joy, a child of God, For -
2. I come with Chris - tians far and near To
3. As Christ breaks bread, and bids us share, Each
4. The Spir - it of the ris - en Christ, Un -
5. To - geth - er met, to - geth - er bound By

giv - en, loved, and free, The life of Je - sus
find, as all are fed, The new com - mu - ni -
proud di - vi - sion ends. The love that made us,
seen, but ev - er near, Is in such friend - ship
all that God has done, We'll go with joy, to

to re - call, In love laid down for me.
ty of love In Christ's com - mu - nion bread.
makes us one, And stran - gers now are friends.
bet - ter known, A - live a - mong us here.
give the world The love that makes us one.

Text: Brian Wren, b.1936, © 1971, 1995, Hope Publishing Co.
Tune: LAND OF REST, CM; American; harm. by Annabel M. Buchanan, 1888-1983, © 1938, 1966, J. Fisher and Bro.

800 O Breathe on Me, O Breath of God

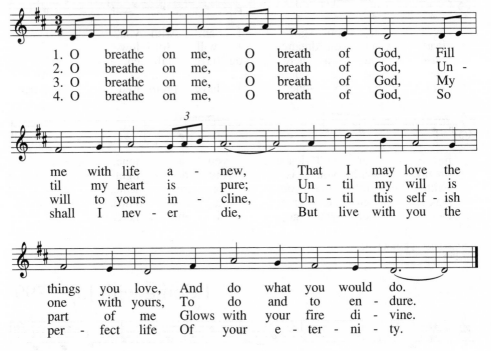

1. O breathe on me, O breath of God, Fill me with life a - new, That I may love the things you love, And do what you would do.
2. O breathe on me, O breath of God, Un - til my heart is pure; Un - til my will is one with yours, To do and to en - dure.
3. O breathe on me, O breath of God, My will to yours in - cline, Un - til this self - ish part of me Glows with your fire di - vine.
4. O breathe on me, O breath of God, So shall I nev - er die, But live with you the per - fect life Of your e - ter - ni - ty.

Text: Edwin Hatch, 1835-1889
Tune: ST. COLUMBA, CM; Gaelic; harm. by A. Gregory Murray, OSB, 1905-1992, © Downside Abbey

801 Christ Be in Your Senses

1. Christ be in your sens - es, marked with sa - cred sign.
2. Christ be in your vi - sion, guard you day and night;
3. Christ be in your breath - ing, con - stant - ly im - part

In the In - car - na - tion, flesh be - came di - vine.
Keep your feet from stum - bling, shine God's ho - ly light.
Grace to ev - 'ry move - ment, peace with - in your heart.

Christ be in your hear - ing, tune you to re - joice;
Christ be in your speak - ing, train your ev - 'ry word.
Christ be in your sens - es, marked with sa - cred sign.

In each shout or whis-per, hear God's call-ing voice.
In your dai-ly wit-ness let God's truth be heard.
In the Spir-it's pres-ence, flesh be-comes di-vine.

Text: Mary Louise Bringle, b.1953
Tune: APPALACHIAN FALL, 11 11 11 11; William P. Rowan, b.1951
© 2002, GIA Publications, Inc.

Sweet Refreshment 802

Refrain

Cantor:
All:
Cantor:

Come to the wa-ter. Come to the wa-ter. Drink of it free-ly.

All:
Cantor:
All:

Drink of it free-ly. Taste God's own Spir-it. Taste God's own

Cantor:
All:

Spir-it. Sweet re-fresh-ment. Sweet re-fresh-ment.

Verses

Cantor:

1. At the dawn of cre-a-tion, your
2. When your peo-ple were cap-tive, you
3. In the wa-ters of Jor-dan, your
4. Liv-ing wa-ters, e-ter-nal,

Spir-it, O God, moved on the wa-ters. You
led them, O God, led them from bond-age. You
Son was bap-tized; with Spir-it a-noint-ed, that
quench ev-'ry thirst, cleanse ev-'ry soul.

D.C.

breathed and the wa-ters were life.
led them through wa-ters to life.
we might be raised to new life.
You are the foun-tain of life.

Text: Based on *Blessing of Water*, Easter Vigil; adapt. by Bob Moore, b.1962
Tune: Bob Moore, b.1962
© 1999, GIA Publications, Inc.

803 Bread of Life from Heaven / Pan de Vida Eterna

Refrain

Bread of life from heav-en, your blood and bod - y giv-en, we
Pan de vi - da e - ter - na, nos das tu cuer - po y san-gre.

eat this bread and drink this cup un - til you come a - gain.
Has - ta que vuel - vas tú, Se - ñor, co - me - mos en tu a -mor.

Verses

1. Break now the bread of Christ's sac - ri - fice; Giv - ing
2. Seek not the food that will pass a - way; Set your
3. Love as the One who, in love for you, Gave him-
4. Take in the light that will nev - er dim, Taste the
5. Dwell in the One who now dwells in you; Make your
6. Drink of this cup and de - clare his death; Eat this
7. *Ven y com -par - te el di - vi - no pan;* *De - mos*
8. *Es - te mis - te - rio es el máx - i - mo* *sa - cri -*
9. *Ven a la me - sa de com - pa -sión,* *re - cor -*
10. *Hoy que co - me - mos del pan de a -mor* *so - mos*
11. *Ce - na que nos re - pre - sen - ta hoy la vi - da,*

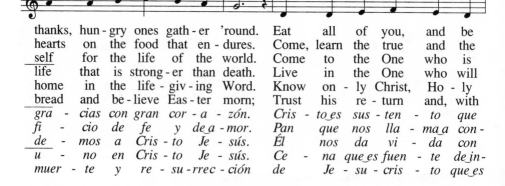

thanks, hun - gry ones gath - er 'round. Eat all of you, and be
hearts on the food that en - dures. Come, learn the true and the
self for the life of the world. Come to the One who is
life that is strong - er than death. Live in the One who will
home in the life - giv - ing Word. Know on - ly Christ, Ho - ly
bread and be - lieve Eas - ter morn; Trust his re - turn and, with
grá - cias con gran cor - a - zón. Cris - to es sus - ten - to que
fi - cio de fe y de a -mor. Pan que nos lla - ma a con -
de - mos a Cris - to Je - sús. Él nos da vi - da con
u - no en Cris - to Je - sús. Ce - na que es fuen - te de in-
muer - te y re - su -rrec - ción de Je - su - cris - to que es

D.S.

sat - is - fied;	in Christ's pres - ence the loaves	will	a - bound.
liv - ing way,	that the full - ness of life	may be	yours.
food for you,	that your hun - ger and thirst	be no	more.
come and then	raise you up at the last	with the	blest.
One of God,	and be - lieve in the truth	you have	heard.
ev - 'ry breath,	praise the One in whom you	are re	- born.
u - ni - rá	a los miem - bros de ca -	da na	- ción.
me - mo - rar	y_a se - guir a Je - sús	Sal - va	- dor.
ple - ni - tud;	Nos pro - te - ge_y nos guí -	a_en su	luz.
spi - ra - ción	pa - ra ser en el mun -	do la	luz.
nues - tro Dios	quien nos lla - ma_y nos da	sal - va	- ción.

Text: Based on John 6; adapt. by Susan R. Briehl, b.1952; Spanish by Jaime Cortez, b.1963
Tune: Argentine folk melody; adapt. and verses by Marty Haugen, b.1950
© 2001, GIA Publications, Inc.

Jesus, Wine of Peace 804

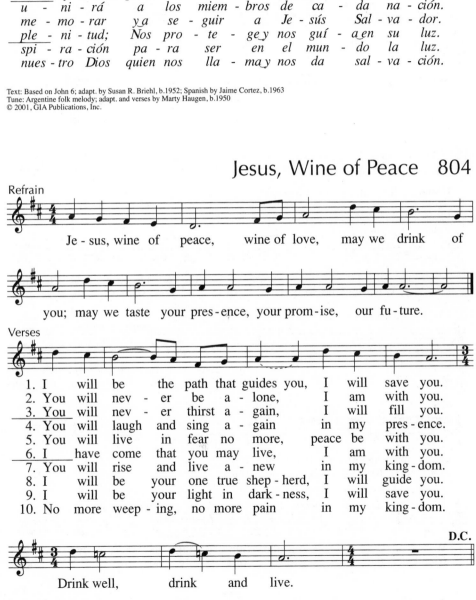

Refrain

Je - sus, wine of peace, wine of love, may we drink of

you; may we taste your pres - ence, your prom - ise, our fu - ture.

Verses

1. I	will be	the path that guides you,	I will	save you.
2. You will	nev - er	be a - lone,	I am	with you.
3. You will	nev - er	thirst a - gain,	I will	fill you.
4. You will	laugh and	sing a - gain	in my	pres - ence.
5. You will	live in	fear no more,	peace be	with you.
6. I have	come that	you may live,	I am	with you.
7. You will	rise and	live a - new	in my	king - dom.
8. I	will be	your one true shep - herd,	I will	guide you.
9. I	will be	your light in dark - ness,	I will	save you.
10. No	more weep - ing,	no more pain	in my	king - dom.

D.C.

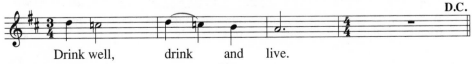

Drink well, drink and live.

Text: David Haas, b.1957
Tune: David Haas, b.1957
© 1985, GIA Publications, Inc.

805 With This Bread

Refrain

With this bread we will walk with each oth - er,

with this cup we will fol-low the Lord. Com - pas - sion,

love o - ver - flow-ing, God's love ev - er know-ing, we

share it in our song.

Verses 1, 2

1. To of - fer as - sis - tance when oth - ers are blind to the need
2. Wash-ing the wounds of di - vi - sion, we seek to ease pain

to give lov - ing care to each oth -
Shar - ing the bur - den of oth -

er is plant - ing God's seed.
ers, like God's gen - tle rain.
Be -

Walk - ing the prom - ise and fall - ing on mer - cy, be -
friend-ing the one who is lone - ly and lost, be -

D.C

liev - ing we'll walk with you.
liev - ing we'll walk with you.

Verse 3

3. We hold the key to our fu - ture as we share our souls,

nur-tur-ing love in a time when com-pas-sion un-folds.

Danc-ing in joy,

D.C.

shar-ing in won - der the prayer that we sing to you.

Text: Kate Cuddy, b.1953
Tune: Kate Cuddy, b.1953
© 2001, GIA Publications, Inc.

Eat This Bread 806

Refrain

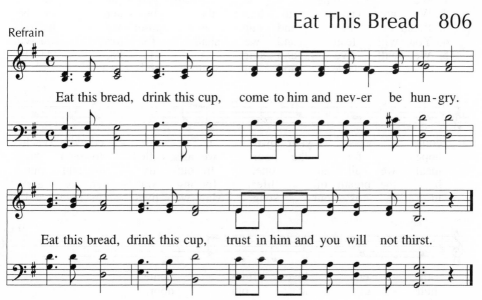

Eat this bread, drink this cup, come to him and nev-er be hun-gry.

Eat this bread, drink this cup, trust in him and you will not thirst.

Text: John 6; adapt. by Robert J. Batastini, b.1942, and the Taizé Community
Tune: Jacques Berthier, 1923-1994
© 1984, Les Presses de Taizé, GIA Publications, Inc., agent

807 Song of the Body of Christ / Canción del Cuerpo de Cristo

Refrain

We come to share our sto-ry, we
Hoy ve - ni - mos a con - tar nues-tra_his - to - ria, com - par-

come to break the bread, We come to
tien - do_el pan ce - les - tial. Hoy ve - ni - mos jun - tos

know our ris - ing from the dead.
a ce - le - brar tu mis - te - rio pas - cual.

Verses

1. We come as your peo - ple, we
2. We are called to heal the bro - ken, to be
3. Bread of life and cup of prom - ise, in this
4. You will lead and we shall fol - low, you will
5. We will live and sing: "A - lo - ha," "Al - le -
   (live and sing your prais - es,)

come as your own, u - nit - ed with each
hope for the poor, we are called to feed the
meal we all are one. In our dy - ing and our
be the breath of life; liv - ing wa - ter, we are
lu - ia" is our song. May we live in love and

D.C.

oth - er, love finds a home.
hun - gry at our door.
ris - ing, may your king - dom come.
thirst - ing for your light.
peace our whole life long.

Verses

1. Hoy ve - ni - mos por - que so - mos tu pue - blo, re - na -
2. A sa - nar al en - fer - mo nos lla - mas, al an -
3. Pan de vi - da y san - gre de la_a - lian - za, haz - nos
4. Nos guia - rás y te se - gui - re - mos. Nues - tro_a -
5. Vi - vi - re - mos can - tan - do "A - lo - ja." "A - le -

ci - dos por tu per - dón, re - u - ni - dos
sio - so, tu_es - pe - ran - za tra - er, y_al ham - brien - to,
u - no_en es - ta co - mu - nión. Que tu rei - no
lien - to vi - tal tú se - rás. Nues - tra luz, en el
lu - ya" es nues - tra can - ción. Que vi - va - mos por

D.C.

en tu_a - mor, y de un co - ra - zón.
nues - tro_a - li - men - to o - fre - cer.
ven - ga en nues - tra trans - for - ma - ción.
dí - a y_en la no - che bri - lla - rás.
siem - pre en paz y fra - ter - na u - nión.

Text: David Haas, b.1957, Spanish translation by Donna Peña, b.1955, and Ronald F. Krisman, b.1946
Tune: NO KE ANO' AHI AHI, Irregular, Hawaiian traditional, arr. by David Haas, b.1957
© 1989, GIA Publications, Inc.

808 Let Us Be Bread

Refrain

Let us be bread, blessed by the Lord, bro-ken and shared,

life for the world. Let us be wine, love free-ly poured.

Let us be one in the Lord.

Verse 1

1. I am the bread of life, bro-ken for all.

Eat now and hun-ger no more.

D.C.

Verse 2

2. You are my friends if you keep my com-mands,

no long - er ser - vants but friends.

D.C.

Verse 3

3. See how my peo-ple have noth-ing to eat.

Give them the bread that is you.

D.C.

Verse 4

4. As God has loved me so I have loved you.

D.C.

Go and live on in my love.

Text: Thomas J. Porter, b.1958
Tune: Thomas J. Porter, b.1958
© 1990, GIA Publications, Inc.

I Received the Living God 809

Refrain

I re-ceived the liv-ing God, and my heart is full of

joy. I re-ceived the liv-ing God, and my heart is full of joy.

Verses

1. Je - sus said: "I am the Bread Knead - ed
2. Je - sus said: "I am the Vine, And my
3. Je - sus said: "I am the Way; And my
4. Je - sus said: "I am the Truth; If you
5. Je - sus said: "I am the Life Far from

long to give you life; You who will par-take of
branch-es you shall be; Come and drink the sav - ing
Fa - ther longs for you; So I come to bring you
fol - low close to me, You will know me in your
whom no thing can grow, But re - ceive this liv - ing

D.C.

me Need not ev - er fear to die."
cup, Till the King - dom you shall see."
home To be one with him a - new."
heart, And my word shall make you free."
bread, And my Spir - it you shall know."

Text: Vss. 1, 3–5, Bernard Geoffroy, tr. anonymous; verse 2, Alan J. Hommerding, b.1956, © 1994, World Library Publications
Tune: LIVING GOD, 7 7 7 7 with refrain; Dom Clément Jacob, adapt.; harm. by Richard Proulx, b.1937, © 1986, GIA Publications, Inc.

810　Come to the Banquet

Refrain

Come to the ban - quet, come to the feast. Eat the bread of

life! Share in the sing - ing, share in the joy.

To verses | *Last time*

Drink the cup of love! love! Share the joy!

Verses

1. Draw near and take the bod - y of the
2. Sal - va - tion's giv - er, Christ, the on - ly
3. Come for - ward then with faith - ful hearts sin -
4. With heav'n - ly bread makes those who hun - ger

Lord. and drink the ho - ly blood for you out - poured.
Son, who by his cross and blood the vic - t'ry won.
cere, and take the prom - ise of sal - va - tion here.
whole, gives liv - ing wa - ters to the thirst - ing soul.

Saved by his bod - y, hal - lowed by his blood, with
Gave up his life for great - est and for least, Him
The Lord, who faith - ful ser - vants loves and shields, to
Be - fore your pres - ence, Lord, all peo - ple bow. In

D.C

souls re - freshed, we give our thanks to God.
self the vic - tim and him - self the priest.
all be - liev - ers life e - ter - nal yields.
this your feast of love be with us now.

Text: *Sancti, venite, corpus sumite,* 7th C., tr. John Mason Neale, 1818-1866, alt.; refrain, James J. Chepponis, b.1956, © 2000, GIA Publications, Inc.
Tune: James J. Chepponis, b.1956, © 2000, GIA Publications, Inc.

Pan de Vida   811

Refrain

*Pan de Vi - da, cuer-po del Se - ñor,

cup of bless - ing, blood of Christ the Lord.

At this ta - ble the last shall be first, **po -

der es ser - vir, por-que Dios es a - mor.

Verses

1. We are the dwell-ing of God,
***2. Us - te - des me lla - man "Se - ñor," me in-
3. There is no Jew or Greek,

fra - gile and wound-ed and weak. We are the
cli - no_a la - var - les los pies: Ha - gan lo
there is no slave or free; there is no

bod - y of Christ, called to be the com -
mis - mo, hu - mil - des, sir - vién - do - se
wom-an or man; on - ly heirs of the

D.C.

pas - sion of God.
u - nos a o - tros.
prom - ise of God.

*Bread of Life, body of the Lord,   **power is for service, because God is Love.
***You call me "Lord," and I bow to wash your feet:
you must do the same, humbly serving each other.

Text: John 13:1-15, Galatians 3:28-29; Bob Hurd, b.1950, and Pia Moriarty, b.1948
Tune: Bob Hurd, b.1950; acc. by Craig S. Kingsbury, b.1952
© 1988, Bob Hurd and Pia Moriarty. Published by OCP Publications.

812 Take and Eat

Refrain

Take and eat; take and eat: this is my bod - y

giv-en up for you. Take and drink; take and drink:

this is my blood giv - en up for you.

Verses

1. I am the Word that spoke and light was made;
2. I am the way that leads the ex - ile home;
3. I am the Lamb that takes a - way your sin;
4. I am the cor - ner - stone that God has laid;
5. I am the light that came in - to the world;
6. I am the first and last, the Liv - ing One;

I am the seed that died to be re - born;
I am the truth that sets the cap - tive free;
I am the gate that guards you night and day;
A cho - sen stone and pre - cious in his eyes;
I am the light that dark - ness can - not hide;
I am the Lord who died that you might live;

I am the bread that comes from heav'n a - bove;
I am the life that rais - es up the dead;
You are my flock: you know the shep-herd's voice;
You are God's dwell - ing place, on me you rest;
I am the morn - ing star that nev - er sets;
I am the bride-groom, this my wed - ding song;

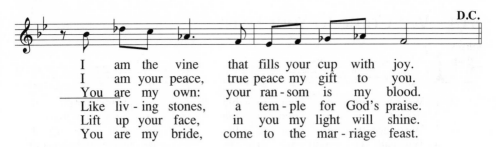

I am the vine that fills your cup with joy.
I am your peace, true peace my gift to you.
You are my own: your ran - som is my blood.
Like liv - ing stones, a tem - ple for God's praise.
Lift up your face, in you my light will shine.
You are my bride, come to the mar - riage feast.

D.C.

Text: Verse text, James Quinn, SJ, b.1919, © 1989. Used by permission of Selah Publishing Co., Inc.; refrain text, Michael Joncas, b.1951, © 1989, GIA Publications, Inc.
Tune: Michael Joncas, b.1951, © 1989, GIA Publications, Inc.

One Bread, One Body 813

Refrain

One bread, one bod-y, one Lord of all,

one cup of bless - ing which we bless. And

we, though man-y, through-out the earth,

we are one bod - y in this one Lord.

Verses

1. Gen - tile or Jew, ser - vant or free,
2. Man - y the gifts, man - y the works,
3. Grain for the fields, scat-tered and grown,

D.C.

wom - an or man no more.
one in the Lord of all.
gath - ered to one for all.

Text: 1 Corinthians 10:16; 17, 12:4, Galatians 3:28; the *Didache* 9; John Foley, SJ, b.1939
Tune: John Foley, SJ, b.1939
© 1978, John B. Foley, SJ, and OCP Publications

814　We Come to Your Feast

Verses

Cantor or choir:

1. We place up - on your ta - ble　　　a gleam-ing cloth of
2. We place up - on your ta - ble　　　a hum - ble loaf of
3. We place up - on your ta - ble　　　a sim - ple cup of
4. We gath - er 'round your ta - ble,　　we pause with - in our

white:　　　　the weav-ing of our sto - ries,
bread:　　　　the gift of field and hill - side,
wine:　　　　the fruit of hu - man la - bor,
quest,　　　　we stand be - side our neigh-bors,

the fab - ric of our lives;　　the dreams of those be -
the grain by which we're fed;　　we come to taste the
the gift of sun and vine;　　we come to taste the
we name the stran - ger "guest."　　The feast is spread be -

fore us,　　　　the an - cient hope - ful cries,
pres - ence　　of him on whom we feed,
pres - ence　　of him we claim as Lord,
fore us;　　　　you bid us come and dine:

the prom - ise of our fu - ture:　our need - ing and our
to strength - en and con - nect us,　to chal - lenge and cor -
his dy - ing and his liv - ing,　his lead - ing and his
in bless - ing we'll un - cov - er,　in shar - ing we'll dis -

nur - ture lie here be - fore our eyes.
rect us, to love in word and deed.
giv - ing, his love in cup out - poured.
cov - er your sub - stance and your sign.

Refrain

We come to your feast, we come to your feast: the young and the old, the fright-ened, the bold, the great-est and the least. We come to your feast, we come to your feast with the fruit of our lands and the work of our hands, we come to your feast.

Text: Michael Joncas, b.1951
Tune: Michael Joncas, b.1951
© 1994, GIA Publications, Inc.

815 Joyous Cup: A Processional for the Easter Season

Verses

Cantor:

All:

1. Slaves and chil - dren, take a stand:
2. Sea, stand straight! And riv - ers, flee:
3. Trem - ble, earth, to see God's face:
4. Heav - ens, sing! O earth, in - tone:
5. Eve and A - dam, tell it plain: Al - le - lu -
6. God, our lov - er, long be - trayed
7. O hap - py fault, O need - ful sin:
8. Go pro - claim a ju - bi - lee:
9. Go pro - claim a ju - bi - lee:

Cantor:

All:

Come to milk and hon - ey land:
Moun - tains, skip like lambs to see:
Flint shall flow with wa - ter's grace:
Death and hell now wail and groan:
ia!   All was lost but more's the gain: Al - le - lu -
Pas - sion has our wed - ding made:
O Christ our sav - ior, Christ our kin:
Nei - ther rich nor poor shall be:
Now from ev - 'ry debt set free:

Refrain

ia!   Christ has died and death is dead: earth and heav - en

bold - ly wed.   Joy - ous cup and heart - y bread.

Al - le - lu - ia.

Text: Based on Psalm 114 and the Exsultet; Gabe Huck
Tune: Tony E. Alonso, b.1980
© 2004, GIA Publications, Inc.

You Satisfy the Hungry Heart 816

Refrain

You sat - is - fy the hun - gry heart With gift of fin - est wheat; Come give to us, O sav - ing Lord, The bread of life to eat.

Verses

1. As when the shep - herd calls his sheep, They
2. With joy - ful lips we sing to you Our
3. Is not the cup we bless and share The
4. The mys - t'ry of your pres - ence, Lord, No
5. You give your - self to us, O Lord; Then

know and heed his voice; So when you call your
praise and grat - i - tude, That you should count us
blood of Christ out - poured? Do not one cup, one
mor - tal tongue can tell: Whom all the world can -
self - less let us be, To serve each oth - er

D.C.

fam - 'ly, Lord, We fol - low and re - joice.
wor - thy, Lord, To share this heav'n - ly food.
loaf, de - clare Our one - ness in the Lord?
not con - tain Comes in our hearts to dwell.
in your name In truth and char - i - ty.

Text: Omer Westendorf, 1916-1998
Tune: BICENTENNIAL, CM with refrain; Robert E. Kreutz, 1922-1996
© 1977, Archdiocese of Philadelphia

817 All Who Hunger

Verses

1. All who hun-ger, gath - er glad - ly; ho - ly man - na
2. All who hun-ger, nev - er stran-gers, seek-er, be a
3. All who hun-ger, sing to - geth - er; Je - sus Christ is

is our bread. Come from wil - der - ness and wan-d'ring.
wel - come guest. Come from rest - less - ness and roam - ing.
liv - ing bread. Come from lone - li - ness and long - ing.

Here, in truth, we will be fed. You that yearn for
Here, in joy, we keep the feast. We that once were
Here, in peace, we have been led. Blest are those who

days of full-ness, all a - round us is our food.
lost and scat-tered in com - mun-ion's love have stood.
from this ta - ble live their lives in grat - i - tude.

Refrain

All:

Taste and see the grace e - ter-nal. Taste and see that God is good.

Text: Sylvia G. Dunstan, 1955-1993, © 1991, GIA Publications, Inc.
Tune: Bob Moore, b. 1962, © 1993, GIA Publications, Inc.

818 Shepherd of Souls

1. Shep - herd of souls, re - fresh and bless
2. We would not live by bread a - lone,
3. Be known to us in break - ing bread,
4. Lord, sup with us in love di - vine;

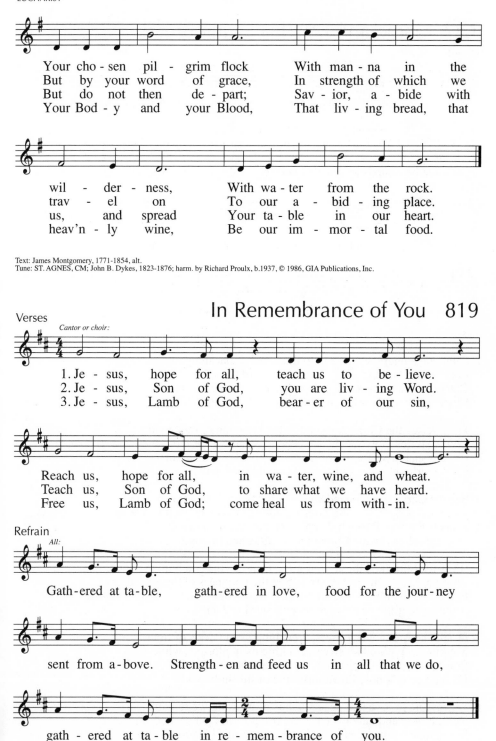

Your cho - sen pil - grim flock With man - na in the
But by your word of grace, In strength of which we
But do not then de - part; Sav - ior, a - bide with
Your Bod - y and your Blood, That liv - ing bread, that

wil - der - ness, With wa - ter from the rock.
trav - el on To our a - bid - ing place.
us, and spread Your ta - ble in our heart.
heav'n - ly wine, Be our im - mor - tal food.

Text: James Montgomery, 1771-1854, alt.
Tune: ST. AGNES, CM; John B. Dykes, 1823-1876; harm. by Richard Proulx, b.1937, © 1986, GIA Publications, Inc.

In Remembrance of You 819

Verses

Cantor or choir:

1. Je - sus, hope for all, teach us to be - lieve.
2. Je - sus, Son of God, you are liv - ing Word.
3. Je - sus, Lamb of God, bear - er of our sin,

Reach us, hope for all, in wa - ter, wine, and wheat.
Teach us, Son of God, to share what we have heard.
Free us, Lamb of God; come heal us from with - in.

Refrain

All:

Gath - ered at ta - ble, gath - ered in love, food for the jour - ney

sent from a - bove. Strength - en and feed us in all that we do,

gath - ered at ta - ble in re - mem - brance of you.

Text: Paul A. Tate, b.1968
Tune: Paul A. Tate, b.1968
© 1997, World Library Publications

820 Come and Eat This Living Bread

Refrain

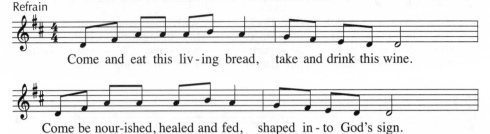

Come and eat this liv-ing bread, take and drink this wine.

Come be nour-ished, healed and fed, shaped in-to God's sign.

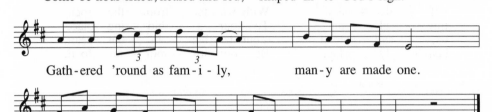

Gath-ered 'round as fam-i-ly, man-y are made one.

Form-ing love's com-mu-ni-ty, one we now be-come.

Verses

1. Saint and sinner welcome in to this meal of harmony.
   Lonely people, next of kin journey toward the glory tree.
   Gathered strangers, scattered sheep, at this table all are fed.
   Blood and body bonds run deep as your kingdom feast is spread.

2. May we see the Christ revealed in the breaking of the bread.
   Living stories, holy meals, we become what we are fed.
   Broken shattered, fragile life, now received by you and me.
   Eating, drinking, joy and strife, Gospel living sets us free.

3. See the Christ in saddened sighs, blood poured out in every land.
   Wounded people, wailing cries lie upon our outstretched hands.
   Jesus is the way through death; truth beyond the present rage.
   Life unfolding, healing breath now enfleshed in youth and age.

4. Bless us, Lord, and these your gifts, fruit of vine and human hands.
   With our hearts and minds we lift all the goodness of these lands.
   Praise and thanks we shout and sing, from your bounty we are blessed.
   Joyfully all gifts we bring to receive our Lord and guest.

5. Death and life in water meet, drenching us in floods of light.
   Marking us with oil so sweet, clothing us in glorious white.
   Priest and prophet, spirit led, we are God's new living sign.
   Feeding on this holy bread, drinking of this holy wine.

6. Witnessing to love and peace, hands of blessing we remain.
   Helping fear and hate to cease, we bring forth God's wondrous reign.
   Strength and power here we find, given in this kingdom feast.
   We go forth to heal and sign everyone, both great and least.

Text: Rob Glover, b.1950
Tune: ADORO TE DEVOTE, 12 12 12 12; verses and arr. Rob Glover, b.1950
© 1997, GIA Publications, Inc.

Life-giving Bread, Saving Cup 821

Refrain

Life-giv-ing bread, sav-ing cup, we of-fer in thanks-giv-ing, O God.

Life-giv-ing bread, sav-ing cup, we of-fer as a sign of our love.

Verses

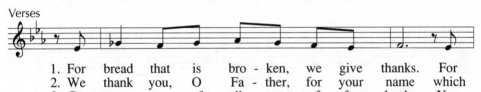

1. For bread that is bro - ken, we give thanks. For
2. We thank you, O Fa - ther, for your name which
3. Cre - a - tor of all, we of - fer thanks. You
4. Re - mem - ber your Church which sings your praise. Per -

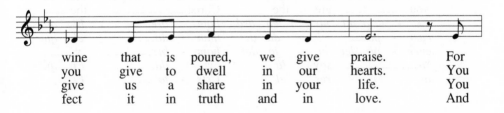

wine that is poured, we give praise. For
you give to dwell in our hearts. You
give us a share in your life. You
fect it in truth and in love. And

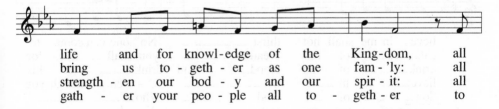

life and for knowl-edge of the King-dom, all
bring us to - geth - er as one fam - 'ly: all
strength - en our bod - y and our spir - it: all
gath - er your peo - ple all to - geth - er to

D.C.

praise to you un - til the end of time!
praise to you un - til the end of time!
praise to you un - til the end of time!
praise you un - til the end of time!

Text: Adapted from the *Didache*, 2nd C.; James J. Chepponis, b.1956
Tune: James J. Chepponis, b.1956
© 1987, GIA Publications, Inc.

822 I Am the Bread of Life / Yo Soy el Pan de Vida

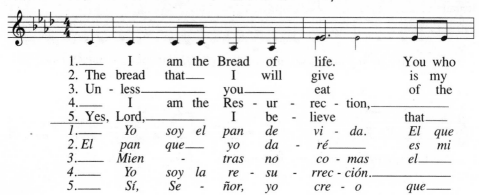

1.___ I am the Bread of life. You who
2. The bread that___ I will give is my
3. Un - less___ you___ eat of the
4.___ I am the Res - ur - rec - tion,___
5. Yes, Lord,___ I be - lieve that___

1.___ Yo soy el pan de vi - da. El que
2. El pan que___ yo da - ré___ es mi
3.___ Mien - tras no co - mas el___
4.___ Yo soy la re - su - rrec - ción.___
5.___ Sí, Se - ñor, yo cre - o que___

come to me shall not hun - ger;___ and who be -
flesh for the life of the world,___ and if you
flesh of the Son of Man___ and___
I___ am the life.___ If you be -
you___ are the Christ,___ the___

vie - ne_a mí no ten - drá ham - bre.___ El que
cuer - po___ vi - da del mun - do,___ y el que
cuer - po del hi - jo del hom - bre,___ y___
Yo___ soy la vi - da.___ El que
tú e - res el Cris - to,___ El___

lieve in me shall not thirst.___ No one can come to
eat___ of this bread,___ you shall___ live for
drink___ of his blood,_ and drink___ of his
lieve___ in___ me,___ e - ven___ though you
Son___ of___ God,___ Who___ has___

cree_en mí no ten - drá sed.___ Na - die___ vie - ne_a
co - ma___ de mi car - ne___ ten - drá___ vi - da_e -
be - bas___ de su san - gre, y be - bas___ de su
cree___ en___ mí,___ aun - que___ mu - rie -
Hi - jo de Dios,_ que vi - no al

me   un - less   the___   Fa - ther   beck - ons.
ev - er,___   you   shall___ live   for   ev - er.
blood,   you   shall   not have life   with - in   you.
die,___   you   shall___ live   for   ev - er.
come   in - to___   the___   world.___
*mí*___   *mien - tras el Pa - dre*   *lla - me.*
*ter - na,*___   *ten - drá*___ *vi - da e - ter - na.*
san - gre,   *no*   *ten - drá*___ *vi - da*   *en ti.*
*ra,*___   *ten - drá vi - da*   *e - ter - na.*
*mun - do*___   *pa - ra sal - var - nos.*

And   I   will   raise   you   up,   and   I   will
Yo   le   re - su - ci - ta - ré,   Yo   le   re -

raise   you   up,   and   I   will   raise   you
su - ci - ta - ré,   Yo   le   re - su - ci - ta -

up   on   the   last   day.
ré   el   di - a   de El.

Text: John 6; Suzanne Toolan, SM, b.1927
Tune: BREAD OF LIFE, Irregular with refrain; Suzanne Toolan, SM, b.1927
© 1966, 1970, 1986, 1993, GIA Publications, Inc.

823 Gather in Your Name

Refrain

When two or more gath-er in your name, and see your pres-ence in each face, we treas-ure the gift of this sa-cred meal, blessed and poured out for all in this place.

Verses

Cantor:

1. Bread, the gift of your bod-y.
2. Bread, our light and our life.
3. Bread, your man-na from heav-en.
4. Bread, your mys-t'ry be-fore us.
5. Bread, the path for our jour-ney.
6. Bread, the food for our long-ing.
7. Bread for those who seek jus-tice.

Wine, your life blood out poured.
Wine, our truth and our way.
Wine, the fruit of your heart.
Wine, the hope of our dreams.
Wine, of wis-dom and grace.
Wine, the sweet taste of love.
Wine for the hum-ble of heart.

All:

Come, join the feast! Take and be-lieve! Be-

D.C.

come what you re-ceive!

Text: Lori True, b.1961
Tune: Lori True, b.1961
© 2003, GIA Publications, Inc.

Behold the Lamb   824

Verses

1. Those who were in the dark are thank - ful for the
2. Peace - ful now, those whose hearts are blessed with un - der-
3. Gen - tle one, Child of God, join with us at this
4. Lord of all, give us light. De - liv - er us from

sun - light; We who live, we who die are
stand-ing Of the wheat, of the wine u -
ta - ble. Bless our lives; nour-ish all who
e - vil. Make us one; be our shield. Make

grate - ful for this gift, thank-ful for God's love.
nit - ed with God's word and the love we share.
hun - ger for this feast; shel - ter them with peace.
still the winds that blow; cra - dle us with love.

Refrain

Be - hold, be-hold the Lamb of God. All who eat,

all who drink shall live; and all, all who dwell in

God, shall come to know God's glo-ry!

Text: Martin Willett, b.1960
Tune: Martin Willett, b.1960; acc. by Craig S. Kingsbury, b.1952
© 1984, OCP Publications

825   Now in This Banquet

Refrain

Now in this ban - quet, Christ is our bread;
Advent: God of our jour - neys, day - break to night;
Lent: Lord, you can o - pen hearts that are stone;

Here shall all hun - gers be fed.
Lead us to jus - tice and light.
Live in our flesh and our bone;

Bread that is bro - ken, wine that is poured,
Grant us com - pas - sion, strength for the day,
Lead us to won - der, mys - t'ry and grace,

Love is the sign of our Lord.
Wis - dom to walk in your way.
One in your lov - ing em - brace.

Verses 1, 2

1. You who have touched us and graced us with love,
2. Let our hearts burn with the fire of your love;

D.C.

make us your peo - ple of good - ness and light.
o - pen our eyes to the glo - ry of God.

Verse 3

3. God who makes the blind to see, God who makes the

*May be sung in canon.

lame to walk, bring us danc - ing in - to day,

D.C.

lead your peo - ple in your way.

Verse 4

4. Hope for the hope - less, light for the blind,

D.C.

"Strong" is your name, Lord, "Gen - tle" and "Kind."

Verse 5

5. Call us to be your light, call us to be your love,

D.C.

make us your peo - ple a - gain.

Verse 6

6. Come, O Spir - it! re - new our hearts!

D.C.

We shall a - rise to be chil - dren of light.

Text: Marty Haugen, b.1950
Tune: Marty Haugen, b.1950
© 1986, GIA Publications, Inc.

826 Alleluia! Sing to Jesus

1. Al - le - lu - ia! sing to Je - sus! His the
2. Al - le - lu - ia! not as or - phans Are we
3. Al - le - lu - ia! Bread of An - gels, Here on
4. Al - le - lu - ia! King e - ter - nal, You the

scep - ter, his the throne; Al - le - lu - ia!
left in sor - row now; Al - le - lu - ia!
earth our food, our stay! Al - le - lu - ia!
Lord of lords we own; Al - le - lu - ia!

his the tri - umph, His the vic - to - ry a - lone;
he is near us, Faith be - lieves, nor ques - tions how:
here the sin - ful Flee to you from day to day:
born of Mar - y, Earth your foot - stool, heav'n your throne:

Hark! the songs of peace - ful Zi - on Thun - der
Though the cloud from sight re - ceived him, When the
In - ter - ces - sor, friend of sin - ners, Earth's re -
You, with - in the veil, have en - tered, Robed in

like a might - y flood; Je - sus out of
for - ty days were o'er, Shall our hearts for -
deem - er, plead for me, Where the songs of
flesh, our great high priest; Here on earth both

ev - 'ry na - tion Has re - deemed us by his blood.
get his prom - ise, "I am with you ev - er - more"?
all the sin - less Sweep a - cross the crys - tal sea.
priest and vic - tim In the eu - cha - ris - tic feast.

Text: Revelation 5:9; William C. Dix, 1837-1898
Tune: HYFRYDOL, 8 7 8 7 D; Rowland H. Prichard, 1811-1887

Taste and See 827

Refrain

Taste and see, taste and see the good - ness of the Lord. O taste and see, taste and see the good - ness of the Lord, of the Lord.

Verses

1. I will bless the Lord at all times.
2. Glo - ri - fy the Lord with me.
3. Wor - ship the Lord, all you peo - ple.

Praise shall al - ways be on my lips;
To - geth - er let us all praise God's name.
You'll want for noth - ing if you ask.

my soul shall glo - ry in the Lord
I called the Lord who an - swered me;
7 Taste and see that the Lord is good;

D.C.

for God has been so good to me.
from all my trou - bles I was set free.
in God we need put all our trust.

Text: Psalm 34; James E. Moore, Jr., b.1951
Tune: James E. Moore, Jr., b.1951
© 1983, GIA Publications, Inc.

828 The Hand of God

Refrain

Last time

The hand of God feeds us, heals us, the hand of God!

Verse 1

Cantor:

1. All your works praise you, your faith - ful ones bless you!

D.C.

Let all pro-claim your glo - ry, your pow - er, your king-dom!

Verse 2

Cantor:

2. All eyes look to you, you feed us in due sea - son.

D.C.

You come with o - pen hands to feed your cre - a - tion!

Verse 3

Cantor:

3. You are just in all things, lov - ing and ho - ly.

D.C.

You are near to all who call your name, who cry out in love and truth!

Text: Psalm 145; adapt. by David Haas, b.1957
Tune: David Haas, b.1957
© 2001, GIA Publications, Inc.

Draw Near 829

Refrain

Draw near, draw near! Take the bod-y of your Lord. Draw near, draw near! Drink the blood for you out-poured.

Verses

1. Draw near and take the bod-y of your Lord,
2. Christ our re-deem - er, God's e - ter-nal Son,
3. Let us ap-proach with faith-ful hearts sin-cere,
4. With heav'n-ly bread makes those who hun-ger whole,

and drink the ho - ly blood for you out-poured:
has by his cross and blood the vic - t'ry won:
and take the pledg-es of sal - va - tion here:
gives liv-ing wa - ters to the thirst-ing soul:

Saved by his bod - y and his ho - ly blood, with
He gave his life for great-est and for least, Him -
Christ who in this life all the saints de-fends, gives
Judge of the na - tions, to whom all must bow, in

D.C.

souls re-freshed we give our thanks to God.
self the of - 'fring and Him-self the Priest.
all be - liev - ers life that nev - er ends.
this great feast of love is with us now.

Text: *Sancti, venite, Christi corpus sumite*, 7th C.; tr. by John M. Neale, 1818-1866, alt.
Tune: Steven R. Janco, b.1961, © 1992, World Library Publications

830 Seed, Scattered and Sown

Refrain

Seed, scat-tered and sown, wheat, gath-ered and grown,
bread, bro-ken and shared as one, the Liv-ing Bread of God.
Vine, fruit of the land, wine, work of our hands, one cup that is
shared by all; the Liv-ing Cup, the Liv-ing Bread of God.

Verses

1. Is not the bread we break a shar-ing in our Lord?
2. The seed which falls on rock will with-er and will die.
3. As wheat up-on the hills was gath-ered and was grown,

D.C.

Is not the cup we bless the blood of Christ out-poured?
The seed with-in good ground will flow-er and have life.
So may the church of God be gath-ered in-to one.

Text: *Didache* 9, 1 Corinthians 10:16-17, Mark 4:3-6; Dan Feiten, b.1953
Tune: Dan Feiten, b.1953; keyboard arr. by Eric Gunnison, R.J. Miller
© 1987, Ekklesia Music, Inc.

831 Come and Eat This Bread

Refrain

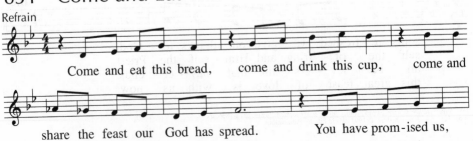

Come and eat this bread, come and drink this cup, come and
share the feast our God has spread. You have prom-ised us,

you are here with us   in the break-ing of the bread.

Verses

1. This   is   the bread of   life,   for   all   to share,   bread of
2. This   is   the cup   of   Christ's own   sac - ri - fice,   blood of
3. Just   as   the scat-tered grains   be - come one bread,   make us
4. And   as   we share one   cup   of   cov - e - nant   make us
5. Each time we   eat   this   bread   and   drink this cup,   we re-

D.C.

hope and   re - demp-tion,   bread to feed a world of   hun-gers.
love and   com - pas - sion,   blood to heal the world's di - vi - sions.
one   in   your Spir - it,   all one Bod - y   in Christ Je - sus.
one   in   com - mun - ion   at   the ta - ble of Christ Je - sus.
mem-ber   your death, Lord   and we cel - e - brate your ris - ing.

Text: Marty Haugen, b.1950
Tune: Marty Haugen, b.1950
© 1997, GIA Publications, Inc.

Let Us Break Bread Together 832

1. Let   us   break   bread to - geth - er   on our   knees;
2. Let   us   drink   wine to - geth - er   on our   knees;
3. Let   us   praise   God to - geth - er   on our   knees;

Let us break   bread to - geth-er   on our   knees;
Let us drink   wine to - geth-er   on our   knees;
Let us praise   God to - geth-er   on our   knees;

When I   fall   on my knees,   With my face to the ris-ing

sun,   O   Lord,   have   mer - cy   on   me.

Text: American folk hymn
Tune: LET US BREAK BREAD, 10 10 6 8 7; American folk hymn; harm. by David Hurd, b.1950, © 1968, GIA Publications, Inc.

833 Table Song

Refrain

We are the bod-y of Christ, Bro-ken and
poured out, prom-ise of life from death,
we are the bod-y of Christ.

Verses

1. Is not the bread of life we break a
2. How shall we make a re - turn to God, for
3. Un - less a grain of wheat shall fall up -
4. Come taste and see the good - ness, the

1. shar - ing in the life of God? Is not the cup of
2. good-ness un - sur - pass - ing? This sav - ing cup we
3. on the earth, it shall re - main a sin - gle grain; but
4. won - ders of the ris - en one! Come bless our God, in

D.C.

1. peace out-poured the blood of Christ?
2. shall hold high, and call out God's name!
3. if it dies, it will come to life!
4. all things, let praise be our song!

Text: David Haas, b. 1957
Tune: David Haas, b. 1957
© 1991, GIA Publications, Inc.

For Living, for Dying 834

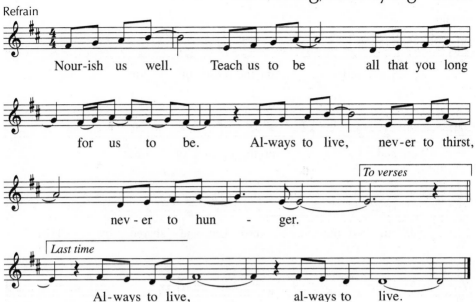

Refrain

Nour-ish us well. Teach us to be all that you long for us to be. Al-ways to live, nev-er to thirst, nev - er to hun - ger.

To verses

Last time

Al-ways to live, al-ways to live.

Verses

1. For living, for dying, Lord, for rising from the dead,
   we praise you with every breath we take.
   We come to you, remember you in the breaking of this bread,
   we drink the cup, the promise that you made.

2. Communion, community, is what we claim this day.
   Your body, your Spirit is our grace.
   With every heart, with every hand, with every word we say,
   of rich and poor, we welcome, we embrace.

3. For loving us, forgiving us, for sharing in our tears,
   for laughter, the tenderness you bring.
   You call to us, we follow. You guard us from our fears.
   Beside you our hearts will always sing.

4. So here we are, a part of you, a part of everyone;
   a river that flows into the sea.
   From east to west, from near and far, from every time and place,
   around the world we all join in your feast.

Text: Donna Peña, b.1955
Tune: Donna Peña, b.1955; arr. by Paul Gerike
© 1999, GIA Publications, Inc.

835 I Myself Am the Bread of Life

Refrain

I my-self am the bread of life.

You and I are the bread of life,

tak - en and blessed, bro - ken and shared by Christ

that the world might live.

Verses

1. This bread is spir - it, gift of the Mak - er's
2. Here is God's king - dom giv - en to us as
3. Lives bro - ken o - pen, sto - ries shared a -

love, and we who share it know that we can be
food. This is our bod - y, this is our
loud, be - come a ban - quet, a shel - ter for the

D.C.

one:
blood: a liv - ing sign of God in Christ.
world:

Text: Rory Cooney, b.1952
Tune: Rory Cooney, b.1952
© 1987, North American Liturgy Resources. Published by OCP Publications.

We Remember, We Believe 836

Refrain

We re-mem-ber in the break-ing of the bread. We re-mem-ber in the cup that we re-ceive. As our thirst is quenched and our hun-ger fed we re-mem-ber and we be-lieve.

Verses

1. More than ear can hear more than eye can see, more pro-found than our minds can un-der-stand, more than mys - ter - y.
2. Stran-gers, lov - ers, friends, neigh-bors, fam - i - ly, in the bod - y our one - ness is dis-played in di - ver - si - ty.
3. Ev - 'ry aisle a path, ev - 'ry step a sign of the jour - ney we walk to - geth - er to the end of time.
4. As we take and eat, so we learn to give. Like the bread, we must break; like wine, be poured so that all may live.

D.C.

Text: Thomas J. Porter, b.1958
Tune: Thomas J. Porter, b.1958
© 1997, GIA Publications, Inc.

837 Look Beyond

Refrain

Look be-yond the bread you eat; See your Sav-ior and your
Lord. Look be-yond the cup you drink;

To verses

See his love poured out as blood.

Final ending

See his life poured out as blood.

Verses

1. Give us a sign that we might be-lieve in
2. I am the bread which from the heav-ens
3. The bread I give you will be my ver - y
4. This man speaks harsh-ly; who can lis - ten to his
5. You, my dis - ci - ples, will you al - so

D.C.

you. Mos - es had man - na from the sky.
came; Those who eat this bread will nev - er die.
flesh; My blood will tru - ly be your drink.
word? We shall no long - er fol - low him.
leave? Lord, to whom can we go?

Present among Us 838

Refrain

Je - sus, Je - sus Christ, pres - ent a - mong us.

Here in this place, bread and wine of grace:

To verses | *To repeat and last time* / *Last time* | Verses

Je - sus Christ. Christ.

Cantor:

1. In the tak - ing,
2. In our sing - ing,
3. In our lis - t'ning,
4. In our search - ing,
5. In our hop - ing,
6. In the ask - ing,
7. In our birth - ing,

in the bless - ing, in the break - ing, in the shar - ing,
in our heal - ing, in our giv - ing, in our lov - ing,
in our seek - ing, in our ques - tions, in our si - lence,
in our ach - ing, in our long - ing, in our griev - ing,
in our reach - ing, in our need - ing, in our weep - ing,
in the hear - ing, in our grop - ing, in our cling - ing,
in our liv - ing, in our suf - f'ring, in our dy - ing,

D.C.

here be-fore you at this ta-ble, now we dine with you.

Text: David Haas, b.1957
Tune: David Haas, b.1957
© 2003, GIA Publications, Inc.

839 Take and Eat This Bread

Refrain

Take and eat this bread. Take and drink this cup.

This is my bod - y and my blood.

When you eat this bread, when you drink this cup,

you live in me and I in you.

Verses

1. This is the bread come down from heav - en;
2. Gath - ered as one a - round one ta - ble,
3. With - in our hands we hold the mys - t'ry,
4. Come all who thirst for life e - ter - nal,

D.C.

this is the cup of our sal - va - tion.
sent forth to wit - ness to sal - va - tion.
dy - ing and ris - ing to sal - va - tion.
come to the ta - ble of sal - va - tion.

Text: Francis Patrick O'Brien, b.1958
Tune: Francis Patrick O'Brien, b.1958
© 1992, GIA Publications, Inc.

At That First Eucharist 840

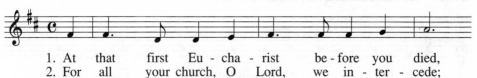

1. At that first Eu - cha - rist be - fore you died,
2. For all your church, O Lord, we in - ter - cede;
3. We pray for those who wan - der from the fold;

O Lord, you prayed that all be one in you;
O make our lack of char - i - ty to cease;
O bring them back, Good Shep - herd of the sheep,

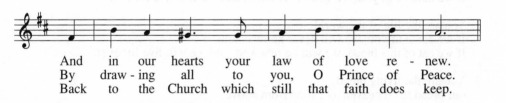

At this our Eu - cha - rist a - gain pre - side,
Draw us the near - er each to each we plead,
Back to the faith which saints be - lieved of old,

And in our hearts your law of love re - new.
By draw - ing all to you, O Prince of Peace.
Back to the Church which still that faith does keep.

Thus may we all one Bread, one Bod - y be;

Through this blest Sac - ra - ment of U - ni - ty.

Text: William H. Turton, 1859-1938, alt.
Tune: UNDE ET MEMORES, 10 10 10 10 with refrain; William H. Monk, 1823-1889, alt.

841   The Living Bread of God

Refrain

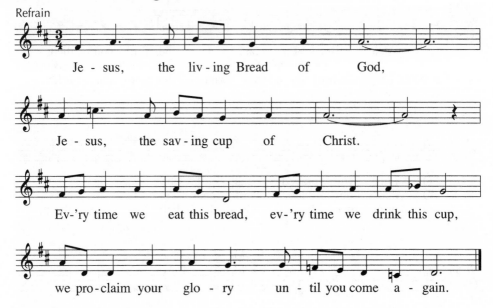

Je - sus,   the liv - ing Bread   of   God,

Je - sus,   the sav - ing cup   of   Christ.

Ev-'ry time we   eat this bread,   ev-'ry time we   drink this cup,

we pro-claim your   glo - ry   un - til you come   a - gain.

Verses

1. You are the bread of life.
   If we come to you, we will never be in need.
   If we believe in you, we will never thirst, and we will live for ever.

2. You are the life of the world.
   If we come to you, we will never know death.
   If we eat of this bread, we will be renewed, and we will live for ever.

3. You are the living bread,
   our bread from heaven, our food from above.
   If we eat and drink, we will be like you, and we will live for ever.

4. You are the living Christ.
   If we follow you, we will see the face of God.
   If we die with you, we will rise again, and we will live for ever.

Text: 1 Corinthians 11:26; David Haas, b.1957
Tune: Kate Cuddy, b.1953
© 1992, GIA Publications, Inc.

Without Seeing You 842

Refrain

With-out see-ing you, we love you; with-out

touch-ing you, we em - brace; with-out know-ing you, we

fol - low; with-out see-ing you, we be - lieve.

Verses

1. We re - turn to you deep with - in, leave the
2. The spar - row will find a home, near to
3. For - ev - er we sing to you of your
4. For you are our shep - herd, there is

past to the dust; turn to you with tears and
you, O God; how hap - py, we who
good - ness, O God; pro - claim - ing to
noth - ing that we need; in green pas - tures we will

D.C.

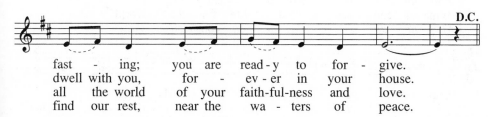

fast - ing; you are read - y to for - give.
dwell with you, for - ev - er in your house.
all the world of your faith-ful-ness and love.
find our rest, near the wa - ters of peace.

Text: Inspired by 1 Peter 1:8; David Haas, b.1957
Tune: David Haas, b.1957
© 1993, GIA Publications, Inc.

843 In the Breaking of the Bread / Cuando Partimos el Pan del Señor

Refrain

In the break - ing of the bread
Cuan-do par - ti - mos el pan del Se - ñor,

We have known him; we have been fed.
lo co - no - ce - mos, nos da de co - mer. Je -

Je - sus the stran - ger, Je - sus the Lord,
sús des - co - no - ci - do, Je - sús Se - ñor,

Be our com - pan - ion; be our hope.
nues - tro com - pa - ñe - ro y fuen - te de fe.

Verses

1. Bread for the jour - ney, strength for our years,
1. *Pan pa - ra_el via - je, Pan de la vi - da,*
2. Bread of the prom - ise, peo - ple of hope,
2. *Pan de pro - me - sa, Pan de_es - pe - ran - za,*

Man - na of a - ges, of strug - gle and tears.
Pan de los si - glos de lu - cha_y do - lor,
Wine of com - pas - sion, life for the world.
Vi - no de vi - da, de su com - pa - sión.

Cup of sal - va - tion, fruit of the land,
y es - te vi - no, fru - to de la tie - rra, ben -
Gath - ered at ta - ble, joined as his bod - y,
En es - ta me - sa, un so - lo cuer - po

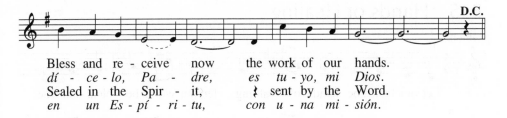

D.C.

Bless and re - ceive now the work of our hands.
dí - ce - lo, Pa - dre, es tu - yo, mi Dios.
Sealed in the Spir - it, sent by the Word.
en un Es - pí - ri - tu, con u - na mi - sión.

Original Verses:

1. Once I was helpless, sad and confused; darkness surrounded me, courage removed.
And then I saw him by my side. Carry my burden, open my eyes.

2. There is no sorrow, pain or woe; there is no suffering he did not know.
He did not waver; he did not bend. He is the victor. He is my friend.

Text: Bob Hurd, b.1950, and Michael Downey, © 1984, 1987; Spanish text by Stephen Dean and Kathleen Orozco, © 1989, OCP Publications
Tune: Bob Hurd, b.1950, © 1984; acc. by Dominic MacAller, b.1959, © 1984, OCP Publications
Published by OCP Publications.

He Healed the Darkness of My Mind   844

1. He healed the dark - ness of my mind The
2. Let oth - ers call my faith a lie, Or
3. Ask me not how! But I know who Has

day he gave my sight to me: It was not sin that
try to stir up doubt in me: Look at me now! None
o - pened up new worlds to me: This Je - sus does what

made me blind; It was no sin - ner made me see.
can de - ny I once was blind, and now I see.
none can do: I once was blind, and now I see!

Text: John 9; Fred Pratt Green, 1903-2000, © 1982, Hope Publishing Co.
Tune: ARLINGTON, LM; David Haas, b.1957, © 1988, GIA Publications, Inc.

845 Hands of Healing

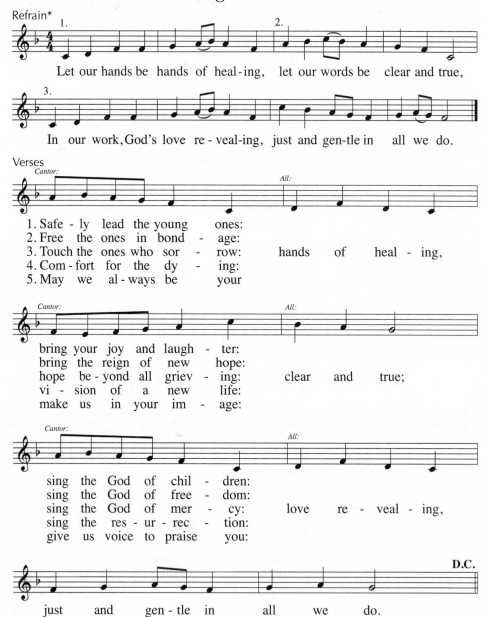

Refrain*

Let our hands be hands of heal-ing, let our words be clear and true,

In our work, God's love re-veal-ing, just and gen-tle in all we do.

Verses

Cantor: / *All:*

1. Safe - ly lead the young ones:
2. Free the ones in bond - age:
3. Touch the ones who sor - row: hands of heal - ing,
4. Com - fort for the dy - ing:
5. May we al - ways be your

Cantor: / *All:*

bring your joy and laugh - ter:
bring the reign of new hope:
hope be - yond all griev - ing: clear and true;
vi - sion of a new life:
make us in your im - age:

Cantor: / *All:*

sing the God of chil - dren:
sing the God of free - dom:
sing the God of mer - cy: love re - veal - ing,
sing the res - ur - rec - tion:
give us voice to praise you:

D.C.

just and gen - tle in all we do.

*May be sung in canon.

Text: Marty Haugen, b.1950
Tune: Marty Haugen, b.1950
© 1999, GIA Publications, Inc.

Jesus, Heal Us 846

Refrain

Je-sus, heal us; Je - sus. Je-sus, hear us now.

Verse 1

1. All who fear the Lord: Wait for God's mer - cy.

D.C.

All who love the Lord: Come, he will fill you.

Verse 2

2. All who fear the Lord: Fol - low the way.

D.C.

All who love the Lord: Hope in God's good - ness.

Verse 3

3. All who fear the Lord: Keep your hearts pre - pared.

D.C.

All who love the Lord: Be hum - bled in God's pres - ence.

Verse 4

4. All who trust the Lord: God will up - hold you. Let us

D.C.

cling to our God; let us fall in the arms of the Lord!

Text: David Haas, b.1957
Tune: David Haas, b.1957
© 1988, GIA Publications, Inc.

847 Precious Lord, Take My Hand

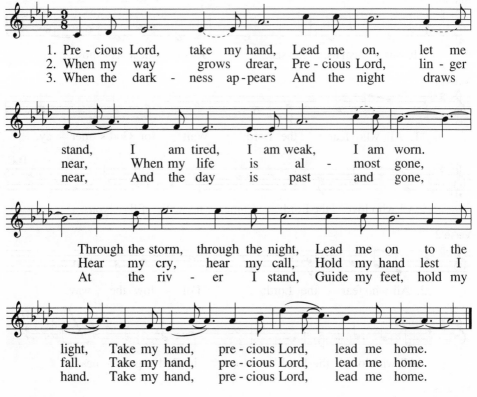

1. Pre - cious Lord, take my hand, Lead me on, let me
2. When my way grows drear, Pre - cious Lord, lin - ger
3. When the dark - ness ap - pears And the night draws

stand, I am tired, I am weak, I am worn.
near, When my life is al - most gone,
near, And the day is past and gone,

Through the storm, through the night, Lead me on to the
Hear my cry, hear my call, Hold my hand lest I
At the riv - er I stand, Guide my feet, hold my

light, Take my hand, pre - cious Lord, lead me home.
fall. Take my hand, pre - cious Lord, lead me home.
hand. Take my hand, pre - cious Lord, lead me home.

Text: Thomas A. Dorsey, 1899-1993
Tune: PRECIOUS LORD, 66 9 D; George N. Allen, 1812-1877; arr. by Kelly Dobbs Mickus, b.1966
© 1938, Unichappell Music, Inc.

848 Forgive Our Sins

1. "For - give our sins as we for - give," You
2. How can your par - don reach and bless The
3. In blaz - ing light your Cross re - veals The
4. Lord, cleanse the depths with - in our souls And

taught us, Lord, to pray, But you a - lone can
un - for - giv - ing heart That broods on wrongs and
truth we dim - ly knew: What triv - ial debts are
bid re - sent - ment cease. Then, bound to all in

grant us grace To live the words we say.
will not let Old bit - ter - ness de - part?
owed to us, How great our debt to you!
bonds of love, Our lives will spread your peace.

Text: Rosamund E. Herklots, 1905-1987, © Oxford University Press
Tune: DETROIT, CM; Supplement to *Kentucky Harmony*, 1820; harm. by Gerald H. Knight, 1908-1979, © The Royal School of Church Music

Our Father, We Have Wandered 849

1. Our Fa - ther, we have wan - dered And hid - den from your
2. And now at length dis - cern - ing The e - vil that we
3. O Lord of all the liv - ing, Both ban - ished and re -

face; In fool - ish - ness have squan - dered Your
do, Be - hold us, Lord, re - turn - ing With
stored, Com - pas - sion - ate, for - giv - ing And

leg - a - cy of grace. But now, in ex - ile
hope and trust to you. In haste you come to
ev - er car - ing Lord, Grant now that our trans -

dwell - ing, We rise with fear and shame, As dis - tant
meet us And home re - joic - ing bring, In glad - ness
gress - ing, Our faith - less - ness may cease. Stretch out your

but com - pell - ing, We hear you call our name.
there to greet us With calf and robe and ring.
hand in bless - ing, In par - don and in peace.

Text: Kevin Nichols, b.1929, © 1980, ICEL
Tune: PASSION CHORALE, 7 6 7 6 D; Hans Leo Hassler, 1564-1612; harm. by J.S. Bach, 1685-1750

850 Softly and Tenderly Jesus Is Calling

1. Soft - ly and ten - der - ly Je - sus is call - ing,
2. Why should we tar - ry when Je - sus is plead - ing,
3. Time is now fleet - ing, the mo - ments are pass - ing,
4. O for the won - der - ful love He has prom - ised,

Call - ing for you and for me; See, on the
Plead - ing for you and for me? Why should we
Pass - ing from you and from me; Shad - ows are
Prom - ised for you and for me; Though we have

por - tals He's wait - ing and watch - ing,
lin - ger and heed not His mer - cies,
gath - er - ing, death - beds are com - ing,
sinned He has mer - cy and par - don,

Watch - ing for you and for me.
Mer - cies for you and for me?
Com - ing for you and for me.
Par - don for you and for me.

Come home, come home, Ye who are wea - ry, come

home; Ear - nest - ly, ten - der - ly,

Je - sus is call - ing— Call - ing, "O sin - ner, come home!"

Text: Will L. Thompson, 1847-1909
Tune: Will L. Thompson, 1847-1909

Remember Your Love 851

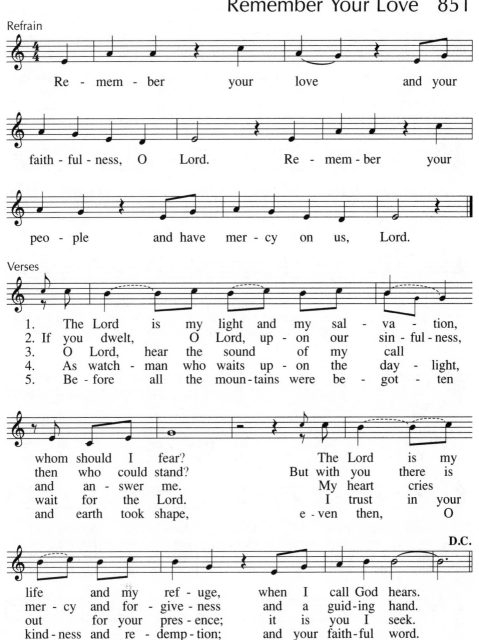

Refrain

Re - mem - ber your love and your faith - ful - ness, O Lord. Re - mem - ber your peo - ple and have mer - cy on us, Lord.

Verses

1. The Lord is my light and my sal - va - tion,
2. If you dwelt, O Lord, up - on our sin - ful - ness,
3. O Lord, hear the sound of my call
4. As watch - man who waits up - on the day - light,
5. Be - fore all the moun - tains were be - got - ten

1. whom should I fear? The Lord is my
2. then who could stand? But with you there is
3. and an - swer me. My heart cries
4. wait for the Lord. I trust in your
5. and earth took shape, e - ven then, O

D.C.

1. life and my ref - uge, when I call God hears.
2. mer - cy and for - give - ness, and a guid - ing hand.
3. out for your pres - ence; it is you I seek.
4. kind - ness and re - demp - tion; and your faith - ful word.
5. Lord, you were our ref - uge through-out ev - 'ry age.

Text: Psalm 27; Mike Balhoff, b.1946
Tune: Darryl Ducote, b.1945, and Gary Daigle, b.1957
© 1978, Damean Music. Distributed by GIA Publications, Inc.

852 Ashes

1. We rise a-gain from ash - es, from the good we've failed to do. We rise a-gain from ash - es, to cre - ate our - selves a - new. If all our world is ash - es, then must our lives be true, An of - fer-ing of ash - es, an of - fer-ing to you.

2. We of - fer you our fail - ures, we of - fer you at-tempts, The gifts not ful - ly giv - en, the dreams not ful - ly dreamt. Give our stum - bl - ings di - rec - tion, give our vi - sions wid - er view, An of - fer-ing of ash - es, an of - fer-ing to you.

3. Then rise a-gain from ash - es, let heal - ing come to pain, Though spring has turned to win - ter, and sun - shine turned to rain. The rain we'll use for grow - ing, and cre - ate the world a - new From an of - fer-ing of ash - es, an of - fer-ing to you.

4. Thanks be to the Fa - ther, who made us like him - self. Thanks be to the Son, who saved us by his death. Thanks be to the Spir - it, who cre - ates the world a - new From an of - fer-ing of ash - es, an of - fer-ing to you.

Text: Tom Conry, b.1951
Tune: Tom Conry, b.1951; acc. by Michael Joncas, b.1951
© 1978, OCP Publications

The Master Came to Bring Good News 853

1. The Mas - ter came to bring good news, The
2. The Law's ful - filled through Je - sus Christ, The
3. To seek the sin - ners Je - sus came, To
4. For - give us, Lord, as we for - give And

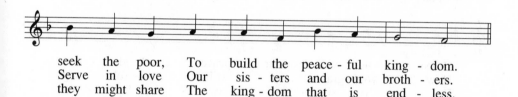

news of love and free - dom, To heal the sick and
man who lived for oth - ers, The law of Christ is:
live a - mong the friend - less, To show them love that
seek to help each oth - er. For - give us, Lord, and

seek the poor, To build the peace - ful king - dom.
Serve in love Our sis - ters and our broth - ers.
they might share The king - dom that is end - less.
we shall live To pray and work to - geth - er.

Fa - ther, for - give us! Through Je - sus hear us!

As we for - give one an - oth - er!

Text: Ralph Finn, b.1941, © 1965, GIA Publications, Inc.
Tune: ICH GLAUB AN GOTT, 8 7 8 7 with refrain; *Mainz Gesangbuch*, 1870; harm. by Richard Proulx, b.1937, © 1986, GIA Publications, Inc.

854 Healer of Our Every Ill

Refrain

Heal-er of our ev-'ry ill, light of each to-mor-row, give us peace be-yond our fear, and hope be-yond our sor-row.

Verses

1. You who know our fears and sad-ness,
2. In the pain and joy be-hold-ing,
3. Give us strength to love each oth-er,
4. You who know each thought and feel-ing,

Grace us with your peace and glad-ness,
How your grace is still un-fold-ing,
Ev-'ry sis-ter, ev-'ry broth-er,
Teach us all your way of heal-ing,

D.C.

Spir-it of all com-fort: fill our hearts.
Give us all your vi-sion: God of love.
Spir-it of all kind-ness: be our guide.
Spir-it of com-pas-sion: fill each heart.

Text: Marty Haugen, b.1950
Tune: Marty Haugen, b.1950
© 1987, GIA Publications, Inc.

855 Love Is the Sunlight

1. Love is the sun-light Shaped of your splen-dor,
2. Love is the spa-cious Qui-et of shad-ows,
3. May we in glad-ness Grow in your sun-shine,

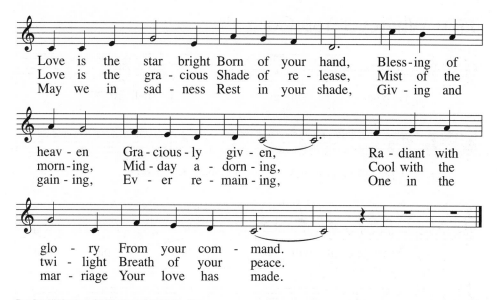

Love is the star bright Born of your hand, Bless-ing of
Love is the gra - cious Shade of re - lease, Mist of the
May we in sad - ness Rest in your shade, Giv - ing and

heav - en Gra - cious-ly giv - en, Ra - diant with
morn-ing, Mid - day a - dorn - ing, Cool with the
gain - ing, Ev - er re - main - ing, One in the

glo - ry From your com - mand.
twi - light Breath of your peace.
mar - riage Your love has made.

Text: Borghild Jacobson, © 1981, Concordia Publishing House
Tune: SHADE, 5 5 5 4 D; David Haas, b.1957, © 1993, GIA Publications, Inc.

When Love Is Found   856

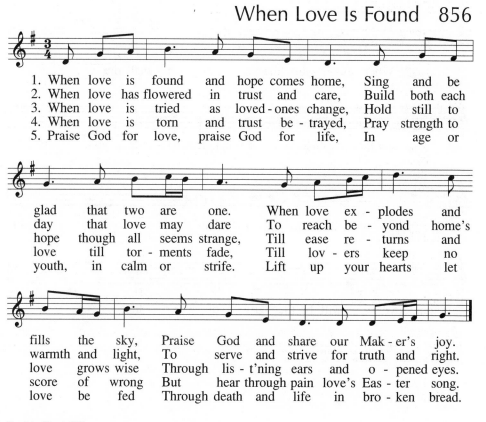

1. When love is found and hope comes home, Sing and be
2. When love has flowered in trust and care, Build both each
3. When love is tried as loved - ones change, Hold still to
4. When love is torn and trust be - trayed, Pray strength to
5. Praise God for love, praise God for life, In age or

glad that two are one. When love ex - plodes and
day that love may dare To reach be - yond home's
hope though all seems strange, Till ease re - turns and
love till tor - ments fade, Till lov - ers keep no
youth, in calm or strife. Lift up your hearts let

fills the sky, Praise God and share our Mak - er's joy.
warmth and light, To serve and strive for truth and right.
love grows wise Through lis - t'ning ears and o - pened eyes.
score of wrong But hear through pain love's Eas - ter song.
love be fed Through death and life in bro - ken bread.

Text: Brian Wren, b.1936
Tune: O WALY WALY, LM; English; harm. by Martin West, b.1929
© 1983, Hope Publishing Co.

857 Wherever You Go

1. Wher-ev-er you go   I shall go.

Wher-ev-er you live   so shall I   live.

Your peo-ple will be   my peo - ple,   and

your God   will be   my God   too.

2. Wher-ev-er you die   I shall die

and there   shall I   be bur-ied be - side   you.

We will be to-geth-er   for ev - er,   and

our love   will be the gift   of our   life.

Text: Ruth 1:16, 17; Weston Priory, Gregory Norbet, OSB, b.1940
Tune: Gregory Norbet, OSB, b.1940; arr. by Mary David Callahan, b.1923
© 1972, 1981, The Benedictine Foundation of the State of Vermont, Inc.

God, in the Planning   858

1. God, in the plan - ning and pur - pose of life,
2. Je - sus was found, at a sim - i - lar feast,
3. There - fore we pray that his spir - it pre - side
4. Praise then the Mak - er, the Spir - it, the Son,

Hal - lowed the un - ion of hus - band and wife:
Tak - ing the roles of both wait - er and priest,
O - ver the wed - ding of bride-groom and bride,
Source of the love through which two are made one.

This we em - bod - y where love is dis - played,
Turn - ing the world - ly to - wards the di - vine,
Ful - fill - ing all that they've hoped will come true,
God's is the glo - ry, the good - ness, and grace

Rings are pre - sent - ed and prom - is - es made.
Tears in - to laugh - ter and wa - ter to wine.
Light - ing with love all they dream of and do.
Seen in this mar - riage and known in this place.

Text: John L. Bell, b.1949, © 1989, Iona Community, GIA Publications, Inc., agent
Tune: SLANE, 10 10 10 10; Irish traditional; harm. by Erik Routley, 1917-1982, © 1975, Hope Publishing Co.

859   A Nuptial Blessing

Refrain

May God bless you, hold and keep you; may God's mer - cy shine on you, guide your work and guard your rest - ing, keep your love for ev - er new.

Verses

1. May God satisfy your longing, be refreshment at your table,
   and provide your daily bread,
   guard your going and your coming, be the solace in your silence:
   life within the lives you wed.

2. May God join your hopeful spirits, fill your hearts with truth and courage,
   trust to share both joy and tears,
   teach love to your children's children; may your household learn to witness
   living faith through all your years.

3. May God make your home a refuge where you warmly welcome strangers
   and the lowly find a place;
   make you caring, kind companions, help you meet the needs of neighbors,
   finding Christ in every face.

Text: Vicki Klima, b.1952; adapt. by Michael Joncas, b.1951, and George Szews, b.1951
Tune: Michael Joncas, b.1951
© 1989, GIA Publications, Inc.

860   Wherever You Go

Refrain

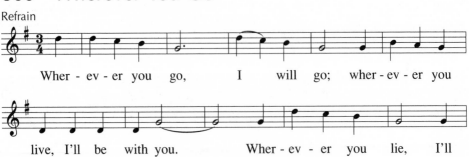

Wher - ev - er you go, I will go; wher - ev - er you live, I'll be with you. Wher - ev - er you lie, I'll

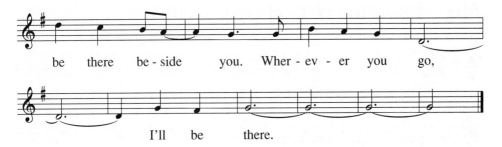

be there be-side you. Wher-ev-er you go,

I'll be there.

Verses

1. Come, set me like a seal upon your heart; a seal protecting your arm.
   Deep waters cannot quench this love; the ocean will not sweep it away.

2. Arise my beloved, come to me; the rains are gone, the winter is past.
   The flowers appear, the vines are pruned, and the dove's song is heard in our land.

3. Wherever you stay, I will stay; your people will be my people.
   Wherever you die, so will I die with you in the arms of God!

Text: Ruth 1:16-17; Song of Songs 2:10-12, 7:6-7; David Haas, b.1957
Tune: David Haas, b.1957
© 1993, GIA Publications, Inc.

May the Angels Lead You into Paradise 861

May the an-gels lead you in-to par-a-dise;

may the mar-tyrs come to wel-come you and

take you to the ho-ly cit-y, the

new and e-ter - nal Je-ru-sa-lem.

Text: *In paradisum; Rite of Funerals*, © 1970, ICEL
Tune: *Music for Rite of Funerals and Rite of Baptism for Children*, Howard Hughes, SM, b.1930, © 1977, ICEL

862 The Hand of God Shall Hold You

Refrain

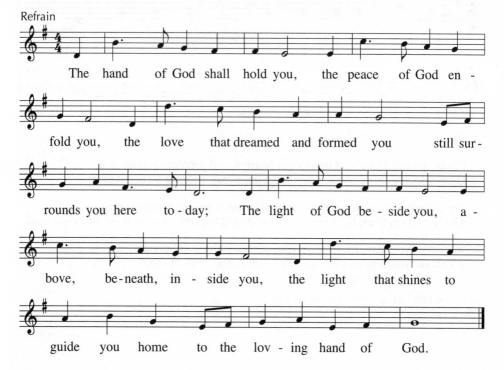

The hand of God shall hold you, the peace of God en-
fold you, the love that dreamed and formed you still sur-
rounds you here to-day; The light of God be-side you, a-
bove, be-neath, in-side you, the light that shines to
guide you home to the lov-ing hand of God.

Verses

1. May God's light shine ever upon you, may you rest in the arms of God;
   may you dwell for evermore in communion with all the blessed.

2. May the angels lead you into paradise; may the martyrs come to welcome you
   and take you to the holy city, the new and eternal Jerusalem.

Text: Marty Haugen, b.1950, © 1994, GIA Publications, Inc.; verse 2 from *In paradisum; Rite of Funerals,* © 1970, ICEL
Tune: Marty Haugen, b.1950, © 1994, GIA Publications, Inc.

863 I Know That My Redeemer Lives

Refrain

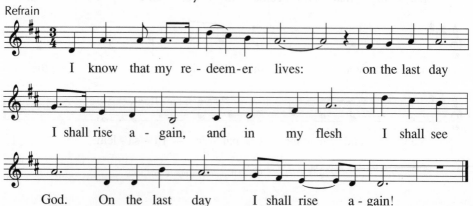

I know that my re-deem-er lives: on the last day
I shall rise a-gain, and in my flesh I shall see
God. On the last day I shall rise a-gain!

Verses

1. I shall see my Sav - ior's face; and my own
2. With - in my heart this hope I hold; that in my

eyes shall be - hold my God. On the last day
flesh I shall see my God. On the last day

I shall rise a - gain!
I shall rise a - gain!

Text: Job 19:25-27; David Haas, b.1957
Tune: David Haas, b.1957
© 1990, GIA Publications, Inc.

The Last Journey 864

1. From the fal - ter of breath, through the si - lence of
2. From frus - tra - tion and pain, through hope hard to sus -
3. From the dim - ming of light, through the dark - ness of
4. From to - day till we die, through all ques - tion - ing

death, To the won - der that's break - ing be - yond;
tain, To the whole - ness here prom - ised, there known;
night, To the glo - ry of good - ness a - bove;
why, To the place from which time and tide flow;

God has wo - ven a way, un - ap - par - ent by
Christ has gone where we fear and has vowed to be
God the Spir - it is sent to en - sure heav'n's in -
An - gels tread on our dreams, and mag - nif - i - cent

day, For all those of whom heav - en is fond.
near On the jour - ney we make on our own.
tent Is em - braced and com - plet - ed in love.
themes Of heav'n's prom - ise are ech - oed be - low.

Text: John L. Bell, b.1949, © 1989, 1996, The Iona Community, GIA Publications, Inc., agent
Tune: IONA BOAT SONG, 12 9 12 9; Scottish traditional, arr. by John L. Bell, b.1949, © 1989, 1996, The Iona Community, GIA Publications, Inc., agent

865 In Paradisum / May Choirs of Angels

In pa - ra - dí - sum de - dú - cant te án - ge - li:
May choirs of an - gels es - cort you in - to par - a - dise:

in tu - o ad - vén - tu su - scí - pi - ant te
and at your ar - ri - val may the mar - tyrs re - ceive

már - ty - res, et per - dú - cant te in
and wel - come you; may they bring you home in -

ci - vi - tá - tem san - ctam Je - rú - sa - lem.
to the ho - ly cit - y, Je - ru - sa - lem.

Cho - rus an - ge - ló - rum te su -
May the ho - ly an - gels wel -

scí - pi - at, et cum Lá - za - ro quon - dam
come you, and with Laz - a - rus, who lived in

páu - pe - re ae - tér - nam
pov - er - ty, may you have

há - be - as ré - qui - em.
ev - er - last - ing rest.

Text: *In Paradisum*, tr. © 1986, GIA Publications, Inc.
Tune: Mode VII; acc. by Richard Proulx, b.1937, © 1986, GIA Publications, Inc.

I Know That My Redeemer Lives 866

Text: *Rite of Funerals,* © 1970, ICEL
Tune: *Music for Rite of Funerals and Rite of Baptism for Children,* Howard Hughes, SM, b.1930, © 1977, ICEL

867 Song of Farewell

Refrain

Dy-ing you de-stroyed our death!   Ris-ing you re-stored our life!

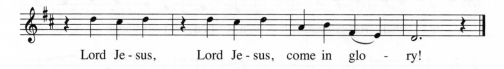

Lord Je-sus,   Lord Je-sus, come in glo - ry!

Verses

1. May Christ who died for you lead you into his kingdom;
   may Christ who died for you lead you this day into paradise.

2. May Christ, the Good Shepherd, lead you home today
   and give you a place within his flock.

Alternate children's verse:

2. May Christ, the Good Shepherd, take you on his shoulders
   and bring you home, bring you home today.

3. May the angels lead you into paradise;
   may the martyrs come to welcome you
   and take you to the Holy City, the new and eternal Jerusalem.

4. May the choirs of angels come to meet you,
   may the choirs of angels come to meet you;
   where Lazarus is poor no longer, may you have eternal life in Christ.

Alternate children's verse:

4. May the choirs of angels come to meet you,
   may the choirs of angels come to meet you;
   and with all God's children may you have eternal life in Christ.

Text: Memorial Acclamation © 1973, ICEL; *In paradisum;* Michael Marchal, b.1951, © 1988, GIA Publications, Inc.
Tune: Michael Joncas, b.1951, © 1988, GIA Publications, Inc.

Go, Silent Friend 868

1. Go, si-lent friend, your life has found its end - ing;
2. Go, si-lent friend, for - give us if we grieved you;

To dust re - turns your wea - ry mor - tal frame.
Safe now in heav - en, kind - ly say our name.

God, who be - fore birth called you in - to be - ing,
Your life has touched us, that is why we mourn you;

Now calls you hence, his ac - cent still the same.
Our lives with - out you can - not be the same.

Go, si - lent friend, your life in Christ is bur - ied;
Go, si - lent friend, we do not grudge you glo - ry;

For you he lived and died and rose a - gain.
Sing, sing with joy deep prais - es to your Lord.

Close by his side your prom - ised place is wait - ing
You, who be - lieved that Christ would come back for you,

Where, ful - ly known, you shall with God re - main.
Now cel - e - brate that Je - sus keeps his word.

Text: John L. Bell, b.1949, © 1996, The Iona Community, GIA Publications, Inc., agent
Tune: LONDONDERRY AIR, 11 10 11 10 D; arr. by John L. Bell, b.1949, © 1996, The Iona Community, GIA Publications, Inc., agent

869 There Is a Place

Verses

1. There's a time for re-mem-b'ring, ᵞ a time to re-
2. There is gold that is gleam-ing, in a past we once
3. There's a prom - ise of God that is writ-ten in the
4. In the quiet of the eve - ning at the close of the

1. call, ᵞ the trials and the tri - umphs, ᵞ the fears and the
2. knew, in our tears and our laugh-ter ᵞ 'twas love brought us
3. stars, ᵞ for all who may trav - el, ᵞ no mat - ter how
4. day, we will rest on our jour - ney to the Lord we will

1. falls. There's a time to be grate-ful for
2. through. There's a road we have trav - eled where
3. far. God will be your com - pan - ion each
4. pray. May we thank God for bless-ings, for the

1. mo - ments so blessed, ᵞ the jewels of our mem - 'ry where
2. sun - light has kissed, ᵞ that car - ries us on - wards when
3. jour - ney you make, in the shad - ow of loved ones to
4. mo - ments we shared, as we seek for to - mor - row, our

[1.]

love is our guest.
loved ones are
light - en your
God will be

[2.-4.]

missed.
way. There is
there.

Refrain

treas - ure in our fields, there is treas - ure in our skies, there is

treas - ure in our dream-ing from the soul to the eye,

for wher - ev - er we gath-er in the light of God's
grace, and for all whom we re - mem - ber, there will
ev - er be a place.

Text: Liam Lawton, b.1959
Tune: Liam Lawton, b.1959; choral arr. by Gary Daigle, b.1957; acc. by Kelly Dobbs Mickus, b.1966
© 2002, GIA Publications, Inc.

God of Adam, God of Joseph   870

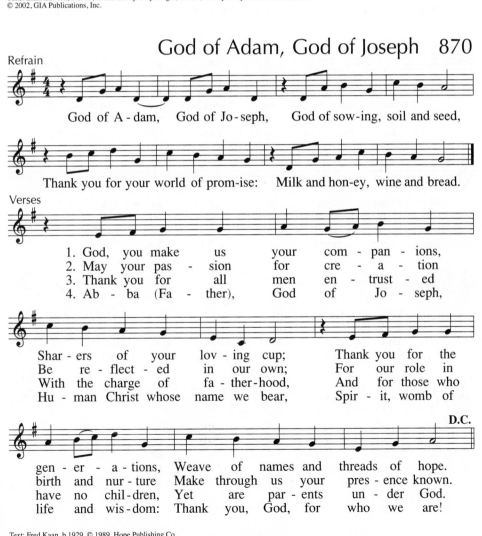

Refrain

God of A - dam, God of Jo - seph, God of sow-ing, soil and seed,

Thank you for your world of prom-ise: Milk and hon-ey, wine and bread.

Verses

1. God, you make us your com - pan - ions,
2. May your pas - sion for cre - a - tion
3. Thank you for all men en - trust - ed
4. Ab - ba (Fa - ther), God of Jo - seph,

Shar - ers of your lov - ing cup; Thank you for the
Be re - flect - ed in our own; For our role in
With the charge of fa - ther-hood, And for those who
Hu - man Christ whose name we bear, Spir - it, womb of

D.C.

gen - er - a - tions, Weave of names and threads of hope.
birth and nur - ture Make through us your pres - ence known.
have no chil - dren, Yet are par - ents un - der God.
life and wis - dom: Thank you, God, for who we are!

Text: Fred Kaan, b.1929, © 1989, Hope Publishing Co.
Tune: FARRELL, 8 7 8 7 with refrain; Thomas J. Porter, b.1958, © 1994, GIA Publications, Inc.

871 God of Eve and God of Mary

Refrain

God of Eve and God of Mar - y,

God of love and moth - er earth, Thank you for the

ones who with us Shared their life and gave us birth.

Verses

1. As you came to earth in Je - sus,
2. Thank you, that the Church, our Moth - er,
3. Thank you for be - long - ing, shel - ter,
4. God of Eve and God of Mar - y,

So you come to us to - day;
Gives us bread and fills our cup,
Bonds of friend - ship, ties of blood,
Christ our broth - er, hu - man Son.

You are pres - ent in the car - ing
And the com - fort of the Spir - it
And for those who have no chil - dren,
Spir - it, car - ing like a moth - er,

D.C.

That pre - pares us for life's way.
Warms our hearts and lifts us up.
Yet are par - ents un - der God.
Take our love and make us one.

Text: Fred Kaan, b.1929, © 1989, Hope Publishing Co.
Tune: FARRELL, 8 7 8 7 with refrain; Thomas J. Porter, b.1958, © 1994, GIA Publications, Inc.

America the Beautiful   872

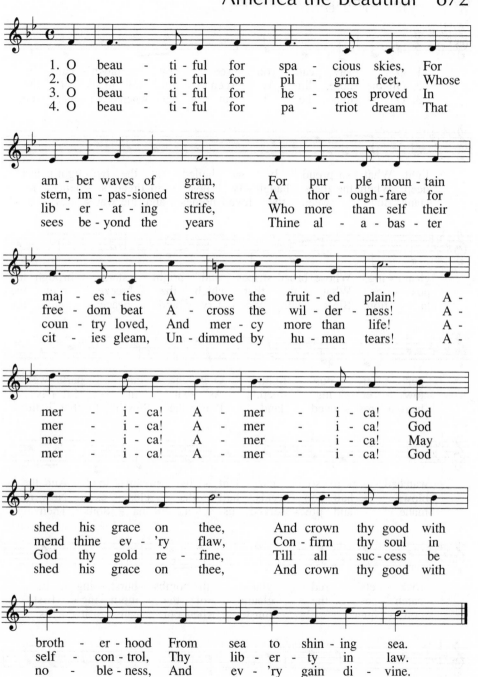

1. O beau - ti - ful for spa - cious skies, For
2. O beau - ti - ful for pil - grim feet, Whose
3. O beau - ti - ful for he - roes proved In
4. O beau - ti - ful for pa - triot dream That

am - ber waves of grain, For pur - ple moun - tain
stern, im - pas-sioned stress A thor - ough-fare for
lib - er - at - ing strife, Who more than self their
sees be - yond the years Thine al - a - bas - ter

maj - es - ties A - bove the fruit - ed plain! A -
free - dom beat A - cross the wil - der - ness! A -
coun - try loved, And mer - cy more than life! A -
cit - ies gleam, Un - dimmed by hu - man tears! A -

mer - i - ca! A - mer - i - ca! God
mer - i - ca! A - mer - i - ca! God
mer - i - ca! A - mer - i - ca! May
mer - i - ca! A - mer - i - ca! God

shed his grace on thee, And crown thy good with
mend thine ev - 'ry flaw, Con - firm thy soul in
God thy gold re - fine, Till all suc - cess be
shed his grace on thee, And crown thy good with

broth - er - hood From sea to shin - ing sea.
self - con - trol, Thy lib - er - ty in law.
no - ble - ness, And ev - 'ry gain di - vine.
broth - er - hood From sea to shin - ing sea.

Text: Katherine L. Bates, 1859-1929
Tune: MATERNA, CMD; Samuel A. Ward, 1848-1903

873 Star-Spangled Banner

1. O say can you see by the dawn's ear-ly
2. On the shore, dim-ly seen thro' the mists of the
3. O thus be it ev - er when free-men shall

light, What so proud-ly we hailed at the twi-light's last
deep, Where the foe's haugh-ty host in dread si-lence re-
stand Be - tween their loved homes and the war's des-o-

gleam-ing, Whose broad stripes and bright stars, through the
pos-es, What is that which the breeze, o'er the
la - tion! Blest with vic-t'ry and peace, may the

per - il - ous fight, O'er the ram - parts we
tow - er - ing steep, As it fit - ful-ly
heav'n - res - cued land Praise the Pow'r that hath

watched, were so gal - lant - ly stream-ing? And the
blows half con-ceals, half dis - clos-es? Now it
made and pre-served us a na - tion! Then

rock - ets' red glare, the bombs burst-ing in
catch-es the gleam of the morn-ing's first
con - quer we must, when our cause it is

air, Gave proof through the night that our
beam, In full glo - ry re - flect-ed now
just, And this be our mot-to, "In

flag was still there. O say does that
shines on the stream, 'Tis the Star - Span - gled
God is our trust." And the Star - Span - gled

Star - Span - gled Ban - ner yet wave O'er the
Ban - ner O long may it wave O'er the
Ban - ner in tri - umph shall wave O'er the

land of the free and the home of the brave?
land of the free and the home of the brave!
land of the free and the home of the brave!

Text: Francis S. Key, 1779-1843
Tune: STAR SPANGLED BANNER, Irregular; John S. Smith, 1750-1836

My Country, 'Tis of Thee   874

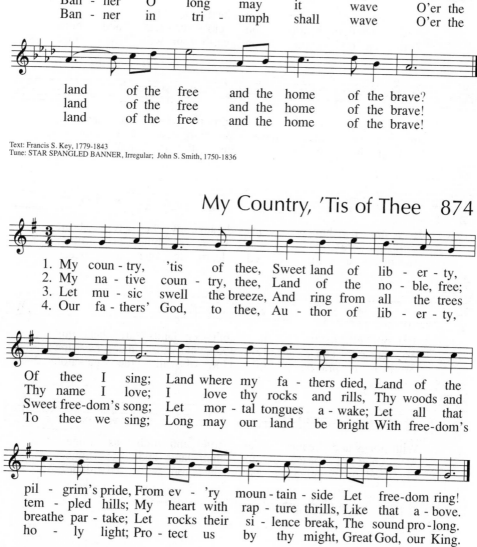

1. My coun - try, 'tis of thee, Sweet land of lib - er - ty,
2. My na - tive coun - try, thee, Land of the no - ble, free;
3. Let mu - sic swell the breeze, And ring from all the trees
4. Our fa - thers' God, to thee, Au - thor of lib - er - ty,

Of thee I sing; Land where my fa - thers died, Land of the
Thy name I love; I love thy rocks and rills, Thy woods and
Sweet free-dom's song; Let mor - tal tongues a - wake; Let all that
To thee we sing; Long may our land be bright With free-dom's

pil - grim's pride, From ev - 'ry moun - tain - side Let free-dom ring!
tem - pled hills; My heart with rap - ture thrills, Like that a - bove.
breathe par - take; Let rocks their si - lence break, The sound pro - long.
ho - ly light; Pro - tect us by thy might, Great God, our King.

Text: Samuel F. Smith, 1808-1895
Tune: AMERICA, 66 4 666 4; *Thesaurus Musicus*, 1744

875 This Is My Song

1. This is my song, O God of all the na-tions,
2. My coun-try's skies are blu-er than the o-cean,
3. This is my prayer, O God of all earth's king-doms,

A song of peace for lands a-far and mine.
And sun-light beams on clo-ver-leaf and pine.
Your king-dom come; on earth your will be done.

This is my home, the coun-try where my heart is;
But oth-er lands have sun-light too, and clo-ver,
Let Christ be lift-ed up till all shall serve him,

Here are my hopes, my dreams, my ho-ly shrine;
And skies are ev-'ry-where as blue as mine.
And hearts u-nit-ed learn to live as one.

But oth-er hearts in oth-er lands are beat-ing
So hear my song, O God of all the na-tions,
So hear my prayer, O God of all the na-tions.

With hopes and dreams as true and high as mine.
A song of peace for their land and for mine.
My-self I give you; let your will be done.

Text: St. 1-2, Lloyd Stone, 1912-1993, st. 3, Georgia Harkness, 1891-1974, © 1964, Lorenz Publishing Co.
Tune: FINLANDIA, 11 10 11 10 11 10; Jean Sibelius, 1865-1957

We Have a Dream 876

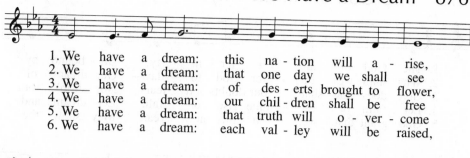

1. We have a dream: this na - tion will a - rise,
2. We have a dream: that one day we shall see
3. We have a dream: of des - erts brought to flower,
4. We have a dream: our chil - dren shall be free
5. We have a dream: that truth will o - ver - come
6. We have a dream: each val - ley will be raised,

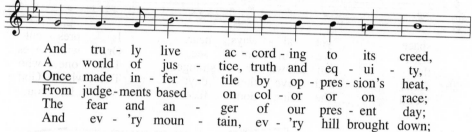

And tru - ly live ac - cord - ing to its creed,
A world of jus - tice, truth and eq - ui - ty,
Once made in - fer - tile by op - pres - sion's heat,
From judge - ments based on col - or or on race;
The fear and an - ger of our pres - ent day;
And ev - 'ry moun - tain, ev - 'ry hill brought down;

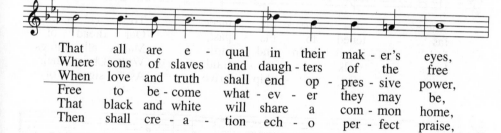

That all are e - qual in their mak - er's eyes,
Where sons of slaves and daugh - ters of the free
When love and truth shall end op - pres - sive power,
Free to be - come what - ev - er they may be,
That black and white will share a com - mon home,
Then shall cre - a - tion ech - o per - fect praise,

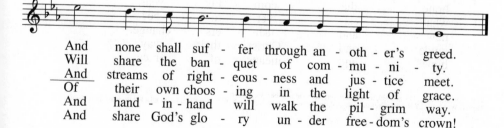

And none shall suf - fer through an - oth - er's greed.
Will share the ban - quet of com - mu - ni - ty.
And streams of right - eous - ness and jus - tice meet.
Of their own choos - ing in the light of grace.
And hand - in - hand will walk the pil - grim way.
And share God's glo - ry un - der free - dom's crown!

Text: Michael Forster, b.1946, © 1997, Kevin Mayhew, Ltd.
Tune: NATIONAL HYMN, 10 10 10 10; George W. Warren, 1828-1902

877 The God of All Eternity

1. The God of all e-ter-ni-ty, Un-bound by
2. What shall we of - fer God to - day— Our dreams of
3. God does not share our doubts and fears, Nor shrinks from
4. Let faith or for - tune rise or fall, Let dreams and
5. God grant that we, in this new year, May show the

space yet al - ways near, Is pres - ent
what we can - not see, Or, with eyes
the un - known or strange: The one who
dread both have their day; Those whom God
world the King - dom's face, And let our

where his peo - ple meet To cel - e -
fas - tened to the past, Our dread of
fash - ioned heav'n and earth Makes all things
loves walk un - a - fraid With Christ their
work and wor - ship thrive As signs of

brate the com - ing year.
what is yet to be?
new and ush - ers change.
guide and Christ their way.
hope and means of grace.

Text: John L. Bell, b.1949, © 1989, Iona Community, GIA Publications, Inc., agent
Tune: O WALY WALY, 8 8 8 8; English traditional; arr. by John L. Bell, b.1949, © 1989, Iona Community, GIA Publications, Inc., agent

Psalm Refrains
from the Lectionary for Mass

Psalm 1   878

Bless-ed are they,   bless-ed are they   who hope in the Lord.

Psalm 4   879

Lord,   let   your   face   shine   on   us.

Psalm 8   880

O Lord, our God,   how won-der-ful your name   in   all the earth!

Psalm 15   881

He who does jus-tice   will live   in the   pres-ence of   the   Lord.

Psalm 15   882

One who does jus-tice   will live   in the   pres-ence of   the   Lord.

Psalm 16   883

You   are my   in - her - i - tance,   O   Lord.

Psalm 16   884

Lord,   you will   show us   the   path   of   life.

885 Psalm 16

You are my in - her - i - tance, O Lord.

886 Psalm 17

Lord, when your glo - ry ap - pears, my joy will be full.

887 Psalm 18

I love you, Lord, my strength, my strength.

888 Psalm 19

Lord, you have the words of ev - er - last - ing life.

889 Psalm 19

Your words, O Lord, are Spir - it and life.

890 Psalm 19

The pre - cepts of the Lord give joy to the heart.

891 Psalm 19

Their mes - sage goes out through all the earth.

892 Psalm 22

My God, my God, why have you a - ban - doned me?

Psalm 22   893

I will praise you, Lord, in the as-sem-bly of your peo - ple.

Psalm 23   894

The Lord is my shep-herd; there is noth - ing I shall want.

Psalm 23   895

Though I walk in the val - ley of dark-ness, I fear no

e - vil, for you are with me.

Psalm 23   896

I shall live in the house of the Lord all the days of my life.

Psalm 24   897

Let the Lord en - ter; he is king of glo - ry.

Psalm 24   898

Who is this king of glo - ry? It is the Lord!

Psalm 24   899

Lord, this is the peo - ple that longs to see your face.

Psalm 25   900

To you, O Lord, I lift my soul, to you I lift my soul.

901 Psalm 25

Your ways, O Lord, are love and truth to those who keep your cov - e - nant.

902 Psalm 25

Teach me your ways, O Lord, teach me your ways.

903 Psalm 25

Re - mem - ber your mer - cies, O Lord.

904 Psalm 25

No one who waits for you, O Lord, will ev - er be put to shame.

905 Psalm 27

The Lord is my light and my sal - va - tion.

906 Psalm 27

I be - lieve that I shall see the good things of the Lord in the land of the liv - ing.

907 Psalm 27

I be - lieve that I shall see the good things of the Lord in the land of the liv - ing.

Psalm 29 908

The Lord will bless his peo-ple with his peace.

Psalm 30 909

I will praise you, Lord, for you have res-cued me.

Psalm 31 910

Fa - ther, in-to your hands I com-mend my spir - it.

Psalm 31 911

Lord, be my rock of safe - ty.

Psalm 32 912

I turn to you, O Lord, in time of

trou - ble, and you fill me with the joy of sal - va - tion.

Psalm 32 913

Lord, for - give the wrong I have done.

Psalm 33 914

Lord, let your mer-cy be on us, as we place our trust in you.

Psalm 33 915

The earth is full of the good-ness of the Lord, the good-ness of the Lord.

916 Psalm 33

Bless - ed the peo-ple the Lord has cho - sen to be his own.

917 Psalm 34

Taste and see the good - ness of the Lord.

918 Psalm 34

The Lord hears the cry of the poor.

919 Psalm 34

The an - gel of the Lord will res - cue those who fear him.

920 Psalm 40

Here am I, Lord; here am I, Lord; I come to do your will.

921 Psalm 40

Lord, come to my aid, Lord, come to my aid!

922 Psalm 41

Lord, heal my soul, for I have sinned a - gainst you.

923 Psalm 42

Like a deer that longs for run - ning streams, my

soul longs for you, my God; my soul longs for you, my God.

Psalm 45   924

The queen stands at your right hand, ar-rayed in gold.

Psalm 46   925

The wa-ters of the riv-er glad-den the cit-y of God, the

ho-ly dwell-ing of the Most High.

Psalm 47   926

God mounts his throne to shouts of joy: a blare of

trum-pets for the Lord.

Psalm 50   927

To the up-right I will show the sav-ing pow'r of God.

Psalm 51   928

Be mer-ci-ful, O Lord, for we have sinned.

Psalm 51   929

Cre-ate in me, cre-ate in me a clean heart, O God.

Psalm 51   930

I will rise and go to my fa-ther.

931 Psalm 54

The Lord up-holds my life.

932 Psalm 62

Rest in God a-lone, rest in God a-lone, my soul.

933 Psalm 63

My soul is thirst-ing for you, O Lord, thirst-ing for you my God.

934 Psalm 65

The seed that falls on good ground will yield a fruit-ful har-vest.

935 Psalm 66

Let all the earth cry out to God with joy.

936 Psalm 67

May God bless us in his mer - cy,

may God bless us in his mer - cy.

937 Psalm 67

O God, O God, let all the na-tions praise you!

938 Psalm 68

God, in your good-ness, you have made a home for the poor.

Psalm 69 — 939
Lord, in your great love, an-swer me.

Psalm 69 — 940
Turn to the Lord in your need, and you will live.

Psalm 71 — 941
I will sing of your sal - va - tion.

Psalm 71 — 942
Since my moth-er's womb, you have been my strength.

Psalm 72 — 943
Jus - tice shall flour - ish in his time, and full - ness of peace for ev - er.

Psalm 72 — 944
Lord, ev-'ry na-tion on earth will a - dore you.

Psalm 78 — 945
The Lord gave them bread from heav - en.

Psalm 78 — 946
Do not for - get the works of the Lord!

947 Psalm 80

Lord, make us turn to you; let us see your face and we shall be saved.

948 Psalm 80

The vine-yard of the Lord is the house of Is - ra - el.

949 Psalm 81

Sing with joy to God! Sing to God our help!

950 Psalm 84

Bless-ed are they who dwell in your house, O Lord.

951 Psalm 85

Lord, let us see your kind - ness, and grant us your sal - va - tion.

952 Psalm 86

Lord, you are good and for - giv - ing.

953 Psalm 89

For ev - er I will sing the good - ness of the Lord.

954 Psalm 89

The son of Da - vid will live for ev - er.

963 Psalm 96

Give the Lord glo-ry and hon - or.

964 Psalm 97

A light will shine on us this day: the Lord is born for us.

965 Psalm 97

The Lord is king, the Lord most high o-ver all the earth.

966 Psalm 98

All the ends of the earth have seen the sav - ing pow'r of God.

967 Psalm 98

The Lord has re-vealed to the na - tions his sav - ing pow'r, his

sav - ing pow'r.

968 Psalm 98

The Lord comes to rule the earth with jus - tice.

969 Psalm 98

Sing to the Lord a new song, for he has done mar-vel-ous deeds.

970 Psalm 100

We are his peo-ple, the sheep of his flock.

Psalm 103 — 971

The Lord is kind and mer-ci-ful; the Lord is kind and mer-ci-ful.

Psalm 103 — 972

The Lord has set his throne in heav - en.

Psalm 103 — 973

The Lord's kind - ness is ev-er - last - ing to those who fear him.

Psalm 103 — 974

The Lord is kind and mer - ci - ful, slow to an - ger, and

rich in com-pas - sion.

Psalm 104 — 975

O bless the Lord, my soul, O bless the Lord.

Psalm 104 — 976

Lord, send out your Spir - it, and re - new the face of the earth.

Psalm 105 — 977

The Lord re - mem - bers his cov - e - nant for ev - er.

Psalm 107 — 978

Give thanks to the Lord, his love is ev-er-last - ing.

979 Psalm 110

You are a priest for ev-er, in the line of Mel-chi-ze-dek.

980 Psalm 112

The just man is a light in dark-ness to the up-right.

981 Psalm 113

Praise the Lord, praise the Lord who lifts up the poor.

982 Psalm 116

I will walk be-fore the Lord, in the land of the liv - ing.

983 Psalm 116

Our bless-ing-cup is a com-mun-ion with the Blood of Christ.

984 Psalm 116

I will take the cup of sal-va-tion, and call on the name of the Lord.

985 Psalm 117

Go out to all the world and tell the Good News.

986 Psalm 118

Al-le-lu - ia, al-le-lu - ia, al-le-lu - ia!

Psalm 118   987

This is the day the Lord has made; let us re-joice and be glad.

Psalm 118   988

Give thanks to the Lord, for he is good, his love is ev - er - last - ing.

Psalm 118   989

The stone re - ject-ed by the build-ers has be-come the cor-ner - stone.

Psalm 119   990

Bless - ed are they who fol - low the law of the Lord!

Psalm 119   991

Lord, I love your com - mands.

Psalm 121   992

Our help is from the Lord, who made heav - en and earth.

Psalm 122   993

Let us go re - joic - ing to the house of the Lord.

Psalm 123   994

Our eyes are fixed on the Lord, plead-ing for his mer - cy.

995 Psalm 126

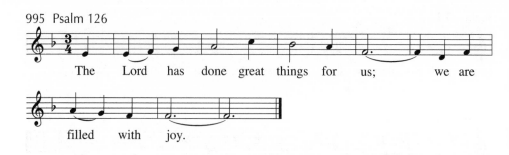

The Lord has done great things for us; we are filled with joy.

996 Psalm 128

Bless-ed are those who fear the Lord and walk in his ways.

997 Psalm 128

May the Lord bless and pro-tect us all the days of our lives.

998 Psalm 128

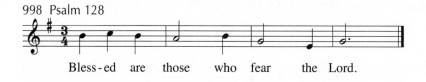

Bless-ed are those who fear the Lord.

999 Psalm 130

With the Lord there is mer - cy, and full-ness of re-demp-tion.

1000 Psalm 131

In you, O Lord, I have found my peace.

1001 Psalm 132

Lord, go up to the place of your rest, you and the ark of your ho-li-ness.

Psalm 137   1002

Let my tongue be si - lenced, if I ev - er for - get you!

Psalm 138   1003

In the sight of the an - gels, I will sing your prais-es, O Lord.

Psalm 138   1004

Lord, on the day I called for help, you an-swered me.

Psalm 138   1005

Lord, your love is e - ter - nal; do not for-sake the work of your hands.

Psalm 139   1006

I praise you, O Lord, for I am won-der-ful-ly made.

Psalm 145   1007

I will praise your name for ev - er, my king and my God.

Psalm 145   1008

The hand of the Lord feeds us; he an - swers all our needs.

Psalm 145   1009

The Lord is near to all who call on him.

1010 Psalm 146

Lord, come and save us.

1011 Psalm 146

Bless-ed the poor in spir-it; the king-dom of heav-en is theirs!

1012 Psalm 146

Praise the Lord, my soul! Praise the Lord!

1013 Psalm 147

O praise the Lord, Je - ru - sa - lem.

1014 Psalm 147

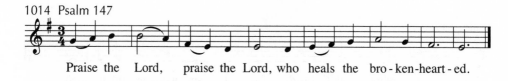

Praise the Lord, praise the Lord, who heals the bro - ken-heart - ed.

1015 Exodus 15

Let us sing to the Lord; he has cov-ered him-self in glo - ry.

1016 Isaiah 12

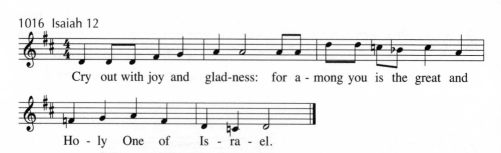

Cry out with joy and glad-ness: for a - mong you is the great and

Ho - ly One of Is - ra - el.

Isaiah 12 1017

You will draw wa-ter joy-ful-ly from the springs of sal - va - tion.

Daniel 3 1018

Glo - ry and praise for ev - er-more.

Luke 1 1019

My soul re - joic-es in my God, my soul re - joic-es in my God.

SERVICE MUSIC

1 © 1986, GIA Publications, Inc.

2 © 1987, GIA Publications, Inc.

3 Text: © 1963, 1986, The Grail, GIA Publications, Inc., agent. Music: © 1985, OCP Publcations. P.O. Box 13248, Portland, OR 97213-0248. All rights reserved. Used with permission.

5 Text: © 1992, GIA Publications, Inc. Harm.: © 1987, GIA Publications, Inc.

6 Music: © 1986, GIA Publications, Inc.

7 Music: © 1986, GIA Publications, Inc.

8 © 1986, GIA Publications, Inc.

10 Text: © William G. Storey. Acc.: © 1975, GIA Publications, Inc.

11 © 1979, GIA Publications, Inc.

13 Text: © 2004, GIA Publications, Inc. Music: © 1979, 1988, GIA Publications, Inc.

14 Harm.: © 1986, GIA Publications, Inc.

15 Music: © 1980, 1993, World Library Publications, a division of J.S. Paluch Company, Inc. Schiller Park, IL 60176. All rights reserved. Used by permission.

16 © 1986, GIA Publications, Inc.

17 Text: © 1989, GIA Publications, Inc., refrain trans. © 1969, ICEL. Music: © 1989, GIA Publications, Inc.

18 Text: © 1993, GIA Publications, Inc.; refrain trans., © 1969, ICEL. Music: © 1993, GIA Publications, Inc.

19 Text: © 1988, GIA Publications, Inc.; refrain III trans. © 1969, ICEL. Music: © 1988, 1994, GIA Publications, Inc.

20 Text: © 1983, GIA Publications, Inc.; refrain trans. © 1969, ICEL. © 1983, GIA Publications, Inc.

21 Text: © 2003, GIA Publications, Inc. English refrain trans. © 1969, ICEL; Spanish refrain trans., © admin. by Obra Nacional de la Buena Prensa. Music: © 2003, GIA Publications, Inc.

22 Text: © 1983, GIA Publications, Inc.; refrain trans. © 1969, ICEL. Music: © 1983, GIA Publications, Inc.

23 © 1986, GIA Publications, Inc.

24 Antiphons: © 1963, The Grail, GIA Publications, Inc., agent. Psalm tone: © 1975, GIA Publications, Inc. Gelineau Tone: © 1963, 1993, The Grail, GIA Publications, Inc., agent

25 Text: © 1993, GIA Publications, Inc.; refrain I trans. © 1969, ICEL. Music: © 1993, GIA Publications, Inc.

26 Text: © 1982, GIA Publications, Inc.; refrain trans. © 1969, ICEL. Music: © 1982, GIA Publications, Inc.

27 Text: © 1985, GIA Publications, Inc.; refrain trans. © 1969, ICEL. Music: © 1985, GIA Publications, Inc.

28 Text: © 2000, GIA Publications, Inc.; refrain trans. © 1969, ICEL. Music: © 2000, GIA Publications, Inc.

29 © 1983, GIA Publications, Inc.

30 Text: Verses, © 1963, 1993, The Grail, GIA Publications, Inc., agent; refrain, © 1985, Paul Inwood. Music: © 1985, Paul Inwood. Published by OCP Publicaitons. P.O. Box 13248, Portland, OR 97213-0248. All rights reserved. Used with permission.

31 © 1993, GIA Publications, Inc.

32 Text: © 1987, 1994, GIA Publications, Inc.; refrain trans. © 1969, ICEL. Music: © 1987, 1994, GIA Publications, Inc.

33 © 1978, 1991, John B. Foley, SJ, and OCP Publications. P.O. Box 13248, Portland, OR 97213-0248. All rights reserved. Used with permission.

34 Text: © 1980, GIA Publications, Inc.; refrain trans. © 1969, ICEL. Music: © 1980, GIA Publications, Inc.

35 Verse text and music: © 1971, 1991, North American Liturgy Resources. Published by OCP Publications. P.O. Box 13248, Portland, OR 97213-0248. All rights reserved. Used with permission. Refrain trans. © 1969, ICEL.

36 Text: © 1983, GIA Publications, Inc.; refrain trans. © 1969, ICEL. Music: © 1983, GIA Publications, Inc.

37 Text: © 1987, GIA Publications, Inc.; refrain I trans. © 1969, ICEL. Music: © 1987, GIA Publications, Inc.

38 Text: © 2003, GIA Publications, Inc.; English refrain trans. © 1969, ICEL; Spanish refrain trans. © 1970, Conferencia Episcopal Española. Music: © 2003, GIA Publications, Inc.

39 Text: © 1963, 1993, The Grail, GIA Publications, Inc., agent; refrain trans. © 1969, ICEL. Music: © 1998, GIA Publications, Inc.

40 © 1963, 1993, The Grail, GIA Publications, Inc., agent. Psalm tone: © Gethsemani Abbey

41 Text: © 1983, GIA Publications, Inc.; refrain trans. © 1969, ICEL. Music: © 1983, GIA Publications, Inc.

42 © 1982, GIA Publications, Inc.

43 Text: Verse adapt., © 1970, Confraternity of Christian Doctrine, Washington, DC. Refrain text and music: © 1987, GIA Publications, Inc.

44 Antiphon I text: © 1969, 1981, ICEL. Antiphon I music: © 1975, GIA Publications, Inc. Antiphon II: © 1979, GIA Publications, Inc. Psalm tone: © 1986, GIA Publications, Inc. Gelineau tone and psalm text: © 1963, The Grail, GIA Publications, Inc., agent

45 © 1982, GIA Publications, Inc.

46 © 1987, 1994, GIA Publications, Inc.

47 © 1982, GIA Publications, Inc.

48 Text: © 1983, GIA Publications, Inc.; refrain trans. © 1969, ICEL. Music: © 1983, GIA Publications, Inc.

49 Verse text: © 1963, 1993, The Grail, GIA Publications, Inc., agent. Alt. text: © 1988, 1993, GIA Publications, Inc., refrain trans. © 1969, ICEL. Music: © 1988, 1994, GIA Publications, Inc.

50 © 1980, GIA Publications, Inc.

51 © 1983, 1994, GIA Publications, Inc.

52 Verse tr.: © 1970, Confraternity of Christian Doctrine, Washington, DC.; refrain tr. © 1969, ICEL. Music: © 1976, GIA Publications, Inc.

53 © 1998, GIA Publications, Inc.

54 Text: © 1989, GIA Publications, Inc., refrain trans. © 1969, ICEL. Music: © 1989, 1994, GIA Publications, Inc.

55 © 1983, 1994, GIA Publications, Inc.

56 © 1983, GIA Publications, Inc.

57 Text and Gelineau tone: © 1963, 1993, The Grail, GIA Publications, Inc., agent. Music: © 1986, GIA Publications, Inc.

58 © 1993, GIA Publications, Inc.

59 Text: © 1983, GIA Publications, Inc.; refrain trans. © 1969, ICEL. Music: © 1983, GIA Publications, Inc.

60 Text: © 1985, GIA Publications, Inc.; refrain trans. © 1969, ICEL. Music: © 1985, GIA Publications, Inc.

61 Text: © 2003, GIA Publications, Inc.; Spanish refrain trans. © 1970, Conferencia Episcopal Española. Music: © 2003, GIA Publications, Inc.

62 Text: © 1987, GIA Publications, Inc.; refrain II trans. © 1969, ICEL. Music: © 1987, GIA Publications, Inc.

63 © 1983, GIA Publications, Inc.

Acknowledgments/*continued*

Acknowledgments/*continued*

452 © 1975, 1979, Robert J. Dufford, SJ and OCP Publications. P.O. Box 13248, Portland, OR 97213-0248. All rights reserved. Used with permission.

453 Text: © 1975, 1995, Hope Publishing Co., Carol Stream, IL 60188. All rights reserved. Used by permission. Tune: © 2003, GIA Publications, Inc.

455 © 1984, Les Presses de Taizé, GIA Publications, Inc., agent

456 Text: from *Oxford Book of Carols,* © Oxford University Press. Acc.: © 1987, GIA Publications, Inc.

458 Text: © 1978, *Lutheran Book of Worship.* Administered by Augsburg Fortress. Used by permission. Tune: © 1975, 1988, Richard Hillert

462 Text and tune: © 1973, Word of God Music. (Administered by THE COPYRIGHT COMPANY NASHVILLE, TN) All rights reserved. International Copyright Secured. Used by permission. Descant harm.: © 1979, CELEBRATION c/o THE COPYRIGHT COMPANY, NASHVILLE, TN) All rights reserved. International Copyright Secured. Used by permission.

464 Text: © 1991, 2003, GIA Publications, Inc. Tune: © 2003, GIA Publications, Inc.

465 © 1988, Iona Community, GIA Publications, Inc., agent

466 Text: © 1978, Hope Publishing Co. Tune: © 1942, 1970, Hope Publishing Co., Carol Stream, IL 60188. All rights reserved. Used by permission.

467 Text tr.: © 1978, *Lutheran Book of Worship.* Administered by Augsburg Fortress. Used by permission. Harm.: from *The English Hymnal,* © Oxford University Press

469 Text: © 1991, GIA Publications, Inc. Tune: from *The English Hymnal,* © Oxford University Press

470 Text tr.: © 1983, Peter J. Scagnelli. Acc.: © Interkerkelijke Stichting voor het Kerklied Den Haag

471 Tune: from *The English Hymnal,* © Oxford University Press

472 Harm.: © 1986, GIA Publications, Inc.

473 © 1997, GIA Publications, Inc.

474 Acc.: © 1975, GIA Publications, Inc.

475 Text tr.: © 1971, John W. Grant. Acc.: © 1975, GIA Publications, Inc.

476 © 1981, 1982, 1987, GIA Publications, Inc.

477 © 1989, GIA Publications, Inc.

478 © 1979, Les Presses de Taizé, GIA Publications, Inc. agent

479 © 1998, Les Presses de Taizé, GIA Publications, Inc., agent.

480 © 2002, GIA Publications, Inc.

481 © 1987, GIA Publications, Inc.

482 Text: © Timothy Wright. Arr.: © 2000, GIA Publications, Inc.

484 © 2002, 2003, GIA Publications, Inc.

485 Text tr.: © 1959, The Liturgical Press. Harm.: © 1958, Ralph Jusko Publications, Inc.

487 Text: © 1986, Hope Publishing Co., Carol Stream, IL 60188. All rights reserved. Used by permission. Tune: © 1993, GIA Publications, Inc.

488 Text: © 1989, Hope Publishing Co., Carol Stream, IL 60188. All rights reserved. Used by permission. Arr.: © 1991, GIA Publications, Inc.

490 Harm.: © 1975, GIA Publications, Inc.

491 Text: from *Enlarged Songs of Praise,* © Oxford University Press

492 Text: © 1941, Irene C. Mueller. Harm.: © 1986, GIA Publications, Inc.

494 Text: © 1966, 1982, Willard F. Jabusch. Administered by OCP Publications. P.O. Box 13248, Portland, OR 97213-0248. All rights reserved. Used with permission. Harm.: © 1986, GIA Publications, Inc.

495 © 1980, GIA Publications, Inc.

496 © 1953, Stuart K. Hine. Assigned to Manna Music, Inc., 35255 Brooten Road, Pacific City, OR 97135. Renewed 1981. All Rights Reserved. Used by Permission. (ASCAP)

497 © 1985, GIA Publications, Inc.

498 © 1989, GIA Publications, Inc.

499 © 1991, GIA Publications, Inc.

500 © 1993, World Library Publications, a division of J.S. Paluch Company, Inc. Schiller Park, IL 60176. All rights reserved. Used by permission.

501 Arr.: © 1997, Iona Community, GIA Publications, Inc., agent.

502 © 1978, John B. Foley, SJ, and OCP Publications. P.O. Box 13248, Portland, OR 97213-0248. All rights reserved. Used with permission.

503 © 2002, GIA Publications, Inc.

504 © 1979, OCP Publications. P.O. Box 13248, Portland, OR 97213-0248. All rights reserved. Used with permission.

505 © 1991, 1992, Jaime Cortez. Published by OCP Publications. P.O. Box 13248, Portland, OR 97213-0248. All rights reserved. Used with permission.

506 © 2002, 2003, GIA Publications, Inc.

507 Text: © 1996, Hope Publishing Co., Carol Stream, IL 60188. All rights reserved. Used by permission. Tune: © 2001, GIA Publications, Inc.

508 © 1992, GIA Publications, Inc.

509 © 1992, Bernadette Farrell. Published by OCP Publications. P.O. Box 13248, Portland, OR 97213-0248. All rights reserved. Used with permission.

510 © 1998, Les Presses de Taizé, GIA Publications, Inc., agent

511 © 1985, GIA Publications, Inc.

512 © 1993, 2000, Bernadette Farrell. Published by OCP Publications. P.O. Box 13248, Portland, OR 97213-0248. All rights reserved. Used with permission.

513 Text and Tune: © 1970, 1975, CELEBRATION (Administered by THE COPYRIGHT COMPANY, NASHVILLE, TN) All Rights Reserved. International Copyright Secured. Used By Permission. Acc.: © 1987, GIA Publications, Inc.

514 Harm.: © 1992, Horace Clarence Boyer

515 © 1966, Vernacular Hymns Publishing Co.

516 © 1984, Utryck, Walton Music Corp.

517 © 1986, Bernadette Farrell. Published by OCP Publications. P.O. Box 13248, Portland, OR 97213-0248. All rights reserved. Used with permission.

518 Text: © 1966, The Hymn Society. (Admin. by Hope Publishing Co., Carol Stream, IL 60188). All rights reserved. Used by permission.

521 © 2002, GIA Publications, Inc.

522 © 1979, Les Presses de Taizé, GIA Publications, Inc., agent

523 Music: from *The English Hymnal,* © Oxford University Press.

524 © 1999, GIA Publications, Inc.

525 Text: © 1991, GIA Publications, Inc. Harm.: © 1986, GIA Publications, Inc.

526 © 1981, Robert J. Dufford, SJ, and OCP Publications. P.O. Box 13248, Portland, OR 97213-0248. All rights reserved. Used with permission.

527 © 1990, GIA Publications, Inc.

528 © 1980, Les Presses de Taizé, GIA Publications, Inc., agent

529 © 1984, Utryck, Walton Music Corp., agent

530 © 1998, Les Presses de Taizé, GIA Publications, Inc., agent

532 Text and tune: © 1981, Ernest Sands. Acc.: © 1986, Paul Inwood. Published by OCP Publications. P.O. Box 13248, Portland, OR 97213-0248. All rights reserved. Used with permission.

Acknowledgments/*continued*

533 © 1998, Les Presses de Taizé, GIA Publications, Inc., agent

534 © 2002, GIA Publications, Inc.

535 © 1979, Les Presses de Taizé, GIA Publications, Inc., agent

536 Descant: © 1953, Novello and Co. Ltd.

537 © 1976, Daniel L. Schutte and OCP Publications. P.O. Box 13248, Portland, OR 97213-0248. All rights reserved. Used with permission.

538 © 1983, 1987, GIA Publications, Inc.

539 Text: © 1972, Hope Publishing Co., Carol Stream, IL 60188. All rights reserved. Used by permission.

540 © 1978, Damean Music. Distributed by GIA Publications, Inc.

541 Text: © 1973, Hope Publishing Co. Tune: © 1973, Jubilate Hymns, Ltd. (Admin. by Hope Publishing Co., Carol Stream, IL 60188). All rights reserved. Used by permission.

542 Harm.: © 1986, GIA Publications, Inc.

543 © 1981, 1993, Roc O'Connor, SJ, and OCP Publications. P.O. Box 13248, Portland, OR 97213-0248. All rights reserved. Used with permission.

544 © 1972, Daniel L. Schutte. Published by OCP Publications. P.O. Box 13248, Portland, OR 97213-0248. All rights reserved. Used with permission.

546 © 1986, 1991, Les Presses de Taizé, GIA Publications, Inc., agent

547 Text: © 1940, The Church Pension Fund. Used by permission of Church Publishing Incorporated, New York.

550 © 1982, 1991, Les Presses de Taizé, GIA Publications, Inc., agent

551 Text: © 1939, 1966, E. C. Schirmer Music Co., Boston, MA. Harm.: © The Royal School of Church Music

552 Harm.: © 1986, GIA Publications, Inc.

553 © 1998, GIA Publications, Inc.

554 © 1995, Veritas Publications/Liam Lawton, GIA Publications, Inc., agent

555 © 1953, Doris M. Akers. All rights administered by Unichappell Music, Inc. International Copyright Secured. All rights reserved.

556 © 2000, GIA Publications, Inc.

557 © 2003, GIA Publications, Inc.

558 © 1989, Iona Community, GIA Publications, Inc., agent

559 © 1987, GIA Publications, Inc.

560 Text: from *Enlarged Songs of Praise,* by permission of Oxford University Press. Harm.: © 1975, Hope Publishing Co., Carol Stream, IL 60188. All rights reserved. Used by permission.

561 © 2002, GIA Publications, Inc.

562 © 2003, GIA Publications, Inc.

563 Text: © 1987, Oxford University Press. Tune: © 2003, GIA Publications, Inc.

564 © 1964 (renewed), Appleseed Music, Inc.

565 © 1997, GIA Publications, Inc.

566 © 1982, Les Presses de Taizé, GIA Publications, Inc., agent

567 Arr.: © 2003, GIA Publications, Inc.

568 Verse text and tune: © 1998, GIA Publications, Inc.

569 © 1988, 1999, Jesse Manibusan. Published by OCP Publications. P.O. Box 13248, Portland, OR 97213-0248. All rights reserved. Used with permission.

570 Text and harm.: © 2003, GIA Publications, Inc.

571 Text: © 2002, GIA Publications, Inc. Tune: © 2003, GIA Publications, Inc.

572 Text: © 1993, Hope Publishing Co., Carol Stream, IL 60188. All rights reserved. Used by permission. Tune: © 2003, GIA Publications, Inc.

573 © 1996, World Library Publications, a division of J.S. Paluch Company, Inc. Schiller Park, IL 60176. All rights reserved. Used by permission.

574 Text: © 1996, Oxford University Press. Tune: © 1998, GIA Publications, Inc

575 Text: © 1992, GIA Publications, Inc. Tune: © 2003, GIA Publications, Inc.

576 © 1998, Les Presses de Taizé, GIA Publications, Inc., agent

577 Text and tune adapt.: © 1997, GIA Publications, Inc.

578 © 1980, GIA Publications, Inc.

580 Text: Verses, © 1963, 1993, The Grail, GIA Publications, Inc., agent; refrain, © 1985, Paul Inwood. Tune: © 1985, Paul Inwood. Published by OCP Publications. P.O. Box 13248, Portland, OR 97213-0248. All rights reserved. Used with permission.

581 © 1989, GIA Publications, Inc.

582 © 1976 by John B. Foley, SJ, and OCP Publications. P.O. Box 13248, Portland, OR 97213-0248. All rights reserved. Used with permission.

583 Tune: © 1984, GIA Publications, Inc.

584 © 1993, World Library Publications, a division of J.S. Paluch Company, Inc. Schiller Park, IL 60176. All rights reserved. Used by permission.

585 © 1976, 1979, Daniel L. Schutte and OCP Publications. P.O. Box 13248, Portland, OR 97213-0248. All rights reserved. Used with permission.

586 Acc.: © 1993, GIA Publications, Inc.

587 Harm.: © 1975, GIA Publications, Inc.

589 © 1994, GIA Publications, Inc.

590 © 1971, Daniel L. Schutte. Published by OCP Publications. P.O. Box 13248, Portland, OR 97213-0248. All rights reserved. Used with permission.

591 © 1976, John B. Foley, SJ and OCP Publications. P.O. Box 13248, Portland, OR 97213-0248. All rights reserved. Used with permission.

592 © 1980, Savgos Music, Inc. Administered by Malaco Music Group. P.O. Box 9287, Jackson, MS 39206

593 © 1979, OCP Publications. P.O. Box 13248, Portland, OR 97213-0248. All rights reserved. Used with permission.

594 Text tr.: © 1978, *Lutheran Book of Worship.* Administered by Augsburg Fortress. Used by permission.

595 © 1975, Daniel L. Schutte and OCP Publications. P.O. Box 13248, Portland, OR 97213-0248. All rights reserved. Used with permission.

596 © 1975, 1978, Robert J. Dufford, SJ, and OCP Publications. P.O. Box 13248, Portland, OR 97213-0248. All rights reserved. Used with permission.

597 © 1969, 1979, Damean Music. Distributed by GIA Publications, Inc.

598 Harm.: © 1988, GIA Publications, Inc.

599 © 1979, OCP Publications. P.O. Box 13248, Portland, OR 97213-0248. All rights reserved. Used with permission.

600 © 1972, Maranatha! Music and CCCM Music (Administered by THE COPYRIGHT COMPANY, NASHVILLE, TN) All rights reserved. International Copyright Secured. Used By Permission.

601 Text tr.: © 1975, 1986, GIA Publications, Inc. Acc.: © 1986, GIA Publications, Inc.

602 © 1969, Concordia Publishing House. Acc.: © 1975, GIA Publications, Inc.

604 Text: © 1992, GIA Publications, Inc.

605 © 2001, GIA Publications, Inc.

606 © Schaff Music Publishing

607 © 1988, GIA Publications, Inc.

608 © 1987, GIA Publications, Inc.

Acknowledgments/*continued*

Acknowledgments/*continued*

Acknowledgments/*continued*

Scripture Passages Related to Hymns/*continued*

Scripture Passages Related to Hymns/*continued*

Scripture Passages Related to Hymns/*continued*

Scripture Passages Related to Hymns/*continued*

1022 Suggested Psalms for the Church Year

ADVENT

Seasonal Psalms
> Psalm 25: To You, O Lord   26
> Psalm 85: Lord, Let Us See Your Kindness   48

ADVENT I
> A - Psalm 122: Let Us Go Rejoicing   68
> Psalm 122: Let Us Go Rejoicing   993
> B - Psalm 80/85/Luke 1: Lord, Make Us Turn to You
> 47
> Psalm 80: Lord, Make Us Turn   947
> C - Psalm 25: To You, O Lord   26
> Psalm 25: To You, O Lord   900

ADVENT II
> A - Psalm 72: Every Nation on Earth   46
> Psalm 72: Justice Shall Flourish   943
> B - Psalm 85: Lord, Let Us See Your Kindness   48
> Psalm 85: Lord, Let Us See Your Kindness   951
> C - Psalm 126: God Has Done Great Things for Us
> 69
> Psalm 126: The Lord Has Done Great Things
> 995

ADVENT III
> A - Psalm 146: Lord, Come and Save Us   1010
> B - Magnificat / Luke 1:46-55   84
> Holy Is Your Name / Luke 1:46-55   83
> Luke 1: My Soul Rejoices   1019
> C - Isaiah 12:2-3, 4, 6   81
> Isaiah 12: Cry Out with Joy   1016

ADVENT IV
> A - Psalm 24: We Long to See Your Face   25
> Psalm 24: Let the Lord Enter   897
> B - Psalm 89: For Ever I Will Sing   49
> Psalm 89: For Ever I Will Sing   953
> C - Psalm 80/85/Luke 1: Lord, Make Us Turn to You
> 47
> Psalm 80: Lord, Make Us Turn   947

CHRISTMAS

Seasonal Psalm
> Psalm 98: All the Ends of the Earth   55

CHRISTMAS/VIGIL
> Psalm 89: For Ever I Will Sing   49
> Psalm 89: For Ever I Will Sing   953

CHRISTMAS/MASS AT MIDNIGHT
> Psalm 96: Today Is Born Our Savior   52
> Psalm 96: Today Is Born Our Savior   961

CHRISTMAS/MASS AT DAWN
> Psalm 97: A Light Will Shine   964

CHRISTMAS/MASS DURING THE DAY
> Psalm 98: All the Ends of the Earth   55
> Psalm 98: All the Ends of the Earth   966

HOLY FAMILY
> Psalm 84: Blessed Are They   950
> Psalm 105: The Lord Remembers   977
> Psalm 128: Blessed Are Those   996
> Psalm 128: Blest Are Those Who Love You   70

MARY, MOTHER OF GOD
> Psalm 67: May God Bless Us   936
> Psalm 72: Lord, Every Nation   944

EPIPHANY
> Psalm 72: Every Nation on Earth   46
> Psalm 72: Lord, Every Nation   944

BAPTISM OF THE LORD
> Psalm 29: The Lord Will Bless   908
> Psalm 104: O Bless the Lord   975
> Isaiah 12: You Will Draw Water   1017

LENT

Seasonal Psalms
> Psalm 51: Be Merciful, O Lord   39
> Psalm 51: Have Mercy, Lord   40
> Psalm 91: Be with Me   50
> Psalm 130: With the Lord There Is Mercy   71

ASH WEDNESDAY
> Psalm 51: Be Merciful, O Lord   39
> Psalm 51: Be Merciful, O Lord   928
> Psalm 51: Have Mercy, Lord   40

LENT I
> A - Psalm 51: Be Merciful, O Lord   39
> Psalm 51: Have Mercy, Lord   40
> Psalm 51: Be Merciful, O Lord   928
> B - Psalm 25: Remember Your Mercies   27
> Psalm 25: Your Ways, O Lord   901
> C - Psalm 91: Be with Me   50
> Psalm 91: Be with Me   957

LENT II
> A - Psalm 33: Let Your Mercy Be on Us   32
> Psalm 33: Lord, Let Your Mercy   914
> B - Psalm 116: I Will Walk Before the Lord   982
> C - Psalm 27: The Lord Is My Light   29
> Psalm 27: The Lord Is My Light   905

LENT III
> A - Psalm 95: If Today You Hear God's Voice   51
> Psalm 95: If Today You Hear His Voice   960
> B - Psalm 19: Lord, You Have the Words   20
> Psalm 19: Lord, You Have the Words   888
> C - Psalm 103: The Lord Is Kind and Merciful   58
> Psalm 103: The Lord Is Kind and Merciful   59
> Psalm 103: The Lord Is Kind and Merciful   971

LENT IV
> A - Psalm 23: My Shepherd Is the Lord   24
> Psalm 23: Shepherd Me, O God   23
> Psalm 23: The Lord Is My Shepherd   894
> B - Psalm 137: Let My Tongue Be Silenced   1002
> C - Psalm 34: Taste and See   34
> Psalm 34: Taste and See   917

LENT V
> A - Psalm 130: With the Lord, There Is Mercy   71
> Psalm 130: With The Lord   999
> B - Psalm 51: Create in Me   37
> Psalm 51: Create in Me   38
> Psalm 51: Create in Me   929
> C - Psalm 126: God Has Done Great Things for Us
> 69
> Psalm 126: The Lord Has Done Great Things
> 995

HOLY WEEK

Seasonal Psalm
> Psalm 22: My God, My God   22
> Psalm 22: My God, My God   892

Suggested Psalms for the Church Year/*continued*

PASSION SUNDAY
Psalm 22: My God, My God   22
Psalm 22: My God, My God   892

HOLY THURSDAY
Psalm 116: Our Blessing-Cup   61
Psalm 116: Our Blessing-Cup   63
Psalm 116: Our Blessing-Cup   983
Psalm 116: The Name of God   62

GOOD FRIDAY
Psalm 31: I Put My Life in Your Hands / Pongo Mi
Vida   31
Psalm 31: Father, Into Your Hands   910

EASTER VIGIL
Seasonal Psalm
Psalm 136: Love Is Never Ending   73

EASTER VIGIL
1 - Psalm 104: Lord, Send Out Your Spirit   60
Psalm 104: Lord, Send Out Your Spirit   976
Psalm 33: Let Your Mercy Be on Us   32
Psalm 33: The Earth Is Full   915
2 - Psalm 16: Keep Me Safe, O God   18
Psalm 16: You Are My Inheritance   883
Psalm 16: You Will Show Me the Path of Life
19
3 - Song at the Sea / Exodus 15   80
Exodus 15: Let Us Sing   1015
4 - Psalm 30: I Will Praise You, Lord   30
Psalm 30: I Will Praise You, Lord   909
5 - Isaiah 12:2-3, 4, 6   81
Isaiah 12: You Will Draw Water   1017
6 - Psalm 19: Lord, You Have the Words   20
Psalm 19: Lord, You Have the Words   888
7 - Psalm 51: Create in Me   37
 -   Psalm 51: Create in Me   38
Psalm 51: Create in Me   929
Psalm 42: Like a Deer   923
Alleluia: Psalm 118: Alleluia, Alleluia   986

EASTER
Seasonal Psalms
Psalm 118: Let Us Rejoice   65
Psalm 118: This Is the Day   64
Psalm 66: Let All the Earth   45

EASTER SUNDAY
Psalm 118: Let Us Rejoice   65
Psalm 118: This Is the Day   64
Psalm 118: This Is the Day   987

EASTER II
Psalm 118: Give Thanks to the Lord   988
Psalm 118: Let Us Rejoice   65
Psalm 118: This Is the Day   64

EASTER III
A - Psalm 16: You Will Show Me the Path of Life
19
Psalm 16: Lord, You Will Show Us the Path of
Life   884
B - Psalm 4: Lord, Let Your Face Shine on Us   879
C - Psalm 30: I Will Praise You, Lord   30
Psalm 30: I Will Praise You, Lord   909

EASTER IV
A - Psalm 23: My Shepherd Is the Lord   24
Psalm 23: Shepherd Me, O God   23

Psalm 23: The Lord Is My Shepherd   894
B - Psalm 118: Let Us Rejoice   65
Psalm 118: The Stone Rejected by the Builders
989
Psalm 118: This Is the Day   64
C - Psalm 100: We Are God's People   56
Psalm 100: We Are His People   970

EASTER V
A - Psalm 33: Let Your Mercy Be on Us   32
Psalm 33: Lord, Let Your Mercy   914
B - Psalm 22: I Will Praise You, Lord   893
C - Psalm 145: I Will Praise Your Name   76
Psalm 145: I Will Praise Your Name   1007

EASTER VI
A - Psalm 66: Let All the Earth   45
Psalm 66: Let All the Earth   935
B - Psalm 98: All the Ends of the Earth   55
Psalm 98: The Lord Has Revealed   967
C - Psalm 67: Let All the Nations   937

ASCENSION
Psalm 47: God Mounts His Throne   36
Psalm 47: God Mounts His Throne   926

EASTER VII
A - Psalm 27: I Believe that I Shall See   906
Psalm 27: I Believe that I Shall See   907
B - Psalm 103: The Lord Has Set His Throne   972
Psalm 103: The Lord Is Kind and Merciful   58
Psalm 103: The Lord Is Kind and Merciful   59
C - Psalm 97: the Lord Is King!   965

PENTECOST
Psalm 104: Lord, Send Out Your Spirit   60
Psalm 104: Lord, Send Out Your Spirit   976

TRINITY SUNDAY
A - Daniel 3: Glory and Praise   1018
B - Psalm 33: Let Your Mercy Be on Us   32
Psalm 33: Blessed the People   916
C - Psalm 8: O Lord, Our God, How Wonderful Your
Name   880

BODY AND BLOOD OF CHRIST
A - Psalm 147: Bless the Lord, My Soul   77
Psalm 147: O Praise the Lord   1013
B - Psalm 116: The Name of God   62
Psalm 116: I Will Take the Cup   984
C - Psalm 110: You Are a Priest For Ever   979

SACRED HEART
A - Psalm 103: The Lord Is Kind and Merciful   58
Psalm 103: The Lord Is Kind and Merciful   59
Psalm 103: The Lord's Kindness   973
B - Isaiah 12:2-3, 4, 6   81
Isaiah 12: You Will Draw Water   1017
C - Psalm 23: My Shepherd Is the Lord   24
Psalm 23: Shepherd Me, O God   23
Psalm 23: The Lord Is My Shepherd   894

ORDINARY TIME
Seasonal Psalms
Psalm 19: Lord, You Have the Words   20
Psalm 27: The Lord Is My Light and My Salvation
29
Psalm 34: Taste and See   34
Psalm 63: My Soul Is Thirsting   43
Psalm 63: My Soul Is Thirsting   44

Suggested Psalms for the Church Year/*continued*

Psalm 63: Your Love Is Finer Than Life 42
Psalm 95: If Today You Hear God's Voice 51
Psalm 100: We Are God's People 56
Psalm 103: The Lord Is Kind and Merciful 58
Psalm 103: The Lord Is Kind and Merciful 59
Psalm 145: I Will Praise Your Name 76

LAST WEEKS IN ORDINARY TIME
Seasonal Psalms
Psalm 122: Let Us Go Rejoicing 68

ORDINARY TIME
SECOND SUNDAY
A - Psalm 40: Here I Am 35
    Psalm 40: Here Am I, Lord 920
B - Psalm 40: Here I Am 35
    Psalm 40: Here Am I, Lord 920
C - Psalm 96: Proclaim to All the Nations 54
    Psalm 96: Proclaim His Marvelous Deeds 962

THIRD SUNDAY
A - Psalm 27: The Lord Is My Light 29
    Psalm 27: The Lord Is My Light 905
B - Psalm 25: Remember Your Mercies 27
    Psalm 25: Teach Me Your Ways 902
C - Psalm 19: Lord, You Have the Words 20
    Psalm 19: Your Words, O Lord 889

FOURTH SUNDAY
A - Psalm 146: Blessed the Poor in Spirit 1011
B - Psalm 95: If Today You Hear God's Voice 51
    Psalm 95: If Today You Hear His Voice 960
C - Psalm 71: I Will Sing 941

FIFTH SUNDAY
A - Psalm 112: The Just Man 980
B - Psalm 147: Bless the Lord, My Soul 77
    Psalm 147: Praise the Lord Who Heals 1014
C - Psalm 138: In the Sight of the Angels 1003
    Psalm 138: The Fragrance of Christ 74

SIXTH SUNDAY
A - Psalm 66: Let All the Earth 45
- Psalm 66: Let All the Earth 935
B - Psalm 32: I Turn to You, O Lord 912
C - Psalm 1: Blessed Are They 878

SEVENTH SUNDAY
A - Psalm 103: The Lord Is Kind and Merciful 58
    Psalm 103: The Lord Is Kind and Merciful 59
    Psalm 103: The Lord Is Kind and Merciful 971
B - Psalm 41: Lord, Heal My Soul 922
C - Psalm 103: The Lord Is Kind and Merciful 58
    Psalm 103: The Lord Is Kind and Merciful 59
    Psalm 103: The Lord Is Kind and Merciful 971

EIGHTH SUNDAY
A - Psalm 62: Rest in God Alone 932
B - Psalm 103: The Lord Is Kind and Merciful 58
    Psalm 103: The Lord Is Kind and Merciful 59
    Psalm 103: The Lord Is Kind and Merciful 971
C - Psalm 92: Lord, It Is Good 958

NINTH SUNDAY
A - Psalm 31: I Put My Life in Your Hands / Pongo
    Mi Vida 31
    Psalm 31: Lord, Be My Rock 911
B - Psalm 81: Sing with Joy 949
C - Psalm 117: Go Out to All the World 985

TENTH SUNDAY
A - Psalm 50: To the Upright 927
B - Psalm 130: With the Lord There Is Mercy 71
    Psalm 130: With The Lord 999
C - Psalm 30: I Will Praise You, Lord 30
    Psalm 30: I Will Praise You, Lord 909

ELEVENTH SUNDAY
A - Psalm 100: We Are His People 970
B - Psalm 92: Lord, It Is Good 958
C - Psalm 32: Lord, Forgive the Wrong 913

TWELFTH SUNDAY
A - Psalm 69: Lord, in Your Great Love 939
B - Psalm 107: Give Thanks to the Lord 978
C - Psalm 63: My Soul Is Thirsting 43
    Psalm 63: My Soul Is Thirsting 44
    Psalm 63: My Soul Is Thirsting 933
    Psalm 63: Your Love Is Finer Than Life 42

THIRTEENTH SUNDAY
A - Psalm 89: For Ever I Will Sing 89
B - Psalm 30: I Will Praise You, Lord 30
    Psalm 30: I Will Praise You, Lord 909
C - Psalm 16: You Are My Inheritance 885
    Psalm 16: You Will Show Me the Path of Life
    19

FOURTEENTH SUNDAY
A - Psalm 145: I Will Praise Your Name 76
    Psalm 145: I Will Praise Your Name 1007
B - Psalm 123: Our Eyes Are Fixed 994
C - Psalm 66: Let All the Earth 45
    Psalm 66: Let All the Earth 935

FIFTEENTH SUNDAY
A - Psalm 65: The Seed that Falls 934
B - Psalm 85: Let Us See Your Kindness 48
    Psalm 85: Lord, Let Us See Your Kindness 951
C - Psalm 19: Your Words, O Lord 889
    Psalm 69: Turn to the Lord 940

SIXTEENTH SUNDAY
A - Psalm 86: Lord, You Are Good 952
B - Psalm 23: My Shepherd Is the Lord 24
    Psalm 23: Shepherd Me, O God 23
    Psalm 23: The Lord Is My Shepherd 894
C - Psalm 15: He Who Does Justice 881
    Psalm 15: They Who Do Justice 17

SEVENTEENTH SUNDAY
A - Psalm 119: Lord, I Love Your Commands 991
B - Psalm 145: I Will Praise Your Name 76
C - Psalm 138: The Fragrance of Christ 134

EIGHTEENTH SUNDAY
A - Psalm 145: I Will Praise Your Name 76
B - Psalm 145: The Hand of the Lord 1008
C - Psalm 95: If Today You Hear God's Voice 51
    Psalm 138: Lord, on the Day 1004

NINETEENTH SUNDAY
A - Psalm 85: Lord, Let Us See Your Kindness 48
    Psalm 85: Lord, Let Us See Your Kindness 951
B - Psalm 34: Taste and See 34
    Psalm 34: Taste and See 917
C - Psalm 33: Blessed the People 916
    Psalm 33: Let Your Mercy Be on Us 32

TWENTIETH SUNDAY
A - Psalm 67: Let All the Nations
   Psalm 67: Let All the Nations   937
B - Psalm 34: Taste and See   34
   Psalm 34: Taste and See   917
C - Psalm 40: Here I Am   35
   Psalm 40: Lord, Come to My Aid   921

TWENTY-FIRST SUNDAY
A - Psalm 138: Lord, Your Love Is Eternal   1005
B - Psalm 34: Taste and See   34
   Psalm 34: Taste and See   917
C - Psalm 117: Go Out to All the World   985

TWENTY-SECOND SUNDAY
A - Psalm 63: My Soul Is Thirsting   43
   Psalm 63: My Soul Is Thirsting   44
   Psalm 63: My Soul Is Thirsting   933
   Psalm 63: Your Love Is Finer Than Life   42
B - Psalm 15: One Who Does Justice   882
   Psalm 15: They Who Do Justice   17
C - Psalm 68: God, in Your Goodness   938

TWENTY-THIRD SUNDAY
A - Psalm 95: If Today You Hear God's Voice   51
   Psalm 95: If Today You Hear His Voice   960
B - Psalm 146: Praise the Lord   1012
C - Psalm 90: In Every Age   955

TWENTY-FOURTH SUNDAY
A - Psalm 103: The Lord Is Kind and Merciful   58
   Psalm 103: The Lord Is Kind and Merciful   59
   Psalm 103: The Lord Is Kind and Merciful   974
B - Psalm 116: I Will Walk Before the Lord   982
C - Psalm 51: Create in Me   37
-   Psalm 51: Create in Me   38
   Psalm 51: I Will Rise   930

TWENTY-FIFTH SUNDAY
A - Psalm 145: I Will Praise Your Name
   Psalm 145: The Lord Is Near   1009
B - Psalm 54: The Lord Upholds My Life   931
C - Psalm 113: Praise the Lord   981

TWENTY-SIXTH SUNDAY
A - Psalm 25: Remember Your Mercies   27
   Psalm 25: Remember Your Mercies   903
B - Psalm 19: Lord, You Have the Words   20
   Psalm 19: The Precepts of the Lord   890
C - Psalm 146: Praise the Lord   1012

TWENTY-SEVENTH SUNDAY
A - Psalm 80: The Vineyard of the Lord   948
B - Psalm 128: Blest Are Those Who Love You   70
   Psalm 128: May the Lord Bless   997
C - Psalm 95: If Today You Hear God's Voice   51
   Psalm 95: If Today You Hear His Voice   960

TWENTY-EIGHTH SUNDAY
A - Psalm 23: My Shepherd Is the Lord   24
   Psalm 23: Shepherd Me, O God   23
   Psalm 23: I Shall Live in the House of the Lord
   896
B - Psalm 90: Fill Us with Your Love   956
C - Psalm 98: All the Ends of the Earth   98
   Psalm 98: The Lord Has Revealed   967

TWENTY-NINTH SUNDAY
A - Psalm 96: Give the Lord   963
   Psalm 96: Proclaim to All the Nations   54
B - Psalm 33: Let Your Mercy Be on Us   32
   Psalm 33: Lord, Let Your Mercy   914
C - Psalm 121: Our Help Comes From the Lord   66
   Psalm 121: Our Help Is from the Lord   992

THIRTIETH SUNDAY
A - Psalm 18: I Love You, Lord   887
B - Psalm 126: God Has Done Great Things for Us
   69
   Psalm 126: The Lord Has Done Great Things
   995
C - Psalm 34: Cry of the Poor   33
   Psalm 34: The Lord Hears the Cry   918

THIRTY-FIRST SUNDAY
A - Psalm 131: In You, O Lord   1000
   Psalm 131: My Soul Is Still   72
B - Psalm 18: I Love You, Lord   887
C - Psalm 145: I Will Praise Your Name   76
   Psalm 145: I Will Praise Your Name   1007

THIRTY-SECOND SUNDAY
A - Psalm 63: My Soul Is Thirsting   43
   Psalm 63: My Soul Is Thirsting   44
   Psalm 63: My Soul Is Thirsting   933
   Psalm 63: Your Love Is Finer Than Life   42
B - Psalm 146: Praise the Lord   1012
C - Psalm 17: Lord, when Your Glory Appears   886

THIRTY-THIRD SUNDAY
A - Psalm 128: Blessed Are Those Who Fear the
   Lord   998
   Psalm 128: Blest Are Those Who Love You   70
B - Psalm 16: Keep Me Safe, O God   18
   Psalm 16: You Are My Inheritance   885
   Psalm 16: You Will Show Me the Path of Life
   19
C - Psalm 98: All the Ends of the Earth   55
   Psalm 98: The Lord Comes to Rule   968

CHRIST THE KING
A - Psalm 23: My Shepherd Is the Lord   24
   Psalm 23: Shepherd Me, O God   23
   Psalm 23: The Lord Is My Shepherd   894
B - Psalm 93: the Lord Is King!   959
C - Psalm 122: Let Us Go Rejoicing   68
   Psalm 122: Let Us Go Rejoicing   993

ASSUMPTION / VIGIL
Psalm 132: Lord, Go Up   1001

ASSUMPTION / DURING THE DAY
Psalm 45: The Queen Stands at Your Right Hand
   924

ALL SAINTS
Psalm 24: Lord, This Is the People   899
Psalm 24: We Long to See Your Face   25

IMMACULATE CONCEPTION
Psalm 98: All the Ends of the Earth   55
Psalm 98: Sing to the Lord   969

1023   Liturgical Index

Liturgical Index/*continued*

Liturgical Index/*continued*

Liturgical Index/*continued*

Topical Index/*continued*

Topical Index/*continued*

Topical Index/*continued*

Topical Index/*continued*

Topical Index/*continued*

Topical Index/*continued*

Topical Index/*continued*

Topical Index/*continued*

Topical Index/*continued*

Topical Index/*continued*

Topical Index/*continued*

Topical Index/*continued*

Topical Index/*continued*

Topical Index/*continued*

Topical Index/*continued*

Topical Index/*continued*

Topical Index/*continued*

81 Isaiah 12: With Joy You Shall Draw Water
528 Laudate Dominum
545 Now Thank We All Our God
445 On the Journey to Emmaus
492 To Jesus Christ, Our Sovereign King
614 What Wondrous Love Is This
718 World Peace Prayer

VOCATION
740 Come to Us
608 God Is Love
779 Hail Mary: Gentle Woman
517 Praise to You, O Christ, Our Savior
655 Take This Moment
540 We Praise You
(also Discipleship)

WATER
797 Baptized in Water
499 Come to the Feast
502 Come to the Water
567 Down to the River to Pray
402 From Ashes to the Living Font
537 Glory and Praise to Our God
564 Healing River
622 I Heard the Voice of Jesus Say
399 Jerusalem, My Destiny
709 Let Justice Roll Like a River
761 Shall We Gather at the River
807 Song of the Body of Christ / Canción del Cuerpo de Cristo
559 Song over the Waters
802 Sweet Refreshment
401 Tree of Life
793 Wade in the Water
842 Without Seeing You

WAY, TRUTH & LIFE
765 Do Not Let Your Hearts Be Troubled
809 I Received the Living God
513 I Want to Walk as a Child of the Light
730 Jesus Christ, Yesterday, Today and for Ever
812 Take and Eat
619 The Clouds' Veil
877 The God of All Eternity
500 Wisdom, My Road

WELCOME
859 A Nuptial Blessing
705 A Place at the Table
741 All Are Welcome
817 All Who Hunger
738 As We Gather at Your Table
820 Come and Eat This Living Bread
747 Come, Host of Heaven's High Dwelling Place

740 Come to Us
729 Diverse in Culture, Nation, Race
735 Gather 'Round This Table
745 Gathered as One
737 God Is Here! As We His People
730 Jesus Christ, Yesterday, Today and for Ever
445 On the Journey to Emmaus
839 Take and Eat This Bread
381 The Aye Carol
641 The Reign of God

WISDOM
524 All Glory Is Yours
729 Diverse in Culture, Nation, Race
616 Eye Has Not Seen
537 Glory and Praise to Our God
779 Hail Mary: Gentle Woman
695 Here Am I, Lord
556 O Lord, the Guardian of My Heart
445 On the Journey to Emmaus
754 Praise and Thanksgiving
20 Psalm 19: Lord, You Have the Words
21 Psalm 19: Words of Everlasting Life / Palabras de Vida Eterna
395 Seek the Lord
604 The Call Is Clear and Simple
521 We Praise You
540 We Praise You
500 Wisdom, My Road

WITNESS
579 A Living Faith
859 A Nuptial Blessing
738 As We Gather at Your Table
666 Go Make of All Disciples
469 Go to the World!
672 Good News
466 Lord, You Give the Great Commission
35 Psalm 40: Here I Am
477 Send Down the Fire
839 Take and Eat This Bread
518 Tell It! Tell It Out with Gladness
770 Transform Us
539 When, in Our Music, God Is Glorified

WORD OF GOD
594 A Mighty Fortress Is Our God
586 Amazing Grace
803 Bread of Life from Heaven / Pan de Vida Eterna
414 Change Our Hearts
486 Come Now, Almighty King
740 Come to Us

507 Fresh as the Morning
402 From Ashes to the Living Font
469 Go to the World!
704 God, Whose Purpose Is to Kindle
672 Good News
676 I Am for You
809 I Received the Living God
581 I Say "Yes," Lord / Digo "Sí," Señor
819 In Remembrance of You
85 Luke 2: Nunc Dimittis
557 Make Us Worthy
748 Morning Has Broken
767 Now Let Your Servant Go
717 O God of Every Nation
445 On the Journey to Emmaus
346 People of the Night
517 Praise to You, O Christ, Our Savior
20 Psalm 19: Lord, You Have the Words
21 Psalm 19: Words of Everlasting Life / Palabras de Vida Eterna
505 Rain Down
600 Seek Ye First
818 Shepherd of Souls
812 Take and Eat
518 Tell It! Tell It Out with Gladness
325 Walk in the Reign
521 We Praise You
627 You Are Mine
525 You, Lord, Are Both Lamb and Shepherd

WORK *(see Labor)*

WORLD
579 A Living Faith
643 As a Fire Is Meant for Burning
527 Canticle of the Turning
724 Dona Nobis Pacem
548 For the Beauty of the Earth
712 For the Healing of the Nations
726 In Christ There Is No East or West
528 Laudate Dominum
723 Let There Be Peace on Earth
808 Let Us Be Bread
602 Lord of All Nations, Grant Me Grace
545 Now Thank We All Our God
757 O Holy City, Seen of John
492 To Jesus Christ, Our Sovereign King
614 What Wondrous Love Is This
601 Where True Love and Charity Are Found / Ubi Caritas

WORSHIP *(see Praise)*

Index of Composers, Authors and Sources/*continued*

Index of Composers, Authors and Sources/*continued*

1026   Metrical Index of Tunes

SM (SHORT METER - 66 86)

428	SOUTHWELL
769 771	SWABIA

CM (COMMON METER - 86 86)

353	ANTIOCH
610	CHRISTIAN LOVE
848	DETROIT
660 764 799	LAND OF REST
641 726	McKEE
347	MORNING SONG
586	NEW BRITAIN
583	SHANTI
818	ST. AGNES
588	ST. ANNE
747 800	ST. COLUMBA
402 416	ST. FLAVIAN

CMD (COMMON METER DOUBLED)

379	CAROL
5 706	FOREST GREEN
622	KINGSFOLD
872	MATERNA
574	MOSHIER
777	THE FLIGHT OF THE EARLS

LM (LONG METER - 88 88)

844	ARLINGTON
334 767	CONDITOR ALME SIDERUM
130	DUGUET
454	DUKE STREET
10	JESU DULCIS MEMORIA
665 690 786 856 877	O WALY WALY
397 407 746	OLD HUNDREDTH
488	PROSPECT
389 461	PUER NOBIS
729	TALLIS' CANON,
474 602	VENI CREATOR SPIRITUS
344	WINCHESTER NEW

LM WITH ALLELUIAS

467 523 790	LASST UNS ERFREUEN
441	STUEMPFLE

LM WITH REFRAIN

579	ST. CATHERINE
323	VENI VENI EMMANUEL

5 5 5 4 D

749	ANDREA
748 754	BUNESSAN
752	EVENING HYMN
855	SHADE

66 4 666 4

874	AMERICA
486	ITALIAN HYMN

7 6 7 6 D

646 679	AURELIA
666	ELLACOMBE
327 448	GAUDEAMUS PARITER
435 570 604 717 849	PASSION CHORALE
421	ST. THEODULPH

7 6 7 6 WITH REFRAIN

618	BALM IN GILEAD
363	GO TELL IT ON THE MOUNTAIN
485	GOTT VATER SEI GEPRIESEN

7 7 7 7 WITH REFRAIN

361	GLORIA
809	LIVING GOD
497	SING OUT

7 7 7 7 7 7

384 548	DIX

77 77 D

383 463	SALZBURG
552	ST. GEORGE'S WINDSOR

77 77 WITH ALLELUIAS

457	EASTER HYMN
439 468	LLANFAIR

8 7 8 7

630	DUNSTAN
631	ST. COLUMBA
345 732	STUTTGART

8 7 8 7 D

466 737	ABBOT'S LEIGH
386 643 750	BEACH SPRING
440 738	HOLY ANTHEM
449	HOSANNA
613 826	HYFRYDOL
442 518 520 704	HYMN TO JOY
603 668	IN BABILONE
354	JOYOUS LIGHT
703	LA GRANGE
644	NETTLETON
776	OMNE DIE
778	PLEADING SAVIOR
465	TRANSFORMATION

8 7 8 7 WITH REFRAIN

612	COMFORT
686	COME AND JOURNEY
870 871	FARRELL
387	GREENSLEEVES
761	HANSON PLACE
598	HOW CAN I KEEP FROM SINGING
492 853	ICH GLAUB AN GOTT

8 7 8 7 D WITH REFRAIN

553 789	WE GIVE YOU THANKS

8 7 8 7 8 7

531	LAUDA ANIMA
85	PEACETIME
525 542 770	PICARDY
369	REGENT SQUARE
675	ROSEMARY
132 642 712	ST. THOMAS

888 WITH ALLELUIAS

491	GELOBT SEI GOTT
446	O FILII ET FILIAE
459	VICTORY

9 8 9 8 D

390 547	RENDEZ À DIEU

Metrical Index of Tunes/*continued*

1027 Index of Tunes

A light will shine on us this day: the Lord is born for us. 964

Abba, I put my life in your hands. 31

Abba, pongo mi vida en tus manos. 31

All the ends of the earth have seen the power of God. 55

All the ends of the earth have seen the saving power of God. 966

Alleluia, alleluia, alleluia! 65 78 986

As morning breaks I look to you to be my strength this day. 3

Be merciful, O Lord, for we have sinned. 39 41 928

Be with me, Lord, when I am in trouble. 50 957

Bless the Lord, my soul, who heals the brokenhearted. 77

Blessed are they who dwell in your house, O Lord. 950

Blessed are they who follow the law of the Lord! 990

Blessed are they, blessed are they who hope in the Lord. 878

Blessed are those who fear the Lord and walk in his ways. 996

Blessed are those who fear the Lord. 998

Blessed the people the Lord has chosen to be his own. 916

Blessed the poor in spirit; the kingdom of heaven is theirs! 1011

Blest are those who love you, happy those who follow you, blest are those who seek you, O God. 70

Come, my children, come to me, and you will know the fear of the Lord. 92

Create in me a clean heart, O God. 37 38 39 929

Cry out with joy and gladness: for among you is the great and Holy One of Israel. 1016

Do not forget the works of the Lord! 946

El cáliz que bendecimos es la comunión de la sangre de Cristo. 61

Every nation on earth will adore you, Lord. 46

Father, into your hands I commend my spirit. 910

Fill us with your love, O Lord, and we will sing for joy! 956

For ever I will sing the goodness of the Lord. 49 953

Give thanks to the Lord, for he is good, his love is everlasting. 988

Give thanks to the Lord, his love is everlasting. 978

Give the Lord glory and honor. 54 963

Glory and praise for evermore. 1018

Go out to all the world and tell the Good News. 985

God has done great things for us, filled us with laughter and music. 69

God mounts his throne to shouts of joy. 36

God mounts his throne to shouts of joy: a blare of trumpets for the Lord. 926

God, in your goodness, you have made a home for the poor. 938

Have mercy, Lord, cleanse me from all my sins. 40

He who does justice will live in the presence of the Lord. 881

Here am I, Lord; here am I, Lord; I come to do your will. 35 920

I believe that I shall see the good things of the Lord in the land of the living. 906 907

I love you, Lord, my strength, my strength. 887

I praise you, O Lord, for I am wonderfully made. 1006

I shall live in the house of the Lord all the days of my life. 896

I turn to you, O Lord, in time of trouble, and you fill me with the joy of salvation. 912

I will arise and go to my God. 37

I will praise you, Lord, for you have rescued me. 909

I will praise you, Lord, you have rescued me, I will praise you, Lord, for your mercy. 30

I will praise you, Lord, in the assembly of your people. 893

I will praise your name for ever, my king and my God. 1007

I will praise your name, my King and my God. 76

I will rise and go to my father. 930

I will sing of your salvation. 941

I will take the cup of life, I will call God's name all my days. 62

I will take the cup of salvation, and call on the name of the Lord. 984

I will walk before the Lord, in the land of the living. 982

If today you hear his voice, harden not your hearts. 51 960

In every age, O Lord, you have been our refuge. 955

In his days justice will flourish. 46

In the land of the living, I will Walk with God all my days. 62

In the morning I will sing glad songs of praise to you. 44

In the presence of the angels, O Lord, may we praise your name. 74

In the sight of the angels, I will sing your praises, O Lord. 1003

In you, O Lord, I have found my peace. 72 1000

In your presence is endless joy, at your side is my home forever. 19

Justice shall flourish in his time, and fullness of peace for ever. 943

Keep me safe, O God, I take refuge in you. 19

Keep me safe, O God: you are my hope. 18

Let all the earth cry out in joy to the Lord. 45

Let all the earth cry out to God with joy. 935

Let my prayer rise up like incense before you, the lifting up of my hands as an offering to you. 75

Let my tongue be silenced, if I ever forget you! 1002

Let the Lord enter; he is king of glory. 897

Let us go rejoicing to the house of the Lord. 68 993

Let us sing to the Lord; he has covered himself in glory. 1015

Let your mercy be on us, O God, as we place our trust in you. 32

Like a deer that longs for running streams, my soul longs for you, my God; my soul longs for you, my God. 923

Lord, be my rock of safety. 911

Lord, come and save us. 1010

Lord, come to my aid, Lord, come to my aid! 921

Lord, every nation on earth will adore you. 944

Lord, forgive the wrong I have done. 913

Lord, go up to the place of your rest, you and the ark of your holiness. 1001

Lord, heal my soul for I have sinned against you. 922

Lord, I love your commands. 991

Lord, in your great love, answer me. 939

Lord, it is good to give thanks to you. 958

Lord, let us see your kindness, Lord, let us see your kindness. 48

Lord, let us see your kindness, and grant us your salvation. 951

Lord, let your face shine on us. 879

Lord, let your mercy be on us, as we place our trust in you. 914

Lord, make us turn to you; let us see your face and we shall be saved. 47 947

Lord, may our prayer rise like incense in your sight, may this place be filled with the fragrance of Christ. 74

Lord, on the day I called for help, you answered me. 74 1004

Lord, send out your Spirit, and renew the face of the earth. 60 976

Lord, this is the people that longs to see your face. 899

Lord, when your glory appears, my joy will be full. 886

Lord, you are good and forgiving. 952

Lord, you have the words of everlasting life. 20 21 888

Lord, you will show us the path of life. 884

Lord, your love is eternal; do not forsake the work of your hands. 1005

May God bless us in his mercy, may God bless us in his mercy. 936

May the Lord bless and protect us all the days of our lives. 997

May the Lord bless us, may the Lord protect us all the days of our lives. 70

My God, my God, why have you abandoned me? 22 892

My prayers rise like incense, my hands like an evening offering. 11

My shepherd is the Lord, nothing indeed shall I want. 24

My soul is thirsting for you, O Lord, thirsting for you my God. 43 44 933

My soul rejoices in my God, my soul rejoices in my God. 1019

My soul, give thanks to the Lord, and bless God's holy name. 57

No one who waits for you, O Lord, will ever be put to shame. 904

O bless the Lord, my soul, O bless the Lord. 975

O God, I seek you, my soul thirsts for you, your love is finer than life. 42

O God, O God, let all the nations praise you! 937

O God, this is the people that longs to see your face. 25

O Lord, our God, how wonderful your name in all the earth! 880

O praise the Lord, Jerusalem. 1013

Oh Dios, crea en mí un corazón puro. 38

One who does justice will live in the presence of the Lord. 882

Open wide your gates; let the King of Glory in. 25

Our blessing-cup is a communion with the Blood of Christ. 61 62 63 983

Our eyes are fixed on the Lord, pleading for his mercy. 994

Our help comes from the Lord, the maker of heaven and earth. 66 67

Our help is from the Lord, who made heaven and earth. 992

Praise the Lord, my soul! Praise the Lord! 1012

Praise the Lord, praise the Lord who lifts up the poor. 981

Praise the Lord, praise the Lord, who heals the brokenhearted. 1014

Proclaim his marvelous deeds to all the nations. 962

Proclaim to all the nations the marvelous deeds of the Lord. 54

Remember your mercies, O Lord. 27 903

Rest in God alone, rest in God alone, my soul. 932

Shepherd me, O God, beyond my wants, beyond my fears, from death into life. 23

Since my mother's womb, you have been my strength. 942

Sing a song to the Lord's holy name. 53

Sing to the Lord a new song, for God has done wonderful deeds. 55

Sing to the Lord a new song, for he has done marvelous deeds. 969

Sing with joy to God! Sing to God our help! 949

Taste and see the goodness of the Lord. 34 917

Teach me your ways, O Lord. 27

Teach me your ways, O Lord, teach me your ways. 902

The angel of the Lord will rescue those who fear him. 919

The earth is full of the goodness of the Lord, the goodness of the Lord. 915

The hand of the Lord feeds us; he answers all our needs. 1008

The just man is a light in darkness to the upright. 980

The Lord comes to rule the earth with justice. 968

The Lord comes to the earth to rule the earth with justice. 55

The Lord gave them bread from heaven. 945

The Lord has done great things for us; we are filled with joy. 995

The Lord has revealed to the nations his saving power, his saving power. 967

Psalm Refrains Set to Music/*continued*

The Lord has set his throne in heaven. 972

The Lord hears the cry of the poor. 918

The Lord hears the cry of the poor. Blessed be the Lord. 33

The Lord is kind and merciful, slow to anger, and rich in compassion. 58 974

The Lord is kind and merciful, the Lord is kind and merciful. 59 971

The Lord is king; he is robed in majesty. 959

The Lord is king, the Lord most high over all the earth. 965

The Lord is my light and my salvation. 101 905

The Lord is my light and my salvation, of whom should I be afraid? 29

The Lord is my shepherd; there is nothing I shall want. 24 894

The Lord is near to all who call on him. 1009

The Lord remembers his covenant for ever. 977

The Lord upholds my life. 931

The Lord will bless his people with his peace. 908

The Lord's kindness is everlasting to those who fear him. 973

The precepts of the Lord give joy to the heart. 890

The queen stands at your right hand, arrayed in gold. 924

The seed that falls on good ground will yield a fruitful harvest. 934

The son of David will live for ever. 954

The stone rejected by the builders has become the cornerstone. 989

The vineyard of the Lord is the house of Israel. 948

The waters of the river gladden the city of God, the holy dwelling of the Most High. 925

Their message goes out through all the earth. 891

They who do justice will live in the presence of God. 17

This is the day the Lord has made; let us rejoice and be glad. 64 65 987

Though I walk in the valley of darkness, I fear no evil, for you are with me. 895

To the upright I will show the saving power of God. 927

To you, O Lord, I lift my soul, to you I lift my soul. 26 28 900

Today Is Born our Savior, Christ the Lord. 52 961

Tú tienes, Señor, palabras de vida eterna. 21

Turn to the Lord in your need, and you will live. 940

We are God's people, the flock of the Lord. 56

We are his people, the sheep of his flock. 970

Who is this king of glory? It is the Lord! 898

With the Lord there is mercy and fullness of redemption. 71 112 999

You are a priest for ever, in the line of Melchizedek. 979

You are my inheritance, O Lord. 19 883 885

You will draw water joyfully from the springs of salvation. 1017

You will show me the path of life, you, my hope and my shelter. 19

Your love is never ending. 73

Your ways, O Lord, are love and truth to those who keep your covenant. 901

Your words, O Lord, are Spirit and life. 889

Index of First Lines and Common Titles/*continued*

Index of First Lines and Common Titles/*continued*

Index of First Lines and Common Titles/*continued*

Index of First Lines and Common Titles/*continued*

Index of First Lines and Common Titles/*continued*

Index of First Lines and Common Titles/*continued*

Index of First Lines and Common Titles/*continued*

Index of First Lines and Common Titles/*continued*